PROCEEDINGS OF THE

FIRST INTERNATIONAL TURFGRASS RESEARCH CONFERENCE

held at
the Old Swan Hotel

HARROGATE, ENGLAND

July 15-18, 1969

International Organizing Committee:

Dr. J. B. Beard, Michigan State University (Chairman).
Mr. J. R. Escritt, Sports Turf Research Institute.
Mr. B. Langvad, W. Weibull A.B.
Dr. J. R. Watson, Toro Manufacturing Corporation.

Local Arrangements Committee:

Mr. J. R. Escritt, Sports Turf Research Institute (Chairman).
Mr. W. F. P. Bishop, British Crop Protection Council.
Prof. Dr. P. Boeker, Bonn University.
Mr. B. Langvad, W. Weibull A.B.
Mr. R. L. Morris, Fisons Limited.
Ir. G. J. Ruychaver, Nederlandse Sport Federatie.
Mr. R. S. Tayler, British Grassland Society.
Mr. B. M. Wood, Sports Turf Research Institute (Treasurer).
Mr. J. P. Shildrick, Sports Turf Research Institute (Secretary).

I

Front row (sitting) (Left to right)	Second row (Left to right)	Third row (Left to right)	Back row (Left to right)
Dr. W. H. Daniel	Mr. J. P. Shildrick	Dr. R. W. Schery	Dr. J. H. Madison
Dr. S. W. Bingham	Dr. P. E. Rieke	Mr. E. Helmbring	Dr. L. E. Janson
Dr. G. M. Wood	Ir. H. Vos	Dr. J. Troll	Dr. R. W. Miller
Dr. E. Ebert-Jehle	Dr. V. I. Stewart	Mr. K. Potter	Dr. R. A. Keen
Mr. R. L. Morris	Mr. R. W. Palin	Mr. J. C. Knolle	Mr. P. Bowen
Prof. P. Boeker	Mr. D. Soper	Dipl. Ing. E. W. Schweizer	
Mr. B. Langvad	Dr. C. E. Wright	Mr. G. Akesson	Dr. C. M. Switzer
Dr. J. R. Watson	Dr. T. A. Aldrich	Dr. L. H. J. Korsten	Dr. C. W. H. M. Schaepman
Dr. J. B. Beard	Ir. J. P. van der Horst	Dr. B. Werminghausen	Mr. J. Andringa
Mr. J. R. Escritt	Dr. H. H. Williams	Mr. E. L. Entrup	Mr. C. Eisele
Ir. G. J. Ruychaver	Dr. R. R. Davis	Dr. P. R. Henderiong	Mr. R. C. O'Knefski
Dr. Z. B. - Kuninska	Mr. A. V. Bogdan	Mr. W. A. Adams	Dr. I. Yoshikawa
Miss M.-L. Denecke	Mr. J. F. Shoulders	Dr. A. Pap	
Mr. W. C. Morgan	Mr. J. L. Kidwell	Dr. L. E. Moser	Mr. W. H. Bengeyfield
Mr. G. S. Robinson	Dr. R. L. Goss	Mr. M. A. Wood	Mr. D. J. Glas
Ir. W. A. Eschauzier	Dr. W. B. Gilbert	Dr. J. Stubbs	Dr. R. E. Schmidt
	Dr. D. B. White	Mr. M. Petersen	Mr. J. A. Simmons
	Dr. T. E. Freeman	Mr. G. G. Fisher	Dr. T. Eggers
	Dr. G. C. Horn	Ir. M. Kamps	Mr. R. Vijn
	Dr. K. Ehara	Mr. J. L. Dawson	Dr. W. W. Huffine
		Dr. R. E. Engel	Dr. J. E. Howland

II

III

IV

OBITUARY

BJARNE LANGVAD

Bjarne Langvad was one of the team which organized the Conference and the European tour. He was known and respected internationally for his advisory and consultative work on athletic fields, golf courses and roadsides.

He was born on 24 June 1925 in Norway and worked on a fruit and vegetable farm during World War II. He began apprentice training at Weibullsholm Plant Breeding Institute in 1947. In 1949 he returned to Norway where he graduated as a horticulturist. After again working at Weibullsholm, he came to the U.S.A. where he completed the Master of Science degree at Michigan State University. He returned to Sweden in 1956 and in recent years concentrated on turfgrass research and education. His career was tragically cut short by a highway accident on 5 December 1969.

He leaves a wife, Brita, and three children, Carl Johan, Magnus and Erika.

Bjarne developed the Weigrass method of hydroseeding large turf areas, and conducted intensive research on sand bed rootzones for fast drainage and compaction tolerance in athletic areas and golf greens. He pioneered soil warming techniques using hot air, hot water and electric heating, and he helped to improve numerous sports fields. He produced the turfgrass cultivars Evergreen turf timothy, Sydsport Kentucky bluegrass and Erika red fescue.

His service within his community was most extensive. He was Chairman for gymnasts in the Landskrona area and also General Chairman of the 1969 European Championship for female gymnasts. His activities in improving recreational facilities in Sweden occupied much of his time.

These Proceedings of the First International Turfgrass Research Conference are a memorial to one who contributed much towards the international understanding of turf improvement.

CONTENTS

INTRODUCTORY SESSION: NATIONAL REVIEWS OF TURFGRASS CONDITIONS,

AND RESEARCH AND ADVISORY BODIES

(Chairman: Dr. J. B. Beard)

TURFGRASS RESEARCH IN CANADA

C. M. Switzer,

Professor and Chairman of the Department of Botany, University of Guelph,

Guelph, Ontario, Canada

The turfgrass industry has been growing rapidly in Canada as it has in most other countries. In spite of this rapid growth and increasing importance there has been little emphasis put on turfgrass research by Universities or Government Experimental Stations until very recently. In fact, although turfgrass research has been conducted at five stations for many years, there has not been one full time turfgrass researcher in Canada until 1968. Undoubtedly, this situation is changing, and it is to be expected that the continuing urbanization of the countryside will force a much increased emphasis on turf research.

Turf is grown in Canada under an extremely wide range of environmental conditions. On the west coast the mild, damp conditions approximate to those of many parts of England. The problems in this area are quite different from those in the Prairie Provinces where the weather is dry and extremely cold during the winter months. In Ontario the weather conditions are similar to those of many parts of the Northern U.S. and the same holds true for most Provinces along the Eastern Seaboard.

The majority of golf courses and lawns in Canada contain primarily Poa and Festuca spp. Merion and Common Kentucky bluegrass (Poa pratensis L.) are used most widely, with Fylking and Windsor showing promise for tees, aprons, and approaches. Pennlawn creeping red fescue (Festuca rubra L. subsp. rubra) has proved to be a useful grass for home lawns and golf courses.

On golf course greens Toronto, C-15, and Penncross bentgrass (Agrostis palustris Huds.) are used most frequently. Northland and Cohansey look very good in research trials in Canada because of their early spring growth.

Annual bluegrass (Poa annua L.) is considered a weed in some areas of Canada but a desirable grass when given proper management in other areas. Generally, a large percentage of the Poa annua plants due during the winter in most parts of Canada, with the notable exception of the Pacific Coast areas.

Variety testing trials are at present being carried out at all five turfgrass research units in Canada. Resistance to winter injury and early spring growth are particularly desirable characteristics in the rigorous climate of Canada.

Broadleaf weeds do not present any great problem in most turf areas in Canada. The weeds commonly found in unsprayed and poorly maintained turf include dandelion (Taraxacum officinale Weber), common plantain (Plantago major L.), ribgrass(Plantago lanceolata L.), black medick (Medicago lupulina L.), heal-all (Prunella vulgaris L.), creeping charlie (Glecoma hederacea L.), mouse-ear chickweed (Cerastium vulgatum L.), Veronica spp., creeping buttercup (Ranunculus repens L.),English daisy (Bellis perennis L.), and several other less frequently found species. Crabgrass (Digitaria spp.) is considered to be a problem in some lawns in Southern Ontario and on the West Coast. However, it does not appear to be a serious pest on most golf courses as it may be readily controlled with several pre-emergence herbicides.

Probably the most serious weed is quackgrass (<u>Agropyron repens</u>(L.)Beauv.).
This weed is found in many turf areas and is particularly a problem of the
sod grower. Creeping bentgrass (<u>Agrostis stolonifera</u> L.) growing in fairways
or lawns also presents a problem in many parts of the country.

The most important disease on putting greens in Canada is snow mould.
This problem has received some attention at Guelph over the past few years,
and effective measures for the control of this disease in Southwestern Ontario
have been established. The most important summer diseases in Southern Ontario
and the West Coast are brown patch and dollar spot. The <u>Helminthosporium</u>
diseases are also common on golf courses and lawns. There are no serious
insect problems on turf in Canada with the exception of local white-grub
infestation from time to time.

Winter killing of grass is probably the major problem on many golf courses
in Canada. The majority of the winter killing is not from the extreme cold
but rather from desiccation during the winter months. Present turf research
in Manitoba is concentrated on various techniques for protecting grass from
winter desiccation. Usually snow mould is related to this problem. Work in
Western Canada showed that injury from snow mould was practically eliminated
when, by using soil-heating cables, the temperature of the turf was not
allowed to drop below freezing.

Considerable quantities of salt are used on roads in Canada during the
winter months. Sometimes this may splash on to adjacent turf areas causing
considerable damage. Some research is being done on the effect of chlorine
levels on various turf species.

There is considerable interest at present in the long-term effects on
turf of continued use of various chemicals. This applies particularly to
herbicides and fungicides. Work is continuing at Guelph on the effects of
growth regulators on turf.

THE TURFGRASS SITUATION IN WEST GERMANY

Peter Boeker,

Institut für Pflanzenbau, University of Bonn, West Germany

In Germany there are big climatic differences from north to south, and from west to east. Some regions have a moist maritime climate; others show a considerable continental influence; while in a small region there is even a slight Mediterranean influence. There are also large areas with hill and mountain conditions. These differences influence the length of the winter, e.g. the days with frost, the amount of rainfall, and the relative humidity of the air. There are also many differences in the soils, which range from peat overlying sand to heavy clay.

Apart from sports turf the interest in turf is relatively new; it arose only recently in connection with the development of the economy. In private gardens in former times vegetables used to be grown, while now people like to have lawns for recreation. Also, communities are now able to spend much more on their public lawns. There is, therefore, a boom in machinery, fertilizers, lawn seeds and special seeds mixtures. The first imports of special lawn seeds into Germany started in 1951 with Chewings red fescue (Festuca rubra L. ssp. commutata Gaud.), from New Zealand. In 1953 Highland browntop bent (Agrostis tenuis Sibth.) was first imported and in 1956 the first real varieties, Astoria and Seaside bent (Agrostis tenuis and A. palustris Huds. respectively).

In general the state of turf is rather poor, although there are some exceptions, particularly golf turf which is the subject of special advice at regular intervals from experts from England, Italy, and some special advisers in Germany. Other sports turf is somewhat better than average, but in very many cases unsatisfactory, despite the efforts by the German Sports Association, including the Football Association. Private lawns are generally rather unsatisfactory, although they have been improving in recent years thanks to the advice given by machinery, seed and fertilizer firms.

Management of public grass areas is somewhat better, because of the higher standard of education of the people who have to care for them, but very often high costs prevent the best management. Only occasionally can the public walk on these grass areas and play on them. This is because the German climate is less favourable for such use than that of England and the area per inhabitant is smaller, so that damage tends to be heavier.

The composition of turf on road verges and beside water courses is very often not adapted to its special requirements. It grows too high and it is necessary to mow it more frequently than would be necessary if low-growing species were used.

Until now there has been insufficient knowledge of turf problems. For a start, there is lack of knowledge on the best adapted grass species for various seeds mixtures. The latter still contain too many species. An extreme example was a mixture containing 58 species which it was proposed to sow on the site of the Olympic winter games in Grenoble. In former times the composition of a mixture was mostly unknown. According to new seed laws it is now obligatory to declare it, and the value of mixtures has improved considerably. For some species which can also be used in agriculture the laws prescribe the use of certified seeds. Through these measures mixtures have become more expensive but on the other hand much better than before.

The breeding of special varieties of grass for turf is very much behind
the development in some other countries. This is because until 1968
the seed laws gave no legal protection for turf varieties. But now at several
places there is intensive breeding work. Nevertheless at the moment the main
part of the special seeds for turf is imported from the Netherlands, Denmark,
Sweden and the U.S.A.

For the evaluation of the new varieties official testing was started
by the Federal Variety Testing Office (Bundessortenamt) in 1967, at 4
stations in the Federal Republic which are ecologically different. This
testing will be extended to some other places in the future. Besides this
there are private trials by firms and institutes.

There is almost no work on the appropriate use of fertilizers. In
general far too few nutrients are applied. There is sometimes strong argument
about whether to use organic or mineral fertilizers. The Society for Turf
Research therefore started some fertilizer trials. The first, with 18
treatments, ran from 1965 to 1968 at 5 places; a second started this year (1969)
at 7 places with 25 fertilizers.

In Germany too many rotary mowers are used and not enough gang mowers,
though the latter seem to have increased in number in recent years. Only on
sports turf and on public grass areas are gang mowers widely used. These
large multiple units are mostly imported from the U.S.A. and Great Britain.
There is a big production of rotary mowers primarily for private lawns.

Research is still only beginning, but promising results can already be
seen. The main gap is because horticultural faculties have hitherto shown
little or no interest in turf. The situation is better at the level of
horticultural schools, perhaps because these are closer to turf practices and
their problems. On the other hand there is much interest in turf at the
agricultural faculties, specially at the institutes dealing with grassland
research, which gives a good starting point for turf research. At least here
can be found a good knowledge of the grasses and their ecological behaviour.
Turf research is in progress at the Universities of Berlin, Bonn, Giessen and
Munich-Weihenstephan.

The biggest turf research station is connected with the Institute for
Grassland and Fodder Crops of the University of Giessen. It was founded in
1965. Another big one will be developed at the Institute of Agronomy of the
University of Bonn, whither the author moved in April 1969. Turf research is
also carried out at several schools of horticulture. The oldest and most
extensive trials are at Weihenstephan, near Munich. In addition the German
Sports Association supports a small sports turf research station at Steinach,
in Bavaria, in connection with the advice given to the owners of sports fields.

The most serious lack is of people working full time on turf research.
At the government-supported institutions there is no-one. With private firms
things are slightly better, as there are already several persons working on
special problems.

Details of Advisory Services are given in a later paper, in Session 5.

Finally, something on the history of turf research in Germany. A group of
people with special interest in turf formed themselves in 1956 into the
Working Party for Turf (Arbeitskreis Rasen). They exchanged experiences and

started the first trials with new seeds mixtures at several places. The work of this group came to an end in 1960 as some of its members took over new appointments at that time and the working party had been quite a loose one without any rules and regulations. But quite soon afterwards there was felt the need for a similar forum which led in 1964 to the foundation of the Society for Turf Research (now the Deutsche Rasengesellschaft, 53 Bonn, Katzenburgweg 5). The Society has now slightly over 200 members of whom about 10% come from Sweden, Denmark, the Netherlands, Switzerland, Italy and Austria. The aim is to facilitate the exchange of information with the help of publications and the organization of seminars, to encourage trials, and to give advice to research stations. The success of this work so far can be seen in the increasing number of members.

In conclusion, although generally speaking turf in Germany is not in good condition, it is hoped - and all the signs seem to support this opinion - that it will improve considerably in the near future.

THE GOLF COURSES OF JAPAN

Isao Yoshikawa, Kansai Golf Union Research Center,

1303-2 Kurando-Yamahata, Takarazuka, Hyogoken, Japan.

The oldest golf course in Japan was founded in 1903 and there are now many famous old golf courses, some of them 40 to 60 years old. There are now about 500 golf courses in Japan. The courses can be divided into two types, the membership or private, and the public or semi-public golf course. The ratio is in fact 9 to 1.

Bentgrass (Agrostis spp.) or ryegrass (Lolium spp.) is used on greens in the Northern regions; zoysiagrass (Zoysia spp.) is generally used in other regions. Moreover, there are golf courses with double putting greens, using zoysiagrass for the summer green and bentgrass or ryegrass for the winter green. Single green golf courses usually use zoysiagrass.

Courses are maintained just like artistic miniature gardens. Rough areas are cut short to help to find lost balls. Weeds on greens have been pulled by hand for many years and the practice still continues. It is one of the caddy's duties to repair divots made by the golfer.

Since the climate of Japan has very high temperatures and high humidities in mid-summer and near the Sea, many turfgrass diseases occur throughout the four seasons and on the different kinds of turfgrasses. One of the most important is the disease on zoysiagrass called "Haruhage" (it literally means "spring patch"). This produces symptoms somewhat similar to those of Spring Dead Spot on bermudagrass in the U.S.A. Other typical diseases of zoysiagrass are fairy rings, Helminthosporium spp. leaf spot, Rust and Yellowing. Slime moulds are also found during periods of high temperatures. Among diseases of other grasses, brown patch (Rhizoctonia solani Kuhn)is one of the major fungus foliar diseases of bentgrass. Fairy rings and Helminthosporium-incited diseases can also be listed. In the cool region, dollar spot (Sclerotinia homoeocarpa F. T. Bennett), Pythium diseases and snow mould caused by Fusarium spp. and Pythium spp.rank among the most important.

TURFGRASS IN THE NETHERLANDS

G. J. Ruychaver, Nederlandse Sport Federatie,

's Gravenhage, the Netherlands

The Netherlands are under the influence of a temperate oceanic climate. The rainfall, taken over a large number of years, is on average 760 mm, with rain falling for about 500 hours. The number of days without sunshine is 66. In the growing season (March-October) the period May-June is a specially difficult one on higher-situated ground, particularly on sandy soils, because insufficient moisture is available for optimum growth. The winters are wet and long frost periods are rare.

The average temperatures during the year are the following:

	Natural day (^{0}C)	daytime only (^{0}C)	days of frost (with maximum temp. below 0^0C)
January	1.9	2.2	5
February	2.3	2.8	3
March	4.9	5.9	
April	8.4	9.7	
May	12.4	14.2	
June	15.2	17.1	
July	17.2	18.9	
August	16.7	18.3	
September	14.2	15.4	
October	9.8	10.6	
November	5.5	5.9	
December	2.4	2.7	4

The landscape is almost totally flat in the delta of the rivers Rhine and Maas. The soil is sandy in the higher regions, that is to say about 20 to 40 m above sea level, and clay and peat in the lower part, from about 5 m below to 5 m above sea level.

Grass growing has been the basis of agricultural effort for a long time. The Dutch Frisian cows are world-famous. Now the Netherlands are highly industrialised so the agricultural income has already been reduced to 10% of the national income.

At the same time sports grounds and recreation grounds have become of more interest to the people who are working in factories and big establishments. Lack of movement is now the root of all evil! Shortage of space is a big problem in Holland, and very big land-reclamation works have been going on for the last 40 years.

The shortage of space for recreation can be solved in two ways. The first is by

establishing new sports grounds. The second - and a very effective one -
is by improving the level of maintenance, including using better grass
varieties, so that the intensity of use can be augmented. The possibility of
multipurpose designs has to be explored so that sports grounds can be used
by anyone who wants recreation, of whatever sort.

Both the ways mentioned are showing up the problem of finding more
wear resistance in varieties of grasses. At the moment there is an intensive
exchange of views between the 8 big breeding firms, research workers of the
University at Wageningen, executive committees and advisory authorities.

In Holland the unique situation has developed that the proceeds of the
football pools are given to help organised sports. The Nederlandse Sport
Federatie is the co-ordinating organisation on a non-commercial basis. By this
means it has been possible -

(a) to found a national sports centre for training and research,
(b) to give subsidies to the affiliated associations for the benefit
     of their work,
(c) to give subsidies for the benefit of large international
     gatherings, and
(d) to found a research station for grasses and hard surfaces.

All this has stimulated the appropriate Ministry to attend to the problems
and needs of sports and recreation. The provision of sports facilities in
Holland depends in most cases on the municipalities, work being done by two
large specialised contractors and some smaller ones. In total, Holland has
about 6000 ha of turf sports grounds.

GREENKEEPING PROBLEMS IN NEW ZEALAND

G. S. Robinson, Agronomy Department, Massey University,

Palmerston North, New Zealand

Investigations into turf culture in New Zealand have so far been very limited, for lack not of problems but of finance. Although the N.Z. Golf Association has led the way in providing funds and instituting research activities, it has had comparatively little support from the other sporting bodies. Government Departments interested in plant and soil research have helped, but no permanent technical staff have been allocated to this field until this year, when the Grasslands Division of D.S.I.R. has appointed a research officer in turf culture. The following are some of the more important problems needing further study.

Manuring

Many of the problems in greenkeeping concern the manurial requirements of turf, and the earliest organised experimental work chiefly sought to find out what fertilizers should be used, how often they should be applied, and what rates were desirable. Valuable information on these points soon became available and resulted in a general recommendation that a 3 to 1 mixture of sulphate of ammonia and superphosphate should be applied at three monthly intervals at the rate of 1 oz. per sq. yd. (34g/sq m). For most circumstances this has proved very valuable in maintaining a healthy vigorous turf relatively free of weeds and at the same time allowing the development of a turf mat and reducing the activity of earthworms.

In recent years it has been possible for greenkeepers to learn more of the nutrient status of their greens through soil tests made by the Department of Agriculture and interpreted by the Advisory Officers of the Institute for Turf Culture. Variations from the normal are then recommended where necessary. pH level indicates whether to continue with sulphate of ammonia or substitute nitrolime, especially over the summer months when dry patches tend to develop on over-acid portions of a green. This generally is advisable when the pH in the top inch is below 5.4.

Excessive or long term use of sulphate of ammonia frequently results in permanent dry patches developing, where pH has dropped below 5, and specially on the crests or high spots of the green. Liming is then necessary, perhaps with coring, slicing or other mechanical treatment to enable water to enter the turf.

Soil tests have focussed attention on phosphate and potash levels: where phosphate is low a 3:2 mixture of nitrogen and superphosphate is recommended until the position improves. On older greens where constant mowing and removal of clippings have depleted potash, more potash dressings are required to maintain vigour of growth. Seasonal variations in the fertilizing programme are adopted where there is little or no artificial watering in the summer. Most of the nutrients should be applied during the main growing period, and nitrolime rather than sulphate of ammonia should be used in dry conditions to avoid excessive surface acidification.

Soil Compaction

This is one of the major problems, primarily on golf greens but also to a

10

limited extent on any turf used when the soil is wet. In New Zealand golf
is largely a winter sport. Courses are seldom closed because of wet conditions and because there are too few courses and too many players, the greens
become so consolidated that healthy grass growth is inhibited and Agrostis
and Festuca species are replaced by Poa annua L.

Trouble is often due to faulty construction of greens laid down on the
original soils without drainage. Many of the larger clubs now use a base of
coarse free draining material such as shingle and sand when they are re-laying
greens. If re-laying is not possible, compaction is reduced by hollow tined
coring or by drilling. Where the compaction goes deep some shattering of the
soil becomes necessary if the treatment is to last for any length of time. A
slow but very effective way is with a garden fork pushed in to whatever depth
is possible, given a slight backward pull and then removed. Slicing machines
are very much quicker and because of the frequency with which they can be easily
used are just as effective as the hand method. Some degree of shattering
occurs with the penetration and passage of the knives, and many greenkeepers
record much more rapid disappearance of water on greens since they have used
this machine.

In some cases, however, the corers and slicers have merely let the water
down to deeper layers where it collects and only seeps away slowly. If there is
then much traffic on the green the surface tends to float on this wet underground layer, and playing conditions can be worse than before. To correct
this condition the Institute for Turf Culture developed a small mole plough,
which, though not yet very intensively tested, is performing satisfactorily,
apparently being quite safe to use on areas of fine turf and not disturbing
the surface unduly. It both shatters the soil to some depth and provides a
channel to draw off the sub-surface water. If conditions are too wet to take
the tractor onto the green a towline can be fitted so that the mole plough
can be pulled through the green without running the tractor on any part of it.

Species

Agrostis tenuis Sibth. and Festuca rubra L.ssp. commutata Gaud. are the
most suitable species for general purpose use. They grow reasonably well at
relatively low pH levels and develop a satisfactory turf mat suitable for golf
greens and yet when suitably top-dressed with soil provide the less springy
turf required for bowling greens. A pH level of between 5 and 5.5 ensures a
high degree of worm control and freedom from weeds. The desire for better
summer growth has resulted in testing a number of Cynodon cultivars from other
countries. They have produced an excellent dense turf, but have been difficult
to maintain because of fungus diseases. Chewings fescue and browntop bent are
still therefore used for fine turf. For coarse turf such as football fields,
racetracks, etc., Cynosurus cristatus L. and Lolium perenne L. are normally added.

For bowling greens, a number of clubs have recently changed from grass to
Cotula pulchella because excessive use of sulphate of ammonia on grass has caused
intense acidity and consequent unthriftiness. Excellent bowling surfaces can
be provided with Cotula but although quite a lot has been learnt about its
manurial requirements and maintenance, complete knowledge of how best to manage
it is still lacking.

Poa annua

Poa annua is certainly the major impurity found in fine turf in New Zealand, associated with any conditions that result in a weakening of the sown species such as heavy traffic causing compaction. Poa annua can per-sist under conditions of shallow rooting, and is favoured by the use of excessive amounts of lime.

Very little success has attended efforts to control Poa annua by manage= ment methods where the traffic is heavy. Better drainage and careful fertili-zing will at best prevent its increase but recent trials with endothal and bensulide for post- and pre-emergence control respectively appear promising.

Height of cutting

Some trial work on the effect of height of cutting on fine turf has been conducted in New Zealand. During the playing season height depends on the requirements of the sport, bowlers and golfers both preferring short turf. For grass vigour it is better to have too much leaf rather than too little, specially where there is heavy traffic on the greens in cold or wet weather, but investigations have shown that allowing too much growth in the off season of play weakens the fine turf species, Density is reduced by excessive shading at ground level with the result that when the turf is again cut to playing height, it is dominated by coarse stemmy material which provides a very poor playing surface.

Chemical weed control

More information is required on the effect of different climatic conditions on herbicide activity. Temperatures vary considerably throughout the length of New Zealand. Rates of application for turf at different stages of growth also need further investigation.

General

Many other problems also need investigation, for example in water used for irrigation the quantities of dissolved salts could have a big effect on the type of turf produced and more information is required on the best frequency and time of applying water.

Techniques for renovation of greens have been worked out for different conditions. Considerable progress has been made in developing suitable machinery for this purpose and in the management of off-season turf but further improvements should be possible if a co-ordinated programme could be carried out in different districts.

Most of these problems require a research team to investigate them. Up to now this has been lacking, but with the establishment of a research section at the Grasslands Division of D.S.I.R., it is hoped that before long many of these problems will be solved.

TURFGRASSES IN SWEDEN

B. Langvad, W. Weibull A.B., Landskrona, Sweden

The main turfgrasses of Sweden are the bluegrasses (Poa spp.), fescues (Festuca spp.), and browntop bent (Agrostis tenuis Sibth.). These are all naturally occurring grasses. Browntop bent in particular is very common, from the far North down to the latitude of Stockholm. Fescue is also very common. Poa pratensis L. and diploid timothy (Phleum bertolonii D.C.) are used in sports fields, for example football pitches, but Poa annua L. soon colonizes the central hard-worn areas.

Poa annua is the main turf problem. There are two possible solutions - better turfgrass varieties, and soil improvement.

The first official trials of turfgrasses started in 1968, and a descriptive list of grass varieties for green areas was published in Spring 1968.

Sports facilities in Sweden include 100 golf courses, and 3,000 stadia under grass. Almost all these stadia have Poa annua but it is hoped that better more persistent varieties of Poa pratensis are on the way.

In addition to this breeding work, research is in progress on better soil systems for football pitches and golf greens, with sand beneath and a peat and soil mixture on top. Studies are also being made on the effect of ice cover on grasses, with a view to increasing the use of turf throughout the year; the reclamation of seaside sandy areas; and methods of sowing roadside verges without having to use the original top soil.

TURFGRASS CONDITIONS IN BRITAIN

J. R. Escritt, Sports Turf Research Institute, Bingley,

Yorkshire, U.K.

To the east of these islands there is the land mass of Europe and Asia; to the west there is the vast expanse of the Atlantic Ocean. These two features are antagonistic, the land mass tending to make the climate drier (warm summers and cold winters) while the oceanic influence tends to make for a wetter climate (cool summers and mild winters). The latter influence is predominant; consequently the weather is rarely very hot or very cold, and rainfall is sufficient at all seasons. In fact the south-west winds from the Atlantic give the winters a higher mean temperature than those in any country in a similar or higher latitude.

The climate is governed by a sequence of anticyclones and depressions, the depressions which bring rain coming from the North Atlantic on a north-east path. In the summer these depressions, because of high pressure systems in the Azores, are pushed further north; consequently there is some sun, or at least less rain, at this time of year. In short, it is the interaction of rainfall, temperature and wind which chiefly control British weather.

The average rainfall is just over 106 cm. This rain is fairly well distributed but on average March to June are the driest months, October to January are the wettest.

The annual average temperature is 9.5^{0}C.
January average is 4 5^{0}C.
July average is 14.2^{0}C.
The maximum shade temperature ever recorded is 38.1^{0}C.
   at Tonbridge, Kent, 1868.
The lowest shade temperature ever recorded is -27.2^{0}C.
   at Braemar, 1895.
The annual average number of hours of sunshine is around
   1400 hours.
The daily average number of hours of sunshine is around
   3.7 hours.
The average number of days without sunshine in the year
   is 75.

Britain has such geographical diversity that many areas have their own peculiarities of weather, e.g. the east with its larger temperature ranges and low rainfall; the softer rainier climate of the west; the heavy rains of mountainous districts, and the breezes of the coasts.

Though a small country, Britain has a fairly wide range of soils. They are mainly mineral soils with quite a good organic matter content. In practice many of the sites used for playing fields and golf courses have been much modified by man over the centuries: frequently one has to deal with worked-out quarries, colliery refuse tips or other unpromising sites which may be entirely devoid of top soil.

The main grasses used are Agrostis tenuis Sibth., Festuca rubra L., Cynosurus cristatus L., Poa pratensis L., Poa trivialis L., Phleum pratense L. and Lolium perenne L. By far the greater part of turf is sown but special areas such as cricket tables and some lawns may be turfed. Only one or two small firms market specially grown turf but a good deal of "natural" turf is marketed from old grassland and there is a tradition (not entirely justified) that turf from the sea marshes (particularly those of Cumberland and Lancashire) is just the thing for bowls.

When sowing new turf, fine grass areas (golf greens and bowling greens) are commonly sown with a mixture of Festuca rubra L. ssp. commutata Gaud. (70-80%) and Agrostis tenuis Sibth.(20-30%). Football fields and similar areas are usually sown with mixtures such as:

        35% Lolium perenne
        20% Festuca rubra ssp. commutata
        20% F. rubra ssp. rubra
        17½% Poa pratensis
        7½% Agrostis tenuis

but Cynosurus cristatus, Poa trivialis, etc., may also be included. For professional football grounds Lolium perenne alone may be used.

Existing turf areas, whether fine or general-purpose turf, usually contain a great deal of Agrostis (A. tenuis or A. stolonifera L.) and annual meadow-grass (Poa annua L.). It has been said that if all the annual meadow-grass were killed out of all fine turf grass there would not be many golf greens or bowling greens fit to play on! In fact original Bingley proposals for research on control of annual meadow-grass in existing turf were discouraged by practical men as being a waste of time since no treatment found to be successful could ever be used. The commonest weeds are daisy (Bellis perennis L.), dandelion (Taraxacum officinale Weber), Cat's ear (Hypochaeris radicata L.), pearlwort (Sagina procumbens L.), creeping buttercup (Ranunculus repens L.) yarrow (Achillea millefolium L.) and white clover (Trifolium repens L.).

The main turf pest in Britain is the earthworm but there is much debate among practical men as to whether its advantages outweigh its disadvantages. Troubles with disease are mainly limited to fine turf areas which may be attacked once or twice a year by Fusarium patch disease (Fusarium nivale, (Fr.) Ces.). Ophiobolus disease (Ophiobolus graminis Sacc. var. avenae E. M. Turner) has become increasingly important both on fine turf and on general areas. Corticium disease (Corticium fuciforme (Berk) Wakef.) occurs quite frequently but is usually not very important. Dollar spot (Sclerotinia homoeocarpa F. T. Bennett) is rare and restricted to Festuca rubra of sea marsh origin.

There is a shortage of skilled groundsmen and golf greenkeepers, this being in part related to low wages and low status in the past. A considerable amount of turf is managed (not altogether badly) on basic principles known to the general public through personal experience of lawns, and the practice of horticulture and agriculture. This basic understanding should not be under-rated: in countries with different traditions untrained operatives have less understanding of turf requirements than untrained people here.

The first advisory services came from the Trade and these are still important. The Sports Turf Research Institute is now the recognised centre for advice on construction and maintenance of turfgrass areas but advises only on a membership basis since subscriptions and advisory fees produce by far the major part of its income. One or two individuals have set up private advisory services and some agricultural colleges and universities do a little advisory work, at least part of it on the private initiative of staff.

As regards research the Institute, though restricted by shortage of funds, has had almost a monopoly for many years, but the work done by a few commercial organisations cannot be ignored. With increasing interest in the universities it may be that the work reported from the University of Aberystwyth will be the start of much more university research on turfgrass matters. The Department of Education and Science has had a Working Party examining the position regarding turfgrass research (specific requirements, etc.), and its report is expected soon, though it is not known whether it will be published.

John F. Cornman, Professor of Ornamental Horticulture, Cornell University,

Ithaca, New York, U.S.A.

The north-eastern United States consists of the New England States plus the three middle Atlantic states, New York, Pennsylvania, and New Jersey. Pasture grasses grow well, by American standards, and much of the agricultural land is too irregular or otherwise unsuited for more intensive cultivation, so dairying is an important part of agriculture in much of the region.

The principal enduring grasses are Kentucky bluegrass (Poa pratensis L.), red fescue (Festuca rubra L.), rough bluegrass (Poa trivialis L.) and the bent-grasses (Agrostis spp.). The chief quick growing grasses used as companions in seed mixtures are redtop (Agrostis alba L.) and the usual ryegrasses (Lolium perenne L. and Lolium multiflorum Lam.). Tall fescue (F. arundinacea Schreb.) is used occasionally for rough, high cut turf on athletic fields. The warm-season grasses, bermudagrass (Cynodon) and Zoysia spp. are used occasionally in the very warmest parts of the region but have made no great inroads into the general turfgrass picture. Throughout the region annual bluegrass (Poa annua L.) is present in all but the driest situations.

Choice of grasses depends less upon locality within the region than upon the management practices and performances expected of the grass. For close-cut putting greens and the occasional bowling greens and grass tennis courts Agrostis spp. are the predominant choice. Mowing is at a height of about ¼ inch (6 mm.). In a few favoured New England locations velvet bent (Agrostis canina L.) can be grown but through most of the north-east the colonial bentgrass A. tenuis Sibth.) and the creeping bentgrasses (A. stolonifera L.) are more logical choices. Frequent irrigation is required throughout the warmer months of the year.

For golf course fairways and lawns that are amply irrigated and are cut at ½-1 in. (1.2 - 2.5 cm), the bentgrasses are the usual survivors even though bluegrasses may sometimes be planted with them. Both here and on putting greens annual bluegrass (Poa annua L.) is a regular invader, and turf superin-tendents in warmer areas have a constant summer struggle to retain or eliminate this uncertain performer.

Turf for average lawn situations, athletic fields, and parks is mowed at a height of 1¼ - 2½ in. (3.2 - 6.5 cm). Artificial irrigation is used often or occasionally in some situations but natural rainfall generally supplies all or most of the moisture received. For these situations Kentucky bluegrass for the good soils with reasonable moisture and fertility in the full sun is the usual choice. For dry soils either in sun or shade red fescues are the predominant choice.

Soils in the north-east are podzols in the higher mountain regions but most agricultural soils are brown or grey-brown podzolic soils. They tend to be leached soils needing lime except for small areas derived from limestone. The general practice is to add ground limestone to soils that test below pH 6.0.

Fertilization is relatively heavy where high standards of turf quality are required. The usual unit for fertilization of established turfgrass is 1 lb. nitrogen per 1000 sq. ft. (ca 0.5 kg/100 sq m) in a complete or incomplete fertilizer. For home lawn and park turf one or two such applications per season

is the usual practice. Where Merion Kentucky bluegrass is grown, 4 to 8
applications or the equivalent per season are necessary if the Merion is to
keep good colour. On more closely cut golf course fairways and lawns, the
equivalent of four applications at the standard rate per year is probably
a reasonable average. On putting greens the equivalent of 1 lb. nitrogen per
1000 sq. ft. per month is generally considered a moderate rate of fertilization. Thus in the north-eastern United States, far more fertilization and
liming is practiced than in Great Britain.

Major dependence is placed on chemical applications for the control of
insects. Careful maintenance, when appropriate, plus general reliance on
chemical treatments, are combined for the control of weeds and of disease
organisms.

There are very few weeds in the north-eastern United States that cannot be
controlled adequately with chemicals. Weeds like Taraxacum officinale Weber
and Plantago spp. die promptly when treated with 2,4-D. Silvex, dicamba and
mecoprop destroy most of the smaller-leaved dicotyledonous weeds. Broad-
spectrum mixtures of 2,4-D with one of the others are usual.

Crabgrass (Digitaria spp.), the chief weedy annual summer grass, for many
years was the outstanding turf weed problem in the warmer regions of the north-
east. Now a number of chemicals are very effective in a single application
made to the turf in the spring, prior to the normal germination time of the
crabgrass. In addition to these pre-emergence treatments, adequate post-
emergence treatments are also available but require repeated use and much more
accurate application for success. There are as yet no really satisfactory
controls, either ecological or chemical, for annual bluegrass or for the
selective control of unwanted perennial grasses like quackgrass (Agropyron
repens L.) and tall fescue.

Major turf insects throughout the region are the larvae of various
beetles. All of these succumb to the usual soil treatments with such
materials as chlordane, dieldrin, and related compounds. These same chemicals,
used at lighter rates when injuries first occur, are effective against sod
webworm (the larvae of Crambus spp.) and chinchbug (Blissus hirtus Montandon).

Fungus diseases are frequent and varied, with at least one turf disease
active at almost any temperature above freezing. On such areas as golf
course putting greens the protection of the turf continuously throughout the
growing season is routine. On lawn type turf the troublesome Helminthosporium
spp. leaf spot of Poa pratensis is avoided by using Merion and similar types
though Merion has its own special disease problems.

The most pressing problems, as indicated by current research emphasis,
are the development of improved turfgrass varieties; the control of Poa annua;
soil amendments to avoid compaction; and the control of thatch.

Unsolved disease problems, especially related to Merion Kentucky bluegrass
are root rot caused by Fusarium roseum (Lk.) Snyd.& Hans. and stripe smut
caused by Ustilago striiformis (West) Niessl.

TURFGRASS RESEARCH IN THE SOUTH-EASTERN UNITED STATES

W. B. Gilbert,
North Carolina State University, Raleigh, North Carolina
U.S.A.

The factors affecting the growth and development of turfgrasses are climate, soil, and management. The latter two can be modified within certain limits, so the grasses adapted to any region are those which can withstand extremes in climatic factors such as temperature, rainfall, and relative humidity in addition to the insects, diseases and weeds of that region.

The southeastern region of the United States probably has more variation in climate than any other region, as the following statistics indicate:

Rainfall:	annual average	100 to 130 cm
	April-September	60 to 75 cm
Temperature:	annual average	10 to 21°C (north to south)
	Frost-free days	180 to 280
	January average	-9 to 10°C
	January minimum	-34 to -18°C
	July average	21 to 27°C
	July maximum	38 to 44°C

The classic climatic descriptions show the south-east goes from cool-humid in parts of six states, to warm-humid in 9 of the 10 states, and hot-humid in Florida and along the coast of six other states.

This variation in temperature means that all cool-season turfgrasses grown in the north-eastern region are also used in the south-east, in addition to the warm-season grasses. In the cool-humid upper south (which includes most of Kentucky, eastern Tennessee, the mountains and upper Piedmont regions of Georgia, South Carolina, North Carolina, Virginia, and Maryland) cool-season grasses such as Kentucky bluegrass (Poa pratensis L.), red and tall fescues (Festuca rubra L. and F. arundinacea Schreb.) and bentgrass (Agrostis palustris Huds.) are used for permanent turf plantings. In the warm and hot-humid sections, Kentucky bluegrass, Poa trivialis L., red fescue, ryegrass (Lolium multiflorum Lam.) and bentgrass are used as overseeded winter turf, primarily on bermudagrass (Cynodon species) golf courses and lawns.

The permanent warm-season grasses used as permanent turf in the warm and hot-humid areas are centipedegrass (Eremochloa ophiuroides (Munro) Hack.) St. Augustinegrass (Stenotaphrum secundatum (Walt.) Kuntze), carpetgrass (Axonopus affinis Chase), bahiagrass (Paspalum notatum Flugge), zoysiagrass (Zoysia species), and many varieties of bermudagrass.

The large number of grasses used in the region presents many opportunities to research personnel, but also creates problems of space and funds to cover the entire field. The following sections describe research on cool and warm-season grasses as reported by the various states in the region.

BENTGRASS (Agrostis palustris)

The use of bentgrass in the upper south showed a tremendous increase following the winter of 1962-63 when many courses lost the bermudagrass on the greens. The most widely used variety is Penncross, a synthetic poly-cross of three selected strains, which is quite well adapted to the area. Penncross is the only recommended seeded variety, with other varieties being vegetatively propagated. A test of five bentgrass varieties was planted at North Carolina state in 1963, with all management treatments being the same on the three replications. Results are given in Table 1.

Table 1: observations on five bentgrass varieties, 1963-6

Variety	Thatch[1] mm	Disease[2]	Dry Wilt[3]
Old Orchard	19	2.2	1.7
Cohansey	17	6.4	7.0
Nimisilla	17	4.4	5.0
Toronto	20	5.5	4.4
Penncross	16	3.2	3.3

1. Average thatch in 1965 and 1966
2. Rating 1-9; 9 = most disease. 5 outbreaks of dollar spot, 4 of brown patch, 2 of Pythium. No preventative fungicide, control only.
3. Average of 3 ratings 1-9; 9 = most wilt

Old Orchard has been the best variety in the trials, with more resistance to disease and dry wilt, with Penncross next, and Cohansey being poorest.

Fertility studies on bentgrass at Virginia Polytechnic Institute and North Carolina State University indicate 3 to 4.5 kg of nitrogen per 100 sq m is adequate for excellent turf. Most of this nitrogen should be applied in the fall and early winter when the grass is rebuilding its root system with very little needed in the spring and almost none in the summer. An experiment is under way at the University of Tennessee on the best type, source and rate of nitrogen for maintaining bentgrass greens during periods of summer stress.

As mentioned above, the severe winter of 1962 started the swing to bentgrass in the upper south, and the summer of 1968 may have reversed this trend. According to weather data from the experimental putting green at Clemson University, this past summer was the worst since 1898 from a high temperature-humidity aspect. It will be remembered as the "Great Pythium Plague", for bentgrass was lost almost overnight on many courses in the upper south. In the early 1960's the Experiment Station at Tifton, Georgia, tested and recommended Dexon at 2 oz. for the control of Pythium on overseeded grasses. Newer chemicals are now available which give promise of better control. States working on Pythium control are Tennessee, South Carolina, Georgia, North Carolina, and Virginia.

KENTUCKY BLUEGRASS (Poa pratensis)

Many words have been written about bluegrass, but the best known passage was by J. J. Ingalls in 1872 ("In Praise of Blue Grass" reprinted in 1948 Yearbook of Agriculture "Grass") who wrote ... "One grass differs from another grass in glory ... But the king of them all, with genuine blood royal, is blue grass". Virginia Polytechnic Institute is co-operating with the north-east region in a Regional Turfgrass Variety Test on bluegrass and will have twenty-six varieties under test, with experimental varieties to be added later on the basis of performance and availability of seed. One of the newer varieties being tested in many states is Fylking, which has semi-dwarf growth habits and thrives on close mowing down to 12 mm. In a variety test at Raleigh, a bluegrass introduction from Afghanistan (PI-269392) had a lateral spread of 66 cm from single seedlings in the first year of growth. It will not be long before a bluegrass is developed for golf fairway use that will have the same desirable qualities as bermudagrass.

The south-eastern states with research on bluegrass are Kentucky, Tennessee, North Carolina, and Virginia. Experiments include variety testing, fertility studies, insect and disease resistance, and management.

TALL FESCUE (Festuca arundinacea)

With the discovery of Kentucky 31 tall fescue in 1931 and the later recognition and promotion of its value, the upper south has had a much greener look. Tall fescue has a wide adaptation to soil types and temperature extremes, and remains green all the year with the occasional exception of mid-summer. In the transition zone between the bluegrass and bermudagrass areas, tall fescue is widely used as a lawn grass and is the major grass used on highway roadsides. It is admittedly a coarse-leaved grass, but when seeded at a heavy rate of 3 to 9 kg/100 sq m, it is more than acceptable for lawn use.

Tall fescue is quite resistant to drought damage, as it usually goes dormant during hot, dry weather, and recovers with the fall rains and cooler temperatures, provided the grass has received proper fertilization. In a fertility experiment at Raleigh which started in 1961, the summer drought of 1968 gave clear evidence of the need for balanced fertilization. On plots fertilized with a 3-1-2 ratio at the rate of 1.5 kg/100 sq m, less than 25% of the grass was lost, while on plots receiving a 3-0-0 and a 3-2-0 ratio, over 75% of the grass died. Evidently, potash fertilization is the key to drought and heat resistance.

In a study at Beltsville, Maryland, by Juska using 80% shade, average turf quality over 4 years showed that tall fescue was about 14% better than Pennlawn red fescue and almost 25% better than common Kentucky bluegrass.

Improved strains of tall fescue are being sought, with finer leaves, more spreading habit and less clumping, and more stress resistance. Kentucky has a breeding programme on tall fescue, with selections being made for turf quality as well as for pasture. Other states also are selecting for improved turf quality.

CENTIPEDEGRASS (Eremochloa ophiuroides)

This is a sod-forming, low maintenance perennial grass from China, introduced around 1910. It is well adapted to the soils and climatic conditions of the warm and hot-humid regions of the south-east, particularly in soils with a pH well into the acid range. Liming the soil to a pH above 6.0 causes a chlorosis due to a less available supply of iron. Oklawn (Oklahoma selection) is the only named variety, but selections for better quality are being made in Florida, Mississippi, and North Carolina.

Management and fertility studies have been conducted in the above states and in Georgia, and are generally in agreement. High rates of fertilization are detrimental, with rates over 2 kg nitrogen/100 sq m per year causing increased iron deficiency symptoms, decreased seed yield, increased "brown patch" incidence, and increased "winter kill" of the grass. In an experiment at Raleigh, centipedegrass cut at 3.8 cm weekly had no winter kill with nitrogen rates above 1 kg/100 sq m. From these studies, the recommended management would be to fertilize with a 4-1-2 ratio, using from 0.5 to 1.5 kg/100 sq m of nitrogen, with the higher rate on sandier soils and further south, and cutting frequently below 5.0 cm in height.

BAHIAGRASS (Paspalum notatum)

This grass was introduced from Brazil in 1914, and is well adapted to the lower south. Bahiagrass is usually seeded, and forms a sod with short stolons. It is the most drought-resistant of the warm-season grasses, and has good shade tolerance, but objectionable seed heads. The Tifton Station reports that high rates of seeding (5 kg/100 sq m) and weekly mowing at 2.0 cm height reduced seed head production , but the low mowing decreases sod density. Florida reports that high rates of nitrogen (4 and 8 kg/100 sq m) caused severe winter killing of seedlings. The generally recommended management is about 1.5 kg of nitrogen and cutting at 5.0 cm. Lower cutting heights generally weaken the grass.

ST. AUGUSTINEGRASS (Stenotaphrum secundatum)

This is a sod-forming grass indigenous to the West Indies and common in tropical Africa, Mexico, and Australia. It is used primarily as a lawn grass from Florida to east Texas, but is generally killed in winter above the hot-humid zone. Some selections are proving more winter-hardy but are of limited distribution. St. Augustinegrass grows best on relatively fertile, well-drained soils, and is quite shade tolerant. It is subject to chinch bug (Blissus spp.) damage, which is the basis for a multi-million dollar business on the Gulf Coast. An experiment at Florida showed that the source and rate of nitrogen had an effect on chinch bug population and the damage caused to the variety Floratine in 1964.

Plots receiving ammonium nitrate per 100 sq m were killed as follows:

8 kg nitrogen	95%
4 kg nitrogen	80%
2 kg nitrogen	50%

(None of the plots receiving organic nitrogen at the same rates was killed, even though chinch bugs were present)

A 4-1-2 ratio of fertilizer appeared to be satisfactory, with 2 kg/100 sq m of nitrogen giving good growth and colour and less winter damage than higher rates.

ZOYSIAGRASS (Zoysia species)

This grass was introduced from North Korea in 1895. The Meyer strain (Z. japonica) was selected in co-operation with the USGA Green Section and released in 1952. It is a medium textured zoysia, quite winter-hardy, but susceptible to damage by billbugs (Sphenophorus spp.). Manilagrass (Z. matrella) has finer leaves, more shade-tolerance but is less winter-hardy than Meyer. Emerald zoysia (Z. japonica x Z. tenuifolia) was released in 1955 and rates superior to other zoysias in turf quality. All strains are drought tolerant, but will turn brown. They will grow and persist on relatively poor soils, but must be well managed to thrive, because they require frequent mowing, fertilization, and occasional watering to maintain desirable characteristics.

Experimental results show a balanced fertilization is best for all zoysias, with a 3-1-2 ratio meeting most requirements. North Carolina results show about 2 kg/100 sq m nitrogen to be optimum on clay-loam soils, while Florida recommends approximately 4 kg for their sandier soils and longer growing season. Auburn results show a chlorosis from high phosphorus.

BERMUDAGRASS (Cynodon species)

The common bermudagrass, C. dactylon, is a major warm-season, sod-forming perennial grass believed to have been introduced from Africa in 1751 or earlier. It is used for pastures, hay, lawns, general-purpose turf, and erosion control. Several other species have been introduced for turf purposes, including C. transvaalensis, C. magennisii, and C. bradleyi. Interspecific hybridizations have been important factors in the development of improved varieties for turf. All the bermudas thrive in sub-tropical areas, and are well adapted to relatively fertile soils in the humid south, but are found as far north as Maryland and the southern part of the central Corn Belt states.

No mention can be made of turf bermudagrasses without saluting Dr. Glenn Burton from the Georgia Coastal Plain Experiment Station at Tifton. The breeding and release of Tiflawn (T-57) in 1952, Tiffine (T-127) in 1953, Tifgreen (T-328) in 1956, Tifway (T-419) in 1960 and Tifdwarf in 1965 are testimonies to his dedication to turf research.

Other bermudagrass varieties of more than passing interest include Ormond, Everglades and Floraturf, all selected or evaluated at the University of Florida. Floraturf has created some excitement since it was discovered to have better turf qualities in partial shade, which is something new for a bermudagrass.

The fertilization and management requirements of the fine strains were under way even before the grasses were released, and research has continued in each of the ten states in the south-east, and west to California. At the present, emphasis is on the requirements of Tifgreen and Tifdwarf, with published and unpublished results from all states having general agreement.

The fertility requirements of bermudagrass for quality putting greens are quite high, with a general recommended rate of 0.75 to 1.0 kg/100 sq m of nitrogen every 2-3 weeks during the growing season. With the multitude of different sources and mixtures available, suffice it to say that almost any source, properly used, will produce good turf.

Nitrogen is not the only element that is required in the proper amount. In an experiment at Raleigh, plugs of Tifgreen and Tifdwarf were taken from an established sod and grown in the greenhouse for 4 months without nutrients, so that all the N, P, and K originally in the soil were reduced to very low levels. Five fertility ratios were then applied and the grass plugs grown in the greenhouse for 3 additional weeks. The plugs were then hardened in a controlled environmental chamber for 4 weeks at $4^{0}C$ and 3000 ft. candles of light for 8 hours each day. This hardening treatment is similar to that of 1 month in the field in the fall. The plugs were then placed in a programmed freezer, some of them removed at various temperatures, and the temperatures were calculated at which 50% of the grass was killed for each fertility ratio. Table 2 shows the results.

Table 2:	temperatures at which 50% of grass was killed	
Nutrient ratio	Tifdwarf	Tifgreen
(N-P-K)	(^{0}C)	(^{0}C)
4-0-0	-4.4	-5.0
4-1-0	-5.6	-5.6
4-0-2	-5.0	-6.1
4-1-2	-7.8	-7.2
4-1-5	-8.3	-8.3

With both varieties, the 4-1-5 ratio was optimum for improving cold resistance with the 4-1-2 ratio quite close. Plants receiving nitrogen only (4-0-0) were the least resistant to the freezing, while the addition of P (4-1-0) and K (4-0-2) improved cold tolerance.

Further parts of the same test also emphasize the importance of a balanced nutrient relationship.

Since potassium is an important nutrient for bermudagrass, Table 3 is of interest. These results were with ammonium sulphate as the nitrogen source. Potassium carbonate and potassium sulphate were significantly better than the other sources, and 1.25 kg was equal to any higher rate. The frequency results are not given in the table, but it made no difference whether the potash applications were split in 4 applications, or all applied at one time.

Generally, when a good job has been done with fertilizing the greens, a thatch tends to build up if not kept under tight control. An excellent study at Mississippi State (Table 4) shows how thatch on Tifgreen is influenced by management practices. In a previous study, topdressing monthly or every two months reduced the thatch more than any other treatment.

Table 3: results of a potassium source-rate-frequency study at
Gainesville, 1966-67 season

Potash source	Kg of potash per 100 sq m			
	0	1.25	2.5	5.0
Potassium chloride (KCl)	4.5	6.4	8.0	7.2
Potassium carbonate (K_2CO_3)	4.6	8.5	8.5	8.6
Potassium sulphate (K_2SO_4)	4.8	8.3	8.3	8.0
Potassium nitrate (KNO_3)	4.8	6.8	8.2	7.2

Rating scale: 9 = excellent turf
1 = very poor turf

Table 4: thatch accumulations (mm) on Tifgreen bermudagrass, 1965

Aerifications per summer	Vertical mowing interval			
	None	2 weeks	4 weeks	6 weeks
0	15	9	12	12
3	15	7	13	11
6	16	9	13	7

In 1965, vertical mowing reduced accumulations of thatch, while aerification tended to prevent any increase, but gave a positive response to turf quality. The conclusions drawn from the study are that a management programme which includes frequent vertical mowings and aerifications during the growing season will reduce thatch accumulation and the number of required topdressings for Tifgreen bermudagrass putting greens.

The research on the control of diseases has progressed in the region, but fortunately the warm season grasses are not quite as susceptible to the various diseases as, for example, bentgrass. Attacks by <u>Pythium</u> spp., brownpatch (<u>Rhizoctonia solani</u> Kuhn), dollar spot (<u>Sclerotinia homoeocarpa</u> F. T. Bennett), and other diseases occasionally break out, but in general are brought under control with the proper use of the various available fungicides. Yet one disease, if so it be, has resisted efforts to identify the cause and to give a satisfactory control. Spring dead spot has caused a lot of damage to bermudagrass, and research workers at the University of Georgia and the Mallinkrodt Chemical Company have extensive research on this puzzling problem.

An indication of the progress being made in turfgrass research in the southeast was the formation of the Southern Regional Turf Research Group in 1967. This involves not only the 10 states in the southeast, but also Arkansas, Oklahoma, and Texas, since many of the grasses are the same and the problems mutual. Annual meetings have been held with a full exchange of ideas, projects, and plans. The future plans for the group are indicated by the following committees and their charges:

1. <u>Bioassays in turf research</u>. To develop or recommend standard techniques for applying herbicides, nematocides, fungicides, etc., to turf research plots; to recommend methods to use in making phytotoxicity measurements, and to collate recommendations of various states as regards specialised chemicals used on turf.

2. <u>Turf Varieties</u>. To develop a list of available vegetative and seed planting stock of turf species, varieties, selections, and accessions by states; to develop a standard procedure for the release of a new turf variety; to develop a master plan in which each state, or selected states, would be responsible for maintaining in a pure state specific genera, species, or varieties of turf.

3. <u>Teaching improvement in turf management</u>. To survey the course offerings in turf for the Southern Region; to recommend new techniques and methods for teaching undergraduate and graduate courses in turf; to recommend a course of study leading to the B.S. degree in turf management; to study the need for a regional brochure on career opportunities in the turf industry.

TURFGRASS IN THE MIDWESTERN UNITED STATES

W. H. Daniel, Turf Specialist, Department of Agronomy, Purdue University,

Lafayette, Indiana, U.S.A.

As one of the six areas in the United States the midwest has a cool humid climate with extremes in duration and frequency of weather which cause extreme stress on turfgrasses. As an example, a series of hot humid nights can intensify attacks by <u>Pythium</u> spp. and <u>Fusarium roseum</u> (Lk.)Snyd.& Hans, while cool nights may dramatically stop the damage.

Hot dry winds may severely stress turf yet in some years little supplemental irrigation may be needed. Thus the turf manager needs to be well informed, well equipped, and mobie in his thinking and scheduling.

Rapid information exchange is characteristic of modern turf managers. Local districts have monthly meetings; States and Regional groups have conferences and field days; and National Conferences encourage and involve all who will participate. Field day reports, conference proceedings, extension and trade literature serve to advance ideas. For example, completely automatic irrigation with central controller, automatic rain cutoff and individual timing of each sprinkler is a reality being shared to-day.

Since 1950 golf courses have increased rapidly throughout the U.S. so that 6,000 courses 20 years ago have increased to 10,000 in 1969. Heavy play and motorized carts for players increase the wear everywhere. Ideally, putting greens in the area are made with cultivars of creeping bentgrass (<u>Agrostis stolonifera</u> L.).

Most fairways are started as <u>Poa pratensis</u> L. and <u>Festuca rubra</u> L. with bluegrass predominating when ample nitrogen and irrigation are used. As elsewhere, the infestation and survival of <u>Poa annua</u> L. and the annual competition of knotweed (<u>Polygonum aviculare</u> L.), crabgrass (<u>Digitaria spp</u>.) and other weeds dictate management techniques and present research workers with great challenges to produce improved varieties and herbicides.

To-day about 500 golf courses are specifically treating with selective chemicals to remove <u>Poa annua</u>. There is a gradual accumulation of arsenic toxicity on fairways, and this, with repeated groove seeding of the newer bluegrass varieties, means that within two years a change from over 90% <u>Poa annua</u> to 99% <u>Poa pratensis</u> can be achieved.

Artificial turf is very expensive and presents some problems in use. Yet in professional stadia its use will expand, for certain management problems are solved and more intensive play and practice can be arranged.

For turf, heavy soils, excess wetness, compaction and poor turf are widespread problems. Re-sodding, vertical trenches for excess water removal and mechanical topdressing are making large improvements. As an example the Busch Stadium in St. Louis, Missouri, has a porous rootzone (with only 10% soil), soil warming, automatic soil sensing irrigation, a powered partial field cover, plus warm and cool season grasses and annual re-sodding. A vigorous aggressive <u>Poa pratensis</u> for sports turf use in the cool humid areas is badly needed.

Lawns for homes, industry and public buildings are now often sodded to achieve "instant lawn". The use of special varieties which are denser, tolerate closer mowing, and provide more disease resistance (e.g. Merion, Windsor and Fylking) has greatly increased.

Grooming of lawns has advanced rapidly: motorized vertical thinners for reducing thatch and regulating competition are widely available as service units for homeowners. Six major crabgrass herbicides, which act when at toxic levels in the soil, are widely available through lawn and turf suppliers. There are estimated to be about 800 sod growers in the U.S., with a concentration in Michigan, Illinois and Wisconsin areas where muck (organic peat) soils are preferred for growing. Mechanical developments are coming fast. Units which cut, roll, load, and unload are being conceived and made by various individuals and these will quickly bring about changes in methods.

The increase of vegetatively propagated varieties has begun in Poa pratensis with the A-10, A-20 and A-34 varieties of Warren's Sod Co. being either patented or trademarked for identification. Future progress here is of keen interest to research and commercial interests for its likely effect on the seed industry.

TURFGRASS IN THE CENTRAL PLAINS

Ray A. Keen, Ph.D.,

Kansas State University, Manhattan, Kansas, U.S.A.

Fine turf is a recent luxury in the heartland of the United States. Only a century ago the first transcontinental railroad was completed across this prairie region. The grazing bison and American Indian were still supreme. Kentucky bluegrass (Poa pratensis L.) had followed the white man into the region and was to become an indicator of overgrazing of the dominant tall and midgrass prairies indigenous to the eastern edge of the Plains along the Missouri River.

The first good lawns and attempts at bentgrass golf greens date from that period of prosperity known as the "Roaring Twenties" between World War 1 and the Great Depression. Seed for lawns and athletic fields was stripped from overgrazed pastures with a considerable seed industry centering around St. Joseph, Missouri. Some sod was also cut from the better pastures in the late twenties.

Golf greens were constructed by adding a bit of peat or composted manure to the local prairie soil and seeding with"brown German bent" or other available bentgrass seed. Traffic was light, the climate extreme and the green-keepers ignorant, so that many greens were replanted annually.

Probably the first turf research on the Plains was performed by Quinlan and Zahnley who applied nitrogen fertilizers to turf and weighed the clippings. There was a direct correlation between rate of application and weight of clippings; however, there was good evaluation of turf quality and weed exclusion by fertilized grass.

The organised professional turf men in Iowa, Oklahoma and Texas were co-operating with their respective Land Grant Universities prior to the Autumn of 1950 when the Central Plains Turfgrass Foundation was organized and the first Central Plains Turf Conference held. This foundation is directed toward raising funds for sponsoring research and holding educational Field Days and Conferences for all turf interests in the Central Plains. The Heart of America (centered in Kansas City) and the Kansas Turfgrass Assn. (centered in Wichita) are loyal supporters of the foundation.

At the present time Dr. Huffine, Dr. Wadsworth and Dr. Young are using a strong team approach to breeding, evaluation, disease and insect control problems of turf at Oklahoma State University in Stillwater, Oklahoma. In Nebraska Dr. Dudeck is concentrating on erosion control along the wide rights-of-way associated with highway construction in the Plains.

Dr. Lobenstein and Dr. Dunn at the University of Missouri in Columbia, Missouri, are initiating an ambitious programme that should result in improved turf for the more humid forest border region; as should the reorganized programme at Iowa State University at Ames, Iowa, following Dr. Elliot Robert's removal to Florida to serve as Department Head there.

In Kansas there is a long-range breeding and selection programme to find turfgrass adapted to the Central Plains climate of extremes and generally alkaline soils. Good progress has been made with bermudagrasses (Cynodon dactylon (L.) Pers.) and Zoysia japonica Steud.

Germ plasm of Festuca rubra L. and Agrostis stolonifera L. is being collected and preserved for breeding cultivars adapted to the Central Plains. High summer temperatures make turfs of either of these species extremely susceptible to disease.

The Plains are a semi-arid grassland or steppe region with a continental climate characterized by rapid and extreme changes. Rainfall decreases from the tallgrass prairies on the eastern border, where an average of 90 cm falls annually, to the shortgrass plains at the foot of the Rocky Mountains, which are responsible for the rain shadow, where only 30 cm falls on the average. Most of the precipitation occurs as thundershowers during the growing season from April to October with a peak in June. With the aid of prairie fires the warm-season grasses are climax vegetation over the entire region except for the moist swales at high altitudes in the west and north where the wheatgrasses (Agropyron spp.) may dominate the shorter buffalograss (Buchloe dactyloides Engm.) and grama grasses (Bouteloua spp.). Buffalograss is the only indigenous sod-forming grass.

Altitude plays an important role in the production of fine turfgrasses on the Plains. At the lower altitudes (200 m) in the east, the soil and night-time temperatures in the summer exceed 30^{0}C. The altitude rises toward the west at a rather regular 3 m per mile except for local low rolling hills where escarpments or cuestas of durable sandstone or cherty limestone cap the softer shales. West of the 99th meridian the altitude exceeds 600 m and the soil and night-time temperatures permit excellent cool-season turfs where irrigation water is available. Diseases are of little concern because the low humidity and constant winds quickly dry the grass after irrigation or rain.

Compared to other regions the soils of the plains are very fertile, having been semi-arid grasslands since pre-Pleistocene time. Only the northeastern portion, east of the Big Blue and north of the Kansas (Kaw) and Missouri Rivers, was glaciated and left with a blanket of till. Glacial action in the Rocky Mountains resulted in great quantities of outwash sands and gravels deposited as outwash plains in the west. Farther east the finer sands were worked by wind into dunes along the rivers and the Sand Hill region of Nebraska. Thousands of square miles are covered by silty loess deposits, with fossil soils corresponding to the major advances and retreats of the Ice Age.

The fertile soils, low relief and grassland vegetation has resulted in maximum utilization of the Plains for agricultural purposes. Less than 2% of the 50,000,000 acres (20 million ha) in Kansas are wasteland. There are no national, state, or regional forests. All recreation and other land uses must be subtracted from farm land. Even so, the demand for urban expansion, airports, golf courses, highways, and giant federal reservoirs is taking over ¼ million acres out of cultivation annually in the Great Plains region. Most of this is being replanted into some form of turfgrass.

REFERENCES

FLORA, S. D. (1948) The Climate of Kansas. Report of the Kansas State Board of Agriculture 62.

GATES, F. C. (1940) Flora of Kansas. Kansas agric. Exp. Stn., Manhattan, Kansas.

U.S. DEPT. OF AGRICULTURE (1948) Grass. The Yearbook of Agriculture. Govt. Printing Office, Washington, D.C.

U.S. DEPT. OF AGRICULTURE (1957) Soil. The Yearbook of Agriculture. Govt. Printing Office, Washington, D.C.

ZAHNLEY, J. W., and QUINLAN, L. R. (1934). Lawns in Kansas. Bull. 267, Kansas agric. Exp. Stn.

THE TURFGRASS SITUATION ON THE WEST COAST OF THE U.S.A.

W. H. Bengeyfield, USGA Green Section, Garden Grove, California, U.S.A

Facilities utilizing turfgrasses in the western United States include golf courses, parks, cemeteries, industrial lawns, home lawns and highways. Golf courses (over 500 in California alone) have the highest degree of turfgrass maintenance. Some golf clubs will spend in excess of $200,000 annually for maintaining an 18-hole course. Seventy percent of this cost goes for labour.

In western U.S.A., irrigation is critical. There are many areas where the rainfall is less than 25 cm annually (California). In other areas, rainfall will exceed 2.5 m per year (Washington State). Automatic irrigation of turfgrass areas has increased tremendously. Approximately 50 per cent of the western golf courses are now under automatic irrigation.

Soil compaction and Poa annua L. are the major problems. Scientifically - prepared soil mixtures designed to resist compaction (USGA Green Section Specifications) are being widely used for putting green construction. Good management (including the use of pre-emergence chemicals, disease control, irrigation techniques, better Agrostis varieties, fertilization and cultural practices) will overcome the Poa annua problem.

One problem apparently will not yield to improved cultural practices, i.e. excessive traffic on turf. Golf cart paths and the "scatter principle" have been partially effective but the day is awaited when an air-cushion type vehicle will be developed and used on the golf course.

SESSION 1A: BREEDING, EVALUATION AND PERFORMANCE

OF TURFGRASSES

(Chairman: Dr. J. B. Beard)

H. Vos and W. Scheijgrond,

Institute for Research on Varieties of Field Crops, Wageningen,

The Netherlands

SUMMARY

The development of grass mixtures over the years has reduced the number of species used, due to the use of good varieties and better information about competition and behaviour of different grasses. For football fields Poa pratensis, Lolium perenne and Phleum pratense or bertolonii are the most important species; for ornamental lawns Agrostis tenuis and Festuca rubra are normally used.

Changes in the botanical composition of mixtures of grass species and varieties under different circumstances are shown in some of the Tables. Agrostis spp. are very aggressive on sandy soil (low pH) but cannot withstand treading. Festuca rubra dominates on clay soil. Treading stimulates Lolium perenne and Poa pratensis. There are great differences between the varieties of different species. Therefore it is necessary in making a choice of mixture to make choice also of varieties. A good combination of species can give bad results if bad varieties are used.

A monoculture in lawns and in sports fields is only possible if very good varieties with a good adaptability are used. Details are given of the seed mixtures for lawns and sports fields which are used in the Netherlands.

INTRODUCTION

There have recently been interesting changes in grass mixtures compared with those of some decades ago. The principle used to be to make the mixture as complex as possible. This principle was valid then because there was a lack of research on, and experience with, the characters and behaviour of species and the competition between them. Also, in general there were no good varieties. It was supposed that mixtures for sports turf should resemble mixtures for lawns. Grasses for both purposes had to be fine-leaved and had to make a dense turf. The great differences in treading resistance were not enough acknowledged.

Mixtures for sports fields or for lawns were composed of the following species (the list includes some old Latin names):-

Sports fields: Agrostis tenuis (Sibth.), Festuca rubra L., Poa pratensis L., Lolium perenne L., Cynosurus cristatus L., Poa trivialis L., Festuca ovina var. duriuscula.

Lawns: Agrostis spp., Anthoxanthum odoratum L., Cynosurus cristatus L., Festuca duriuscula, Festuca heterophylla Lam., Festuca ovina angustifolia, Festuca rubra L., Poa nemoralis L., Poa pratensis L., Lolium perenne L., (Paceys, for quick effect), Aira flexuosa L.

The proportions of each species were mostly left to personal judgment.

Since 1948 recommendations on grass mixtures for several purposes have been included in the Dutch list of varieties. The mixtures are marked by symbols showing the purpose, e.g. BG 5 is a general purpose mixture for permanent grassland, SV denotes mixtures for sports fields, GZ mixtures for lawns. When modern mixtures for different purposes are compared with old ones it is striking that the number of species has decreased considerably. Mixtures for lawns and for sports fields also diverge much more than they used to. It has been shown that most of the fine-leaved species are not resistant against treading, and they are therefore not included in the principal mixture for football fields. Apart from these differences it is more and more clear that the choice of good varieties is as important as, or sometimes even more important than, the choice of good species.

GRASSES FOR LAWNS AND SPORTS FIELDS

Knowledge about grasses for lawns and sports fields is based on many trials, made on the most important types of soil. Varieties of different species are tested under conditions appropriate for lawns and sports fields, and are also given special treatments, e.g. special mowing and special application of fertilizers and growth-inhibitors. Sports grasses are tested under normal playing conditions on sports fields or under artificial playing conditions. It has been the authors' experience that the behaviour of varieties of a certain species under lawn treatment is comparable with the results under sports field conditions. The persistency ranking under different treatments or in a mixture remains the same, because the mowing system has a great influence. The influence of play, in changing the botanical composition of a mixture of different species, is comparable to the influence of mechanical pressure (compaction by wheels, etc.) viz. increase of Lolium perenne and Poa pratensis and decrease of Agrostis tenuis and Festuca rubra.

The most important species for fine lawns are Agrostis tenuis, Agrostis canina ssp. canina, Festuca rubra ssp. commutata, Festuca rubra ssp. rubra, Of less importance are Poa pratensis, Festuca longifolia, Festuca tenuifolia. Agrostis stolonifera and Poa nemoralis are seldom used in modern mixtures. Very important for sports fields (e.g. football fields) are Poa pratensis, Lolium perenne, Phleum pratense and Phleum bertolonii. For special circumstances Festuca rubra is used, and sometimes Agrostis tenuis and Cynosurus cristatus.

AGROSTIS TENUIS

This grass is by nature widely distributed on acid poor sandy soil. In lawns it is favoured by application of nitrogen and on sandy soils with low pH it tends to dominate other species. For sports fields it is aggressive against species such as Lolium perenne, Poa pratensis and Phleum in the initial period when mowing is the only treatment. When the games start the disadvantage of Agrostis becomes very clear: this species is not resistant against repeated treading. Agrostis tenuis gives a nice, very dense lawn and is drought-resistant to a certain degree.

Table 1 gives the result of a trial field of good varieties of different species. Every variety was partly mixed with Lolium perenne.

ground cover percentages of good varieties of different species growing in competition with Lolium perenne on a poor sandy soil

	1 year after sowing			After 2 years of football		
	sown spp.	Lolium perenne	unsown spp.	sown spp.	Lolium perenne	unsown spp.
Agrostis tenuis	95	5	-	20	30	50
Festuca rubra ssp. rubra	85	10	5	55	25	20
Festuca longifolia	75	15	10	5	25	70
Festuca tenuifolia	60	20	20	5	35	60
Poa pratensis	80	15	5	60	30	10

The lawn treatment in the first year gave a dominance of the fine-leaved grasses, especially of Agrostis tenuis.

After two years of football, only the mixture of Lolium perenne with Poa pratensis still had a low percentage of weeds.

Table 2 shows the average differences of lawns sown on a sandy and on a clay soil (means of 2 trials on each type of soil).

This table shows:

1. A great dominance of Agrostis tenuis on sandy soil.

2. On a clay soil Festuca rubra is dominant and not Agrostis spp. In other trials less than 5% Agrostis species was found on clay soil.

3. If Agrostis is dominant there are nearly no weeds.

4. Agrostis tenuis and the Festuca species cannot stand treading though in the trial described in Table 1, Festuca spp. were better than Agrostis spp.

Table 2: botanical composition of some mixtures on different soils, expressed as weight percentages of the component species

Seed Mixture	Stage and soil type	Agrostis tenuis	Agrostis canina ssp. canina	Festuca rubra ssp. commutata	Festuca rubra ssp. rubra	Unsown spp.
GZ1	At sowing	25		75		
	Established turf on sandy soil	81		19		
	Established turf on clay soil	41		55		4
GZ2	At sowing	20		40	40	
	Established turf on sandy soil	89			11	-
	Established turf on clay soil	31			62	7
GZ4	At sowing		25	75		
	Established turf on sandy soil		69	30		1
	Established turf on clay soil		20	66		14
GZ5	At sowing		20	40	40	
	Established turf on sandy soil		69		30	1
	Established turf on clay soil		10		79	11

AGROSTIS CANINA

Velvet bent (Agrostis canina ssp. canina) is a very fine-leaved grass of damp or wet soil. Most of the varieties have a very light colour. Good fertilization and water are necessary for their use in ornamental lawns. The tendency to dominate is similar to that of Agrostis tenuis; it also has a bad resistance against treading. Agrostis canina ssp. canina produces under very good conditions a sward even more dense than Agrostis tenuis and has a very good recovery, e.g. after a period of drought.

Brown bent (Agrostis canina ssp. montana) is, on the contrary, drought-resistant but in general the colour for lawns is not so attractive. Also, this grass is very susceptible to various diseases.

AGROSTIS STOLONIFERA

This grass grows under conditions different from those preferred by Agrostis tenuis and can compete better with Festuca rubra on clay soil. It is, however, much more susceptible to Fusarium nivale (Fr.) Ces. Good varieties of Agrostis canina ssp. canina and especially of Agrostis tenuis are more tolerant of close mowing than Agrostis stolonifera under Dutch conditions.

FESTUCA RUBRA

Festuca rubra is sub-divided into (a) Festuca rubra ssp. commutata (2n = 42; Chewings fescue) that occurs in general on poor sandy soil or waste ground, and (b) Festuca rubra ssp. rubra (creeping red fescue) which prefers better conditions, and includes long-rhizome varieties with 2n = 56 and short-rhizome varieties with 2n = 42.

Festuca rubra is drought resistant and tends to dominate on clay soil with high pH and under dry and poor lawn conditions. Festuca rubra ssp. rubra is, in comparison with Festuca rubra ssp. commutata, more competitive on clay soil than on sandy soil (see Table 2). Festuca rubra is moderately resistant against treading (Table 1) and occurs in sports fields often only at the sides of the fields as is shown in Table 3.

POA PRATENSIS

Meadow grass occurs on dry, well drained rather good soil. The good varieties are very resistant against treading and drought. The winterhardiness is very good. The authors found on a wet soil where Poa trivialis is normally more persistant, that Poa pratensis survived a severe winter in which Poa trivialis had been killed by frost.

Tolerance to close mowing is moderate. Resistance against Helmintho-sporium vagans Drechsler is the main determining factor of persistency under lawn or under sports field conditions. Though Poa pratensis has excellent qualities for sports fields, it is not very frequent in botanical analysis of many sports fields in the Netherlands. Some reasons can be mentioned:

1. Initial establishment of Poa is difficult, especially when it is sown late in autumn, too early in spring, or under dry conditions.

2. Good varieties have only recently been introduced into

mixtures for sports fields.

3. Fertilizer treatment has not always been very good.

4. The percentage of Poa pratensis in the mixture was often too low.

For a good development of Poa pratensis in a mixture, a good application of NPK fertilizer is necessary. In a trial with different nitrogen levels, Poa pratensis dominated over Festuca rubra ssp. rubra at a high N-level. On a low N-level Festuca rubra ssp.rubra dominated over Poa pratensis, viz:-

	Poa pratensis	Festuca rubra	unsown species
Cover percentages at high N-level	70%	22%	8%
Cover percentages at low N-level	32%	62%	6%

Table 3: botanical composition of mixture SV 2 on a sandy soil

Species	Composition of seed mixture	One year after sowing	After 4 years' playing sides of the field	After 4 years' playing middle part of the field
Lolium perenne	20	20	18	29
Poa pratensis	20	3	29	32
Phleum pratense	20	2	4	1
Festuca rubra ssp. rubra	20 }	56	35	10
Festuca rubra ssp. commutata	10 }			
Agrostis tenuis	10	19	6	3
Unsown spp.	-	-	8	25

LOLIUM PERENNE

The persistent, late flowering, winterhardy, strong tillering varieties are used for sports fields. Lolium perenne is in the Dutch climate a real "tread plant" that follows human civilization. Foot traffic or mechanical pressure and a good fertilization level stimulate its development in a mixture; tolerance to close mowing is moderate. After four years of artificial treading the percentage of Lolium perenne went up from 20% to 60% in one mixture. As already mentioned, this only occurs with winter-hardy and persistent varieties. In competition with Agrostis tenuis there is a striking difference on a sandy soil compared with a clay soil (Table 4).

To get sufficient Lolium perenne on a sandy soil it is necessary to omit Agrostis.

Table 4: difference in percentage of Lolium perenne with and without competition of Agrostis tenuis on different soil types, assessed in the established turf two years after sowing without playing

Seed mixture	Stage and soil type	Lolium perenne	Phleum pratense	Poa pratensis	Agrostis tenuis	Festuca rubra ssp. commutata	Festuca rubra ssp. rubra	Unsown spp.
SV2	At sowing	20	20	20	10	10	20	
	Established turf on sandy soil	13	-	9	67	9		2
	Established turf on clay soil	60	19	3	12	4		2
SV4	At sowing	30	10	60				
	Established turf on sandy soil	56	5	29				10

PHLEUM SPECIES

The Phleum species are very winterhardy and need good soil. There is a great range of varieties. Late flowering, strong tillering varieties which are three weeks later in heading than early flowering varieties, are much more persistent and tolerant of close mowing and treading. Establishment and winter colour are better than with Poa pratensis.

Most of the varieties belong to the hexaploid Phleum pratense. Phleum bertolonii has some characters which are better than those of Phleum pratense and it has finer leaves. The present varieties of Phleum bertolonii are susceptible to drought.

OTHER SPECIES

In Table 1 it is shown that Festuca tenuifolia and Festuca longifolia do not withstand heavy treading. The good varieties of these grasses are sometimes used in lawns, but they are not very aggressive and the choice of a good companion grass is difficult.

Poa trivialis gives good establishment and is aggressive under wet conditions. It is, however, very susceptible to drought and cannot stand treading.

Gaps of lawns and sports fields are spontaneously invaded by Poa annua, a well-known annual, susceptible to drought owing to its shallow root system.

Cynosurus cristatus can stand treading but is not very winterhardy. Artificial freezing trials showed the following survival percentages:-

Lolium perenne	46%
Cynosurus cristatus	10%

It is possible that breeding work could improve the winterhardiness of the varieties of Cynosurus cristatus.

THE EFFECT OF NEW VARIETIES

Cultivars are in the Netherlands, as in some other countries, protected by a law giving Breeders' rights. A breeder can ask for registration of a variety he has produced and this will be given if a cultivar can be distinguished from other cultivars, is sufficiently homogeneous and sufficiently stable. The method of multiplication is taken into account.

Apart from testing for registration, all varieties are tested for possible recommendation in the list of varieties.

In the last decade or so varieties for lawns and playing fields have been very much improved by breeding work, especially in persistency, colour, fineness of leaf, winterhardiness and resistance to diseases.

Appreciation of colour is a personal taste and of course subject to fashion. Nevertheless, there is general agreement on what is good or bad within each category of colour. There is, for instance, no doubt that the colour of one new bred variety of hard fescue is much better than that of turf grown from the old commercial seed.

Some results underline advantages of good varieties. In one trial, the authors found the percentages of good and bad varieties of Poa pratensis, Lolium perenne and Festuca rubra shown in Table 5.

The percentage of unsown species was much less in areas sown with good varieties than in areas sown with bad varieties.

In mixtures of Agrostis tenuis and Festuca rubra the same thing was found. Under lawn management, the mixture with good varieties had, after four years, hardly any unsown species; the mixture of bad varieties had 14% unsown species. Striking differences in disease resistance are well-known, especially for the following species shown with their main disease:-

Poa pratensis	Helminthosporium vagans Drechsler
Lolium perenne	Puccinia coronata Corda
Agrostis spp.	Fusarium nivale (Fr.) Ces.
Festuca rubra	Corticium fuciforme (Berk.) Wakef.

Improvements in tolerance to very close mowing, e.g. on golf greens, have now been made with varieties of some species, e.g. Agrostis tenuis and Festuca rubra.

In the Dutch list of varieties, which is published yearly, a description is given of the recommended varieties of the different species for lawns and sports fields.

Table 5: some examples of differences in ground cover percentages of good and bad varieties sown as monocultures

| Species | After 2 years of mowing | | After 2 years of playing | |
	Good variety	Bad variety	Good variety	Bad variety
Poa pratensis	90%	40%	80%	5%
Lolium perenne	85%	25%	90%	10%
Festuca rubra ssp. rubra	95%	55%	55%	30%

MONOCULTURE OR MIXTURE?

.In the Netherlands there is a certain tendency towards monoculture in lawns and in sports fields. The first requirement for this is a good variety. The purpose of a monoculture is a uniform lawn or field without aggressive companion species. Good characters of a certain variety are thus better realised. The disadvantages are that invasion by weed grasses or an attack of disease is more disturbing.

Mixtures are better under conditions which are insufficiently known or which are irregular and sometimes difficult to predict; moreover, a mixture generally suffers less damage from diseases, but mixtures which are too complex may allow the dominance of the wrong species. Examples are demonstrated in Tables 1 and 3 of too great a dominance by Agrostis tenuis or Festuca rubra. The disadvantage of this dominance on sports fields was apparent because these species did not stand heavy treading.

SUMMARY OF MIXTURES

For ornamental lawns the favourite remains the classic English lawn mixture Agrostis tenuis with Festuca rubra. When a light colour is preferred one can take light varieties; under wet conditions Agrostis canina ssp. canina is often used instead of Agrostis tenuis.

The following simple mixtures for lawns, included in the Dutch list of varieties, have given good results if good varieties are used:

| | Lawn mixtures | | |
	GZ 1	GZ 2	GZ 4
Agrostis tenuis	25%	20%	
Agrostis canina ssp. canina			20%
Festuca rubra ssp. commutata	75%	40%	40%
Festuca rubra ssp. rubra		40%	40%

With creeping red fescue, the varieties with short rhizomes have given the best results. For special purposes, e.g. lawns subject to heavy wear and tear, a certain percentage of good varieties of Poa pratensis is included. The mixture GZ2 is also used for greens in the Netherlands. For sports fields (football, etc.) the accent is more and more on Poa pratensis (owing to the improved quality of varieties) combined with late varieties of Lolium perenne and of Phleum pratense or Phleum bertolonii. In very dry conditions a certain percentage of Festuca rubra is added instead of Phleum.

The following mixtures SV4 and SV5 are given in the Dutch list of varieties, in which also good varieties for sports turfs are described. These mixtures are used for football fields in the Netherlands.

Sports field mixtures

	SV4 (for most circumstances)	SV5 (for very dry, poor soil)
<u>Poa</u> <u>pratensis</u>	60%	50%
<u>Lolium</u> <u>perenne</u> (late flowering)	30%	20%
<u>Phleum pratense</u> (late flowering) or <u>Phleum bertolonii</u>	10%	
<u>Festuca</u> <u>rubra</u> ssp. <u>rubra</u>		20%
<u>Festuca</u> <u>rubra</u> ssp. <u>commutata</u>		10%

These mixtures can also be used for tees and fairways.

As already mentioned, mixtures for several purposes are recommended in the Dutch list of varieties and revised in accordance with new results of trials with mixtures and improved varieties.

TESTING RYEGRASS VARIETIES FOR BRITISH AGRICULTURE

D. T. A. Aldrich,
National Institute of Agricultural
Botany, Cambridge, U.K.

SUMMARY

An outline is given of the testing procedures used by the National Institute of Agricultural Botany, Cambridge, for assessing the value of new varieties of Lolium spp. for agriculture. Varieties are first tested in Preliminary trials at two centres after which the better varieties are assessed in Main trials at five centres throughout England and Wales. Testing at regional centres over a period of years makes possible an analysis of the reaction of a new variety to climatic conditions.

The main characters recorded are dry matter yield, feeding value, persistency, winter hardiness and disease resistance. Three of these characters - persistency, winter hardiness and disease resistance - are of direct interest in both turf research and agricultural research. For persistency and winter hardiness special tests have developed at N.I.A.B. to provide more detailed data than can be obtained from Main trials. Some results from these supplementary tests are summarised.

INTRODUCTION

A paper on testing grasses for their agricultural value may at first sight appear out of place in an international Turfgrass Research Conference. There are, however, two reasons why agricultural research workers may be able to make some contribution to turfgrass research:-

(1)   The testing of agricultural grasses has been developed over many years and in England and Wales there has been an N.I.A.B. Farmers Leaflet on Grass Varieties since 1960. Some of the general principles of variety testing which have been evolved in this work may be of interest to those concerned with the relatively new field of turfgrass variety evaluation.

(2)   The ryegrasses (Lolium spp.) are widely used for amenity purposes, and it seems probable that some of the data on ryegrass collected by grassland agronomists may be of value to the turfgrass worker. The reverse is, of course, equally true. It would seem useful to explore this area in which interests overlap and see how far an exchange of information can be to mutual advantage.

This paper will be largely concerned with these two points.

TESTING PROCEDURES IN USE AT THE N.I.A.B., CAMBRIDGE

The National Institute of Agricultural Botany is a national centre for variety testing of agricultural crops and grasses for England and Wales, and it is also a centre for certification schemes, for seed testing, and for the technical aspects of variety registration and plant breeders' rights. It deals, in fact, with all matters relating to agricultural needs.

The Institute was founded fifty years ago and in the first twenty-five years of its life dealt mainly with arable crops. Since the Second World War the N.I.A.B. has taken an increasing interest in grasses and now publishes annually a Recommended List of Grass Varieties.

The testing procedure falls into three phases:

(1) Preliminary Trials

New varieties are first grown in relatively simple two replicate trials at two centres (Cambridge and Trawscoed, Wales). About 15 to 20 new varieties of ryegrass enter this stage each year, and after two years of testing the more promising ones enter more detailed tests known as Main trials.

(2) Main Trials

These trials represent the primary source of data for the preparation of the Recommended List. They are carried out at five centres and each variety is sown for three consecutive seasons. The trials are recorded for one or two years depending on the facilities available at each centre. Results for each variety are, therefore, available from fifteen trials (five centres x three sowings). The trials are run under two contrasting managements - a four cut system being equivalent to a series of conservation cuts and a nine cut system to simulate rotational grazing.

The five centres were chosen to represent the full range of climatic conditions within lowland England and Wales as it has been possible to study the data statistically to assess the importance of variety x centres and variety x year interactions. These interactions have been somewhat smaller than was anticipated and, normally, similar results are obtained from the various centres and in different years. (Aldrich 1969).

However, on occasion, an abnormal season has resulted in variety x year interaction and occasionally certain varieties have reacted to the climatic conditions at a particular centre, resulting in variety x centre interaction. Some of these interactions can be explained in terms of simple climatic factors such as frost or moisture deficit,but others remain unexplained, posing some very interesting problems for future investigation.

The more important records taken in the Main trials are

(1) Dry matter yield (under two contrasting managements).
(2) Herbage quality. (Digestibility, Crude Protein and soluble carbohydrate content).
(3) Persistency.
(4) Winterhardiness.
(5) Disease resistance.

(3) Supplementary Tests

Main trials were designed primarily to measure yield and quality. They provide some information on winter hardiness, disease resistance and persistency but for each of these three supplementary tests have been required to give a full assessment.

(a) Winter hardiness. Results are only of real value in seasons when the winter is fairly severe. It is possible for a variety to complete its three years under test in a succession of mild winters without its susceptibility to winter damage being fully determined. For this reason a laboratory procedure has been evolved for measuring frost hardiness. Seeds are sown in 5 in. pots in July and are allowed to grow and harden naturally in the open under normal winter conditions. The pots are placed in a freezing cabinet in January and held at -10°C for 24 hours. They are then returned to normal outdoor conditions. This always takes place in the late afternoon to avoid a sudden change of temperature after treatment. The plants are assessed for damage two weeks and six weeks after treatment. The method has given some useful results (Table 1) but the main problem is the difficulty in getting uniform temperature conditions within the cabinet.

(b) The assessment of disease resistance is at present limited to recording the natural occurrence of diseases in trial plots. The diseases appear in an irregular and unpredictable way and it is difficult to get consistent results. Colleagues working with cereals have had similar problems and have found it necessary to develop special tests based on the artificial inoculation of seedlings, and there will certainly have to be a move in this direction if there is to be real progress in the breeding and testing of disease resistant grasses.

(c) The measurement of persistency presents slightly different problems. The cutting treatments used in trials are to some extent artificial in that many grasses are mainly used for grazing and have to survive in the grazing environment. Some workers have questioned the validity of predicting persistency under grazing from data obtained under cutting, but Clouting and Hawkins (1966) showed that the relationship between the two estimates was very good (Table 2). Furthermore, they showed that by a very intensive cutting system it was possible to obtain a persistency rating in only one year, which would not be apparent under grazing for three or four years. In practice, special grazing tests are still being used to supplement the persistency estimates; from cut plots. These grazing persistency trials are relatively simple to carry out and provide a valuable opportunity to observe new grass varieties growing in the truly realistic environment of the grazed pasture.

APPLICABILITY OF AGRICULTURAL GRASS TESTING TO TURF GRASS STUDIES

The agronomist busy providing fodder for livestock and the turf specialist creating fine lawns would not, at first sight, appear to have much in common. But although the turf specialist is not concerned with yield and digestibility, he has a common interest with the agriculturist in persistency, in winter hardiness and in grass diseases.

Table 1: scores for frost damage in perennial ryegrass varieties six weeks after freezing at - 10°C for 24 hours

(Scale = 0 - 9, 0 = no damage. 9 = severe damage).

	Mean Score	Range
One variety from New Zealand	7.9	-
Mean of six varieties from U.K.	6.4	6.0 - 6.9
Mean of fifteen varieties from the Netherlands	5.5	4.5 - 6.0

Table 2: persistency (% ground cover) of perennial ryegrass: correlations between grazed trials and 4 in. cutting technique averaged over three years
(From Clouting and Hawkins, 1966)

Variety	Grazed trial	Cutting technique	
	(Mean of 10 centres)	After 1 year	After 2 years
		Mean of 1960-61, 62-63, 63-64	Mean of 1960-62, 62-64, 63-65
	1958-61		
Melle pasture	63	85	83
Aberystwyth S.23	63	90	67
Barenza pasture	62	82	67
Mommersteeg's pasture	58	83	62
McGillsmith evergreen	60	80	63
Kent indigenous	60	78	58
G.O.L. pasture	60	78	47
Aberystwyth S101	59	57	28
Heraf pasture	58	77	42
G.O.L. dual purpose	52	67	32
Aberystwyth S.24	54	58	35
Viktoria	58	35	14
Hunsballe Late	47	31	7
Mean	57	69	47
Range	16%	59%	76%
Correlation coefficient		+ 0.90***	+ 0.89***

(1) <u>Persistency.</u> Experience with agricultural grasses suggests that, assuming freedom from winter kill and freedom from disease, each variety has a characteristic degree of persistency which can be measured on a scale relative to known control varieties (N.I.A.B. 1968). The actual length of life of a variety in terms of months and years will depend on such factors as frequency of cut and height of cut. Persistency is also much influenced by soil moisture supply. All varieties are less persistent in dry seasons and at low rainfall centres. But relative differences between varieties remain remarkably constant over a wide range of conditions.

Work in New Zealand (Edmonds 1966) has suggested that special problems may arise under severe treading and poaching but these studies have not been repeated to date under European conditions.

(2) <u>Winter hardiness.</u> Both field evidence and trials data have shown that winter damage is normally less severe in short swards, such as turf, than in fields that have been cut for silage or hay production. There have been clear cut differences in varietal resistance to winter damage with varieties bred in mild environments being more susceptible to damage than Continental or Canadian material. It has also been found that high levels of fertilizer nitrogen (300 units N/acre/year and above) have resulted in increased winter damage and it is now widely agreed that winter-hardy ryegrass varieties will be required for these high nitrogen systems.

(3) <u>Disease.</u> Fungus diseases are of less importance in agriculture than in turf maintenance and this is a field in which agricultural research workers have much to learn from turf specialists. The comparatively limited experience at the N.I.A.B. has found more grass disease problems in the milder climate of the South and West. The most serious fungus disease in ryegrass at present is crown rust (<u>Puccinia coronata</u> Corda). The use of high levels of nitrogen fertilizer in trials has reduced the incidence of this disease to such an extent that consideration is being given to growing special plots at a low nitrogen level to encourage the disease and make possible the measurement of variety differences in resistance to this disease.

There is much concern at the increasing evidence of virus diseases in grasses (Carr 1968). In perennial ryegrass Barley Yellow Dwarf virus is known to be widespread and in cocksfoot the two viruses Mottle and Streak can be quite serious under some circumstances.

To sum up, there are several problems concerned with the maintenance of healthy, persistent stands of grass which are of direct interest to all working with grass, whether on the farm or on the fairway.

REFERENCES

ALDRICH, D. T. A. (1969)   Herbage Variety evaluation – problems of regions and numbers: in "Grass and Forage Breeding," British Grassland Society, Occasional Symposium (In the press).

CARR, A. J. H. (1968)   Virus diseases of grasses. Span $\underline{11}$, 2.

CLOUTING, G. M., and HAWKINS, R. P. (1966)   A technique for measuring the persistency of grass varieties. J. nat. Inst. agric. Bot., $\underline{10}$, 621-627.

EDMOND, D. B. (1966)   The influence of animal treading on pasture growth. Proc. 10th Int. Grassld. Congr., 1966, 453.

N.I.A.B. (1968)   Farmers Leaflet No. 16. Varieties of Grasses (1968/69).

TURFGRASSES IN KENYA

A. V. Bogdan,

Commonwealth Bureau of Pasture and Field Crops,Hurley, Maidenhead,
Berks., U.K.

SUMMARY

In Kenya, at altitudes above 2000m, Kikuyu grass (Pennisetum
clandestinum) is most suitable as a turf grass and is extensively used for
this purpose. At lower altitudes, S. African varieties of Cynodon are very
popular. Other important turf grasses are Digitaria swazilandensis for lawns,
Brachiaria humidicola for sports grounds, and Paspalum notatum for shaded
places and steep slopes. Arachis prostrata, a creeping plant of the pea
family, showed good promise as a lawn plant. Sixteen other local and
introduced plants, all except one grasses, were tested as turf plants with
varying results.

INTRODUCTION

A number of turf grasses have been grown for some 15 years at the
Grassland Research Station, Kitale, Kenya. This station is situated in W. Kenya
at an altitude of 1800 m above sea level and has an annual rainfall of 1100 mm.
Pasture and fodder crops naturally receive the main attention at the Kitale
station. Turf grasses were studied only as a side line and only a few
occasional trials with them could be afforded.

Kenya has a unique variety of climates from true tropical in the coastal
area to temperate at high elevations and from wet, with over 2500 mm annual
rainfall, to dry where the rainfall is under 250 mm.   Only species of
tropical and sub-tropical origin are grown in Kenya. Temperate grasses can
grow reasonably well at high altitudes but in the areas where the rains
continue throughout the whole year, or where dry seasons are short, they are
usually ousted by the strong and widespread Kíkuyugrass .

It should be noted that the main turf species used in Kenya produce little
or no seed and they practically always are propagated vegetatively.

IMPORTANT TURF GRASSES

1. KIKUYUGRASS (Pennisetum clandestinum Hochst.) is indigenous to East
African high elevations where it thrives at roadsides and forest edges, but
mainly on land recently cleared from forest where the soil is still fertile.

Kikuyugrass is a strong and aggressive perennial which spreads by
underground rhizomes and also by thick, surface creeping stolons with numerous
short internodes; both rhizomes and stolons root freely. At elevations above
1800 m and under an annual rainfall of 900-1000 mm or more, Kikuyugrass
establishes itself freely from rhizomes, stolons or seed and invades lawns sown
or planted with other grasses. Temperate turf grasses, such as Agrostis
stolonifera L., can grow reasonably well at high elevations, as can
Festuca rubra L. ssp. commutata Gaud., but they are unable to compete with
Kikuyugrass which almost invariably finds its way into the turf. If this
happens, the best policy is not to fight a losing battle, but to accept
Kikuyugrass and to manage its turf as well as possible.

Grown on fertile soil and periodically cut, Kikuyugrass forms an
attractive cover, somewhat springy, thick and soft, and of bright salad-green

colour. To maintain a Kikuyugrass lawn in a good condition, periodic surface dressing with good garden soil or compost is essential. It is tolerant of shade and it grows well under trees. In the areas of high rainfall it can stay green for the whole year round, but under marginal rainfall of 800-900 mm or at marginal elevations of 1500-2000m it turns brown soon after the onset of dry season. The leaves are somewhat succulent and not fibrous, and the turf can be easily cut and kept low. Long white filaments sticking out some 4-5 cm above the ground level are characteristic of a Kikuyugrass lawn at some periods of the year; they appear in the morning and wilt later in the day. These filaments belong to the flowers of short fertile shoots, which produce a few large seeds each. Although Kikuyugrass can be established from seed it is usually planted from stolons or rhizomes spaced 15-30 cm apart; they take well and spread rapidly. Kikuyugrass makes an ideal turf for croquet but may not withstand heavier games.

2. CYNODON SPECIES. Large stoloniferous types of Cynodon occur naturally in Kenya, but they form only loose cover and are unsuitable as turf grasses. Only S. African varieties of Cynodon form dense turf and some of them make excellent lawns and sports grounds in Kenya. The main types introduced from S. Africa are Royal Cape grass, Bradley grass and Magennis grass.

(a) ROYAL CAPE GRASS which, according to Hurcombe (1948) belongs to Cynodon dactylon (L.)Pers., is a strong rhizomatous species which forms a very dense growth of fine, wiry stems and narrow and relatively short leaves. When unchecked it grows to about 20-30 cm high and produces numerous flowering heads, but in Kenya no seed is produced. Royal Cape grass is fairly drought resistant and is much used in semi-arid areas. It remains green for a considerable time after the termination of rains but eventually the herbage, which is dull bluish-green in colour, dries out and turns pale-brown, fresh growth appearing in the next season. Only in areas with a relatively short dry season, can it remain green throughout the year.

Royal Cape grass should be kept low right from establishment; once overgrown it can be cut only with great difficulty and only with a motor-mower. The stems are wiry and flexible and even turf which is not overgrown is not easily cut. Planting is done by splits placed 20-40 cm apart. Spreading begins with the above-ground stolons which creep rapidly, branch in all directions and cover the ground with a network of stolons; at this stage the lawn looks untidy and unattractive. The underground rhizomes spread more slowly and a growth of tillers originating from these rhizomes makes a dense and attractive cover. No weeding is normally required except when the lawn is invaded with strong rhizomatous sedge, Cyperus rotundus L., which can be removed only by digging out all rhizomes.

Royal Cape grass can be used for sports ground but particularly heavy trampling results in bare whitish patches with the rhizome and soil exposed. Similar patches often appear in places if the soil was not sufficiently levelled and the grass cut low; soil or compost should then be spread over the bare spots. Royal Cape grass is very persistent and once established will stay practically for ever and it tends to encroach upon the adjacent flower-beds.

(b)   BRADLEY GRASS (Cynodon bradleyi Stent)is a low-growing species which is much less strong than Royal Cape grass and needs much care during establishment; weeding is required even for well-established turf. The hairy leaves are of dull-green colour, not very attractive in lawns; this grass is popular mainly in golf greens where colour is of secondary importance, and it is widely grown in Kenya golf courses. Its management in golf greens has been described in detail by Graham (1945).

(c)   MAGENNIS GRASS (Cynodon magennisii Hurcombe) is a creeping grass with very fine, thread-like stolons and very narrow bright-green leaves. Of all grasses tried in Kenya it forms the finest turf and makes very attractive lawns but needs frequent weeding. It is also not drought resistant. It is best suited for crazy pavements where it produces a very attractive effect. Planted from splits it spreads very rapidly. Transvaal or Florida grass (Cynodon tranvaalensis Burtt Davy) is very similar to Magennis grass in appearance and in behaviour in lawns.

(d)   OTHER TYPES OF CYNODON. There are other types of Cynodon which can be found occasionally in Kenya lawns,"Uganda grass" which resembles Bradley grass being the most common. An interesting introduction is Tifgreen, a hybrid type developed at the Coastal Plain Experiment Station, Tifton, Georgia, U.S.A. This grass is characterised by a very low growth and short leaves, shorter than in any other type of Cynodon, and it requires no cutting. It may be a good substitute for Bradley grass in golf greens.

3.   SWAZIGRASS (Digitaria swazilandensis Stent) is a stoloniferous grass widely grown in Kenya lawns, but it is not strong enough for sports grounds. Newly established Swazigrass produces numerous flowering stems (which disappear in the second year) and flowers profusely but only very occasional seeds are formed and planting is done from splits spaced 15-20 in. apart; the stolons, which are sparsely branched, grow fast. When fully established, Swazigrass forms very dense growth, which, if overgrown, is difficult to cut back, and cutting should begin from the early stages of establishment.

Swazigrass is not drought resistant and although it seldom dies out during the dry seasons, its leaves become dry and turn pale-brown soon after the rains terminate. It is often subjected to weed invasions, the main weeds being Digitaria scalarum (Schweinf.) Chiov., Cyperus rotundus and Trifolium semipilosum Fres. Shade tolerance of Swazigrass is satisfactory.

4.   SIGNAL GRASS (Brachiaria humidicola (Rendle) Schweick.) is a stoloniferous perennial with bright green, short and broad leaves 25-50 mm long and 10-15 mm wide. The stems terminate in a few horizontally-spreading racemes resembling a railway signal. In a Rhodesian variety the stems are numerous only during the establishment period and only occasional stems appear in mature turf. Signal grass is unsuitable for fine lawns but is an excellent grass for green covers and sports grounds. Only occasional seeds are formed and the grass is established from splits. Splits containing 2-3 shoots produce new stolons and cover the ground quicker than when large pieces of turf are planted. The established turf is dense and requires little cutting, but if cutting is needed it can be done easily with any type of cutting machine because the leaves are crisp. In Kenya Signal grass has been

used with success for sports grounds and withstood considerable wear. It is unsuitable for steep slopes and cannot tolerate shade. It has a strong competitive ability and only Cyperus rotundus and occasionally also Digitaria scalarum can invade the turf.

5.   BAHIAGRASS (Paspalum notatum Fluegge) is a stoloniferous perennial with thick, slow-growing stolons. In Kenya the flowering stems are sparse in the first year of growth and usually absent in a well-established turf. This grass is usually established from stolons, although seed can be obtained in the U.S.A. Bahiagrass is not drought resistant and its leaves dry out and turn dark-brown soon after the onset of dry weather. It is shade-tolerant and is particularly suitable for drives lined with trees. It is also suitable for steep slopes and is often used in Kenya for soil conservation. Bahiagrass spreads slowly and is planted at distances of 15-20 cm. It is strong and requires little if any weeding (Thomas 1942) but is not suitable for sports grounds because trampling soon exposes the stolons and the soil. The variety in general use in East Africa has emerald-green leaves of medium size but more recent introductions include several types differing in leaf size, colour and hairiness. One variety with relatively narrow, bright-green leaves is of particular interest for lawns.

NEW TURF PLANTS - LOCAL AND INTRODUCED

Several other grasses and two plants other than grasses, all described below, have been tried at Kitale with varying success.

CARPETGRASS (Axonopus compressus (Swartz) Beauv.) A stoloniferous perennial with fine flowering stems numerous in the first year of growth. This grass can be propagated from splits or from seed. The dense and low turf has a natural nap. Cutting is needed only in the first year of growth and occasionally in the second year. In Kenya Carpetgrass showed poor resistance to weeds and drought.

CENTIPEDEGRASS (Eremochloa ophiuroides (Munro) Hack.) is a stoloniferous perennial with the stolons very densely covered with short harsh leaves. It forms an exeeptionally dense growth but, contrary to American data, spreads very slowly and 2-3 years were needed at Kitale to establish a continuous cover. Under Kenya conditions, it is not drought resistant.

ZOYSIAGRASS (Zoysia matrella (L.) Merr.) was grown at Kitale where the establishment was extremely slow and only a partial cover was obtained after 3 years of growth, during which period the soil was repeatedly eroded and needed replacement.

ST. AUGUSTINEGRASS (Stenotaphrum secundatum (Walt.) Kuntze). Two varieties of this stoloniferous perennial were tried, one from Portugal and the other from the U.S.A. The Portuguese variety was planted from stolons and may well be a clone; it developed only occasional flowering heads but no seed. This variety formed a vigorous, dense complete cover of dark green leaves and relatively fast growing stolons. When fully established it resisted weed invasion, was fairly drought resistant, and showed good promise as a turf grass. The American variety was weak, and formed numerous flowering heads containing some seed; the turf it formed was thin and suffered from drought.

PEMBAGRASS (Stenotaphrum dimidiatum (L.) Brongn.) A stoloniferous perennial which occurs naturally in East Africa, and in Zanzibar and Pemba islands, on

coastal sands, often in shade under coconut trees. It resembles St.
Augustinegrass but its stolons have longer internodes and longer semi-
erect leaves resulting in looser turf. No seed is usually produced and this
grass is propagated from stolons. It forms an attractive green cover and
is used for lawns at the coast and occasionally on higher ground as, for
example, at the Hunter's Lodge hotel, Kiboko, 900 m altitude. It grew well
at Kitale but was slower to spread than in the coastal areas.

RHODES GRASS (Chloris gayana Kunth) is a stoloniferous perennial which is
tall and unsuitable for turf. A special low-growing and dense variety
"Usenge" had been developed at Kitale (Bogdan, 1965) with a view to using it
as a turf grass. It is a good seeder and can be easily grown from seed
and can be a substitute for better turf when quick establishment is essential.

PANGOLA GRASS (Digitaria decumbens Stent). A stoloniferous perennial of
S. African origin which is easily propagated from splits. Under favourable
conditions on fertile soil, it forms dense, vigorous and relatively low
growth and can perhaps be used in sports grounds.

GINGERSPIKE (Chrysochloa orientalis (Hubbard) Swallen) is a very low growing
stoloniferous grass with bright-green leaves. In some parts of Kenya it grows
on occasionally waterlogged plains with black-clay soil and it is well worth
a trial on such soils which cover a part of Nairobi township where a good
lawn grass would be welcomed. On poor sandy loam of Kitale, it was weak,
easily invaded by weeds and not drought-resistant.

SWEET BLUESTEM (Bothriochloa insculpta (Hochst.) A. Camus). This stoloniferous grass forms stolons only in open ground, but is of a tufted habit
in stands of tall grass. When cut and kept low it forms continuous but only
mediocre turf. The advantages of this species are that it can be established
from seed and that it can be grown on seasonally water-logged black clays.

LOVEGRASS (Eragrostis barbinodis Hack). A creeping perennial of S. African
origin propagated from seeds or stolons. It had been tried at Kitale but
without much success.

SODA DROP SEED (Sporobolus marginatus Hochst. ex A. Rich.). A creeping low-
growing stoloniferous perennial which forms an attractive turf but only on
soils rich in soda. When tried at Kitale it soon died out on local acid
soil. It sets seed well, but vegetative propagation is preferred.

COUCH DROP SEED (Sporobolus phyllothrichus Hochst.) A rhizomatous perennial,
pale-green in colour, with soft, narrow, fairly short and slightly hairy leaves.
In the year of establishment it produces numerous fine stems terminating in
small loose panicles but a mature sward has relatively few flowering shoots.
It forms a fair amount of seed but can be better propagated from rhizomes
which spread rapidly. This grass makes fairly dense but not very low cover
and, when cut low, time is required before the leaves develop again.

ETHIOPIAN BLUESTEM (Andropogon sp. aff. amethystinus Steud.). This grass was
brought from Alamaya in Ethiopia. It has soft light-green leaves which form
dense cover about 5 cm in height and thin flowering stems abundant in the year
of establishment but disappearing after repeated cutting. It has a
stoloniferous habit and although spreading slowly, it forms a continuous
cover. The herbage turns pale-brown almost immediately after the onset of dry
weather but recovers remarkably quickly as soon as the rains begin. It
shows some promise as a turf grass, but not for areas where dry seasons would
interrupt its growth.

CROWFOOT GRASS (Dactyloctenium sp.) A creeping perennial forming a dense low growth of leaves in dry parts of Kenya where the annual rainfall is below 500 mm and it is well worth a further trial as a turf grass for dry conditions. The stems are tall and rather thick, but frequent cutting may reduce their numbers.

CREEPING GROUNDNUT (Arachis prostrata Benth.) A low-growing creeping perennial of the pea family. It produced at Kitale a dense growth of dark-green leaves 5-10 cm high, tolerated mowing well and was kept as short as desired. Bright yellow flowers which rise slightly above the leaf level, make the lawn attractive. Creeping groundnut produced no seed and was propagated from cuttings which took well and spread rapidly. The newly planted cuttings first sent out numerous stolons which spread flat on the ground and at this initial stage the lawn was not attractive. Meantime the rhizomes spread under the ground and sent up shoots which made the final dense cover. Creeping groundnut is a strong plant which withstood competition from most weeds except Cyperus rotundus and Oxalis corniculata L. Shade tolerance of of Creeping Groundnut was satisfactory and it was drought resistant enough to remain green throughout the three months of the Kitale dry season. It is very persistent; once planted it may stay for years. This very promising plant should be tried more extensively.

PHYLA (Phyla nodiflora Greene). An interesting ornamental lawn was made at Kitale from this creeping herb which has small leaves and mauve-coloured flowers gathered in small heads. It seeds well but can be established more easily from rooting stolons. It dries out early in the dry season but recovers again when the seasonal rains begin. The second year's growth is however less attractive that that of the first year.

REFERENCES

BOGDAN, A. V. (1965) Cultivated varieties of tropical and sub-tropical herbage plants in Kenya. E. Afr. agric. For. J. 30, 330.

GRAHAM, M. D. (1945) Golf greens and lawns in East Africa. E. Afr. agric. J. 11, 94.

HURCOMBE, R. (1948) A cytological and morphological study of cultivated Cynodon species. In "Experiments with Cynodon dactylon and other species at the South African Turf Research Station", Frankenwald, 36.

THOMAS, A. S. (1942) The uses of Paspalum notatum in Uganda. E. Afr. agric. J. 7, 236.

THE EVALUATION OF A NEW TURFGRASS

W. H. Daniel,
Turf Specialist, Department of Agronomy, Purdue University,
Lafayette, Indiana, 47907, U.S.A.

SUMMARY

The paper gives a list of points to be considered in preparing an evaluation programme and makes detailed suggestions on assessment techniques.

PRINCIPLES OF EVALUATION

Although research workers are vitally concerned with techniques of testing, they face the equally difficult question of WHY, WHAT, WHO, WHERE, WHEN and HOW TO TEST AND REPORT.

1. WHY TEST?

    (a) To seek improvement in performance.

    (b) To satisfy diverse local conditions or needs.

    (c) To anticipate local marketing of a variety.

    (d) To meet legal requirements for tests before marketing is permitted.

    (e) To test just because seed is offered.

    (f) To retest an old variety as a standard when testing the new.

Anything research workers can do to expedite the culling process and reduce the entries to be arranged, planted, maintained, observed and reported would be a contribution to turf improvement. This is especially true of old varieties and marginal material.

II. WHAT TO TEST?

    (a) Species:
  1. Which does the climate demand?
  2. Is there reason to specialise in one, or a few, species?
  3. Which do the management methods require?

    (b) Varieties:
  1. What new qualities are needed in the area?
  2. What uses are worth investigating?(e.g.
     (i) appearance,(ii) athletic use,
     (iii) blending)

    (c) Experimental facilities:
  1. On what basis can the effort be justified?
  2. On what basis are sources to submit samples for test?
  3. What load can be assumed, by source or by co-tester?

III. WHO?
(a) is willing to undertake testing ?
(b) has interest, technique, resources, contacts?
(c) is in a potential marketing area?
(d) is part of an organised co-testing programme?

IV WHERE?

This is closely related to "Who?" The desire for superior performance at consumer level is basic. Currently economics and government conditions greatly affect sales by the seed industry. Shall testing be done:

(a) by all states, or a representative in each region?
(b) by all in a common market, or all required by law?
(c) only by public institutions, or only by private companies, or by both?

V. WHEN?

In other words, at what stage of varietal development? Must the Breeder protect himself by releasing the variety completely on his own, or can co-testing serve to help guide him in varietal selection? How can the Breeder obtain help early and wide enough to secure the benefit of co-testing? The alternatives are:

(a) Co-testing as a component part of the basic early screening:

1. On numbered experimental material, before decisions on potential varieties are made.

2. Can be a second step, after the first local tests.

3. Use 50% of the earliest seed harvest for distribution to selected co-testers.

4. Reporting back annually all data on experimental and standard material.

(b) Co-testing of new variety, after naming and release:

1. For wider adaptation and wider acceptance and to spread sales.

2. To conform to laws requiring approval as a condition prior to sale; tests to be made by designated test stations.

3. For local information-sharing by researchers.

4. For observations by consumers.

VI. REPORTING

Perhaps the most difficult phase of all is the rapid exchange of information. All possible effort to reduce, cull and discard inferior selections promptly will help.

(a) Early screening stage (see V.(a) above).

1. All data on the experimental material and the standard to be sent back to breeder annually.

2. Visits and personal communications also, as much as possible.

3. Share summaries with co-workers in research meetings, as desired.

4. After two years, a summary to the breeder.

5. Data to be published only if variety is released, but then anything the consumer audience needs should be published.

(b) Reporting on a new variety (see V. (b) above).

1. After two years, a summary to the breeder and to co-workers.

2. Publish anything the consumer audience needs.

3. To conform to laws, publish information as required, e.g. whether the variety is:
   (i) recommended, suggested or not recommended.
   (ii) proven, adapted, or has only limited or special uses.
   (iii) registered, not tested or not registerable.
   (iv) approved on the basis of co-testers' reports from elsewhere.
   (v) not submitted, or requested, for test, and so not tested.

VII. FEES FOR CO-TESTING

In view of the wide variation in requirements, needs and responsibilities it is obvious that each potential co-tester must establish his own plan or code of fees for various tests, e.g.

A-1 Turf test (replicated plots) (to be charged for first two years)
A-2 Mowed individual spaced plants (10-100) (to be charged for first two years)
A-3 Unmowed spaced plants (10-100) (to be charged for first two years)
A-4 Disease inoculations and incubations (to be charged by arrangement only).

Such charges are only in effect after entry forms are adequately completed, and seed forwarding is arranged by co-testers and source.

Experiment Station research material should be subject to the same conditions, except the fees, by arrangement.

TECHNIQUES OF EVALUATION

The legal obligation for varietal testing in some countries and the numerous available experimental selections show the need for more uniform testing procedures.

The broad concept of variety comparison (ignoring all the possible details of procedures) can make use of ratings, percentages, rankings and objective measured data.

I. RATINGS

These are essentially based on a range of character expression. There are two possible approaches:

A.   Comparison with the PERFECT IDEAL (a mental picture).

   (i) One trained person must repeatedly do the judging.
  (ii) This method can reveal trends.
 (iii) No plot can show a character to an extreme degree.
  (iv) All may be similar (good, average or bad).
   (v) Ratings may be plotted as accumulation of value with time, e.g. putting green quality on 1st April was average (3-5) but on 1st June was good (1-2) for all varieties.

B. Comparison with OTHERS in test.

   (i) several observers can make concurrent judgments.
  (ii) anyone can make valid comparisons.
 (iii) one or more plots must show highest value.
  (iv) one or more plots must show lowest value.
   (v) all plots are rated comparatively.

C.   Methods of expressing ratings.

	Score for most desired character ←	Score for least desired character →	Comments
Method (i)	1 2 3 4	5 6 7 8 9	fits punch cards: 0 is used for loss of plot.
Method (ii)	5 4	3 2 1	Used in some disease lesion work.
Method (iii)	1 2	3 4 5	equivalent to alternate numbers in method (i)
Method (iv)	10 9 8 7 6	5 4 3 2 1	requires 2 lines on punch cards: easy to confuse with percentages.

As an example the 1-9 system (method (i)) can be used thus for response to range of nitrogen rates:

1.   Is the most (perhaps an excessive) growth response.
2.   Is very ample: perhaps more than conditions normally need.
3.   Is an adequate response for the use intended.
4.   Is a marginal response for the use intended.
5.   Is average response for the use intended.
6.   Is a definitely weak response.
7.   Is little response.
8.   Is a response just more than the check (control).
9.   Is the worst, the same as the untreated check (control).

II PERCENTAGES

    A. Visual estimates. These permit fast comparison, for example,

        100, 99, 98, 96, 94,/ 90, 85, 80, 75, 70, 60, 50 and reverse to 0.

        close estimates   general estimates

    B. Actual MEASUREMENTS with top value of 100%, for example 85% of seed germinated by count.

    C. Conversion to a BASE of 100%, for example if a standard variety, such as Merion Kentucky bluegrass, is assigned 100, all other varieties in trial can be assessed as more or less than the standard.

III. OBJECTIVE MEASUREMENTS (Metric when applicable)

    A. Numbers (of tillers, shoots, rhizomes, lesions, spots, etc.)

    B. Height (of leaves, seedheads, sheaths, regrowth, etc.)

    C. Width (of leaf when mowed, leaf unmowed at high N, etc.)

    D. Size (of seedhead, seed, lesions, spots, spread, etc.)

    E. Weight (of clippings, seed, etc.)

IV. RANKINGS

The ranking of the varieties being compared is useful:

    a. When several items need be reduced into one judgment.
    b. When weighted values for importance need to be assigned: for example, is spread more important than colour, or how are large lesions to be compared with small dots?

V. DATA PRESENTATION

Data on area size (metric) should not give more than 3 digits per unit area, for example:-

0.12	kg/ha
8.2	$kg/100m^2$
125	gms/m^2
425	$shoots/dm^2$
15	$leaves/cm^2$

The reader is helped to understand detailed work if it is reported in standard units with few figures.

CO-TESTER   SOURCE OR BREEDER   _____ entry name

_____ name   _____ name   _____ or number

_____ address   _____ address   _____ amount of
                                                                           seed

_____   _____   _____ lot no.

_____   _____   _____ date of
                                                                           request

_____   _____   _____ date seed
                                                                           received

                                                            _____ date seed
                                                                           planted
                                                            _____ location

                              HISTORY

years tested_____

source _____

early history _____

no. of generations so far _____

other places having tests underway _____

comments _____

              DESCRIPTION - compared to standard = _____ variety

establishment rate _____

Rhizome vigour _____

height of leaves unmowed _____

   "   "   seedheads _____

density as TURF _____

colour _____

close mowing tolerance _____

shade   "   _____

disease   "   _____

_____

fertility preference _____

chromosome counts _____

current status in plans _____

seed also being sent to _____

promising uses of entry _____

comments _____

A general assessment of a variety should study the effect of, and recovery from:

Weather
Wear
Damage
Heavy use, and
Competition

For the three possible uses (A, B and C), the detailed characters should be as shown. The letter "r" means the character is expressed as a rating, by comparison with all varieties in use;   the range of ratings is 1-9 1 denoting the most and 9 the least desired expression of the character.

	A	B	C
	Lawns, cemeteries, non-use	Trees, Fairways, sports	Roadsides, Rotary-mowed roughs
short leaf rather than long (less clippings)	r 1	1	1
short partial sheath	r 2	2	2
wide angle leaf to stem (more density)	r 3	3	3
maximum leaves per shoot or tiller	r 3	3	3
thick firm leaf (heavy cuticle, stiff)	r 3	3	3
colour (dark, medium or light green)	r 2	3	5
early spring growth (often needed)	r 2	2	2
hot weather survival (reduces need for irrigation)	r 4	4	4
disease resistance (or, at least, tolerance)	r 2	3	5
shade tolerance	r 2	4	5
turf density (dense or sparse) measured by shoots/dm^2)	r 2	3	5

Rhizomes

	A	B	C
long, rather than short (to fill in better)	r 2	2	2
large, rather than small (to give more reserves)	r 4	4	4
weak apical dominance (to allow more spurs)	r 5	5	5
deep, rather than shallow (to escape damage better)	r 3	3	3

Seedlings

	A	B	C
fast establishment (rather than slow)	r 1-5	1-5	1-5
strong (rather than weak or variable)	r 1-3	1-3	1-3
rhizomes and new leaves formed early	r 1-2	1-2	1-2
low-growing (rather than tall "spindle")	r 1-3	1-3	1-3

As mature single plant		A	B	C
low to medium seed yielder (not high)	lb./ac.	300	300	500
seedhead short rather than high	cm	20-30	30-40	40-60
strong stems, full heads, late maturity	r	1-3	1-3	1-3
seed weight (heavy to very heavy)	seed/gm	4,000	4,000	< 4,000
no severe seed field diseases	r	1-3	1-3	1-3
seed with little "cotton" (easy to clean)	r	1-3	1-3	1-3
leaf (mature) without competition (leaf should be short, not long)	cm	5-10	5-12	6-15
leaf (mature) with dense competition	cm	10-20	10-24	12-30
leaf wide rather than narrow	cm	2-4	3-5	4-7
leaf thick, stiff, with thick cuticle	r	1-5	1-5	1-5

TURFGRASS BREEDING IN WEST GERMANY

E. L. Entrup,
Deutsche Saatveredelung Lippstadt-Bremen G.m.b.H., Lippstadt,
West Germany

SUMMARY

German turfgrass breeding was restricted by a Seed Law which only
protected grass varieties with purely agricultural value, but a stop-gap
ruling and finally the new Seed Law enabled turfgrasses to get protection. In
expectation of this, German breeders had achieved good preparatory work, so
that when the new Seed Law came into effect four strains were already protected
and twenty-two further varieties had been accepted into the official system.

In breeding, the German Research stations aim for suitability for fine
ornamental turf, normal general purpose lawns, playgrounds and playing
fields, or even embankments.

The ecological wild stocks of Central Europe are predominantly used as
parent material, since these offer the best adaptation to the constantly
changing climatic conditions.

Three points are suggested for consideration by the Conference:

1. International co-operation on methods of breeding for
    disease resistance.

2. Standardisation of testing methods.

3. Study of the most suitable seed multiplication areas.

Today if one is to give an account of turfgrass breeding in Germany
one must not forget to cast a backward glance on the beginnings with their
many associated difficulties. Only the recognition of this past history can
give understanding why German breeding work in turfgrasses has not yet caught
up completely with that of foreign partners, who have already been culti-
vating lawn grasses for decades.

The old Seed Law of 1953 confined itself in the Varieties Protection
division to grass varieties which were catalogued in the so-called "List of
species". The species dealt with were those of importance agriculturally,
whereas the species or sub-species to which the most important turfgrasses
belong were not adequately protected. The demand for seed of turfgrass
was therefore predominantly met by varieties from the agricultural sphere or
else taken care of by cheap imports of an unsatisfactory quality.

The breeders as well as the consumer very soon recognised that not every
species or variety was suited for lawn purposes and quality became more and
more important. The demand for lawn seed had an upward swing and it appeared
worthwhile for the breeder to take up work on turf grasses alongside breeding
work on fodder grasses.

In the absence of a better legal foundation the Variety Registration
Office (Bundessortenamt) created a temporary solution for those species which

had been introduced into the list of varieties, but which are not of cultural value in the agricultural sense. In the catalogue test, these varieties had to fulfil the conditions but were declared "Export strain" and were not subject to a quality test.

To the breeders this stop-gap solution was by no means encouraging. Nevertheless variety protection was given to two varieties of Poa pratensis L. and two varieties of Festuca rubra L. ssp. commutata Gaud. during this time.

Stimulated by this temporary solution and in expectation of a new Seed Law that would adequately cover these matters, numerous breeding stations began to take a closer interest in turfgrass. Finally, the new Seed Law of 1st July 1968 brought an alteration so that to-day even lawn grass varieties can receive protection from the Variety Registration Office.

In the drawing up of aims, breeders limited themselves to four different applications:

1. the fine ornamental lawn.
2. the normal general-purpose lawn.
3. playgrounds and playing fields.
4. embankments, slopes and dykes.

1. The fine ornamental lawn

This is to be purely ornamental, to beautify the domestic surroundings together with floral decoration. The grass species and varieties required are those which give a thick growth, possess the narrowest possible leaf, and present a uniform attractive colour consistently throughout the year. To achieve this, both persistence and resistance to disease are the main aim of the breeder. A good toleration of close mowing guarantees a good appearance at a distance at any season of the year, and under all light conditions. Therefore the breeders confine themselves to the following grass species:

(a) Festuca rubra L. ssp. rubra
(b) Festuca rubra ssp. commutata
(c) Agrostis tenuis Sibth.
(d) Agrostis canina L.
(e) Poa pratensis

2. The normal general-purpose lawn

This type of grass is increasing in area and will continue to do so in the future as it provides space round houses and playing areas during leisure time for children. In contrast to the fine ornamental lawn, the absolutely necessary quality is durability. This lawn must be wear-resistant because it is to serve for recreation as well as being a childrens' playground. Species and varieties with good tillering and runner formation, and strong regenerative ability, receive preference here. In contrast to this prevailing breeder's aim, the appearance aspect is of lesser importance, but persistence and resistance to diseases must be good. German breeding stations are chiefly working on the following species:

(a) Poa pratensis
(b) Festuca rubra ssp. commutata
(c) Agrostis tenuis
(d) Lolium perenne L.

3. Turfgrass for playgrounds and playing fields

In the turf of playgrounds, which has to resist the most demanding uses, thickness and robustness are mainly of interest. Fine structure of leaf and attractive colour are subordinate. The decisive factor is a powerful root formation, especially by subterranean runners as in some varieties of Poa pratensis.

Along with an excellent regenerative ability, the persistence and health of the varieties and strains must be good. The chief species with character-istics corresponding to these requirements for playgrounds and playing fields are:

  (a) Poa pratensis
  (b) Lolium perenne
  (c) Festuca rubra ssp. commutata
  (d) Festuca rubra ssp. rubra
  (e) Cynosurus cristatus L.
  (f) Phleum pratense L.

Apart from these species, Poa annua L. is being investigated in the hope of finding types which are up to the requirements of a heavily worn playing field. Many types of Festuca arundinacea Schreb. might likewise be useful on heavily used turf such as race courses.

4. Embankments, slopes and dykes

The qualities of species and varieties which find application in the technical sphere differ basically in many attributes from those of the normal ornamental turfgrass. To limit erosion they should grow rapidly and strengthen the soil with their roots. Moreover, they must possess a good ability to adjust to both soil and climate. It is the breeder's aim to breed varieties for use on embankments, slopes and road sides which need only one mowing per year and on the whole can do without attention. Nevertheless, a pleasing aspect must be preserved for these green surfaces.

One property which the breeder must take into special consideration is salt tolerance for grasses on dykes and road sides. The species on which work is being done are:

  (a) Festuca rubra
  (b) Agrostis tenuis
  (c) Agrostis canina
  (d) Festuca ovina L.
  (e) Poa pratensis
  (f) Lolium perenne
  (g) P. bertolonii DC

Whereas turfgrass breeding has been pursued for decades in other countries, it is still in its infancy in Germany, due to the aforementioned circumstances. Nevertheless the opinion among breeders is that in the natural populations of grasses, there are good and even excellent forms and types available which can be considered for lawn purposes and which are well adapted to central European climatic conditions. Building upon this parent material, the German turfgrass breeders hope soon to achieve successes.

The Breeder's work extends therefore over a comprehensive collection of ecological types. Valuable sources of discovery are heavily used playing fields,

much used pathways and old grazing pastures.   Moreover, commercial seed and
existing varieties are used for selecting and crossbreeding. They are
selected further under simultaneous use of various testing methods, to
obtain a turfgrass variety which achieves the breeder's aim.

At the beginning of the 1960's an institution was formed, to give more
attention to turfgrass problems, namely the "Society of Turfgrass Research".
This organization can advise the breeder on many questions, and also has the role
of making investigations, giving advice and awaking a real awareness of
varieties in the consumer.

The Research Establishment at the Institute for Grassland Farming and
Fodder Production at the Justus-Liebig-University in Giessen has set itself
a similar aim under the leadership of Dr. Skirde. Both in quality ratings
of lawn grasses and in the appropriate test methods, valuable work has been
achieved at this Research station up to this time.

If present-day German turfgrass breeding has made any considerable
advances, then credit is certainly due to these Research Stations.

Success, and the present state of turfgrass breeding in Germany, are best
reflected in the number of varieties which have been registed at the Variety
Registration Office for variety protection. Those which are now undergoing
tests are:

Poa pratensis	5 varieties
Festuca rubra	7 varieties
Agrostis alba L	1 variety
Agrostis tenuis	1 variety
Agrostis canina	2 varieties
Lolium perenne	6 varieties
	22 varieties

The fact that, apart from some varieties already licensed, another 22
are under test, is a sign of the intensive work on lawn grasses by German
breeders. It may also be an indication of the intensity of research that
breeding work on the following species is in progress at various breeding
stations:

(a)   Festuca ovina
(b)   Phleum pratense
(c)   Cynosurus cristatus
(d)   Festuca arundinacea
(e)   Poa annua
(f)   Poa trivialis L.

It is clear that the multiplicity of breeding aims with turfgrasses is
by no means exhausted, if one thinks of the seed multiplication of high grade
lawn grasses. What use is a variety equipped with ideal properties if it
cannot be multiplied? Vegetative and reproductive growth in a plant are in
conflict with each other. But here it can be seen too that climatic
and photoperiodic factors play a role. It might therefore be useful to
have species and varieties which behave vegetatively under central European
climatic conditions and which represent ideal lawn grasses, and to grow them
under quite different conditions for seed multiplication. In this connection
the example of German lucerne and clover varieties may be recalled; they have

very good seed yields under the Californian climate, which can hardly ever be attained in their country of origin. In this respect an International Turfgrass Research Conference might have a real purpose.

But there is first of all another wish of breeders, to be addressed to this International Conference, on the subject of resistance to diseases in turfgrasses. There are many fungal diseases and other plant pests which create more and more difficulties in breeding work. It must be possible in the field of international co-operation to do something in breeding for resistance.

A second wish of the breeders is linked to this, and appears just as important; that is the wish for standardised testing methods for lawn grasses. Uniform test methods ensure comparable results so that the factors affecting a grass strain are more easily comprehensible.

The third point is the wish of the breeders to find the most favourable region for seed multiplication of each species.

It would be welcome if this first working conference were to reach decisions. A great service would be rendered in many respects to the breeder, to the branches of trade concerned with turfgrasses, and to the consumer.

TURFGRASS BREEDING IN THE NETHERLANDS

W. A. Eschauzier,

Senior Plant Breeder, N.V.H. Mommersteeg's Zaadteelt & Zaadhandel,

Vlijmen, The Netherlands

SUMMARY

Turfgrass breeding in the Netherlands had already started on a small scale before 1920,when the first steps in this field were taken by a private breeder. Since then several private breeding stations have taken up this work and at present they number 8, working on either a large or small scale. In the 44th Dutch Descriptive List of Varieties of 1969, 51 Dutch cultivars are listed, belonging to 12 different botanical species or sub-species, suitable for use in lawns and sporting grounds. Of these 51 cultivars, 27 have been registered on one or more foreign Lists of Varieties, whilst 48 new cultivars are under test both in the Netherlands and other countries.

In this paper attention is given to the botanical species and the cultivars in the breeding programme of the 8 firms, and the breeding methods employed by them.

INTRODUCTION

This paper aims to give a brief summary of the breeder's work on turfgrasses in the Netherlands. As with forage grasses, this work has always been in the hands of private firms, working from their own financial resources without any state subsidies.

The government institutes,very active in the field of forage grasses, limit themselves to breeding research, and from time to time basic material resulting from this research is issued to the breeders as initial material for further breeding. These institutes, however, have, not yet worked on turfgrasses. Even before the twenties the first steps in turfgrass breeding had been taken by a private company. During the following years other firms followed gradually, but only after 1940 was this work tackled on a much larger scale by 4 breeders. Later another 4 breeding firms followed, so that there are now 8 in total, which apart from their breeding programme on forage grasses, have also, on a larger or smaller scale, a programme for turfgrass breeding.

For commercial reasons the activities of the 8 firms will be summarised in general, and the activities of each breeding firm will not be considered separately, nor will the names of the developed cultivars be mentioned.

THE BREEDING FIRMS

The eight Breeding firms breeding grasses for lawns and sports turf are, in alphabetical order:

1. Barenbrug's Zaadhandel N.V.,Arnhem.
2. Cebeco,Rotterdam.
3. N.V. Kweekbedrijf C.I.V., Ottersum.
4. Gebrs. van Engelen's Zaadteelt en Zaadhandel N.V.,Vlijmen.
5. Kon. Kweekbedrijf D.J. van der Have N.V., Kapelle-Biezelinge.

6.   J. Joordens Zaadhandel N.V., Venlo-Blerick.
7.   N.V.H. Mommersteeg's Zaadteelt en Zaadhandel, Vlijmen.
8.   Zwaan en de Wiljes Zaadteelt en Zaadhandel N.V.,Scheemda.

THE DUTCH DESCRIPTIVE LIST OF VARIETIES AND TRIALS IN OTHER COUNTRIES

In 1924 the first official "Descriptive List of Varieties" was
published. In 1941 a national law came into force granting protection to the
breeder, and furthermore the Institute for Research on Varieties of Field
Crops (I.V.R.O.) was founded in 1942. Consequently breeding work received
a considerable stimulus though at that time more interest was given to
species than to varieties.

In the 21st list in 1946, a special chapter "Lawns and sporting turf"
was included for the first time, in which a dozen varieties for this purpose
were mentioned. In the 44th List in 1969 (6), this number had increased to
51 cultivars.

After the second world war interest in lawns, parks and sports turf rose
considerably. The rapid increase in population, the higher standard of
living and the need of more active and passive recreation was no doubt
connected with it (2).

In an increasing number of European countries grasses are now tested in
official trials for their turf quality, although in many countries there still
does not exist an official List of Varieties of Turf grasses such as is
found in Belgium,France and the Netherlands. In Germany, it has for some time
been possible to present cultivars for registration; these are then specially
tested on their performance in multiple tests. In England, trials are
carried out at the Sports Turf Research Institute, Bingley.

Over the last few years, as a result of the Paris Convention for Breeders'
Rights coming into operation, protection for breeders of lawngrasses has been
stimulated in more and more countries, although in most countries turf grass
cultivars cannot as yet be protected, in spite of being tested in trials at
Institutes or with various commercial firms; nevertheless a lively export
trade is being done with these varieties.

COMMENTS ON SPECIES AND CULTIVARS

A survey is given below for each separate species or subspecies, with
brief comments on the position in the Netherlands and on the cultivars
developed there. The 51 Dutch turf cultivars shown in the Descriptive List
of 1969 (6) are ranged in Table 1 according to species or subspecies. The
table shows how many cultivars the 8 breeding firms have developed, the
number of new cultivars under test in the Netherlands and abroad, and the
number of Dutch cultivars included in one or more foreign list of varieties.
The botanical names used, given in full in the Tables, are in accordance with
the International Code of Botanical Nomenclature, 1966 (1).

1.   AGROSTIS TENUIS

This is considered in the Netherlands one of the most important species
for high class ornamental lawns. It is fine leaved and aggressive, produces
a dense turf and is very tolerant to close mowing. In most cases, both for
use in high-grade lawns and in golfgreens, it is sown with 75-80% Festuca rubra
ssp. commutata on the model of the "classic" English lawn mixture. Sometimes,

71

Table 1: summary of cultivars in the 1969 Descriptive List

Botanical species or subspecies	Number of cultivars in the Dutch List of Varieties	Number of firms responsible for cultivars in preceding column	Number of new cultivars under test in the Netherlands	Number of Dutch cultivars in one or more foreign lists	Average yearly seed production 1964-1968 in the Netherlands in ha (1 ha = 2.47 acres)
Agrostis canina L. ssp. canina	3	3	1	2	⎫
Agrostis canina L. ssp. montana Hartm.	2	2	-	2	⎬ 41
Agrostis tenuis Sibth.	5	5	3	2	-
Agrostis stolonifera L.	1	1	-	-	-
Cynosorus cristatus L.	-	-	-	-	3
Festuca longifolia Thuill.	1	1	-	1	209 (Note 1)
Festuca rubra L. ssp. commutata Gaud.	5	4	10	4	699
Festuca rubra L. ssp. rubra	7	5	6	5	1228
Festuca tenuifolia Sibth.	2	2	1	2	88
Lolium perenne L.	10	7	8	4	1216 (Note 2)
Phleum bertolonii DC	-	-	-	-	-
Phleum pratense L.	5	5	1	1	36 (Note 3)
Poa nemoralis L.	3	3	-	1	127
Poa pratensis L.	7	5	17	3	4582 (Note 4)
Poa trivialis L.	-	-	1	-	24
Total	51		48	27	

Note 1. Increased rapidly from 1964 to 1968
"   2. permanent pasture varieties, used also for forage
"   3. hay-type varieties included
"   4. Merion bluegrass included

however, Festuca rubra ssp. rubra or F. tenuifolia are added to these two species. On fairly acid sandy soils A. tenuis has a strong suppressive tendency and even with very small percentages such as 2% or 3% in the seeds mixture, in several tests on such soils, lawns dominated by Agrostis were obtained within 2 years. On clay soils with higher pH values A. tenuis is much less aggressive.

Its disadvantages are that it is susceptible to some diseases (such as Corticium fuciforme (Berk.) Wakef., Fusarium nivale (Fr.) Ces., Sclerotinea homoeocarpa F. T. Bennett and Ophiobolus graminis Sacc), is rather susceptible to drought and does not have a high tolerance to wear.

Three of the 5 Dutch cultivars all produce a dense turf, and have a rather dark colour whereas the other two are of a lighter green. The summer colour of these 5 varieties is much more attractive than that of the Highland bent imported from the U.S.A., but conversely their winter colour is less attractive than that of the latter. Three of the Dutch varieties have shown an excellent performance in German trials (4).

2.   AGROSTIS CANINA SSP. CANINA

In broad outlines the same applies for this species as mentioned for A. tenuis. Susceptibility to disease is about the same, but A. canina ssp. canina is of a much lighter colour and has a considerably finer leaf.

In 1969, however, after a rather long period of snow covering in the Netherlands, the susceptibility of A. canina ssp. canina to Fusarium nivale turned out to be higher.

In trials in Germany, the drought resistance of the two Dutch varieties turned out to be better than that of A. tenuis (5), but it is still uncertain whether this has been fully proved. A canina ssp. canina remains an attractive proposition for those who prefer bright, fine leaved lawns with light cultivars of F. rubra ssp. commutata in the seeds mixture, but in general the interest is less great than for A. tenuis.

The 3 Dutch cultivars are very fine textured and have a very light colour. They differ only fractionally from each other, and their performance has been good in German trials (4). A. canina ssp. canina is not suitable for playing fields or sporting turf.

3.   AGROSTIS CANINA SSP. MONTANA

On account of its sometimes disappointing persistency and a dark, somewhat dull green colour, this subspecies is much less valuable for lawns than the two Agrostis species already mentioned. It can perhaps be of some value for lawns under very dry conditions, but one should consider its high susceptibility to diseases such as Corticium fuciforme and Ophiobolus graminis. It is not used for sports grounds.

There is little difference between the two Dutch cultivars.

4.   AGROSTIS STOLONIFERA

This species is little used in the Netherlands. It produces extensively creeping stolons,has a light green colour and is fine leaved. A Dutch cultivar has recently been produced, which may perhaps become of importance alongside Penncross bent from the U.S.A. which has given a good performance in lawns there (3) and in Germany (5).

5.   CYNOSURUS CRISTATUS

This species is sometimes added to sports turf mixtures, yet its use is limited, as its winterhardiness leaves much to be desired. Up to the present time there is no registered Dutch cultivar. After a series of mild winters interest in this species often increases. On a very limited scale, an attempt is being made to build up a variety for use in sports turf by selecting more winterhardy types.

6.   FESTUCA LONGIFOLIA

This botanical species (also named Festuca ovina var. duriuscula) has in its generally known form as commercial seed an unattractive bluish-green colour, and it also forms a poor turf.

In the Netherlands, however, a type was found which appeared to have a fresh, dark green colour, and because of its drought resistance, good turf production, fine leaves and tolerance to Corticium fuciforme could be developed into a good turf cultivar. On sandy soil, however, it is sometimes rapidly suppressed by A. tenuis. Turf monocultures of this cultivar are sometimes invaded by Poa annua which the breeder is therefore seeking selective means to control, with hopeful results already. In the meantime the variety has turned out to give an excellent performance in mixtures with some Poa pratensis cultivars for playing grounds. A cutting height of not lower than 1 inch (2.5 cm) is recommended.

In Germany this variety has shown an outstanding performance in playing fields for family recreation (4).

7.   FESTUCA RUBRA SSP. COMMUTATA

This subspecies - also named Festuca rubra fallax or Chewings fescue - is considered to be one of the most important components in ornamental lawns; being noted for its fine leaves, an often attractive colour, dense growth and tolerance of close mowing. By these features it complies with very high requirements in seed mixtures of the classic English composition: 75-80% F. rubra ssp. commutata and 25-20% Agrostis tenuis.

On sandy soils it is often suppressed by A. tenuis, but is more aggressive on clay soils. The Dutch List of Varieties includes 5 Dutch cultivars, some of which are outstanding in the quality of their colour, fine leaves and dense turf production. With regard to leaf colour, summer and winter colour in a lawn, and the growth rhythm, clear-cut differences between these varieties are to be noted. In Germany 2 of these varieties for ornamental lawns and 2 for playing grounds have given an excellent performance (4). All 5 varieties have 42 chromosomes and some of them produce more or less short creeping rhizomes.

For sports turf under drier conditions their inclusion in the seeds mixture may sometimes have some value, though F. rubra ssp. commutata is in general not sufficiently tolerant to wear.

8. FESTUCA RUBRA SSP. RUBRA

Of the 7 cultivars of this sub-species (also named F. eurubra or genuina) in the Dutch List of Varieties, all except one have 56 chromosomes.

They produce mostly slender creeping rhizomes; have a somewhat coarser leaf than F. rubra ssp. commutata; are somewhat less resistant to drought; and notwithstanding their strong creeping capacity, they produce a less dense sward in monoculture. For these reasons they are less suitable for high-class lawns, but for playing turf, some types of sporting grounds, camping sites, or road-verges, they are very useful. One of these cultivars with 42 chromosomes takes a special place for its shorter runners, finer leaves, and better turf production; consequently it is very suitable for ornamental lawns. There are obvious differences between these varieties in leaf colour, turf production and their speed of establishment in sward formation. In Germany 1 of the 7 cultivars turned out to be very suitable for ornamental lawns and 3 for playing grounds (4).

9. FESTUCA TENUIFOLIA

This species has not proved to be of great importance in lawns. In monoculture it has the tendency to whorl, and in mixtures on moist soils it is suppressed by other grasses, especially by A. tenuis on sandy soils. As a component in a seeds mixture for road verges on drier soils it can be of importance for its low growth and fine leaves. The two Dutch varieties on the List show little difference.

10. LOLIUM PERENNE

The use of this species in lawn mixtures belongs more and more to the past. Its leaves are too coarse for Dutch requirements and it has little tolerance of close mowing; furthermore its drought resistance is poor. For sports turf, however, it has very good properties, such as good wear tolerance and rapid recovery provided that sufficient fertiliser is applied.

In climates with very low winter temperatures the winter-hardiness of some cultivars is insufficient. On sandy soils it is often suppressed by Agrostis spp., which is why they are at present not included in seeds mixtures for sports turf. Over a period of years it has been shown that most of the late-flowering, persistent, winter-hardy, strong tillering and prostrate-growing pasture types of L. perenne developed by Dutch breeders for permanent pastures, are very satisfactory in sports turf mixtures.

About 10 of the Dutch pasture varieties comply with the high requirements for sports turf, though they are not all equal in their performance, differing somewhat in turf density, winter-hardiness, persistency, and heading time.

Now that better and more resistant varieties of Poa pratensis are coming on the market, more and more European experts are of the opinion that L. perenne in seeds mixtures for sports turf will give way to Poa pratensis.

11. PHLEUM SPECIES

The late-flowering, prostrate-growing types of Phleum have proved to be very valuable for use in sporting and playing grounds for their tolerance to wear, their frost resistance, and their green winter colour. Sometimes on account of its slow initial growth, <u>Phleum</u> may be suppressed by too high a proportion of <u>L. perenne</u> in a mixture.

The erect-growing types of <u>Phleum</u> are less tolerant of close mowing and do not appear to be persistent.

11a. Phleum pratense L.(42 chromosomes)

In the Dutch List of Varieties 1969 one can find 5 Dutch cultivars all of which having a good tillering capacity, having good to very good persistency and a prostrate growth habit.

They are all adapted to sports turf mixtures on not too dry soils. The seed is usually expensive, as the plant's seed production is low.

11b. Phleum bertolonii DC (14 chromosomes)

This species (also known under the name of <u>P. nodosum</u>) is very prostrate growing and finer-leaved than <u>P. pratense</u>. Dutch varieties have not yet been presented for registration, but some breeders have a limited breeding programme for this species.

12. POA PRATENSIS

In the last few years the breeding of <u>Poa pratensis</u> has been enormously expanded. At present 17 new varieties developed by 4 breeding firms in the Netherlands are under test and there are indications that in the coming year this number will increase considerably.

Two characteristics are very typical for this species:

1. The existence of apomictic forms, by which it is possible to breed extremely uniform varieties.

2. The high susceptibility to leafspot disease (<u>Helminthosporium vagans</u> Drechsler) of many types collected in nature, on account of which persistency under close mowing conditions is often greatly reduced.

As in some other countries Dutch breeders are intensively searching for apomictic types with a fair seed production; tolerant to leafspot disease, rust and powdery mildew; with an attractive colour at least in summer, and if possible also in winter; and producing a dense sward. Some breeders have set up a big programme for this purpose.

For high grade ornamental lawns in the Netherlands and in Germany, <u>P. pratensis</u> is considered too coarse-leaved, but for sports turf and playing grounds good varieties can be of great importance. It has been difficult to surpass foreign varieties such as Merion and Fylking, but this will certainly be the case in the near future, some very good varieties already being under test.

Of the 7 Dutch cultivars, some are to an extent susceptible to leafspot disease in several regions, but not in all climatic zones. Some of them have given a very good performance both in the Netherlands and in other countries.

Table 2: number of Dutch breeding firms (out of 7: 1 did not give an opinion) which consider the species or subspecies suitable for the purposes shown

	Suitable for high-grade lawns	Suitable for playing-grounds	Suitable for sportsturf (football)
Agrostis canina L. ssp. canina	6	-	-
Agrostis canina L. ssp. montana Hartm.	-	-	-
Agrostis tenuis Sibth.	7	4	-
Agrostis stolonifera L.	1	-	-
Cynosurus cristatus L.	-	-	2
Festuca longifolia Thuill.	3	1	-
Festuca rubra L. ssp. commutata Gaud.	7	6	4
Festuca rubra L. ssp. rubra	3	5	5
Festuca tenuifolia Sibth.	2	-	-
Lolium perenne L.	-	4	7
Phleum bertolonii DC	1	4	4
Phleum pratense L.	-	1	7
Poa nemoralis L.	-	-	-
Poa pratensis L.	1	7	7 (see note)
Poa trivialis L.	1	-	-

Note: only when varieties tolerant of Helminthosporium vagans are used.

13. POA NEMORALIS

This is often used under trees, but it soon disappears when mown regularly. For shaded lawns it is therefore not of great importance. In the Netherlands 3 cultivars of it were produced, one of which is somewhat more persistent than the other two.

14. POA TRIVIALIS

One breeder in the Netherlands is occupying himself with this species and has presented one variety for registration, but little is known about it.

NOTES ON BREEDING METHODS

The following notes summarise information given by the 8 Dutch breeders with regard to the breeding methods followed by them.

(a) Breeding and selection methods

    1. Plant and Clone-selection based on collected plant material in the Netherlands and abroad: (done by all 8 breeders).

    2. Selection after induced mutation: (done by 3 breeders).

    3. Crosses between existing varieties: (done by 2 breeders).

    4. Improvement based on chromosome doubling (polyploidy breeding): (done by 1 breeder).

(b) Selection for disease resistance

All 8 breeders in some way or the other have done selection on disease resistance, not through inoculation methods, but by estimating the material visually, i.e. in lawn trials.

(c) Testing of new trial-selections (potential varieties)

These as a rule are tested for several years in lawn-trials under close mowing. Sports turf varieties are mostly tested in private company trials; but sometimes they are given to the Netherlands Sports Federation for trial purposes.

(d) Suitability of botanical species for various purposes

In the inquiry form the 8 breeders were asked to indicate which botanical species they considered to be most suitable for:

    1. high grade lawns
    2. playing grounds (i.e. turf for private use, as play-space for children and the like)
    3. sports turf (in this paper the word "sports turf" refers to football fields or similar)

Seven of the eight breeders have replied to this question. The result can be found in Table 2. It should be remembered that, in many cases, particular cultivars of these species were being borne in mind.

REFERENCES

1. HUBBARD, C.E. (1968) Grasses, Pelican Books.

2. 25 JAAR I.V.R.O. (25 Years I.V.R.O.) 1967, 53.

3. REED FUNK, C., ENGEL, R.E.,and HALISKY, P.M. (1966) Performance of bentgrass varieties and selections. Report on turfgrass research at Rutgers University 1966, 41.

4. SKIRDE, W. (1968) Artenkombinationen und Sortenfragen beim Aufbau von Mischungen für Zier - und Gebrauchsrasen. Das Gartenamt 1968, 104.

5. SKIRDE, W. (1968) Ergebnisse aus dem Trockensommer 1967 für Rasenpflege und Rasengräserzuchtung. Rasen und Rasengräser 2, 21.

6. 44e Rassenlijst voor Landbouwgewassen 1969. (44th Dutch list of varieties 1969).

EVALUATION OF WARM-SEASON TURFGRASSES

Wayne W. Huffine,

Department of Agronomy, Oklahoma State University, Stillwater, Oklahoma, U.S.A.

SUMMARY

Research devoted to the evaluation of warm-season turfgrasses includes both basic and applied studies. Basic research generally is concerned with genetics and plant breeding, physiology, and nutrition. This paper reviews recent work in the first two fields.

GENETICS AND PLANT BREEDING

1.   Results presented by Burton and Hart (1) leave little doubt that many clones of Cynodon dactylon (L.) Pers. are highly self-incompatible. A high proportion of hybrid plants can be produced if even partially self-incompatible clones are freely pollinated with suitable pollen. The nature of self-incompatibility in C. dactylon is not known, although a compatability relationship of the diploid personate type of multiple oppositional factors has been suggested by Burton. These data indicate that most unrelated plants of C. dactylon will be cross-compatible.

There can be no doubt, Burton and Hart report, but that bermudagrass clones can be found that will give rise to F_1 hybrids that will have an average forage yield potential equal or superior to that of the parent clones. Therefore, a breeding programme designed to develop parents for commercial F_1 hybrid seed of bermudagrass may well begin with a search of high yielding plants that possess other desired agronomic traits. Since bermudagrass is a highly cross pollinated species, according to Burton et al., these plants will probably be singlecrosses. Most of these plants, if unrelated, will probably be self-incompatible but cross-compatible, and most of these clones should give rise to F_1 hybrids that will yield, on the average, about as much forage as their parents. Once two superior self-sterile cross-fertile clones that give good hybrids are isolated, seed fields can easily be established, they report, by vegetatively planting alternate rows of the two clones. In order to provide the best opportunity for cross-fertilization, these rows should probably not be more than 1 m apart, according to the authors.

2.   St. Augustinegrass (Stenotaphrum secundatum (Walt.) Kuntze) is one of the most popular lawn grasses in the Gulf Coast Region of the United States. The uniform and attractive turf produced by this grass and its tolerance to shade make it particularly useful for home lawns, parks, cemeteries, and similar areas in this region. Until recently the species was assumed to be highly self-sterile, Long and Bashaw (4) reported, and it has always been propagated vegetatively.

Plants used for studies of chromosome numbers and microsporogenesis reported in their paper may be grouped into three morphological types: a coarse-textured, purple-stigma type; a medium-textured, purple-stigma type; and a yellow-stigma type that comprises the common St. Augustinegrass generally used for lawns. Vegetatively propagated common St. Augustinegrass and its seedling progeny were used in the study of the yellow-stigma type, Long and Bashaw reported. The seedlings varied in morphological characteristics ranging from coarse-textured upright types to fine-textured prostrate types.

Microsporogenesis was studied from inflorescences of plants growing in

80

the field and in the greenhouse that were collected and fixed in Carnoy solution (6:3:1), and the pollen mother cell smears were stained with iron-acetocarmine. Chromosome numbers were determined in early anaphase I figures. Photomicrographs were taken with a Kine-Exakta VX 35 mm camera mounted on a Bausch and Lomb research microscope.

The results of these studies showed three cytological groups based on chromosome numbers. The yellow-stigma types had 18 chromosomes. Three purple-stigma types had 27 chromosomes, and one had 36.

Meiotic behaviour was normal in the yellow-stigma types, according to Long and Bashaw. Those types with 27 chromosomes, representing triploids, showed considerable variation in meiotic behaviour. High sterility was common in the triploid types. Normal meiotic behaviour was exhibited by the 36-chromosome type and it showed high sterility.

3. Overseeding bermudagrass (Cynodon dactylon (L.) Pers.) with cool-season grasses in the fall to provide green winter lawns involves three interactions between dormant and actively growing grasses, report Kneebone and Major (3). These are: (1) the transition from the warm-season bermudagrass to the cool-season species in the fall, (2) the growth during the winter of the cool-season species, and (3) the transition in spring from the cool-season species back to the bermudagrass. The authors point out that little attention has been given to the effects of genetic differences among bermudagrasses on the performance of species overseeded on them nor to the smoothness of transition in the fall or spring that can be made.

Initial stands of Pennlawn fescue (Festuca rubra L.), annual ryegrass (Lolium multiflorum Lam.), roughstalk bluegrass (Poa trivialis L.), and a mixture of highland bentgrass (Agrostis tenuis Sibth.), Kentucky bluegrass (Poa pratensis L.), and Pennlawn fescue exhibited marked reductions when overseeded on certain varieties of bermudagrass. The initial stands of all cool-season grasses were above 90%. These stands were maintained until the spring transition on seeded Arizona bermudagrass (C. dactylon) while stands of the ryegrass declined to less than 75% in late February and March on the bermudagrass varieties Tiflawn, Tifway, and Ormond. Ryegrass stands on Tufcote, Beltsville No. 1 and Midway bermudagrasses averaged 89% in the spring compared to 94% on the seeded Arizona bermudagrass.

PHYSIOLOGY

1. Bermudagrass is the most important of the introduced grasses for the southern states both for forage and turf. Improved strains must be established by planting vegetative parts, hereafter called sprigs, which may be from rhizomes, stolons, or both, report Chiles et al. (2). These methods are expensive and often there is difficulty in establishing stands. Four forage-type bermudagrass varieties (Coastal, Midland, Greenfield, and a common selection) were included in this study.

A field experiment was designed to establish the influence of depth of planting of sprigs on sprouting. Twenty-five three-node sprigs were planted 9.16 cm (4 in.) apart in each row. Plantings were at five different depths placed vertical with tip protruding and placed horizontally at 0, 2.54, 5.08, 7.62, and 9.16 cm (0, 1, 2, 3 and 4 in. respectively). A rain of 2.54 cm occurred the next day and the plots were watered on the 7th and 14th day after planting. The sprouting sprigs were counted 10, 16, 23 and 31 days after planting. There was both a delay in emerging sprouts and a decrease in percentage of sprigs sprouting as planting depth increased from 2.54 to 9.16 cm (1 to 4 in.) for all four varieties.

A laboratory study examined the effects of storage time on the viability of bermudagrass sprigs under wet and dry conditions. The sprigs were divided into two 1.69 cu m (4 bu.) samples for each of the four varieties. One set of samples was stored dry and the other wet. The dry-stored sprigs were placed on a dry concrete floor and covered with burlap material. The wet-stored sprigs were placed on a sand floor, sprinkled lightly, and then covered with burlap. They were sprinkled and stirred on alternate days to maintain moisture content. Four replications with 25 three-node sprigs in each replication for each variety, stored wet and dry, were placed in the germinator at each of 0, 4, 8, 12 and 16 days of storage. The sprigs were rolled in moist paper towels and a plastic cover placed around the roll. Counts were made on sprouting sprigs and also total buds sprouted. A commercial model of the "Da-Lite" water curtain-type seed germinator was used. The temperature changed each 12 hours from 30^{0}C during the day to 20^{0}C during the night.

Wet-stored sprigs had higher average percent sprouting of both sprigs and buds for all four varieties. Dry storage reduced percent moisture content, vigour of sprouts, and the number of sprouting buds throughout a 16-day period. Less mould growth and disease damage developed with wet storage conditions.

2.   Research on the shade tolerance of several selections of bermudagrass and other turfgrass species was conducted by McBee and Holt (5). In the first experiment, six grasses were used: Pensacola bahiagrass (Paspalum notatum Flugge), common St. Augustinegrass (Stenotaphrum secundatum (Walt.) Kuntze), Tifway bermudagrass (Cynodon spp.), Meyer zoysia (Zoysia japonica Steud.); and Q-2 bermudagrass (Cynodon spp. Kansas selection). In the second experiment Q-2 and Meyer Zoysia were omitted and T-135 bermudagrass (Cynodon spp. Texas selection) was added.

Plot size was 1.52 m by 1.83 m with three replications in a randomized block design. Plots were seeded or plugged on 2 June 1964 in the first trial. Fertilizer was applied at the time of establishment. The experimental area was relocated for the second experiment and the grasses seeded or sprigged on 23 April 1965. Plots were fertilized at the time of establishment and on the first of each month during the growing season.

Three levels of light were used the first year. They were 100% (full sunlight) and approximately 60 and 35% of incident light. Small wooden frames supported approximately 15.24 cm above the turf and designed to cover individual plots, were covered with one or two layers of an open-mesh cloth to attain 60 and 35% incident light. Two and three layers of cloth were used in the second experiment to permit passage of approximately 35 and 25% of incident light, respectively. Frames were placed over the plots approximately 2 weeks after planting the grasses. Level of light intensity was determined with an Eppley pyrheliometer and Leeds and Northrup potentiometer.

All plots were watered as needed with a sprinkler type irrigation system. They were mowed on a 7- to 10-day schedule at the height of 3.81 cm.

The greatest effect of shading on these turfgrasses was on percent of ground cover and type of growth. The bermudagrass variety No-Mow (FB-137)

exhibited exceptional tolerance to low light intensity, McBee and Holt
reported. Turf quality of No-Mow was better when grown under reduced light
than when exposed to full sunlight, and reportedly exhibited more shade
tolerance than common St. Augustinegrass. Other grasses, including
Pensacola bahiagrass, Meyer zoysia, and two other varieties of bermudagrass,
generally were unsatisfactory in growth habit and percent ground cover.

REFERENCES

1.   BURTON, G. W., and HART, R. H. (1967) Use of self-incompatibility
         to produce commercial seed-propagated F1 bermudagrass hybrids.
         Crop Sci. 7, 5, 524.

2.   CHILES, R. E., HUFFINE, W. W., and LYND, J. Q. (1966) Differential
         response of Cynodon varieties to type of sprig storage and
         planting depth. Agron. J. 58, 2, 231.

3.   KNEEBONE, W. R., and MAJORS, G. L. (1969) Differential survival
         of cool season turfgrass species overseeded on different
         selections of bermudagrass. Crop Sci. 9, 2, 153.

4.   LONG, J. A., and BASHAW, E. C. (1961) Microsporogenesis and
         chromosome numbers in St. Augustinegrass. Crop Sci. 1, 1, 41.

5.   McBEE, G. G., and HOLT, E. C. (1966) Shade tolerance studies on
         bermudagrass and other turfgrasses. Agron. J. 58, 5, 523.

GRASSES FOR THE TRANSITION ZONE

Ray A. Keen, Ph.D.,
Kansas State University, Manhattan, Kansas, U.S.A.

SUMMARY

The transition zone in the U.S. is at the latitude of the Mediterranean
Sea. It is too warm in summer for most cool-season grasses which succumb
to disease. Winters are severe enough to kill most warm-season turfgrasses.

Kentucky bluegrass has been long used in this region and is best for
shaded areas. Kentucky - 31 tall fescue at 2 kg/100 sq m makes an excellent
coarse lawn when mowed above 5 cm. Ryegrasses and red fescues are temporary
winter grasses.

Japanese lawngrass performs very well in the transition zone, as do the
hardy clones of bermudagrass and centipedegrass.

A plane flying due east from Manhattan, Kansas, would fly over Kansas
City; St. Louis, Missouri; Cincinnatti, Ohio; Washington, D.C., and enter
Europe at Lisbon, cross the toe of Italy's boot and pass over Athens, Greece.
One degree either side of the 39°N. parallel is a zone, roughly 200 miles wide,
too far south for cool-season grasses in summer and too far north for warm-season
grasses in winter. Europe avoids this dilemma because its mountains run east-
west to produce a Mediterranean climate with olive and orange groves in the
area corresponding to the U.S. "Crabgrass Belt" (Digitaria spp.)

Kentucky bluegrass (Poa pratensis L.) has been one of the more successful
cool-season grasses in the transition zone, especially on the limestone soils
of Kentucky and Kansas and in the shade further south. Most of the breeding
and selection of Poa pratensis has been in regions much cooler than the
transition zone, so that the resultant cultivars are susceptible to warm-
season diseases. When mowed above 5 cm and carried at a low rate of nitrogen
fertility, Poa pratensis will survive most summers if irrigation water is
applied before any wilting occurs. If allowed to wilt when soil temperatures
exceed 30°C. it will usually remain dormant until late summer or autumn when
the soil cools.

Most of the fine leaved fescues (Festuca rubra L.) fail to survive the
summer in the transition zone because of disease problems, especially if well
fertilised. A strong programme of breeding and selection at Rutgers University
and initial screening at Oklahoma State and Kansas State Universities shows
promise of improving on the many selections made in cooler climates. The
author's bias in this opinion is based on the generally superior performance of
the Kentucky - 31 selection of tall fescue (Festuca arundinacea Schreb.)
compared with Alta selected in Oregon. Breeding to produce a rhizomatous
cultivar of this grass is progressing under Dr. Felix Juska at Beltsville,
Maryland, near Washington, D.C. Though quite coarse in texture, this grass
performs well in dense stands on lawns and athletic fields in the transition
zone.

The ryegrasses (Lolium spp.) are useful for temporary green cover in
summer and for overseeding warm-season grasses in autumn to give green colour
while Cynodon or Zoysia are dormant. In the western portion of the transition
zone the ryegrasses are weakened by rust and fail to persist. Farther east
they may survive as bunches until close mowing and high temperatures eliminate

them. Some of the newer cultivars of <u>Lolium perenne</u> L. may persist more than year in the east if mowed fairly tall. One lot from certified seed lasted four years 1951-1954 when mowed at 7.5 cm in the Kansas trials. At shorter mowing it died the first summer and other seed lots since then have failed except for scattered plants.

From the transition zone in Asia has come one of the best grasses for the equivalent U.S. zone, Japanese lawngrass (<u>Zoysia japonica</u> Steud.). It forms a tough traffic-tolerant turf that is green from April to November. Winter hardiness has been good, even two hundred miles farther north where the short summer season limits its use. With widespread planting of the Meyer clone of <u>Zoysia japonica</u>, some difficulty has been experienced with rust, billbugs and, on alkaline soils, iron deficiency chlorosis. Many criticise <u>Zoysia</u> for slow spread from vegetative propagules but this is easily overcome by close mowing at 1 or 2 cm. Other available clones are used less.

The good hot weather tolerance of bermudagrass (<u>Cynodon dactylon</u> (L.) Pers.) was introduced into the transition zone by the relatively hardy clone U-3. It was widely planted until attacked by a "disease complex" described by Dr. Wadsworth of Oklahoma as "Spring dead spot."

Since 1956 the breeding programme at Kansas Agricultural Experiment Station has resulted in clones which are completely hardy under prairie conditions. Screening of the new hardy clones for resistance to Spring dead spot has been delayed by inconsistent results when inoculations are attempted. One clone has been released under the name Midway. A second will probably be named Belmar and released jointly with the U.S. Department of Agriculture and the Maryland Agricultural Experiment Station. Tolerance of winter traffic, while <u>Cynodon</u> is dormant, is a highly desirable character, because athletic fields and golf courses in the transition zone are much used during the open winter months. The release is expected by Dr. Huffine of new clones from the world-wide collection at Oklahoma.

In the southern half of the transition zone the Oklawn clone of centipedegrass (<u>Eremochloa ophiuroides</u> (Munro) Hack.) has proved hardy and adapted for low maintenance turf. Oklawn has survived -29°C. with no snow cover at Manhattan, Kansas, and more than thirty years at Woodward, Oklahoma, prior to its release by the Oklahoma Agricultural Experiment Station.

REFERENCES

HANSON, A. A. (1965) Grass varieties in the United States. Agriculture Handbook No. 170. U.S.D.A. Washington, D.C.

JUSKA, F. V., and HANSON, A. A. (1964) Evaluation of bermudagrass varieties for general-purpose turf. Agriculture Handbook No. 270. U.S.D.A., Washington, D.C.

KEEN, R. A., and QUINLAN, L. R. (1966) Lawns in Kansas. Circular 327, Kansas agric. Exp. Stn.

MUSSER, H. B. (1962) Turf Management. McGraw-Hill Book Co. Inc., New York and London.

SCHERY, R. W. (1961) The Lawn Book. The Macmillan Co., New York.

U.S. DEPT. OF AGR. (1948) Grass. The Yearbook of Agriculture. Govt. Printing Office, Washington, D.C.

BREEDING AND TRIAL TECHNIQUES IN SWEDEN

Bjarne Langvad, M.Sc.,

W. Weibull A.B., Landskrona, Sweden

SUMMARY

Up to recent times the garden architects, engineers and specialists who have recommended mixtures of turfgrass species have not mentioned varieties in their instructions on how to make turf areas. To educate people to be "variety minded" is one of the main objects of turf specialists in Sweden, working for a better turf standard within the country. The breeding stations bring new and better turfgrass varieties onto the market and some of the special aims of breeding are described. The latest arrangements for variety trials in Sweden are outlined.

INTRODUCTION

The rise in the standard of living and social development which has taken place in the post-war years has given rise to demand for more beautiful environments and a more beautiful landscape.

Grass holds a central place in this connection, and intensified breeding and research work has steadily increased. Private housing is occupying larger and larger areas in which the lawns are the dominant feature; green belts are important features in town planning; and increased spare time and the need for recreation have extended the need for sports grounds such as football grounds, golf courses, etc.

The annual turnover in trade in lawn grasses runs into millions of Swedish crowns. But with Sweden's exposed climatic situation, it has been a matter of urgency to breed grass varieties suitable for various special applications, which means better winter hardiness and lawns with longer life. Hand in hand with these breeding activities there is constant investigation of various problems connected with laying down areas to turf.

BREEDING PROBLEMS

When sowing green surfaces of various kinds, the question of variety is of the greatest importance. Clean and fresh seed of a good variety will produce fine and resistant stands, whereas seed of the opposite kind will give inferior stands which often have to be resown and in which, moreover, weeds often gain a footing.

Breeding work constantly tries to improve the resistance of varieties to disease, such as fungus attacks during the winter and leaf spotting during the summer. These are the two most common grass diseases in Sweden, though many more have been recorded.

The colour of the grass varies greatly in the different varieties. An attractive lawn should have a warm, light colour, and attention is always paid to this in selection work, especially in trying to find varieties which become green early in the spring. To remain verdant for a few weeks longer each year is worth a lot in Swedish climatic conditions. Grass varieties must be hardy all the way up to the Arctic area, and they must be able to make attractive lawns far above the timber line. Through heating experiments and experiments under artificially frozen ice these important qualities can be studied at Weibullsholm. Resistance is therefore a very important quality, which must be considered in the breeding.

A good lawn variety should form a thick carpet, which prevents the invasion of weeds, but without being too aggressive towards other desirable grass components in a mixture.

There is thus quite a lot that a grass breeder has to keep in mind in his endeavours to produce better varieties. More differentiated varietal material is also being aimed at; e.g. a narrow-leaved meadow-grass for residential garden lawns, an intermediate type for football grounds, and a broad-leaved type for racecourses and camping grounds. It is therefore important that the landscape gardener should give a correct account of the material in his directions for the layout and sowing of grass surfaces.

The turf timothy (Phleum bertolonii DC) Evergreen is one of the greatest gains which has been made for several years in the turfgrass sector and is a result of the breeder's endeavours to raise the standard of varieties available in northern Europe.

VARIETY TRIALS

At Weibullsholm testing of varieties has been done over more than twenty years. Testing areas have been chosen all over Scandinavia, up to the far north.

In August 1968 official variety tests of turfgrass started under the University of Agriculture, Alnarp. The turfgrass varieties will be tested at three stations: Alnarp in the south, Uppsala in the middle part of the country and in Norrland.

In December 1968 the first official list of turfgrass varieties was accepted, and a descriptive list of grass varieties for green area use was published in spring 1968. (Aktuellt fran Lantbrukshogskolan, Nr. 118 Mark Vaxter 19-Tradgard 5).

TURFGRASS VARIETY TRIALS IN THE U.K.

J. P. Shildrick,

Sports Turf Research Institute, Bingley, Yorkshire, U.K.

SUMMARY

The paper reviews the present methods of turfgrass variety testing at the Sports Turf Research Institute, and discusses some of the problems of assessment. The effects of seed size may make it difficult to compare varieties for initial establishment, and the effects of disease on weed grasses complicate comparisons of disease resistance. Some results on persistency are compared with those obtained in agricultural testing, and some suggestions made on recording colour. To ensure that testing is realistic, and is not diverted into recording characters which are simply the most convenient to record, those responsible for variety testing need to obtain, if possible, clear indications from seed users, advisers and research workers on the qualities they look for in varieties.

INTRODUCTION

The recognised centre for turfgrass trials in the U.K. is the Sports Turf Research Institute at Bingley, (Latitude 53.54 N; altitude 600 ft. (183 m); annual rainfall approx. 40 in. (100 cm)). The Institute is an independent body, neither profit-making nor Government-controlled. Some seed firms in the U.K. conduct trials or grow observation plots, but there are no turfgrass trials by Government or University bodies in the U.K. The recent report of the Government-appointed Committee on Herbage Seed Supplies (1968) advocated a large extension of trials on turfgrass varieties, and recognised Bingley as the place for this work to be done.

Trials on turfgrass species, and some of the main types within species, have been conducted since the Institute's foundation in 1929, but it was in 1957 that major trials for variety comparison were started. Results have been reported in the Institute's Annual Journal since 1959, on the numbers of varieties, selections and commercial types shown below:

Agrostis species	24
Cynosurus cristatus L.	3
Festuca rubra L.	33
F. Longifolia Thuill.) F. ovina L.,) and F. tenuifolia) Sibth.)	13
Lolium perenne L.	37
Phleum pratense L.) and P. bertolonii DC)	7
Poa pratensis L.	31

In addition, some varieties and types of Dactylis glomerata L.,

Festuca pratensis Huds., _Festuca arundinacea_ Schreb.. and _Poa trivialis_ L. have been on trial.

To develop the Institute's variety testing more systematically, trials will in future be at two levels of complexity. Preliminary trials will give a first simple assessment of a variety under only one or two treatments, to show whether or not it is likely to be outstanding in any respect. If it is not, it will nevertheless go through a secondary trial, which will in effect repeat the preliminary trial, to verify its results. If, however, a variety is outstanding, or of particular interest, it will go into main trials where it can be given more treatments and more detailed examination.

TRIAL METHODS

1. Pure or mixed sowings

Varieties have been grown either as pure stands or in mixtures. Generally, most information has been obtained from pure stands. Complex mixtures have shown two disadvantages - first, the extra variability due to having several species (sown or weed), and second the difficulty of isolating for examination the species under trial. In one recent trial, however, it has proved valuable to combine two species. With a range of red fescue varieties, half of each plot was oversown with _Agrostis tenuis_ Sibth., and conversely with a range of _Agrostis_ varieties half of each plot was oversown with Chewings fescue (_F. rubra_ ssp. _commutata_). The trial has been mown for 5 years at 3/16 in. (5 mm) and the half-plots with the companion species have given useful information on comparative persistency of varieties, often more strikingly than the pure half-plots.

2. Sowing rates

Table 1 shows the seed rates which have been used in recent years. These sowing rates have not normally been adjusted for seed germination or seed size, but in new sowings adjustment will be made for germination, and in some trials plots will be sown at rates adjusted for the seed size of each variety sample, to compare with plots sown at the normal rate.

3. Plot size

Plot size has usually been between 3 and 6 sq. yd. (2.5 - 5.0 sq m) although observation plots have sometimes been smaller, and plots comparing mixtures have been as large as 24 or 32 sq. yd. There have generally been two replicates of each variety treatment, but it is proposed in future to increase this to three as a minimum.

4. Mowing treatments

Treatments have often been adapted to the circumstances of individual trials, but currently the mowing treatments for species in various trials are:

Agrostis spp.	3/16 in. (5 mm) cuttings removed
Cynosurus cristatus	3/16 - 7/16 in. (5-11 mm) cuttings removed
Festuca rubra	3/16 - 7/16 in. (5-11 mm) cuttings removed
Other fine fescues	3/16 in. (5 mm) cuttings removed
Lolium perenne	¾ - 1 in. (19-25 mm) cuttings left on the plot

Table 1: sowing rates recently used for trials at S.T.R.I.

Species	Seed rates		Approx. no. of seeds per gram	Approx. no. of seeds	
	oz./sq. yd.	g/sq m		per sq. yd.	per sq m
Lolium perenne	½	17	500	7,000	8,500
Festuca rubra	½ - ¾	17 - 25.5	1,000	14-21,000	17-26,000
Festuca longifolia	½	17	1,250	18,000	21,000
Cynosurus cristatus	½	17	2,000	28,000	34,000
Festuca tenuifolia	½	17	3,000	43,000	51,000
Phleum spp.	¾	25.5	3,000	64,000	77,000
Poa pratensis	½ - ¾	17 - 25.5	4,000	57-85,000	68-102,000
Agrostis spp.	¼	8.5	15,000	106,000	127,000

Phleum spp.   7/16 - 1 in. (11-25 mm) cuttings
                                      removed

Poa pratensis   ½ - 1 in. (13-25 mm) cuttings removed

5.   Fertilizer treatments

      Most plots receive a standard treatment in spring and again in late
summer of 1½ oz./sq. yd. of a powdered general fertilizer mixture containing
7% N, 10% P_2O_5 and 4% K_2O. The two doses represent an annual application per
acre of 60 lb. N, 90 lb. P_2O_5 and 36 lb. K_2O (67 kg N, 100 kg P_2O_5, 40 kg K_2O
per hectare). Where necessary, particularly for Poa pratensis, this annual
dose is increased by ⅓, to 2 oz./sq. yd. Supplementary nitrogen is also usually
given during the summer, as 2 x ½ oz. doses of sulphate of ammonia, giving an
extra 60 lb. N per acre. The fertilizer for the higher cut plots is generally
given as a proprietary granular compound.

ASSESSMENT OF RESULTS

      The main characters recorded are:-

      1.   Speed and density of initial establishment.
      2.   Persistency under mowing treatments.
      3.   Disease resistance.
      4.   Colour, leaf fineness and other qualities that affect
            the attractiveness or playing surface of the turf.

      In the following sections the present methods of the Institute are
described with some examples of results obtained, and comment is also made on
possible ways of improving recording techniques.

1.   Speed and density of establishment

      This character has normally been assessed as the ground cover in plots
during establishment. A uniform sowing rate, however, makes no allowance for
seed size or germination. Establishment assessments of plots sown at uniform
rates therefore measure sample characteristics of seed size and germination
as much as variety characteristics.

      The difference in seed size between samples can be considerable. For
example, among samples of 32 varieties of Festuca rubra submitted for trial in
1969, the average 1000 seed weight varied from 0.82 to 1.43 g - a difference
of 25-30% either side of the median value of 1.10 g. These differences were
reflected in speed of seed germination, when tested in soil boxes in a
greenhouse, larger seeded samples having greater "germination vigour" (see
footnote).* Although some differences could be attributed to difference in
chromosome number between subspecies, or to genuine varietal characters, others
were probably due to the accidental conditions of seed production and cleaning.

      If differences in seedling vigour are followed by comparable differences in
speed of tillering, response to cutting, and ability to crowd out weeds in the

---

*   Thousand seed weight = x
    $\dfrac{\text{% seedlings at interim count (9-11 days)}}{\text{% seedlings at final count (18-20 days)}} \times 100 = \dfrac{\text{germination}}{\text{vigour}} = y$

    y = 34.02 x 44.84 (significant at P = 0.01)

early stages of the turf: then the nature of the turf even several months after sowing may be a reflection of seed characters rather than **of** variety.

2.   Persistency under mowing treatments

Some species are tested under more than one height of cut, for example Festuca rubra, of which the two subspecies differ greatly in their response to height of cut. Persistency is normally assessed in terms of apparent ground cover, by a general visual estimate, but more accurate methods may occasionally be necessary.

In one trial on Lolium perenne (Jackson, 1962) botanical analyses were made to assess persistency after two years under four different conditions of companion species and height of cut. The results are presented in Table 2 and illustrate two points:-

1. The broad pattern of persistency is similar to that established by other workers in the U.K., notably the National Institute of Agricultural Botany in its agricultural testing where pure stands are cut at about 1¼ in. height. The most recent N.I.A.B. ratings, for all but two varieties, are shown in brackets in Table 2 (Aldrich 1968, N.I.A.B. 1968). There is therefore justification for taking advantage, in turfgrass work, of some of the results obtained in agricultural testing, provided that conditions are more or less comparable. Lolium perenne and Phleum pratense are the two main dual-purpose species of this kind in the U.K. Two other less important dual-purpose species are Festuca pratensis and F. arundinacea (which may be used on race courses).

2. Although some differences between treatments in Table 2 are undoubtedly not significant, the changing positions of Heraf and S101, for example, suggest that ranking may vary according to treatment, and that at very low mowing the ranking may differ from that under cuts of 1-1½ in. In order to verify this, more accurate assessment methods would probably be needed than the normal visual estimate of ground cover, even though a trained observer can give very satisfactory estimates when the situations to be assessed show clear contrasts.

Although the S.T.R.I. assessment of persistence has generally only been under frequent cutting, it is hoped also to introduce wear treatments in the near future. These may lead to co-operation with the agricultural trial workers who wonder whether persistency under animal grazing and treading is the same as under cutting.

Alternatively, small-scale easily-standardized tests in pots or boxes may give the necessary information to predict variety behaviour under mowing or treading, more quickly and more reliably than in normal field plots. For example, tests for response to cold or drought may be quicker and more useful than mere repetition of cutting.

3.   Disease resistance

Assessment for disease resistance has depended largely on whether disease has occurred naturally on trials. Where it has occurred, scoring has normally

Table 2: persistency ranking of eleven varieties of <u>Lolium perenne</u> based on sward percentage assessed by botanical analysis (July 1961) two years after sowing. (N.I.A.B. persistency ratings in brackets: 7½ denotes most persistent ryegrass)

Ranking order	In mixture with F. rubra and Agrostis tenuis		Pure stands	
	1 in. cut	½ in. cut	½ in. cut	¼ in. cut
1	Melle pasture (7½)	Melle pasture (7½)	S.23 (7½)	Heraf
2	S.23 (7½)	S.23 (7½)	Heraf	S101(6)
3	Pelo (7)	Sceempter pasture (7)	Melle pasture (7½)	S.23 (7½)
4	S101 (6)	Pelo (7)	Sceempter Pasture (7)	Melle Pasture (7½)
5	Sceempter pasture (7)	Heraf	S101 (6)	Sceempter pasture (7)
6	Heraf	S101 (6)	Pelo (7)	Pelo (7)
7	Barlenna* (5)	Barlenna (5)	Barlenna (5)	Barlenna (5)
8	S.24 (5)	Animo (6)	Animo (6)	Animo (6)
9	Devon eaver (5)	S.24 (5)	Devon eaver (5)	Devon eaver (5)
10	Animo † (6)	Devon eaver (5)	S.24 (5)	S.24 (5)
11	N. Irish	N. Irish	N. Irish	N. Irish
Percentage in sward of No. 1 and	57%	56%	61%	50%
No. 11	10%	11%	18%	8%

* Previously Barenza late hay
† " " " Mommersteeg's late hay

93

been on a simple severity scale (e.g. 0-5). Table 3 illustrates this, in the results obtained on one trial of five Poa pratensis varieties, which was covered with snow for about a month and showed conspicuous symptoms of Fusarium nivale (Fr.) Ces. in March when the snow cleared. The figures show the greater incidence on plots of the 'Danish' commercial stock, on plots receiving high nitrogen, and on plots mowed at ½ in. The plots had been sown in June 1957, but some were quite heavily infested with Poa annua L., particularly those of the 'Danish' stock, so that the disease scores are primarily a picture of disease on areas sown and managed in a certain way, and do not necessarily show varietal differences. It may therefore be preferable to try to establish varietal differences by greenhouse testing.

The principal other diseases which have occurred in trials are Corticium fuciforme (Berk.) Wakef., Helminthosporium vagans Drechsler and Sclerotinia homoeocarpa F. T. Bennett, although in few cases has it been possible to obtain such clear results as in Table 3.

4.   Colour

Leaf characters are often obvious to see, but difficult to record consistently. Colour is one of the most important. It can to some extent be judged on a scale in the mind's eye ranging from dark to light, with allowance for blue-greens and yellow-greens; but such a scale is very subjective, and the scoring of plots according to it even more so. One possible improvement is to use the Horticultural Colour Chart (Wilson, 1939 and 1942). It includes 29 greens, of which about 10 might be appropriate for grass leaf colour. Each colour sheet has four tints. As it is impracticable to use all 40 tints, about five can be selected as reference colours for visual assessment. The most appropriate colours may vary from season to season, but in an April scoring of Poa pratensis, for example, the following five tints appeared to cover the range of leaf colour (as determined by laying cut leaves on the colour sheets).

000858	Leek green
00962	Parsley green
0960	Spinach green
860	Scheeles green
861	Lettuce green

Because the colour of leaves within a plot varies greatly, it is useless to lay the colour sheets directly on to plots, and differences in light strength and angle of incidence on leaves, and the effect of straw-coloured dead leaves, make it difficult to match colour sheet and plot from a distance. The method adopted so far has been to select the tint which most nearly gives the same impression as the plot. At the April scoring referred to, three varieties approximated to the rather dark grey (almost blue-grey) green 000858: one to the dark green 0960; four to the rather lighter green 860, and two to the yellower green, 861.

Colour does not, however, depend only on the green leaf: discolouration at the leaf tip, due to mowing or frost, affects it, and the proportion of dead and senescent leaves in turf is an even more conspicuous element in appearance. It is a major problem not only to assess the elements of appearance objectively, but also to relate them to each other in a way that is meaningful to the seed user. For example, in the Poa pratensis trial just described, the variety that was dark green (0960) in April and which was

Table 3: incidence of _Fusarium nivale_ in plots of 5 _Poa pratensis_ varieties under different nitrogen and cutting regimes, March 1969

(Scored 0-5. 0 = no attack. 5 = severe attack: 20% or more killed)

	Nitrogen rates (see footnote)			Height of cut		Average of all treatments
	Low	Medium	High	½ in.	1 in.	
Arista	0	0.5	2.5	1.2	0.8	1.0
"Danish" commercial stock	0	1.8	4.3	2.5	1.5	2.0
Fylking	0	0	1.0	0.7	0	0.3
Prato	0.3	0.5	1.3	1.0	0.3	0.7
Windsor	0.3	0.8	2.3	1.0	1.2	1.1
Average of all varieties	0.1	0.7	2.3	1.3	0.8	

Nitrogen rates –   low - 3 lb. per 1000 sq. ft. per annum
medium - 6 lb. " " " " " "
high - 10 lb. " " " " " "

95

judged by several people to be the most attractive, had in January shown so much dead brown leaf due to winter kill that it was without question the least attractive variety in the trial.

DISCUSSION

After this brief review of the present methods of variety testing at the Sports Turf Research Institute, and the indication of some obvious problems, it is appropriate to consider variety testing in relation to the seed user, for whom the work is done.

Table 4 reproduces from the Report of the Committee on Herbage Seed Supplies (1968), its estimates of seed use in 1966-67. Three species predominate - perennial ryegrass, red fescue and browntop bent (Agrostis tenuis). At first sight it is in these species that the greater part of the effort of variety testing, and the education based on it, should be made. On the other hand, it is also necessary to ask what value there is in variety testing, and for whose benefit it is done.

A large, though indefinable, proportion of seed is used in situations varying from private gardens to public works, where the conditions of maintenance, and the lack of critical appreciation by the user, probably make it immaterial what variety is sown. This is not to say that there is no scope for variety selection. Perhaps insufficient attention has been paid, in testing, to ease of maintenance and performance under conditions of semi-neglect, for example in road verges, where a non-productive ryegrass variety, with its growth peaks levelled out or falling at times when work can most easily be done, would be more useful than a conventional agricultural variety, however persistent.

Nevertheless much seed use, particularly of perennial ryegrass, red fescue and bent, will depend solely on seed trade factors such as price and availability, and no varietal differences of the sort apparent today will matter in the least.

In more specialised turf uses, however, and mainly in sports turf, variety choice can be important, although it is questionable whether full use is being made of the comparatively simple information already available on varieties, let alone the more complex and detailed information likely to come from elaborate trials. For example, on football pitches in the U.K. tests and experience have shown that a useful renovation mixture is 50% Grasslands Ruanui perennial ryegrass and 50% S.23. The S.23 (N.I.A.B. persistency rating 7½) contributes persistency while the Grasslands Ruanui (rating 5) gives better short term results. Tests showed that Northern Irish (rating not published: probably about 3) was definitely not persistent enough for such uses. There may however be scope for more testing on the best balance of types and the sort of persistency ratings to aim for, before it becomes necessary to get more data than is already available on varietal persistency. It may even be that in such situations a character such as large seed size, for quick establishment, or some hitherto unappreciated quality, is more important than persistency.

The turfgrass seed user's real requirements are still not well enough known for the variety tester to understand what he ought to measure. In such a situation there is a grave danger of the characters which can most easily be measured becoming accepted as the most important. Such a situation becomes

Table 4: turfgrass seed use in the U.K.: quantities and estimated value in 1966-7

Quantity of seed used	cwt.	Estimated retail value of seed	£
Perennial ryegrass (estimate)	35,000	Creeping red fescue	880,000
Creeping red fescue	27,000	Perennial ryegrass	474,000
Chewings fescue	12,000	Chewings fescue	471,000
Agrostis spp.	10,000	Agrostis spp.	355,000
Smooth-stalked meadow-grass	5,000	Smooth-stalked meadow-grass	162,000
Crested dogstail	3,000	Crested dogstail	102,000
Rough-stalked meadow-grass	3,000	Rough-stalked meadow-grass	89,000
Fine fescues	1,000	Fine fescues	55,000
	96,000		2,588,000

Percentages of all grass seed used in the U.K.

Turfgrasses	18%		27%
Agricultural grasses	82%		73%

an advertiser's paradise, with numerous differences between varieties to exploit as selling points; but if the characters are not relevant to turf use, the performance of varieties will not appear to justify the claims made for them, and the user's confidence will be undermined so that even the relevant information is ignored along with the irrelevant.

Another problem is that illustrated in the previous section on assessment of colour. If one variety is outstanding at one time of the year, and a second is outstanding at another, which is the user to choose? If, as he probably will, he blends the two, his blend is going to perform no better over the year than the majority of inconspicuous varieties in trial. In other words, no advantage can be taken of either variety, and until a perfect variety is produced - if ever - there may be no practical advantage to the user from the laborious evaluation of appearance.

To summarise, the variety tester needs to know from seed users, or their advisers and seedsmen, or the research workers who support them:-

1. The situations in which each species is used or could be used.

2. The most important characters in each situation.

3. The degree of precision which is required: for example, is a 5% difference in persistency after two years worth spending time to verify, or do only 50% differences matter?

The tester will not get simple answers from other people; he will not even get them when he has to sit down and provide the answers himself; but the questions are nevertheless worth asking frequently.

REFERENCES

JACKSON, N. J. (1962) Further notes on the evaluation of some grass
              varieties. J. Sports Turf Res. Inst. 38, 394.

ALDRICH, D. T. A. (1968) A summary of performance trial results for 35
              grass varieties, etc. J. natn. Inst. agric. Bot.
              11, 293.

N.I.A.B. (1968) Farmers leaflet No. 16. Varieties of grasses (1968/69).

WILSON, R. F. (1939 and 1942) Horticultural Colour Chart. (2 volumes)
              London; Wilson Colour Ltd., British
              Colour Council and Royal Horticultural
              Society.

Report of the Committee on Herbage Seed Supplies (1968). London: Her
    Majesty's Stationery Office.

DISCUSSION

VARIETY LISTS

R. W. Schery (Ohio, U.S.A.)

In the U.S.A. the state of Maryland tries on the basis of limited experience and opinion to legislate what cultivars can be sold as "permanent lawngrasses" in the state. To what extent are the official variety lists mentioned for the Netherlands, Germany, etc., exclusive of older varieties or those for other reasons not appearing on the lists? I think we can not be so sure of our knowledge as to exclude cultivars upon the basis of subtle differences at the variety level.

H. Vos (Netherlands)

There are two lists in the Netherlands - the register of varieties and the advisory list. To qualify for registration in the Netherlands a variety must be new, homogeneous and stable. All registered varieties may be sold. In the advisory list of varieties, on the other hand, consumers are given recommendations on using only the best varieties. As the Netherlands is a small country, there are no important regional differences in variety performance.

B. Langvad (Sweden)

Good varieties are available for use throughout Sweden, but the limiting factor in turf improvement is the need to educate seed users; efforts are being made to teach them to make the best use of available varieties.

C. Eisele (West Germany)

Any variety may be sold in the Common Market Countries if inscribed in the Official List of Varieties. Any variety can get on this list, if it is named, homogeneous and stable. So value is not a restrictive character.

P. Boeker (West Germany)

With the amendment of the German seed laws in 1962 official evaluation trials with new varieties of grasses for lawns were started at 4 locations, dealing with 29 varieties. These trials have one sowing year and 4 main observation years. The main characters for assessment are establishment, performance (e.g. homogeneity), colour, persistency and resistance to disease. In 1969 a second series was started, with 48 varieties. Species included are Agrostis canina L., Agrostis tenuis Sibth., Festuca ovina L., Festuca rubra L., Lolium perenne L., and Poa pratensis L. It is intended to bring the number of trials centres up to 6. It would be useful to have a uniform evaluation scheme, at least in Europe, to make easier the comparison of results from different countries.

TESTING FOR WEAR TOLERANCE

R. L. Morris (U.K.)

Does Dr. Huffine think that some method of simulating wear could be used with advantage at an early stage in variety selection in order to conserve effort by eliminating varieties prone to wear?

W. W. Huffine (Oklahoma, U.S.A.)

Several machines to simulate wear have been developed at universities in the U.S.A. The first one was described by Dr. Youngner of California.

D.B. White (Minnesota, U.S.A.)

I question the value of such machines, particularly since they do not reproduce true wear conditions: for example, they do not simulate the turning movement of players' feet.

J. B. Beard (Michigan, U.S.A.)

There are two aspects of traffic to be considered, the wear effect on the plant and the soil compaction effect.

W. H. Daniel (Indiana, U.S.A.)

Most machines simply exert weight and pressure but they do not give side thrust or tear the plant, as would happen with skidding in football.

G. G. Fisher (U.K.)

Because of the deficiencies of wear machines, the use of animals may help in breeding for wear resistance. The Welsh Plant Breeding Station is including resistance to animal poaching in the selection of pasture varieties of grasses.

SELECTION FOR LOW GROWTH HABIT

C. M. Switzer (Canada)

Many people are working on growth regulation with various chemicals, but I would like to know of any work that is being carried out at the present time to breed varieties with low growth habit. The maximum benefit from the use of growth regulators would be obtained if they were applied to varieties selected for short growth.

W. H. Daniel (Indiana, U.S.A.)

We are interested in selecting dwarf types to conserve carbohydrates for continued horizontal growth and rhizome development, rather than for upright growth which is lost through clipping removal.

D. B. White (Minnesota, U.S.A.)

I have been testing advanced selections with growth regulators and herbicides, partly with this aspect in view.

J. B. Beard (Michigan, U.S.A.)

Two factors are involved in low-growing plants, (a) growth habit and (b) vertical growth rate. Many dwarf types show correlation between these two factors. There may however be establishment problems with plants which are very slow growing.

DURATION OF VARIETY TESTING

R. A. Keen (Kansas, U.S.A.)

It has been asked if we can make rapid evaluations on newly established turf, but I consider these would not show up the long term effects of factors such as climate which change the pattern of variety response. I think, however, there is a need for standardising testing procedures, which may be a subject for the next conference.

J. B. Beard (Michigan, U.S.A.)

We can use short-term testing in the early stages of breeding but before final release of a variety I should want to evaluate it for at least 6 years.

W. W. Huffine (Oklahoma, U.S.A.)

In variety testing we need to discuss and understand clearly the uses to which varieties will be put, and test them accordingly, e.g. for shade tolerance.

VARIABILITY AMONG SEED LOTS

P. R. Henderlong (Ohio, U.S.A.)

I want to make a brief comment in response to the point made by Mr. Shildrick in introducing his paper, concerning the possible range of variability among seed lots of a given variety with respect to germination and seedling vigour. Recent research in the U.S.A. suggests that seedling vigour of establishment in cereals may be related to the protein content of the seed. If there is a similar relationship in turfgrass seed, the seed production cultural programme will become increasingly important in influencing seed lot variability of a given turfgrass variety.

SESSION 1B: ECOLOGY   OF   TURFGRASS   COMMUNITIES

(Chairman: Dr. J. B. Beard)

COOL-SEASON TURFGRASS COMMUNITIES IN THE UNITED STATES

R. R. Davis,

Professor of Agronomy, Ohio Agricultural Research and Development Center and Ohio State University, Wooster, Ohio, U.S.A.

SUMMARY

The most common turfgrass community on lawns of much of the cool humid area of the United States is Poa pratensis L./Festuca rubra L. Experimental evidence and observations indicate that F. rubra tends to dominate this polystand over some of the region. Agrostis spp. (Bentgrass)/P. pratensis communities are also common. Bentgrass eventually dominates over most of the region. Festuca arundinacea Schreb./P. pratensis communities are used on home lawns in the cool region-warm region transitional zone and for roadsides, playfields and industrial grounds over all but the extreme northern part of the cool region. Bentgrass/Poa annua L. or P. pratensis/P. annua communities are the rule on golf courses throughout the region. P. annua is favoured by irrigation and short mowing. Lolium spp. and Agrostis alba L. are used in seed mixtures for quick establishment, often to the detriment of the permanent grass community. The composition of turfgrass communities can be altered by cultural practices including height of mowing, rate of nitrogen fertilization, irrigation and pest control.

INTRODUCTION

Most of the turfgrass areas in the cool, humid region of the United States are seeded to two or more species of grass. With a large number of Poa pratensis cultivars and selections becoming available, a recent trend is to use a blend of two or more cultivars of a single species with different characteristics. Both mixtures and blends will be called "polystands" in this discussion.

Golf course greens and a few other special areas are usually planted, either vegetatively or with seed, to a single selection of one species ("monostand"). Warm-season grasses are usually planted in monostand, but when they are overseeded with cool-season grasses the use of polystands for overseeding is common. The subject of overseeding for winter colour is covered in other papers.

The communities discussed in this report are either established intentionally or develop in response to climate and cultural practices.

POA PRATENSIS/FESTUCA RUBRA COMMUNITIES

If there is any "standard" polystand of turfgrass in the cool, humid region of the U.S. it is the P. pratensis/F. rubra mixture. Few seed mixtures of "permanent" lawn grass fail to contain these two species. It is also the typical mixture (more quickly establishing grasses often included) seeded in parks, school grounds, industrial lawns and cemeteries. A high percentage of golf course fairways are seeded to these two species, later to be invaded by Poa annua, particularly when cut short and irrigated.

Most writing for laymen (Schery 1961) and some research reports state or imply that P. pratensis/F. rubra will stay in polystand indefinitely in sunny locations if properly managed. Although discouraged by heavy nitrogen fertilization and irrigation, Davis (1968) found that F. rubra tends to dominate the mixture (Table 1) at Wooster, Ohio, U.S.A. Juska and Hanson (1959) reported earlier that F. rubra dominated common P. pratensis in experiments at Beltsville, Maryland. Many observations on home lawns confirm these experimental findings. The adaptation and dominance of F. rubra in shaded locations is well known. (Beard, 1965).

POA PRATENSIS/AGROSTIS COMMUNITIES

Twenty years ago it was common practice in the U.S. to include bentgrass (A. palustris Huds. or A. tenuis Sibth.) with P. pratensis in polystands for lawns. Davis (1958), Juska and Hanson (1959) and Musser (1948) reported that bentgrass was very aggressive in polystands and eventually elminated other species used with it. As a result of these reports and many confirming observations, bentgrass is now usually omitted from lawn seed mixtures. It still remains as a common weed in P. pratensis turf.

The precise manner by which bentgrass is able to dominate a polystand is not well understood, but apparently it merely overcomes and smothers the competition with its aggressive, stoloniferous habit. High mowing and moisture deficiency reduce its competitive advantage, but these factors only serve to delay the process. Seed sources of A. tenuis in the U.S. contain stoloniferous types that differ little in competitive ability from A. palustris.

Table 1: change in F. rubra content of sod, 1965-66, from seeding Sept. 1964

	Seeded grass by wt.	% F. rubra in sod	
		1965	1966
A	100% F. rubra	90	89
B	90% F. rubra 10% P. pratensis	83	83
C	60% F. rubra 40% P. pratensis	57	68
D	30% F. rubra 70% P. pratensis	28	48
E	10% F. rubra 90% P. pratensis	14	26

FESTUCA ARUNDINACEA/POA PRATENSIS COMMUNITIES

Most polystands seeded on roadsides contain F. arundinacea and
P. pratensis. Under low fertility and infrequent, high mowing, F. arundinacea
usually dominates. This polystand is frequently used on athletic fields.
F. arundinacea usually makes up 90% or more (by weight) of the seeded mixture.
Miller (1966) reported that heavy nitrogen fertilization(3.5 kg/100 sq m/year) and
irrigation encourages P. pratensis to the point of dominating the polystand.
The same cultural practices also increase the likelihood of winter kill of
F. arundinacea.

F. arundinacea is a major component of many turfgrass communities in the
transitional zone between the cool humid zones and the warm humid zones of
the U.S.A. Washington D.C. (Latitude about 39°N) is near the northern limit
and Atlanta, Georgia (Latitude about 34°N) near the southern limit of this
zone in which F. arundinacea is commonly used in home lawns as well as in other
general lawn areas.

Other areas where polystands dominated by F. arundinacea are commonly used
include airports, high traffic areas and industrial grounds. In scattered
clumps, it is one of the most serious weeds in P. pratensis lawns.

COMMUNITIES OF AGROSTIS OR POA PRATENSIS WITH POA ANNUA

Where bentgrass is mowed at 13 mm (½ in.) or less and irrigated, P. annua
is usually a substantial part and often the dominant grass in the polystand
although it is never deliberately seeded. Golf greens, tees and fairways are
included in this classification. P. annua is likely to die during a hot, humid
period of summer, particularly in the southern part of the cool humid region,
and is subject to winter injury in the northern part of the region (Beard and
Olien 1963). This lack of dependability results in its classification as a
weed by most turfgrass managers.

P. pratensis is also likely to be invaded by P. annua when mowed 32 mm
(1¼ in.) or shorter. It is common practice to mow fairways seeded to
P. pratensis about 20 mm (¾ in.). At this height of cut P. annua is almost
certain to be present.

THE ROLE OF OTHER COOL SEASON GRASSES

Lolium perenne L. and Lolium multiflorum Lam. are common components of
turfgrass seed mixtures. Domestic seed sources in the U.S. usually contain both
species. Their role in the past has been to provide quick establishment but
not remain a permanent part of the polystand. A few unsightly scattered clumps
is all that usually remains after a few years when the common types are used.
Too much Lolium in the seed mixture results in serious competition with other
grasses. New disease-resistant and cold-hardy varieties of L. perenne offer
promise of permanent monostands of this grass.

Agrostis alba is another common component of turfgrass seed mixtures. It,
too is used for quick establishment. Davis (1968) has reported that redtop
remains in the polystand indefinitely and should generally not be used.

Poa trivialis L. is sometimes seeded and is common in moist shaded locations in old polystands. Phleum pratense L. and Dactylis glomerata L. are
seldom seeded but are common weeds in turfgrass polystands. Agropyron
cristatum L. is sometimes used as a turfgrass in the northern Great Plains.

Certain cultural practices can greatly alter the composition of polystands independent of climatic factors. The influence of mowing height on the competitive advantage of bentgrass and P. annua has already been discussed. P. pratensis and F. rubra are much more resistant to the invasion of many weed species, including Digitaria sanguinalis (L). Scop. and D. ischaemum (Schreb.) Muhl. when mowed at 51 mm (2 in.) than when mowed 25 mm (1 in.) (Table 2).

Fertilization with nitrogen may also greatly influence the composition of a polystand. F. rubra is favoured by a low level of nitrogen while P. pratensis is favoured by a relatively high rate of nitrogen fertilizer (Table 3). Also, resistance to invasion of Trifolium repens L. and other weeds by P. pratensis is increased substantially by nitrogen fertilization (Table 4).

The composition of a polystand may also be altered with irrigation. Already mentioned is the increased competitive advantage of P. annua and bentgrass under irrigation. In a polystand with P. pratensis, F. rubra is less competitive under irrigation (Table 5).

Table 2: percentage of a 3-year old sod composed of D. sanguinalis and D. ischaemum

Grasses seeded	Mowed 25 mm	Mowed 51 mm
P. pratensis 'Merion'/A. alba	3	0
F. rubra 'Pennlawn'	20	0
P. pratensis	20	1
Lolium spp./P. pratensis	36	2
Average 20 polystands	15	1

Table 3: F. rubra content of 4-year old sod as influenced by nitrogen fertilization

Seeded Grass	% F. rubra	
	2.5 kg N/100 sq m	0.75 kg N/100 sq m
F. rubra Pennlawn	72	91
F. rubra	62	90
F. rubra Pennlawn/P. pratensis	32	68
F. rubra/P. pratensis Merion	21	31

Still another practice which can greatly alter the turfgrass community is pest control. Most weed species can be prevented or eliminated with herbicides. Diseases that are more destructive on one species or cultivar than another can often be controlled. Insects which may be a serious problem on one species and not damage another, can be controlled.

Thus, the composition of a turfgrass community is determined by the characteristics and quantity of grasses in the initial seeding, weed contamination, climatic factors, and the cultural practices applied by the manager. All are important in determining the utility and beauty of the polystand or monostand.

Table 4:   influence of nitrogen fertilization on weed invasion of a
3-year old P. pratensis Merion monostand

kg N/100 sq m	Weeds/sq m	% T. repens in sod
5.0	0	0
3.5	1	0
2.5	4	1
1.0	9	5
No N	24	13

Table 5:   influence of irrigation on 2-year old polystand of
P. pratensis/F. rubra

	Seeded grass, by wt.	% F. rubra	
		Irrigated	Not irrigated
A	100% F. rubra	92	94
B	90% F. rubra 10% P. pratensis	80	87
C	60% F. rubra 40% P. pratensis	70	66
D	30% F. rubra 70% P. pratensis	41	55
E	10% F. rubra 90% P. pratensis	16	36

REFERENCES

BEARD, J. B. (1965) Factors in the adaptation of turfgrasses to shade. Agron. J. <u>57</u>, 457.

BEARD, J. B., and OLIEN, C. R. (1963) Low temperature injury in the lower portion of <u>Poa annua</u> L. crowns. Crop Sci. <u>3</u>, 362.

DAVIS, R. R. (1958) The effect of other species and mowing height on persistence of lawn grasses. Agron. J. <u>50</u>, 671.

DAVIS, R. R. (1968) Grass mixtures for lawns and golf courses. West Virginia Univ. Misc. Publ. 5. 34.

JUSKA, F. V., and HANSON, A. A. (1959) Evaluation of cool-season turfgrasses alone or in mixtures. Agron. J. <u>51</u>, 597.

MILLER, R. W. (1966) The effect of certain management practices on the botanical composition and winter injury to turf containing a mixture of Kentucky bluegrass (<u>Poa pratensis</u> L.) and tall fescue (<u>Festuca arundinacea</u> Schreb.). 17th Illinois Turfgrass Conf. Proc. 39.

MUSSER, H. B. (1948) Effects of soil acidity and available phosphorus on population changes in mixed Kentucky bluegrass-bent turf. J. Am. Soc. Agron. <u>40</u>, 614.

SCHERY, R. W. (1961) The Lawn Book. The Macmillan Co., New York.

THE TWO-GRASS SYSTEM IN FLORIDA

H. G. Meyers and G. C. Horn,
Extension Turf Specialist and Professor of Ornamental Horticulture (Turf)
respectively, University of Florida, Gainesville, Florida,   U.S.A.

SUMMARY

The establishment and maintenance practices of the two-grass system in
Florida are described, and results given of several trials of mixtures of
cool-season grasses. Appearance ratings of mixtures depended on the quality
and number of the components, and three-grass mixtures were, on the whole, the
best. Four mixtures, of two or three grasses, are recommended, subject to
review after the conclusion of work still in progress.

INTRODUCTION

Florida's year-round semitropical climate and 8,426 miles of coastline
have established its worldwide reputation as a vacation resort. Its popularity
is further evidenced by that fact that more than 19,500,000 tourists visited
the state in 1967.

Horticultural beauty plays an important economic role in Florida's
tourist business because of its general aesthetic value and also in the case
of turf because of its functional value in outdoor recreation and sports
such as golf. Generally, it is said, because of tourism, it must always be
spring, summer or fall in Florida. This is the reason for a two-grass system
in which permanent warm-season grasses are overseeded each fall with species
of Agrostis (bentgrass), Poa (bluegrass), Festuca (fescue) and Lolium (ryegrass),
for winter colour. The effectiveness of this horticultural practice is
evidenced by the fact that it is becoming increasingly popular with homeowners
and commercial enterprises. In some areas overseeding is a necessity especially
on golf courses and at other business establishments where a green colour is a
must and the warm-season grasses become dormant during the tourist season.

Overseeding is not complicated although certain steps and horticultural
procedures are recommended for best results. Essentially this practice can
be divided into 3 categories; selection of a cool-season grass or mixture,
establishment and maintenance.

SELECTION OF GRASS OR GRASSES

A primary factor to be considered, prior to selection, is overall
appearance which is dependent upon colour and texture. In many instances
selection based on colour is a matter of personal preference; however, on golf
courses and other specialised areas colour is extremely important since it is
often used to mask-out Poa annua L. where this weed is a problem. Because of
their darker colours bent, blue and fescue grasses emphasize the lighter
coloured Poa annua, whereas Poa trivialis L. and domestic ryegrass are more
compatible. Selection based on texture is usually governed by the texture of
the permanent warm-season grass. For this reason coarse-textured St. Augustinegrass (Stenotaphrum secundatum (Walt.) Kuntze), bahiagrass (Paspalum notatum
Flugge), and centipedegrass (Eremochloa ophiuroides (Munro) Hack.) are usually
overseeded with domestic ryegrass, whereas bermudagrasses (Cynodon spp.) and
zoysiagrasses (Zoysia spp.) may be overseeded with any of the cool-season
grasses. Intended use is also important. Specialised surfaces such as golf

course greens require fine textured grasses for superior putting quality which is one reason why bents, fescues and bluegrasses are often preferred over ryegrass.

Other factors to be considered prior to selection include; rate of establishment, availability of seed, maintenance costs and transition back to warm-season grasses in the spring. As previously stated, bents, fescues and bluegrasses are finer textured and have better putting quality than domestic ryegrass but seed and maintenance costs are higher and rate of establishment of bents and bluegrasses slower. Under ideal conditions ryegrass germinates in 3-4 days whereas bents, fescues and bluegrasses may require 5-7, 5-7 and 17-21 days, respectively. In addition, ryegrass requires approximately 4 weeks for establishment whereas bents, fescues and bluegrasses require 6, 4 and 10 weeks respectively. Since bents and bluegrasses are very slow to become established they are often mixed with ryegrass and fescues which provide colour quickly and in the case of golf courses, a suitable putting surface during the interim period. Use of mixtures complicates selection, however, since colour, texture, germination, rate of establishment, insect and disease problems and rate of transition vary with grass type and variety. For this reason research has been conducted over the past 3 years with pure stands and mixtures of cool-season grasses to determine best compatability and overall performance. Results to date are included in this paper.

ESTABLISHMENT

Time of planting varies with location and annual temperature fluctuations but in general is accomplished between October and December throughout the state. Pre- and post-planting procedures vary with the type of warm-season grass to be overseeded, the cool-season grass mixture, intended use of the area and level of maintenance required. Because of their lower maintenance requirements, St. Augustine, centipede and bahia grasses are used around most homes, motels, hotels and other establishments. Preplant preparation of these grasses usually consists of scalping and removing all clippings prior to planting with ryegrass. Seeded areas are then watered lightly each day until germination is completed at which time watering frequency is decreased but amount per application increased. Because of the coarse texture and open growth of St. Augustine, centipede and bahia grasses, scalping and subsequent watering are usually sufficient to produce an excellent stand of ryegrass. Ryegrass is not only the most compatible in texture, but the least expensive, hardiest and easiest of the cool-season grasses to establish and maintain.

Preparation of specialised surfaces is much more exacting than general turf areas. These areas are usually aerified with a plugging device approximately 4-6 weeks prior to seeding. Failure to allow sufficient recovery time from plugging can result in an unsightly checkerboard effect due to germination of seeds in aerifier holes. Immediately prior to seeding, these areas are vertically mowed twice, the second time at right angles to the first, If additional vertical mowing is necessary for proper seedbed preparation, then subsequent direction of cut is changed so that it is different from preceding cuts. A ½ in. (12 mm) blade spacing is normally used and depth of cut set to include slight soil penetration to improve seedbed characteristics. Following vertical mowing, the areas are scalped as low as possible with greens mowers and all clippings removed. Vacuum sweepers are used in many instances as a final cleanup to remove all loose chaff prior to seeding. Seeded areas are next topdressed with approximately 1-2 mm sterilised topsoil, dragged once with a burlap-covered steel drag to smooth topsoil and then watered lightly. The final step in overseeding consists of spraying with an appropriate fungicide to control damp-off caused by <u>Rhizoctonia</u> and <u>Pythium</u> spp. Water is applied lightly, twice daily, until germination is completed at which time frequency is decreased but amount per application is increased.

MAINTENANCE

General turf areas are usually mowed once or twice weekly at a height
of cut consistent with that of the permanent grass and best appearance,
ranging from ¾ in. (20 mm) on overseeded bermudagrasses to 3 in. (75 mm) on
bahiagrasses. These areas are usually fertilized every 4-6 weeks with a
water-soluble source of nitrogen at 1 lb. N/1000 sq. ft. (0.5 kg/100 sq m).
Specialised turf areas such as golf greens are mowed daily at ca. ¼ in. (6 mm) as
soon as the grass attains sufficient height to be mowed. Greens are normally
fertilized every other week with a water-soluble source of nitrogen at the
rate of 1.0 lb. nitrogen per 1000 sq. ft.

Cool-season grasses usually remain in excellent condition until March
or April at which time the transition back to warm-seascn grasses begins.
This is caused by rising air and soil temperatures which make conditions
unfavourable for growth of cool-season grasses. Transition back to warm-
season grasses usually occurs in the same order as germination and establishment. In other words, ryegrass dies out first followed in order by fescue,
bent and bluegrasses. Rapid die-out of ryegrass (poor transition) in
contrast to slow decline (good transition) of the other cool-season grasses
is another reason why these grasses are often preferred to ryegrass.

RESEARCH

There has been much work with pure stands of cool-season grasses in
Florida, but no research work was available on performance of mixtures.
Therefore on 21 November 1966 two identical experiments were initiated in
Gainesville, Florida, utilising a randomized block design with 40 treatments
replicated 3 times. One was located at the Horticultural Unit of the
Agricultural Experiment Station on established Tifdwarf bermudagrass
maintained under putting green conditions, and the other on a Tifgreen-328
bermudagrass practice putting green at the University of Florida golf course.
The reason for the latter location was to evaluate performance under actual
field conditions of heavy wear. The purpose of the experiments was to
evaluate the performance of established stands of 5 commonly used cool-
season grasees seeded individually and in mixtures. Also included for
evaluation in the experiments were pure stands of 7 experimental ryegrasses.

Grasses and seeding rates (lb./1,000 sq.ft.) used for pure stands were:
Penncross bent (4.2), Pennlawn fescue (30), Kentucky bluegrass (10),
domestic ryegrass (50) and Poa trivialis (10). Mixtures consisted of all
possible combinations of the 5 grasses which produced mixtures containing
2, 3, 4 and 5 grasses. The seeding rate for each grass in a mixture was
obtained by dividing its pure stand rate by the number of grasses in the mixture.
Experimental ryegrasses were not included in mixtures but were planted
individually at the rate of 50 lb. seed per 1000 sq. ft. Individual plots
for all grasses were 3 x 4 ft. and seed required per plot was determined on
the basis of 12 sq. ft. Milorganite was mixed with seed prior to planting
at the rate of 40 lb. per 1000 sq. ft. for ease of distribution with shaker
cans. Procedures used for plot preparation were the same as those previously
outlined for establishment of cool-season grasses on specialised surfaces.
Plots at both locations were periodically rated during the 1966-67 growing
season utilizing a visual appearance rating scale of 1-9 in which 1 was
poorest and 9 best. An average appearance rating of 6.0 was considered to be
the lowest acceptable rating for a grass mixture. Results of this work are

112

combined and averaged for both locations and reported in the 1966-67 (Gainesville) column of Table 1. For simplicity Table 2 lists treatments 32-40 separately, since these treatments were changed each year when plots were established at new locations.

The same experiment with modifications (treatments 32-40) was established in the fall of 1967 at Gainesville, Orlando, Miami Beach and Fort Lauderdale for evaluation during the 1967-68 growing season. Of the 4 locations only those plots at the Orlando and Fort Lauderdale sites are reported in this paper. Results of this work are listed in the 1967-68 columns of Table 1. Treatments 32-40 are listed in Table 2 under the same years. Modifications consisted of eliminating all plots not receiving seed (check plots) and all experimental ryegrasses with the exception of N-106 (Pelo) and NK-100. In place of the experimental ryegrasses these plots were seeded with pure stands of N-106, NK-100 and various bents, bluegrasses and fescues. A mixture containing equal parts of N-106 and NK-100 was also included for evaluation since previous work in the northeastern states indicated that NK-100 was superior to N-106 during the early part of the growing season whereas the reverse occurred during the latter portion.

Treatments 32-40 (Table 2, 1968-69) were again modified and the same experiment established at 4 new locations in 1968 for evaluation during 1968-69. Modifications consisted of substituting N-106, NK-100 and a mixture containing equal parts of both for ryegrass in certain mixtures. It was hoped that substitution of these grasses for ryegrass would improve appearance because of their superior qualities. Results of this work have not been completely tabulated and are therefore not included in this paper.

Overall results so far indicate that the appearance ratings of established mixtures are never better than the pure stand rating of the best grass in the mixture and in many instances not as good. For example, in 1966-67 the appearance rating of a mixture of bent and bluegrass (treatment 7, Table 1) was no different from that of pure bent (treatment 1) and not as good as that of pure bluegrass (treatment 3) which had the higher pure stand rating of the two grasses. The appearance of the same mixture in 1967-68 was no different at either location from those of pure stands of either grass. When bent was mixed with Poa trivialis (Treatment 9, Table 1) the resultant mixture had an average appearance rating of 5.80 in 1966-67 and 6.29 and 6.50 in 1967-68 at Orlando and Fort Lauderdale respectively. When compared to pure stands of the same grasses, however, the appearance of the mixture was poorer than either in 1966-67. During 1967-68 the appearance of the same mixture at Orlando was 6.29 which was no different statistically from a pure stand of Poa trivialis (5.63) and poorer than Penncross bent (7.79) which was the better of the two grasses. The performance of the mixture at Fort Lauderdale was no different from pure stands of either grass.

The preceding results indicate that the ultimate appearance of a specific mixture appears to be dependent upon the quality of the individual grasses. Also, apparently, the appearance of a mixture is dependent not so much on the resultant homogeneous effect of the combination but rather on the requirement that each grass be in sufficient quantity so as not to lose its individual characteristics. Seemingly the appearance of each grass is not additive in a mixture, but decreases as individual characteristics are lost. This is substantiated by the fact that during 1966-67 appearance decreased as the number of grasses in a mixture increased. Specifically, all but one of the pure stands and 6 of the two- and three-grass mixtures had appearance ratings above 6, the lowest acceptable value, whereas none of the 4 and 5-grass mixtures was acceptable. The preceding relationship was not as obvious in Orlando during

Treatment Number	Variety or species: see footnote for abbreviations (in brackets, lb. seed/1000 sq. ft.)	Average appearance rating (D)		
		1966-67 Gainesville	1967-68 Orlando	1967-68 Ft. Lauderdale
1(B)	PB (4.2)	6.52	7.79	7.42
2	PF (30)	6.33	3.46	1.50
3	KB (10)	6.97	7.42	6.33
4	R (50)	4.65	2.88	3.42
5	PT (10)	6.45	5.63	5.17
6(C)	PB (2.1) PF (15)	5.90	6.00	5.92
7	PB (2.1) KB (5)	6.40	6.88	6.50
8	PB (2.1) R (25)	4.88	5.58	5.67
9	PB (2.1) PT (5)	5.80	6.29	6.50
10	PF (15) KB (5)	7.00	6.88	5.67
11	PF (15) R (25)	4.90	3.08	3.50
12	PF (15) PT (5)	6.07	4.29	4.17
13	KB (5) R (25)	4.68	5.08	5.25
14	KB (5) PT (5)	5.89	6.67	6.50
15	R (25) PT (5)	6.23	4.04	4.42
16	PB (1.4) PF (10) KB (3.3)	6.30	6.71	5.75
17	PB (1.4) PF (10) R (16.7)	5.05	7.13	3.92
18	PB (1.4) PF (10) PT (3.3)	6.53	6.54	5.50
19	PB (1.4) KB (3.3) R (16.7)	5.53	7.38	6.08
20	PB (1.4) KB (3.3) PT (3.3)	5.28	6.88	5.58
21	PB (1.4) R (16.7) PT (3.3)	5.85	7.58	6.08
22	PF (10) KB (3.3) R (16.7)	4.50	4.71	3.92
23	PF (10) KB (3.3) PT (3.3)	5.88	4.67	5.33
24	PF (10) R (16.7) PT (3.3)	5.28	3.54	4.58
25	KB (3.3) R (16.7) PT (3.3)	5.48	4.79	5.83
26	PB (1.05) PF (7.5) KB (2.5) R (12.5)	5.13	7.54	4.33
27	PB (1.05) PF (7.5) KB (2.5) PT (2.5)	5.65	6.83	5.17
28	PB (1.05) PF (7.5) R (12.5) PT (2.5)	5.75	7.58	5.08
29	PB (1.05) KB (2.5) R (12.5) PT (2.5)	5.68	7.00	5.50
30	PF (7.5) KB (2.5) R (12.5) PT (2.5)	5.15	4.33	5.50
31	PB (0.84)PF (6) KB (2) R (10) PT (2)	5.50	7.67	4.92
	LSD .05	0.53	1.27	1.58

Abbreviations - PB = Penncross bent, KB = Common Kentucky bluegrass,
PF = Pennlawn fescue, R = domestic ryegrass, PT = Poa trivialis

Notes:
(A) Visual appearance rating scale, 1-9 (1 - poorest; 9 - best). An appearance rating of 6 or above is acceptable for putting greens.

(B) Treatments 1 to 5 are pure stands.

(C) The seeding rate for each grass in a mixture is obtained by dividing its pure stand rate by the number of grasses in the mixture. For example, treatment No. 6 requires 2.1 lb. of Penncross bent and 15 lb. of Pennlawn fescue per 1000 sq. ft.

(D) Appearance ratings may be statistically compared within a given year but not from year to year. For example, when comparing treatments at Gainesville there must be a difference of 0.53 between 2 treatments before there is a difference in appearance. When making comparisons at Orlando and Ft. Lauderdale there must be a difference of 1.27 or 1.58 respectively (LSD values listed at bottom of respective columns).

Table 2:   appearance ratings of modified treatments (32-40)

Treatments	Pure stands and/ or mixtures (1b. of seed per 1000 sq. ft.)	Average appearance rating (see notes)	
1966-67		Gainesville	
32	Check (not overseeded)	3.28	
33	Check (black plastic cover: not overseeded)	3.55	
34	NK-100 ryegrass (50)	5.98	
35	Wimmera " (50)	3.63	
36	N-106 (Pelo) " (50)	6.80	
37	N2-31 " (50)	3.56	
38	N2-33 " (50)	5.38	
39	N3-37 " (50)	2.85	
40	N9-127 " (50)	2.70	
	LSD .05	0.53	
1967-68		Orlando	Ft. Lauderdale
32	N-106 (Pelo) ryegrass (50)	3.17	4.67
33	NK-100 " (50)	2.88	4.83
34	N-106 + NK-100 " (25+25)	3.54	5.83
35	Highland bent (4.2)	5.79	2.92
36	Seaside bent (4.2)	6.42	7.25
37	Park bluegrass (10)	7.50	7.92
38	Newport bluegrass (10)	5.25	5.33
39	Chewings fescue (30)	4.50	4.17
40	Illahee fescue (30)	5.58	5.83
	LSD .05	1.27	1.58

Notes - (A) Visual appearance rating scale, 1-9 (1 - poorest: 9 - best).
            An appearance rating of 6 or above is acceptable for putting greens.
        (B) Appearance ratings may be statistically compared within a given
            year and location, but not from year to year or location.

1967-68 in which 4 of the 5 four-grass mixtures had appearance ratings in excess of 6. This apparent discrepancy was due to poor germination of Pennlawn fescue at all locations during 1967-68 as a result of using seed carried over from 1966-67 tests. Poor performance of fescue caused these mixtures to perform as three-grass mixtures with a resultant increase in appearance. This effect became less noticeable as the number of grasses in a mixture decreased. In many instances poor performance of Pennlawn fescue had a detrimental effect on appearance of two-grass mixtures since it contributed 50% of the seed in comparison to 25 and 20 percent respectively in four- and five-grass mixtures. Variable effects of Pennlawn fescue on appearance of mixtures were less pronounced at the Fort Lauderdale site. In fact these plots closely followed the pattern previously established during 1966-67 in which none of the four- and five-grass mixtures had appearance ratings of 6 or better. Different planting dates are a possible explanation of the differential effects of Pennlawn on appearance at Orlando and Fort Lauderdale. A planting date one month earlier at Orlando permitted a greater period of time for mixtures to become established. These plots were thus able to overcome the detrimental effects of Pennlawn to a greater extent than those at Fort Lauderdale. Further evidence regarding differential establishment is demonstrated by the fact that 16 mixtures had appearance ratings of 6 or better at Orlando in comparison to 5 at Fort Lauderdale.

Effects of Pennlawn fescue on mixtures illustrates the obvious fact that as the number of grasses in a mixture increases its appearance is less affected by poor performance of one of those grasses. As previously indicated, however, where all grasses performed equally well the appearance of a mixture increased as the number of grasses decreased. These two factors indicate that best overall performance on a year-to-year basis can be expected from three-grass mixtures since their appearance is superior to four- and five-grass mixtures but not as adversely affected as two-grass mixtures by poor performance of one of the varieties. Table 3 lists two- and three-grass mixtures currently recommended for overseeding greens. Selection of these mixtures was based on a combination of quality and consistency of performance, since other mixtures had higher ratings during one of the two years tested. Future mixture recommendations may differ, however, depending upon results of the 1968-69 tests.

Since seed prices may vary from year to year, depending upon supply and demand, other research has been conducted with pure stands of various bents, bluegrasses, fescues and other grasses. The purpose of this work was to determine relative varietal quality for purposes of substitution in mixtures. Results of this work indicate that some varieties may be used interchangeably in mixtures without affecting appearance (Table 4). Substitution in a mixture without a concomitant effect upon its appearance is noteworthy since it permits changes based on seed costs.

Table 3: mixtures recommended for overseeding greens

Treatment Number (A)	Grasses (lb. seed/1000 sq. ft.) (B)
7	Penncross bent (2) plus Kentucky bluegrass (5)
10	Pennlawn fescue (15) plus Kentucky bluegrass (5)
16	Penncross bent (2) plus Kentucky bluegrass (4) plus Pennlawn fescue (10)
18(C)	Penncross bent (2) plus Kentucky bluegrass (4) plus Poa trivialis (4)

Notes - (A) Treatment numbers are identical with those in Table 1.
       (B) Seed quantities are slightly higher than those in Table 1 since, they have been rounded off to the nearest whole pound.
       (C) Recommended especially where Poa annua is a problem. (If Poa annua is a major problem the use of 50 lb. of ryegrass per 1000 sq. ft. is recommended).

Table 4: variety substitution (varieties within the same column may be used interchangeably in a mixture without affecting its appearance)

Bents	Fescues	Bluegrasses
Penncross	Pennlawn	Kentucky (common)
Seaside	Illahee	Newport
Highland	Chewings	Delta
		Park

EFFECTS OF REAL AND SIMULATED PLAY OF NEWLY SOWN TURF

M. Kamps,
Plant Breeding Station, Gebr. van Engelen Ltd., Vlijmen (NB), The Netherlands

SUMMARY

Experimenting with grasses under sportsfield conditions imposes many
serious limitations on the lay-out of the trials and on the treatments
and/or seeds mixtures that can be tested. The use of a play simulator in
trial fields would give the experimenter more freedom in planning his
experiments and possibly reduce the number or the size of the samples that
must be analysed. In spring 1968 a set of mixtures was sown in a sportsfield
and in a trial field in which a part of each plot was treated at weekly
intervals with a play simulator; results with two of these mixtures are
reported in this paper. There was good agreement between the changes in
botanical composition of the plots in the sportsfield and those under a
system of simulated play. Playing started about six months after sowing. The
five species in these trials can be grouped into three classes, according
to their resistance to playing:

most sensitive	:	Festuca rubra L. and Agrostis tenuis Sibth.
medium sensitive	:	Poa pratensis L.
relatively resistant	:	Lolium perenne L. and Phleum pratense L.

INTRODUCTION

In recent years much time and money has been spent on the construction and
maintenance of sportsfields. Many people spend part of their leisure time on
the sportsfield, either as sportsman or as spectator. It is therefore important
that much attention is paid to the establishment and to the management of a
turf that can withstand a high level of playing intensity. However,
experimenting with grasses under sportsfield conditions offers many difficulties,
e.g.:

1. The intensity of play is not constant over the field.

2. Local lesions of the turf due to playing are not regularly
   distributed over the field.

3. Differences in management practices are difficult to include in
   trials in sportsfields: e.g. differences in cutting height, cutting
   intervals and fertiliser treatments are difficult to apply on
   sportsfields in use, that need to have a smooth surface to ensure
   even playing conditions all over the field.

4. Treatments that might have an adverse effect on the turf will meet
   serious objections.

5. Comparisons of trials in different fields are very difficult, as
   playing conditions between the fields are different: one match
   under bad field conditions can cause big changes.

Consequently.the lay-out of trials in sportsfields is seriously restricted:

1. Only a small part of a sportsfield can be used for trials, i.e. that
   part of the field where the intensity of play does not vary too much
   within one replicate.

2. The plots must be fairly large with more replicates than usual and many sampling areas have to be examined in order to minimize as much as possible the influence of lesions distributed at random.

3. The choice of treatments is limited to those that do not interfere too much with playing conditions.

The greater part of these difficulties could be avoided if it were possible to conduct the tests in trial fields instead of actually used sportsfields. However, an essential requirement for such trials is that the plots can be treated in such a way that the treatment acts in the same way upon the botanical composition of the plots as actual playing does on sportsfields.

Some authors have reported investigations on wear resistance of turf grasses. Morrish and Harrison (1948) analysed the influence of heavy traffic on an established turf and found considerable differences in wear resistance. However, the conditions in this trial were greatly different from sportsfield conditions.

Youngner (1961) constructed an accelerated wear apparatus to study the strength of the turf and the necessary time for recovery. He did not analyse the influence of repeated wear over a longer period on the botanical composition.

Goss and Roberts (1964) modified an aerifier in order to simulate playing.

Cordukes (1968) used this machine and studied the changes in physical properties of the soil.

The trials referred to in this paper were mainly designed to compare the changes in botanical composition of several mixtures under actual sportsfield conditions with changes under a system of simulated play. Figures of two mixtures will be given in more detail to illustrate the general trends.

MATERIALS AND METHODS

1. Seeds mixtures

The following seeds mixtures and varieties were used:

Mixture A
25% Lolium perenne L.   (Combi pasturetype)
25% Poa pratensis L.   (Arista)
25% Phleum pratense L.   (Olympia)
25% Festuca rubra L. spp. rubra   (Oasis)

Mixture B
20% Lolium perenne L.   (Combi pasturetype)
20% Poa pratensis L.   (Arista)
20% Agrostis tenuis Sibth.   (Brabantia)
20% Festuca rubra L. ssp. rubra   (Oasis)
20% Festuca rubra L. ssp. commutata Gaud.   (Highlight)

Both mixtures were sown at a rate of 120 kg/ha.

2.   Sportsfield

In a football ground in Amsterdam the mixtures were sown on 27 May 1968 in plots of 2 x 5 m in 4 replications. The plots were situated near the centre of the field at a distance of 10-15 m from the side lines.

The first sampling for botanical analysis was made on 11 September 1968, a few days before playing started. The second analysis was made about two months later and the third at the end of the season.

3.   Trial field with play simulator

In the lawn trial fields the mixtures were sown on 19 July 1968 in plots of 1 x 4 m also in 4 replicates. In this trial three intensities of treatments were maintained with the play simulators:

> 6 treatments per week (144 steps/sq m)
> 2 treatments per week (48 steps/sq m)
> 0 treatments (control)

Each plot was divided into sub-plots of 1 m x 1 m receiving the 3 above-mentioned treatments. The plots were sampled for botanical analysis on 3 January 1969 and 17 April, 1969.

For the construction of a play-simulator the frame of a Brabantia aerifier (working width ca. 100 cm) was used. After removing the knives artificial feet were mounted in three independently rotating groups of 8 artificial feet each; within each group the 8 feet were arranged in 2 sets of 4 mutually perpendicular feet; the two sets are mounted at the axle at a distance of 15 cm and with an angle of 45^0 between the sets. The artificial feet measured 10 x 10 cm; the distance between two opposite feet is 35 cm. In one treatment with this play simulator 24 steps/sq m are made.

4.   Sampling and botanical analyses

Sampling was done by the method described by de Vries (1937):   4 borings of exactly 25 sq cm each were taken at random near the centre of each plot or sub-plot in each of the 4 replicates.

The botanical analysis was made by means of tiller-counts;   each tiller was counted, irrespective of the number of roots.

The data given below refer to the number of tillers of each species per sq dm.

RESULTS AND DISCUSSION

Table 1 gives the botanical composition of the plots in the sportsfield in Amsterdam. Table 2 summarises the figures of the trial field in Vlijmen. Finally Table 3 indicates the significant F values of the analyses of the variances.

In Amsterdam there was from the beginning a relatively high percentage of invading weed grasses, mainly Poa annua. This species increased with time. Festuca rubra ssp. rubra disappeared almost completely within two months. Poa pratensis and also Agrostis tenuis decreased rapidly. In the case of mixture A in fact a Lolium perenne/Phleum pratense mixture was left, badly contaminated with Poa annua. In mixture B the only sown species that

120

Key to species in Tables 1, 2, 3:

      L.p.   -   Lolium perenne

      Poa p.   -   Poa pratensis

      Phl.p.   -   Phleum pratense

      F.r.   -   Festuca rubra

      Agr.   -   Agrostis spp.

Table 1: numbers of tillers per sq dm on the Amsterdam sportsfield

Mixture	Sampling date	L.p.	Poa p.	Phl.p.	F.r.	Agr.	unsown
Mixture A	11 Sep. 1968	37	15	22	18	-	25
	21 Nov. 1968	29	3	16	2	-	36
	30 Apr. 1969	27	9	18	0	-	15
Mixture B	11 Sep. 1968	23	14	-	30	64	16
	21 Nov. 1968	19	6	-	4	35	53
	30 Apr. 1969	18	9	-	0	15	23

Table 2: numbers of tillers per sq dm on the trial field in Vlijmen

Mixture and treatment	Sampling date	L.p.	Poa p.	Phl.p.	F.r.	Agr.	Unsown species
Mixture A							
control	3 Jan. 1969	43	69	42	70	-	5
"	17 Apr. 1969	48	38	34	73	-	2
48 steps/sq m	3 Jan. 1969	49	47	49	66	-	3
" " " "	17 Apr. 1969	50	46	36	46	-	8
144 steps/ ""	3 Jan. 1969	29	32	36	28	-	4
" " " "	17 Apr. 1969	30	31	40	17	-	23
Mixture B							
control	3 Jan. 1969	20	30	-	34	226	-
"	17 Apr. 1969	30	27	-	58	145	4
48 steps/sq m	3 Jan. 1969	35	16	-	22	162	-
" " " "	17 Apr. 1969	16	18	-	32	120	4
144 " " "	3 Jan. 1969	17	22	-	9	126	4
" " " "	17 Apr. 1969	24	21	-	12	67	21

Table 3: significance of F values from analyses of variance

    * = significant
    ** = highly significant
    -- = not significant
    0 = no calculation possible

Source of variation		L.p.	Poa p.	Phl.p.	F.r.	Agr.
Amsterdam:	mixtures	**	-	0	-	0
	sampling dates	-	*	-	**	**
Vlijmen:	mixtures (M)	**	**	0	**	0
"	treatments (T)	--	**	--	**	**
"	sampling dates (S)	--	--	--	--	**
"	M x T	--	--	0	*	0
"	M x S	--	--	0	--	0
"	T x S	--	--	--	--	--
"	M x T x S	--	--	0	--	0

remained was <u>Lolium perenne</u>. Due to the disappearance of the other sown species in the latter mixture, there was much more space for <u>Poa annua</u> to establish and to increase.

The trial field at Vlijmen showed a higher number of tillers and much less infection with unsown species. Here it was very clear that <u>Agrostis tenuis</u> is a very aggressive species that suppresses the other components of a mixture: e.g. mixture A contained 25% <u>Festuca rubra</u> and mixture B 40%: however, in mixture A, 70 tillers/sq dm came to establishment and in mixture B only 34.

This situation is often met in sportsfields: the longer the period of establishment, the more seriously the other species are attacked; not only is there a decrease in the number of tillers of the desired, more or less play-resistant species, but also the remaining tillers are weakened. After releasing such fields for play the <u>Agrostis</u> tillers will disappear and none of the other species can take over its place, giving an open turf. Under a system of simulated play again <u>Festuca rubra</u> disappeared most rapidly. <u>Agrostis tenuis</u> also diminished considerably, whilst <u>Lolium perenne</u> and <u>Phleum pratense</u> showed a relatively good resistance against artificial play. <u>Poa pratensis</u> was intermediate, showing a considerable difference at the first sampling date but it could maintain itself in the second part of the winter.

CONCLUSIONS

1. A close agreement was found between the changes in the botanical composition in a football ground and in a trial field on which the described play simulator worked at weekly intervals.

2. If playing starts about six months after sowing, <u>Festuca rubra</u> and <u>Agrostis tenuis</u> were found to be most sensitive: <u>Poa pratensis</u> showed initially a considerable decrease but increased again in late winter or early spring: <u>Lolium perenne</u> and <u>Phleum pratense</u> proved to be the best.

3. On many soils <u>Agrostis tenuis</u> has to be considered as a harmful component of mixtures for sportsfields; it is very aggressive against other species during the period of establishment and is thereafter seriously reduced under playing conditions, leaving an open sod in which weed grasses easily can invade.

REFERENCES

CORDUKES, W. E. (1968) Compaction. The Golf Superintendent <u>36</u>, 8, 20.

GOSS, R. L., and ROBERTS, J.   (1964) A compaction machine for turfgrass areas. Agron. J. <u>56</u>, 522.

MORRISH, R. H., and HARRISON, C. M. (1948) The establishment and comparative wear resistance of various grasses and grass-legume mixtures to vehicular traffic. J. Am. Soc. Agron. <u>40</u>, 168.

VRIES, D. M., DE (1937) Methods of determining the botanical composition of hay fields and pastures. Rep. Fourth Int. Grassld. Congr., Aberystwyth.

YOUNGNER, V. B. (1961) Accelerated wear tests on turfgrasses. Agron. J. <u>53</u>, 217.

OVERSEEDING COOL-SEASON TURFGRASSES ON DORMANT BERMUDAGRASS FOR WINTER TURF

R. E. Schmidt,
Virginia Polytechnic Institute, Blacksburg, Virginia, U.S.A.

SUMMARY

Cool-season grasses must be overseeded in the fall to provide winter turf on dormant Cynodon spp. Winter turf quality is dependent upon the cool-season grass used, the rate of overseeding, thatch build-up, seed bed preparation, time of seeding, and winter fertilisation. Best winter turf is obtained when overseedings are delayed until the soil temperatures start to decline. To ensure adequate winter turf, competition of bermudagrass should be lessened by close vertical mowing immediately prior to overseeding. Soil topdressing at once after overseeding enhances germination and seedling vigour.

The cool-season grass should be selected to provide a gradual spring transition period and to compete during the winter with Poa annua L. infestation. Control of thatch build-up and applying fertiliser during the winter months appears to be essential to maintain winter turf on dormant bermudagrass.

Bermudagrass (Cynodon spp.), one of the main turfgrasses adapted to warm, humid regions of the United States, characteristically turns brown and becomes dormant during the winter months. Winter turf is provided by overseeding it with a cool-season grass in the fall. The cool-season grasses must provide adequate ground cover and colour for a period ranging from seven months in the northern limits of the warm, humid region to three months in southern limits (4,3). Satisfactory winter turf on dormant warm-season grasses depends on the cool-season grass used, the rate of overseeding, thatch control, the seedbed preparation, the time of seeding, and winter fertilisation.

Desirable winter turfgrasses must give good colour, density and wear resistance throughout the entire winter months and also provide a gradual return to bermudagrass in the spring. The high seeding rates that are essential to provide satisfactory winter turf delay the warm-season grasses' spring development. Therefore, it is essential that the cool-season grasses used for winter turf should not deteriorate rapidly in spring before the warm-season grasses develop.

Timing of overseeding in the fall is critical. Best winter turf has been obtained when overseedings were done when the soil temperatures start to decline. If overseeding is too early in the fall, temperatures are warm enough to enhance bermudagrass vigour and it competes with the seedlings of the cool-season grasses. Overseeding too late inhibits germination of the cool-season grasses. The exact date of overseeding will vary depending upon location. Experiments conducted in Virginia showed that overseeding in early October was better than in mid-September (5). Satisfactory winter turf was obtained in Florida when overseedings were delayed to late November (3).

Preparation of the seedbed has also been shown to have a pronounced effect (5,1). The most satisfactory winter turf was obtained by reducing the competition of bermudagrass by vertical mowing or close clipping immediately prior to overseeding and then assuring the seed comes in contact with the soil by topdressing immediately following the overseeding operation.

The annual ryegrass (Lolium multiflorum Lam.) that has been traditionally used for overseeding purposes, generally, is abruptly lost with the warm spring weather. This is especially critical on putting turf where heavy seeding rates are essential to provide the density needed for good putting surfaces. In tests, it has been shown that Festuca rubra L., variety Pennlawn, had maintained good density on fine bermudagrass putting turf during the winter and provided an excellent spring transition (5). The Agrostis species were slow to become established in the fall and provided inferior turf during the winter but were excellent prior to and during the spring transition.

Results from Florida indicated there were no differences in appearance of pure stands of overseeded Agrostis palustris Huds. variety Penncross, Festuca rubra variety Pennlawn, Poa pratensis L. or Poa trivialis (3). The Virginia results agreed with those obtained in Texas that showed that Poa trivialis is one of the first overseeded grasses to become inferior with the approach of hot weather (2,5).

It has been shown that pure stands of cool-season grasses used for winter turf are generally superior to mixtures of two or three grasses (3). However, mixtures of L. multiflorum and Festuca rubra variety Pennlawn (2-1 seeded at 2200 kg/ha) were more desirable than pure stands on areas infested with Poa annua. Pennlawn overseeded with the L. multiflorum and/or Agrostis palustris variety Seaside maintained winter turf quality and a satisfactory spring transition period. Although all cool-season grasses used for overseeded winter turf on dormant Cynodon spp. turf offer competition to Poa annua development, both Lolium multiflorum and Lolium perenne inhibit Poa annua development.

Tests have shown that bensulide at 5.5 kg/ha applied 30 days prior to overseeding had controlled Poa annua satisfactorily without phytotoxic effects on overseeded Festuca rubra and Lolium multiflorum.

The rate of overseeding depends on how many seedlings of a particular species will develop during the winter months. The amount of overseeding must be relatively high because of the high mortality due to surface seeding and continual play and the fact these grasses will not develop much beyond the seedling stage during the winter months. For satisfactory winter putting greens Festuca rubra should be overseeded at about 2150 kg/ha; Lolium multiflorum, 2500 kg/ha; Agrostis spp., 200-500 kg/ha; and Poa spp. at 500 kg/ha (4,3). The overseeding rate of various cool-season grasses for lawns are: Festuca rubra 250 kg/ha; Lolium spp., 500 kg/ha; Agrostis spp., 50 kg/ha; and Poa spp. 150 kg/ha (6).

Fertility must be maintained throughout the winter months to provide satisfactory turf. It appears that approximately 50 kg/ha of nitrogen from a quickly available source is necessary each month to provide desirable turf development during the winter. Higher rates may cause injury especially in areas where desiccation may become a problem.

It has also been shown that poor winter turf cover often results where heavy thatch exists. Where thatch was removed from bermudagrass during the summer months, better winter turf resulted than when the thatch had not been removed.

125

<u>REFERENCES</u>

1. GILL, W. J., THOMPSON, W. R.,Jnr., and WARD, C. Y. (1967) Species and methods for overseeding bermudagrass greens. The Golf Superintendent <u>35</u>, 9, 10.

2. MCBEE, G. G. (1967) Performance of certain cool season grasses in overseeding studies on a Tifgreen bermudagrass golf green. Prog. Report 2457. Texas A. & M. Univ. Texas agric. Exp. Stn.

3. MEYERS, H. G., and HORN, G. C. (1967) Selection of grasses for overseeding. Proc. Univ. Fla. Turfgrass Mgmt. Conf. <u>15</u>, 47.

4. SCHMIDT, R. E., and BLASER, R. E. (1961) Cool season grasses for winter turf on bermuda putting greens. USGA Journal and Turf Management <u>14</u>, 25.

5. SCHMIDT, R. E., and BLASER, R. E. (1962) Establishing winter bermuda putting turf. USGA Journal and Turf Management <u>15</u>, 30.

6. THOMPSON, W. R., Jnr., and WARD, C. Y. (1966) Prevent thatch accumulation on Tifgreen bermudagrass greens. The Golf Superintendent <u>34</u>, Sept.-Oct.

DISCUSSION

POA PRATENSIS/FESTUCA RUBRA MIXTURES

J. P. van der Horst (Netherlands)

We try to sow Poa pratensis L. not later than 10 September in mixtures with Festuca rubra L. Otherwise, the Poa pratensis is very slow in establishing and the Festuca rubra is dominant from the beginning. What is the situation in Ohio?

R. R. Davis (Ohio, U.S.A.)

In late summer sowings, we aim to sow between 15 August and 15 September, preferably the earlier date. Late sowing probably does favour Festuca rubra but my concern is not seedling vigour, but the trend over the long term, in which Festuca rubra becomes increasingly dominant.

J. P. van der Horst (Netherlands)

Does Dr. Davis use a wear machine in his trials? If this were done, would not Poa pratensis form a greater part of the sward than is shown in Table 1 of Dr. Davis' paper?

R. R. Davis (Ohio, U.S.A.)

We do not make wear tests on Festuca rubra/Poa pratensis mixtures, as they are mainly used in lawns and non-traffic areas. For playing fields, we use Festuca arundinacea Schreb., with a little Poa pratensis.

OVERSEEDING BERMUDAGRASS

H. H. Williams (California, U.S.A.)

I have some results from trials on overseeding Tifgreen bermudagrass (Cynodon hybrid) in November and December at Los Angeles:-

1. Scalping bermudagrass early in the fall eliminates the necessity for mulching, results in the early return of colour, and permits late overseeding of the cool-season grasses when the growth of bermudagrass is not too competitive.

2. Seeding rates may be varied widely without affecting colour in winter.,

3. Germination time appeared to decrease from earlier to later plantings, contrary to what is normally expected.

4. Desirable colour was obtained regardless of overseeding date.

5. Poa annua L. was suppressed in all plots except those inadvertently overseeded at low rates.

6. Lolium perenne variety Norlea produced excellent colour until 1 June, after which time it faded and became fibrous and difficult to mow.

7. The long time required for Poa pratensis to become established rules it out for late seeding.

W. B. Gilbert (North Carolina, U.S.A.)

Can one use grass suppressants on bermudagrass so that overseeded cool-season grasses may be seeded earlier and avoid the competition of re-growth by the bermudagrass?

G. C. Horn (Florida, U.S.A.)

We have tested MH-30 (maleic hydrazide) for controlling bermudagrass growth and eliminating competition to the overseeded grass. The results have been disappointing in Florida and we do not recommend MH-30 for this use. We try to sow as late as possible, to avoid disease, especially Pythium. If Poa pratensis is overseeded in September, it establishes in 3 weeks: if overseeded in November it takes 6-7 weeks, but gives very good colour in January and February.

R. E. Schmidt (Virginia, U.S.A.)

There have been no studies on chemicals for depressing the activity of warm-season grasses prior to overseeding for winter turf. The chemicals that are available, such as MH-30, have not appeared very promising. We feel that with proper timing of overseeding the changing environment is enough by itself to create conditions favourable for the development of winter turf on dormant warm-season grasses.

EARTHWORMS AS A POSSIBLE AID FOR OVERSEEDING

V. I. Stewart (U.K.)

Earthworms are not wanted on golf greens or bowling greens and much research is concentrated on the turf requirements for these games. But there is a risk that advice based on this research may not be directly applicable to other sports field conditions or to lawns. For example, speakers describing preparations for overseeding mention the need to aerate, scarify and top-dress with loam. This advice can only be followed if the appropriate machinery is available. The private lawn owner is likely to be reluctant to top-dress annually with loam or to use a fork to aerate and a rake to scarify, especially when an active earthworm population might do these jobs for him. I am surprised therefore that noone discussing overseeding has considered the possibility that techniques may differ according to whether earthworms are present or absent.

R. R. Davis (Ohio, U.S.A.)

In our area, we grow cool-season grasses all the year round, and do not overseed. I can accept that some surface disturbance is needed for overseeding, but the type of worm common in Ohio is large (15-20 cm) and makes large casts which cause an unattractively rough surface. The mower may hit these casts if mowing is below 3.75 cm. We prefer fertiliser and mechanical treatments, e.g. aeration, to produce satisfactory soil conditions without the assistance of worms.

R. A. Keen (Kansas, U.S.A.)

Although we have many types of earthworm, they are not common nor are they surface-casting types. The most serious problem is from night-crawling worms which eat grass.

W. H. Daniel (Indiana, U.S.A.)

At the turf research plots of the University of Illinois, earthworms are plentiful and remove all thatch as it occurs. This is an accepted part of the maintenance programme.

RECOLONIZATION OF BARE PATCHES

W. A. Adams, (U.K.)

Mr. Kamps showed a picture of _Poa annua_ invading a bare area produced by simulated wear on turf. Comments were made on the tolerance of wear by some species, but can any information be given on the ability of grass species present in the original turf to re-colonize or invade bare areas produced by simulated wear?

M. Kamps (Netherlands)

The trial has not been conducted long enough to see whether the damaged spots will be filled by invading weed grasses or by the sown species. Much depends on the weed content of the soil and the turf species.

SESSION 1C: SEED PRODUCTION AND TESTING

(Chairman: Dr. J. B. Beard)

SEED TESTING OF TURFGRASSES IN WEST GERMANY

Christoph H. Eisele,

Hessische Saaten G.m.b.H. (Hesa), Darmstadt, West Germany

SUMMARY

Up to now the quality of seed is tested according to the needs of agriculture. Foreign seeds found in a seed sample are divided into weed seeds and other crop seeds. It is shown that in turf culture these definitions lead to misunderstandings. Eleven species are named which are really harmful to turf culture in Germany and probably in all regions of the moderate climatic zone. A translation of the German rules for turf seed testing is given. These rules include sections dealing with harmful contaminants of a seed lot, and with the fact that a test result can only apply to the sample examined. Proposals are made to develop international rules and have them adopted by I.S.T.A.

There is no doubt that information on seed quality is of great value to everybody dealing with or using seed. Rules have been developed and seed tested according to these rules, and the International Seed Testing Association has been founded to promote this work. Until quite recently grass seed was mainly used in agriculture, and when the International Rules for testing grass seeds were drawn by I.S.T.A. they conformed to agricultural requirements.

In turf culture the definitions of purity and germination of I.S.T.A. are quite acceptable, but for dealing with "foreign" seeds in a seed lot special definitions must be developed. "Foreign" seeds currently are divided into two categories, weed seeds and other crop seeds.

A weed is regarded as a harmful plant whereas other crop seed "shall include seeds of plants grown as crops", according to the definition of the I.S.T.A. To distinguish between the two it may be said that a weed is bad whereas a crop species is good.

In turf culture this obviously is not applicable. For example Rumex spp. are harmful in agriculture but Dactylis glomerata L. improves almost any ley. In turf Rumex presents no problem whatsoever because there are herbicides to kill it, and in any case places where a lawn is to be planted are often heavily infested with broad-leaved weeds. Coarse grasses, however, like Dactylis glomerata, are really harmful to turf culture.

The German Society of Turf Culture (Gesellschaft für Rasenforschung) decided early in 1966 to take up this matter. Rules for turf seed testing were established in collaboration with German I.S.T.A. stations (see appendix). Fortunately, Robert W. Schery, Director of The Lawn Institute of Marysville, Ohio, made a very complete survey on lawn weeds. He listed a great number of weeds and then eliminated those which are practically never found in a seed lot, those which are found in seed lots but generally disappear naturally, and those which are quite easily controlled with familiar herbicides. He came to the conclusion that special attention should be paid to 12 species only. Schery's investigations were adapted to German needs and were incorporated into the Rules for Turf Seed Testing, which established two groups as follows:

Group I: Harmful species

      Agropyron repens L.
      Bromus spp.
      Dactylis glomerata L.
      Holcus spp.
      Veronica spp.

Group II: Species harmful under special circumstances

      Festuca arundinacea Schreb.
      Festuca pratensis L.
      Lolium spp.
      Phleum pratense L.
      Poa annua L.
      Poa trivialis L.

There was another problem to be dealt with, the analysis of a seed mixture. I.S.T.A. did not pay special attention to this point because testing a sample of a seed mixture does not give results which are representative of the seed lot the sample was drawn from. This applies especially to the composition of the mixture, primarily because no mixture really is homogeneous and secondarily because the analyst is not capable of distinguishing subspecies such as Festuca rubra L. ssp. rubra and Festuca rubra L. ssp. commutata Gaud.

The German rules in the appendix are presented to stimulate discussion. A small group of experts might be formed to try to agree internationally on rules for testing lawn seed, which could be approved by the Second Turfgrass Conference and then passed on to I.S.T.A. If I.S.T.A. agreed to incorporate such rules into theirs, F.I.S. (Fédération Internationale des Semences) might then inform the international seed trade so that these rules could be used for grass seed for turf.

This would help growers, processors and the international seed trade to deliver seed that is free of really harmful species and thus help to produce better lawns.

REFERENCES

EISELE, C. H. (1967) Richtlinien zur Prüfung von Rasensaatgut. Mitteilungen der Gesellschaft für Rasenforschung 2, 3, 72.

I.S.T.A. (1966) International Rules for Seed Testing. Proc. Int. Seed Test. Ass. 31, 1, 1.

SCHERY, R. W. (1965) Lawn seed and lawn weeds. Seed World 9, 9, 6.

Introduction

Often the needs of agriculture and horticulture differ from the needs of turf culture. For instance, the definition of a weed in agriculture is related to yield losses caused whereas in turf culture beauty is the main criterion. This and many other reasons lead to drawing of special rules for turf seed testing.

1.0

The rules for turf seed testing follow closely the International Rules for Seed Testing of I.S.T.A.

2.0

"Turf Seed" is defined as follows: Seed, mixed or not mixed, intended for sowing

        A Lawns
        B Sports Turf
        C Other areas for non-agricultural purposes

3.0

Turf seed not mixed

As opposed to the needs of agriculture and horticulture, foreign seeds in a seed lot must be treated differently according to sections 5.0 to 5.3 of these rules. The certificates, therefore, must be marked clearly "Certificate for Turf Seed".

3.1

With the exception of the special attention given to the content of foreign seeds (par.5.0 to 5.3) turf seed shall be examined according to I.S.T.A. rules. The I.S.T.A. prescriptions for sampling are applicable.

4.0

Turf seed in mixtures

Seed of different species cannot be mixed with the guarantee of obtaining an absolutely homogeneous mixture. Even if the sample prepared for testing is large compared to the total lot and even if it is drawn very carefully it is impossible for the testing station to give a certificate establishing the connection between the analysis result and the seed mixture to which the sample refers. The station can only give a certificate comparable to the Blue International Certificate, stating clearly that the analysis result is valid only for the sample tested and not for the mixture the sample was drawn from.

4.1

The certificate must be marked clearly "Certificate for Turf Seed".

4.2

Sampling of a turf seed mixture must be done in the following manner:

In seed lots consisting of 5 bags or less every bag must be sampled; in seed lots of 6 to 10 bags every second bag must be sampled; in seed lots of more than 10 bags every third bag must be sampled. In each case the samples must be drawn from top, middle, and bottom of every bag chosen. The sample obtained must be mixed thoroughly.

4.3

The station must be given, together with the sample, information about the composition of the mixture as declared by the seller or required by the buyer. The minimum size of sample is related to the number of the components of the mixture. For a mixture of up to 4 components a minimum of 300 g is required, with 30 g more for every additional component. The station divides this sample into three equal parts by a mechanical divider. One part is for test, the other two parts being sealed and reserved by the station. They may be given to the person submitting the sample on request.

4.4

The station examines the sample to determine the following:

        (a)   proportions of the different declared species
              (or groups of species).

        (b)   percentage of inert matter.

        (c)   percentage of foreign seeds.

        (d)   number of harmful seeds (section 5.2 and 5.3)
              per 100 g.

A report can then be made on purity, composition, content of inert matter, content of foreign seeds (all in percent), and content of harmful seeds (in number per 100 g). The certificate shall show clearly that the information under item (a) is only valid for the sample tested.

4.5

The germination of the species declared and/or other useful species not declared but found in the sample, must be ascertained separately for each species. Useful species are:

      (a)   for lawns: Agrostis spp.
                            Cynosurus cristatus L.
                            Festuca rubra s. lat.
                            Festuca ovina s. lat.
                            Lolium perenne L.
                            Poa pratensis L.

      (b)   for sports turf, additionally:

                            Phleum pratense L.
                              Phleum bertolonii DC
                            Poa annua L.
                            Poa trivialis L.

The average germination shall then be calculated according to the following formula:

$$DK = \frac{(R1 \times K1) + (R2 \times K2) + (R3 \times K3)}{SR} \quad \text{etc.}$$

Where DK = average germination

135

                    SR   - sum of the components by percentage
                    R1, etc.   = percentage of purity of the components
                    K1, etc.   = percentage of germination of the components

4.6

The genuineness of the declared or found species shall if possible be
determined, if such a determination is asked for especially. The certificate
shall report these species separately.

4.7

The genuineness of declared varieties shall be determined, if possible,
on special request. Normally this will require a field test. In any case
the station must give a separate certificate if reporting on the genuineness
of a variety.

5.0

Foreign seeds

If seed is tested according to these rules no difference is made between
"crop" seeds and "weed" seeds.

5.1

If the percentage of any "foreign" species exceeds 1% the exact percentage
must be mentioned on the certificate. Otherwise it is sufficient if the
different species are named.

5.2

Group 1; harmful species: Agropyron repens L.
                                Bromus spp.
                                Dactylis glomerata L.
                                Holcus spp.
                                Veronica spp.

For these species the number of seeds per 100 g must be mentioned on the
certificate, if they are found. The germination will be determined on special
request.

5.3

Group 2; species harmful under special circumstances:

                                Festuca arundinacea Schreb.
                                Festuca pratensis L.
                                Lolium spp.
                                Phleum pratense L.
                                Poa annua L.
                                Poa trivialis L.

Of these species the number of seeds per 100 g need only be mentioned on
the certificate if they are not included in the declared composition of the lawn
mixture. If the content of any of these species exceeds 0.5% it is sufficient
to declare on the certificate this percentage.

TURFGRASS SEED PRODUCTION IN THE U.S.A.

Robert W. Schery,

The Lawn Institute, Route 4, Kimberdale, Marysville, Ohio 43040,

U.S.A.

SUMMARY

Turfgrass seed production in the USA has grown into a specialised industry requiring considerable skill, capital, and established trade channels. Today it centres especially in Oregon and Washington. Careful growing by the farmers is increasingly important, with preventive weeding in the field to provide contaminant-free seed. Backing up good field practices is experienced seed cleaning meticulously done by responsible handlers in established producing regions. Some contamination does occur, especially with rough grasses. A check of numerous lots of quality species, however, showed over 40% without any foreign seeds, and few lots contained foreign seed (both weed and crop) of a kind, or in quantities, to become persistent pests in the lawn. The burgeoning sod industry has brought demand for especially high quality, but there are other uses where differing standards are appropriate (such as for the roadside).

Lawn seed production now represents a flourishing small industry specialising more and more away from its field seed background. Growers, handlers, and marketers today must keep in mind the end use - fine turf - and cater to the special standards required. Very seldom, these days, is the same kind of seed used for both pastures and lawns.

Detailed attention is important - for example, roguing out off-type plants at their first appearance. Equipment must be adequate for meticulously tending the fields, harvesting the unusually small seeds and threshing and cleaning them without contamination by other types. It is hardly the activity to go into on a shoestring. It is doubly difficult in regions where the specialised practices are not historically part of the farming tradition.

So skilful have lawn seed farmers become, and so specialised the handlers of their seed, that even traditional producing areas in less favoured climates are losing out to localised intensive cropping notably in Oregon and Washington.

Of course by using advanced techniques the clever farmer anywhere can produce good yields of quality seed. But does he have access to buyers who would absorb his production and suggest the most profitable varieties? Are technical help and special products readily available to keep his seed fields free from weeds and genetically different strains of grass? Are specialised equipment and experienced labour available for seasonally rushed operations; or would expensive equipment remain idle much of the time?

As in good farming of any type, the farmer who will be in business tomorrow is the one who takes advantage of advanced technical aids suited to his soil and crop variety. He will be large enough to use equipment efficiently and well enough capitalised for progressive farming. Thousands of dollars may be tied up for years, especially with new growers who must first rid the fields of weeds (perhaps involving a year of fallow), then proceed with planting and meticulous care for at least 2 years before profitable yields arrive. To become competitive in lawn seed production may require $200,000 in capital.

The lawn seed producer of tomorrow will have to be precise about what he is producing. Increasingly, the market is for genetically identified grass. This will involve laying plans years ahead to secure foundation or registered seed of an appropriate variety and arrange for its production under certification.

Even natural ("common") Kentucky bluegrass from the Midwest which has the virtue of a broad genetic base, will need to be distinguished from polyglot "common" (which includes almost anything that cannot be sold as a named variety).

The farmer will have to make sure that his plantings remain true-to-type. Appreciable genetic deviation, as from volunteer grass, uncontrolled cross-pollination, or mutation, will reduce the value and sales possibilities of the seed. Just how this might best be handled varies with the kind of grass. Kentucky bluegrass, highly apomictic (producing seed without fertilisation of pollen), does not offer quite the problems that do sexually-crossing species such as fine fescues and bentgrasses, the other quality lawn favourites. But even so, limitation of the number of generations allowed under certification will add to production expenses.

Fields should be as free as possible of any other seed. It is much easier to prevent contaminants in seed fields, than to count on getting rid of them at the cleaning plant. Dissimilar plants (broad-leaved weeds and markedly different grasses) can be readily spotted in the seed fields and rogued by hand or spot treated chemically. Newer pre-emergence weeding can even prevent them from ever appearing. Constant diligence is needed.

Few farmers are large enough to invest in their own seed threshing and cleaning plants. Usually farmers bring seed to a centralised facility for purchase by the cleaner-dealer, or to have it cleaned for a fee. Here, too, procedures must be carefully watched. Some seed cleaning machinery is not very effective in screening out contaminating seed carried in lawn seed. Research may develop better techniques, but care and judgment can not be replaced.

It is unwise to alternately clean two different types of seed on the same machine if one might be considered a contaminant in the other. For example, the elite sod-growing market for Kentucky bluegrass seed demands that no bentgrass at all be contained. If a lot of bentgrass is cleaned before a bluegrass run, it is almost impossible to rid the equipment of every last bentgrass seed, and contamination is risked. Not only in cleaning, but in blending and packaging operations as well, be sure the equipment is clean.

Tables 1-4 attest that uncontaminated seed of quality types is not uncommon on the market, but that care must be exercised in choice of kind, lot and supplier.

These are not just theoretical considerations. Better genetic and mechanical quality already brings a premium. Leading lawn seed packagers increasingly demand clean, essentially weed-free seed for their better blends. This has been instrumental in raising quality standards above what is acceptable for a field seed.

Of course a "price" market remains and will continue as long as unsophisticated purchasers buy bargain-basement offerings, not caring what is contained.

Table 1: ten most frequent species in Kentucky bluegrass (Poa pratensis L.)
309 lots checked: 42% without foreign seeds

Contaminant	% of lots
Canada bluegrass (Poa compressa L.)	17
Annual bluegrass (Poa annua L.)*	16
Sedges (Cyperaceae)	13
Chickweed (Cerastium spp.)	11
Rough bluegrass (Poa trivialis L.)	10
Water foxtail (Alopecurus geniculatus L.)	8
Shepherd's purse (Capsella bursa-pastoris L.)	7
Windgrass (Apera spica-venti L.)	6
Pennycress (Thlaspi spp.)	6
Timothy (Phleum pratense L.)	6

* mainly in imported seed

Table 2: ten most frequent species in red fescue (Festuca rubra L.)
135 lots checked: 46% without foreign seeds

Contaminant	% of lots
Rat-tail fescue (Festuca myuros L.)	30
Slender wheatgrass (Agropyron trachycaulum (Link) Malte)	22
Bromegrass (Bromus spp.)	21
Ryegrass (Lolium spp.)	20
Orchardgrass (Dactylis glomerata L.)	14
Pennycress (Thlaspi spp.)	10
Velvetgrass (Holcus lanatus L.)	8
Sorrel (Rumex acetosella L.)	7
Kentucky bluegrass (Poa pratensis L.)	7
Tall fescue (Festuca arundinacea Schreb,)	7

Table 3: ten most frequent species in tall fescue (F. arundinacea Schreb.)
46 lots checked: 24% without foreign seeds

Contaminant	% of lots
Orchardgrass (Dactylis glomerata L.)	78
Chess (Bromus secalinus L.)	46
Ryegrass (Lolium spp.)	44
Bromegrass (Bromus inermis Leyss.)	33
Dock (Rumex spp.)	26
Sedges (Cyperaceae)	26
Kentucky bluegrass (Poa pratensis L.)	11
Sweet clover (Melilotus spp.)	11
Sorrel (Rumex acetosella L.)	9
Wild onion (Allium canadense L.)	9

Table 4: ten most frequent species in red top (Agrostis alba L.)
55 lots checked: None without foreign seeds

Contaminant	% of lots
Yarrow (Achillea millefolium L.)	100
Timothy (Phleum pratense L.)	75
Kentucky bluegrass (Poa pratensis L.)	44
Black-eyed susan (Rudbeckia hirta)	40
Sneezeweed (Helenium)	33
Deptford pink (Dianthus armeria L.)	29
Sedge (Cyperaceae)	25
Fleabane (Erigeron annuus)	22
Rush (Juncus spp.)	20
Cinquefoil (Potentilla spp.)	16

The public is becoming more knowledgeable about gardening and no doubt will increasingly demand quality in lawn seed. Equally important, technical specialists purchasing for roadsides, institutional grounds, golf courses, and so on, are adopting quality standards that the industry must meet.

Most quality-conscious of all is the burgeoning sod-growing business. This multi-million dollar industry insists on the highest quality in the seed it plants. By the time a sod grower has spent 20 cents a square yard for production and as much for handling and marketing, he wants to be sure that he has a competitive product to sell; that is, one free of weeds and off-type grasses.

Providing seed for the sod industry has demonstrated that top quality is possible. One of these days most lawn seed will be at a comparable level. This is not to say that all lawn seed should be of a uniformly elevated standard. For some uses it is foolish to think in terms of select varieties, elaborately cleaned. For the roadside full of seeds and volunteer grass, pure Merion Poa pratensis, a variety that will probably not survive under poor maintenance, should hardly be chosen. Some home lawns are not much different. Not every homeowner cares to plant an elite variety, and give it the pampering it deserves. So, we can look towards more individualised markets, pin-pointing allowable deviations from the very high standards required, say, for sod-growing.

SESSION 2A: TURFGRASS SOILS AND THEIR

MODIFICATION

(Chairman: Mr. B. Langvad)

ADEQUATE SOIL TYPE FOR SPORT TURFGRASSES

Lars-Eric Janson,

V.B.B., Stockholm, Sweden

SUMMARY

A definition of an adequate turfgrass soil type on the basis of the grain-size distribution method is given. Theoretical and practical investigations have led to a specification of a turfgrass soil with a high water permeability as well as a sufficiently high water retention capacity.

INTRODUCTION

Irrespective of any attempts made to prolong the growing season for turfgrass by artificial means, it is an established fact that there is an optimum formula for football ground construction from the point of view of growth. The guiding factors in determining suitable principles of construction are both geohydrological and biological. First of all it is well known that difficulties in achieving rapid drainage of football grounds after rain result in exceptionally heavy wear and lead to considerable damage to the grounds. The best resistance to wear is to be found in a fully-grown rather dry grass sward. The first condition for rapid drainage is good water transmission through the top soil.

It is, however, possible to go too far in the matter of permeability, since a certain capacity for water retention is also desirable. The ideal solution in this respect has proved to be a top layer of fine sand mixed with peat, the latter acting as a water retainer.

By choosing a mixture of peat and sand instead of mould for the root zone of the grass favourable conditions are created for a deep root system, since water, air and nutriment are permitted to penetrate the surface layer to a considerable depth. This results in a drought-resistant grass environment during the growth period. A further advantage is that the root zone material is not saturated with water but ventilated during the winter, thereby establishing good conditions for the survival of the grass during the cold months of the year. Early in spring, when the earth is frozen, dry soil means a rapid thawing process and easy downward drainage. Excess of water and shortage of oxygen in the ground can thus be avoided. This type of football ground construction which ensures disposal of surplus water in the spring also creates favourable conditions for a lengthy period of growth. Optimum conditions are obtained so that it is possible to compensate for low ground temperatures in spring by introducing an artificial heating system for the root zone.

The football ground should be designed so that the capacity of the drainage system corresponds to the amount of precipitation which, depending on the permeability of the type of soil, can penetrate the densest layer of the drainage system described above. The densest layer of a properly constructed system consists of the grass-growing top soil which overlies a sandy, gravelly material with good drainage qualities. The last mentioned, in turn, should form the link, either directly or via a thin bed of gravel, with the drainage pipe system. How to choose an adequate top soil material with the grain size distribution as a basis is dealt with below.

THE GRAIN-SIZE DISTRIBUTION METHOD

The permeability of various water-saturated pure soils in natural stratification is fairly well known and is indicated by Darcy's coefficient k m/s. In soil, water has a laminar flow condition and its movement is accounted for by Darcy's law

$$v = kI$$

where v = the velocity of the water (m/s) calculated for the whole cross section and I = the hydraulic gradient. The following approximate values of k apply to various fractions:-

Gravel	d = 20	– 2 mm	$k = 10^{-1}$ to 10^{-3} m/s
Sand	d = 2	– 0.2 mm	$k = 10^{-3}$ to 10^{-5} m/s
Fine sand	d = 0.2	– 0.02 mm	$k = 10^{-5}$ to 10^{-7} m/s
Silt	d = 0.02	– 0.002 mm	$k = 10^{-7}$ to 10^{-9} m/s
Clay	d < 0.002 mm		$k = 10^{-9}$ to 10^{-12} m/s

On the basis of these values it is possible to estimate approximately how long it would take a particular amount of precipitation to penetrate various kinds of soils. Thus the following times apply for the drainage of 100 mm rain in various soils:-

Gravel	10 seconds
Sand	17 minutes
Fine sand	28 hours
Silt	4 months (the evaporation velocity dominates)
Heavy clay (uncracked)	320 years (the evaporation velocity dominates)

A heavy compaction of the material can approximately double these theoretical times. In the case of a football ground, where it is desirable to remove large quantities of precipitation in a short time, the limit of suitable soil from the point of view of drainage lies in the fine sand fraction. Large quantities of silt and clay should thus be avoided in the upper soil layer if a dry and firm ground surface is pursued.

The figures given above apply to pure soil materials with a uniform grain size. In natural soil, however, the grains are not of equal size. If the pores of a coarse-grained material are filled with fine-grained material, it will be the latter that determines the permeability of the mixture. In order to estimate the magnitude of the k-value, it has been necessary to introduce the concept of effective grain diameter d_e as the diameter of grains of uniform size which would yield the same k-value as the natural soil material. Usually d_e is approximately the diameter that divides the material into 10% fine and 90% coarse, that is to say the width of mesh in the sieve on which 90% of the material remains. The effective diameter d_e corresponds therefore to the grain diameter d_{10} in the grain size diagram. From this it follows that it is impossible to influence for all practical purposes the permeability of silt or clay by the admixture of small quantities of sand; to do so would require large quantities. On the other hand an admixture of sand in a light top soil, composed for example of silty sand, would have a practical effect on the permeability. It is therefore important that the right material is chosen from the start to form the top soil layers.

It may be said that the permeability of the grass-grown soil layers can be greater than may appear from the figures given above, chiefly on account of the occurrence of root channels and cracks, but the figures can be used by way of general comparison in estimating the relative penetration capacity of the various kinds of soil. In this connection it is necessary to distinguish between permeability dependent on grain size distribution (the texture) and the permeability dependent on the structure, which, in the latter case, is determined by aggregate formation, admixture of humus, root channels, cracks and holes made by worms. As a rule a well-developed root system in an already established condition means that the structural permeability will be many times greater than the textural. In the re-laying of sport turf it is not possible, however, to take the structural permeability into account, since the ground must have good water penetration capacity from the start of the first playing season. The latter is a condition for the grass to survive the hard wear and tear of the first seasons, in which the structural features already mentioned will not have had sufficient time to develop to any significant extent.

If the textural permeability alone is to determine the material for the top soil layer, it follows from what has already been said that d_{10} should not be less than 0.02 mm if the ground is to be designed to absorb 100 mm rain in 24 hours. This results in soil coarser than that regarded by many people as normal vegetable mould. But it should be borne in mind that in this case we are concerned with the planting of a specially advanced grass culture, exposed from the beginning to very great stress. This leads in turn to the need for a rather extensive fertilising programme, which can exercise a negative effect on the structure. Thus chemical stabilisation in certain fine-grained soils can result from the reaction of certain fertilising substances on the particles of soil. For this reason a reduced permeability of the top soil may be encountered during the first stage, culminating in a reduced strength of the ground surface in rain. As a consequence of the gradually increasing density of the top layers there will be some concentration of nutrients on the ground surface at the expense of the deeper layers, which are to some extent starved of oxygen and nutriment. The roots do not therefore seek greater depths in search of nutriment and water, but prefer to remain near the surface. The result is turf of poor quality. If, on the other hand, coarser-grained top soil is chosen with greater water permeability the fertilising substances can be more easily carried to deeper levels by precipitation. This leads to the conditions necessary for a luxuriant deep-level root system which, on account of its great volume, also can give the turf that softness, elasticity and resilience which is otherwise found as a rule only in fine-grained top soils.

As regards other grain size limits for the top soil, it should be recalled that due to the flow susceptibility of the silty soils when saturated with water a low content of these types of soil is advisable. We thereby reach the left-hand limit of the shaded area in the diagram on Fig. 1, showing the lower limit for suitable top soil. With regard to the form of the curve, it should be observed that uneven grain size distribution in the soil (indicated as a rule by the relationship d_{60}/d_{10}) should be low to prevent the soil becoming dense and impermeable as a result of compaction. An even grain size distribution yields

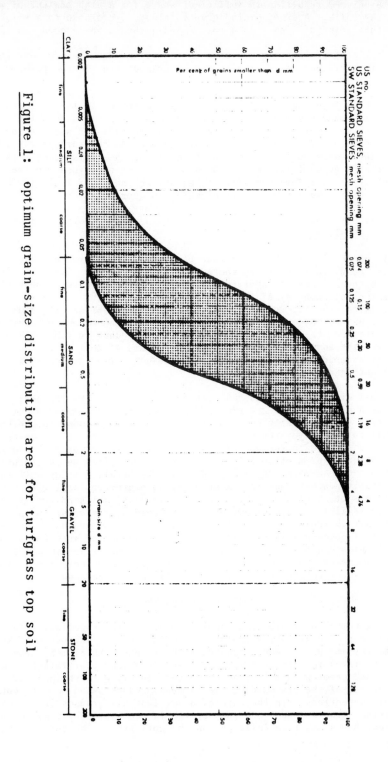

Figure 1: optimum grain-size distribution area for turfgrass top soil

a large pore volume, resulting in sufficient space for a high content of water and air in the earth. A steep grain curve is always preferable to a slight curve from this point of view. As a rule d_{60}/d_{10} should not exceed 10-15.

In determining the upper grain size curve for an adequate top soil (the right-hand limit of the shaded area in the diagram on Fig. 1) two principles apply.

First, it is important to ensure, with regard to the football ground's requirements of water and fertiliser, that the water retention capacity of the soil should not be lower than is necessary by the demands for satisfactory drainage. Second, it is probable that wear and tear of the turf is considerable in cases of too coarse-grained soils, as a result of the roots being pressed between particles of soil set in motion by pressure on the ground surface. On this account it is therefore advisable to establish the upper limit for d_{10} at 0.2 mm and to limit the largest grain diameter to approx. 4 mm.

A specification of an adequate top soil for advanced sports turf may therefore be slightly silty, fine sand.

In this connection it should be made clear that too coarse a soil, with regard to the conditions described above, can within certain limits be made suitable as a top soil by the admixture of peat. This increases, above all, the water retention capacity of the soil material (without reducing to any significant extent the air volume), and also in all probability resistance to wear and tear as well as elasticity are similarly improved. As an example it can be mentioned that a sandy soil with a k-value equal to 1.5 10^{-4} m/s in one case after the admixture of 40 per cent by volume of peat increased its water retention capacity from 8 per cent (dry weight) to 60 per cent without any significant change of the k-value.

A top soil with clay content can also be made suitable by the addition of sand in certain circumstances. A pre-condition is that the clay content should not be too high and preferably below 5%. In such cases the admixture of an amount of sand equal to the clayey top soil will reduce the original clay content by half. If it is desired to reduce the content of clay to 1%, top soil and sand must be mixed in the proportion 1:4 in terms of weight, from which it follows that it can often be a more economic proposition to obtain a sandy soil for direct cultivation rather than to mix an existing clayey top soil with sand. In spite of this it should be emphasised that even a slight sand admixture in a dense top soil is always of advantage in regard to the volume proportions of water and air in the soil. Thus the addition of coarse grains to the fine-grained material makes possible an increase in the number of such large pores (macropores) which can be emptied in drainage. These pores are then filled with air, which means that the volume of air is favourably increased at the expense of the water retention capacity which is thereby reduced.

PRACTICAL EXPERIENCE

In 1965 a number of football grounds in Sweden were investigated in order to obtain a general impression of soil conditions in various well-known arenas. The results have been arranged in accordance with Fig. 1. The results of the investigation covering resilience analyses, determination of pore volume, and chemical analysis agree rather closely with the general impression gained of the standard of the various grounds based on data obtained from various inspections. In the case of older football grounds it is possible to say that the structure due to a root system in the course of many years of development has a positive influence on the soil type. The soil can absorb water more easily when a luxuriant growth of roots has been established, even if that growth is not specially deep down in the soil. A healthy growth of roots even makes the soil more resistant to compaction. It is therefore necessary to pay regard to the humus content when reading off the results of analyses. In otherwise dense soil, organic substances in the form of root fibre and similar materials can exercise a positive influence. Nevertheless the organic substances can be so broken down that they become colloids. To a great extent these have the same characteristics as clay colloids and must be referred to the particle size category. Thus a very high humus content in a coarse-grained soil can in certain circumstances have an unfavourable effect on the permeability.

The grain size distribution method for selecting top soil material was tested for the first time in full scale when new football grounds were built at the Ullevi Stadium in Gothenburg in 1965 and at the Solna Football Stadium and the Söder Stadium in Stockholm in 1966. At the Ullevi Stadium the top soil consists of a 8 cm thick layer of somewhat silty, very fine sand. The 8 cm thick soil layer was transported from a cultivation area outside the town and re-laid in the stadium on a gravel bed. In spite of the high textural permeability of the top soil the practical water penetration capacity was not sufficient in heavy rain during the first season. This was found among other things to be due to the fact that the soil had a very high content of broken-down organic substances and that the layer of this material was too thick. Thus the roots had not in sufficient degree had time to grow down into the gravel bed and in such a way that a high structural permeability could compensate for the unsatisfactory penetration capacity.

Next season, however, after extensive aerification of the soil in order to stimulate the root growth the permeability of the top soil was quite sufficient.

Even at the Solna Football Stadium the soil was transported from a cultivation area out of town and re-laid on a gravel bed. The available vegetable mould, however, was not as coarse-grained as desired. Thus a somewhat clayey silty fine sand had to be accepted as top soil material. To compensate for the fine-grained soil the thickness of the soil was only 3 cm. Because of this thin soil layer the roots grew down in the gravel bed very fast, thus giving rise to a high structural permeability. It was found, however, that a coarse-grained soil should have been preferred with regard to the high compaction susceptibility of the actual soil, if it had been possible.

The experiences from the two football grounds referred to above indicated that it should be better to use a pure sandy soil artificially mixed with peat as a top soil instead of natural vegetable moulds, even if they were sandy. Thus when building up the Söder Stadium football ground which was to be utilised as an artificially frozen ice-track during the winter, it was decided to use a mixture of pure sand and peat as top soil. By mixing 60 per cent by volume of fine sand (0.02 - 2 mm) with 40 per cent by volume of peat, and adding fertilisers, a most suitable vegetable mould was created. The turfgrass was sown in a 5 cm thick layer of this soil mixture. In all relevant respects the result was optimum — high permeability, high water retention capacity and a deep root system of the turfgrass.

REFERENCES

JANSON, L.-E. (1967) A longer football season. The Swedish Football
    Association, Solna 1967.   (Reprinted in English, 1969).

JANSON, L.-E., and LANGVAD, B. (1968) Prolongation of the growing season
    for sport turfgrasses by means of artificial heating of the root zone.
    Weibulls Grästips, Landskrona, Sweden, 1968.

JANSON, L.-E. (1969) Artificial heating of sport fields. Proc. I.A.K.S.
    Congress, Cologne, May, 1969.

TURFGRASS SOILS AND THEIR MODIFICATION:

USGA GREEN MIXES

W. H. Bengeyfield, USGA Green Section, Garden Grove,
California,   U.S.A.

SUMMARY

The USGA specifications for constructing golf greens are outlined and
the soil requirements described in some detail.

In 1960, the USGA Green Section staff published an article in the USGA
Journal and Turf Management entitled "Specifications for a Method of Putting
Green Construction." The article sparked off a considerable amount of
controversy about the concept even though the various principles embodied in
the method are widely accepted and readily demonstrable.

Nine years have passed since the Specifications were introduced and well
over 2,000 greens have been built by this method. There is no question that
the method is both practical and successful. There are, however, some questions
which continue to arise. There are some who have failed to grasp the
significance and the importance of each single step in the construction process,
and there are some who have experienced partial failure because they only
partially followed the Specifications.

The seven steps outlined in the Specifications are:-

       1. Subgrade preparation.

       2. Tile line installation.

       3. Gravel and sand base.

       4. "Ringing" the green.

       5. The soil mixture.

       6. Soil placement, smoothing and firming.

       7. Sterilisation of soil and establishment of turf.

Of particular concern here is Step No. 5, "the soil mixture."

A covering of topsoil mixture at least 12 in. (30 cm) in thickness should
be placed over the subgrade and prepared green base. This soil mixture must
meet certain physical requirements.

Permeability should be such that after compaction at a moisture content
approximately at field capacity as described by Ferguson, Howard and Bloodworth,
a core of the soil mixture will permit the passage of not less than ½ in.
(1.25 cm) of water per hour and not more than 4 in. (10 cm) per hour when subjected to a hydraulic head of ¼ in. (0.65 cm).

Total pore space in a sample of the soil mixture after compaction should
be at least 33%. Of this pore space, the large (non-capillary) pores should
comprise from 12 to 18% and capillary pore space from 15 to 21%.

Information with respect to bulk density, moisture retention capacity, mechanical analysis, and degree of aggregation may enable a soil physicist to evaluate further the potential behaviour of a putting green soil.

Few natural soils meet the requirements stated above. It will be necessary to use mixtures of sand, soil and organic matter. Because of differences in behaviour induced by such factors as sand particle size and gradation, the mineral derivation and degree of aggregation of the clay component, the degree of decomposition of the organic matter, and the silt content of the soil, it is impossible to make satisfactory recommendations for soil mixtures without appropriate laboratory analysis.

The success of the USGA Green Section Specifications is dependent on the proper physical characteristics of the soil and the relationship of that soil to the drainage bed underlying the green. Therefore, a physical analysis of the soil should be made before construction is begun. When the proper proportions of the soil components have been determined, it becomes extremely important that they be mixed in the proportions indicated. A small error in percentages in the case of a plastic clay soil can lead to serious consequences. To ensure thorough mixing and the accurate measurement of the soil components, "off site" mixing is recommended.

MODIFICATION OF SANDY SOILS

G. C. Horn,

Professor of Ornamental Horticulture and Turf, University of Florida, Gainesville, Florida, U.S.A.

SUMMARY

The sand soils and rainfall conditions of Florida make some soil amendment desirable on high-value turf areas. The results are given from a 10 year study, still continuing, of the effects of using four amendment materials at different rates and depths of incorporation. In the first two years, the best mixture was one of those containing all four amendment materials - vermiculite, colloidal phosphate, fired clay and peat.

INTRODUCTION

Warm temperatures throughout most of the year and high rainfall have left Florida with soils that are predominantly sandy. The best mineral soils of Northwest Florida are classed as fine sandy loams with a clay content around 10%. Most of the soils are classified as fine sands with clay contents usually less than 5%.

High microbial activity has reduced the organic matter in these soils to an extremely low percentage. Very few soils in Florida have organic matter contents as high as 10% and most have less than 5%. In extreme south Florida many of the soils have less than 1% organic matter.

When the above facts are considered two things become obvious about Florida soils. First, they have very low base exchange capacities and, second, very low water-holding capacities. These two factors are very important in the production of quality turfgrasses.

Research has found that most sandy soils of Florida will contain about 0.3 in. (8 mm) of available water and that in actively growing turf the evaporation-transpiration loss in June, July, August and September averages about 0.3 in. per day. Therefore when it doesn't rain, it is necessary to irrigate every day during this period to keep the turf alive. Average rainfall is about 55 in. (140 cm) per year but the distribution is not good enough to supply turf needs. Much of this water falls within a short period of time and most is wasted as far as turf needs are concerned.

The best solution is to improve the sandy soils by adding amendments. Most of these amendments are colloidal clays or some form of organic matter. The objectives are to slow down the water infiltration rate, increase the capacity of sandy soil to hold water and fertilisers, and to provide a better root environment for turfgrass roots. Addition of amendments is very expensive and usually is limited to high value turf areas such as golf putting greens, bowling greens and other intensively maintained areas.

The research discussed in the rest of this report deals with amending sandy soils for building putting greens.

Very little research has been done on the adding of amendments to sandy soils to improve them for putting green use. An extensive study was started in Florida in 1959 by Dr. Ralph Smalley. This project was Dr. Smalley's dissertation problem and since his graduation in 1961 this experiment has been maintained as a long term soil amendment study. Periodic studies of physical and chemical properties of these amended plots have been made during this 10 year period. A complete soil study is at present in progress and comparisons are being made between physical and chemical properties as they exist now, and those found 10 years ago.

EXPERIMENTAL METHODS AND MATERIALS

The native soil used for this experiment was Arredondo loamy fine sand. This soil was found to be 88% sand, 3.95% coarse silt, 0.45% fine silt and 7.60% clay. Four materials were selected for amending this soil: Number 2 vermiculite (Terra-lite), colloidal phosphate, crushed calcined montmorillonite clay (Turface) and European peat. All amendments were added on a volume basis as follows: vermiculite 0, 10 and 20%; colloidal phosphate 0, 5 and 10%; fired clay 0 and 10%; and peat 0 and 10%. These materials and rates were combined in a factorial arrangement to form sub-plots in a split-plot experiment. Main plots were depth of adding amendments, namely 6 in. and 12 in. (15 and 30 cm). Because of the expense and amount of labour required, two replications of the 6 in. depth and two replications of the 12 in. depth of incorporation of amendments was used. It was hoped that no significant difference between the two depths of amendments would be found and then the sub-plots would be replicated 4 times. This was found to be true in 1961 and preliminary investigations to date indicate the same to be true 10 years later. The experimental unit was a 6 ft. x 9 ft. block of Tifgreen bermudagrass (Cynodon hybrid) maintained under putting green conditions.

This green is mowed daily during the summer and as needed during the winter. Nitrogen is added every two weeks at the rate of 1 lb. nitrogen per 1,000 sq. ft. (ca. 500g/100 sq m) per application. K is used at the rate of 1 lb. K per 1,000 sq. ft. per month. Phosphorus was found to be high and none has been added since the amendments were incorporated. Nematicides are applied at least once each year and more often if an analysis indicates a high population of parasitic nematodes. Insects and diseases are controlled when the need arises.

Turf evaluations have included yields, quality ratings, drought resistance ratings and root studies. Soil measurements have included organic matter determinations, soil test results, total exchange capacity, compaction tests, zones of compaction, hydraulic conductivity, total pore space including capillary and non-capillary pore space and moisture retention capacities at various moisture tensions. All results have been analysed statistically by use of an IBM punch card computer.

RESULTS

Results are shown in the five Figures. Some of them compare the original data with the averages for the 9 year period beginning in 1960.

The main results of this experiment are summarised below.

(a) The incorporation of amendments to a depth of 6 in. was found to be as good as mixing them to a depth of 12 in.

(b) Addition of vermiculite to Arredondo loamy fine sand increased both yield and quality of Tifgreen bermudagrass. Compaction was reduced below the 1 in. zone by adding vermiculite. Vermiculite was found to increase capillary pore space, available water and cation exchange capacity. Vermiculite additions significantly

152

increased the extractable MgO content of the mix. Also, it was found that 10% vermiculite was equal to or better than 20% when added to the native soil.

(c) Fired clay increased both capillary and non-capillary pore space, permeability, cation exchange capacity and extractable CaO, MgO, and K_2O. The addition of fired clay decreased both yield and quality of the bermudagrass, compaction tendencies and the percentage available water.

(d) Colloidal phosphate, when used as an amendment, increased depth of rooting, amount of roots in the upper 3 in., capillary pore space, cation exchange capacity and extractable MgO. Colloidal phosphate decreased non-capillary pore space and permeability. The addition of 5% colloidal phosphate by volume was better than 10%.

(e) Peat increased penetrability below 1 in., capillary pore space, percentage available water, percentage of organic matter and extractable MgO but only for one year. Most of the 10% peat was oxidized the first year of the experiment.

(f) The best mixture for the first two years was one that contained 20% vermiculite, 5% colloidal phosphate, 10% fired clay and 10% peat. This was treatment 33. Recent data indicate that treatment 15 which is the same as No. 33 but had no peat added originally is its equal.

This experiment will be continued as a long term soil amendment study.

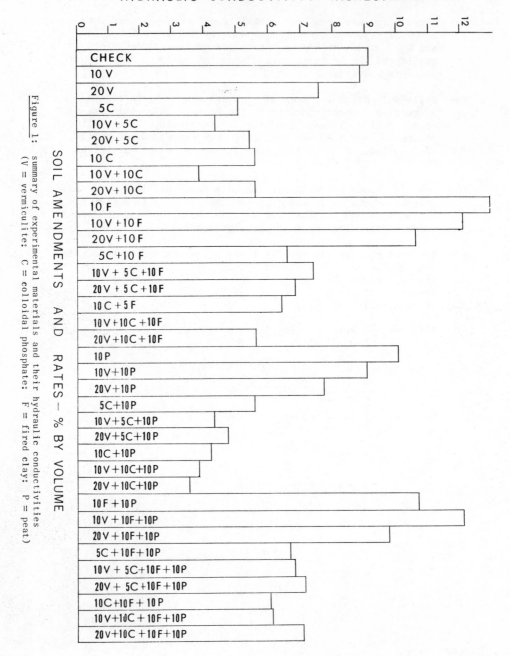

HYDRAULIC CONDUCTIVITY – INCHES / HOUR

SOIL AMENDMENTS AND RATES – % BY VOLUME

CHECK
10 V
20 V
5 C
10 V + 5 C
20 V + 5 C
10 C
10 V + 10 C
20 V + 10 C
10 F
10 V + 10 F
20 V + 10 F
5 C + 10 F
10 V + 5 C + 10 F
20 V + 5 C + 10 F
10 C + 5 F
10 V + 10 C + 10 F
20 V + 10 C + 10 F
10 P
10 V + 10 P
20 V + 10 P
5 C + 10 P
10 V + 5 C + 10 P
20 V + 5 C + 10 P
10 C + 10 P
10 V + 10 C + 10 P
20 V + 10 C + 10 P
10 F + 10 P
10 V + 10 F + 10 P
20 V + 10 F + 10 P
5 C + 10 F + 10 P
10 V + 5 C + 10 F + 10 P
20 V + 5 C + 10 F + 10 P
10 C + 10 F + 10 P
10 V + 10 C + 10 F + 10 P
20 V + 10 C + 10 F + 10 P

Figure 1: summary of experimental materials and their hydraulic conductivities
(V = vermiculite; C = colloidal phosphate; F = fired clay; P = peat)

154

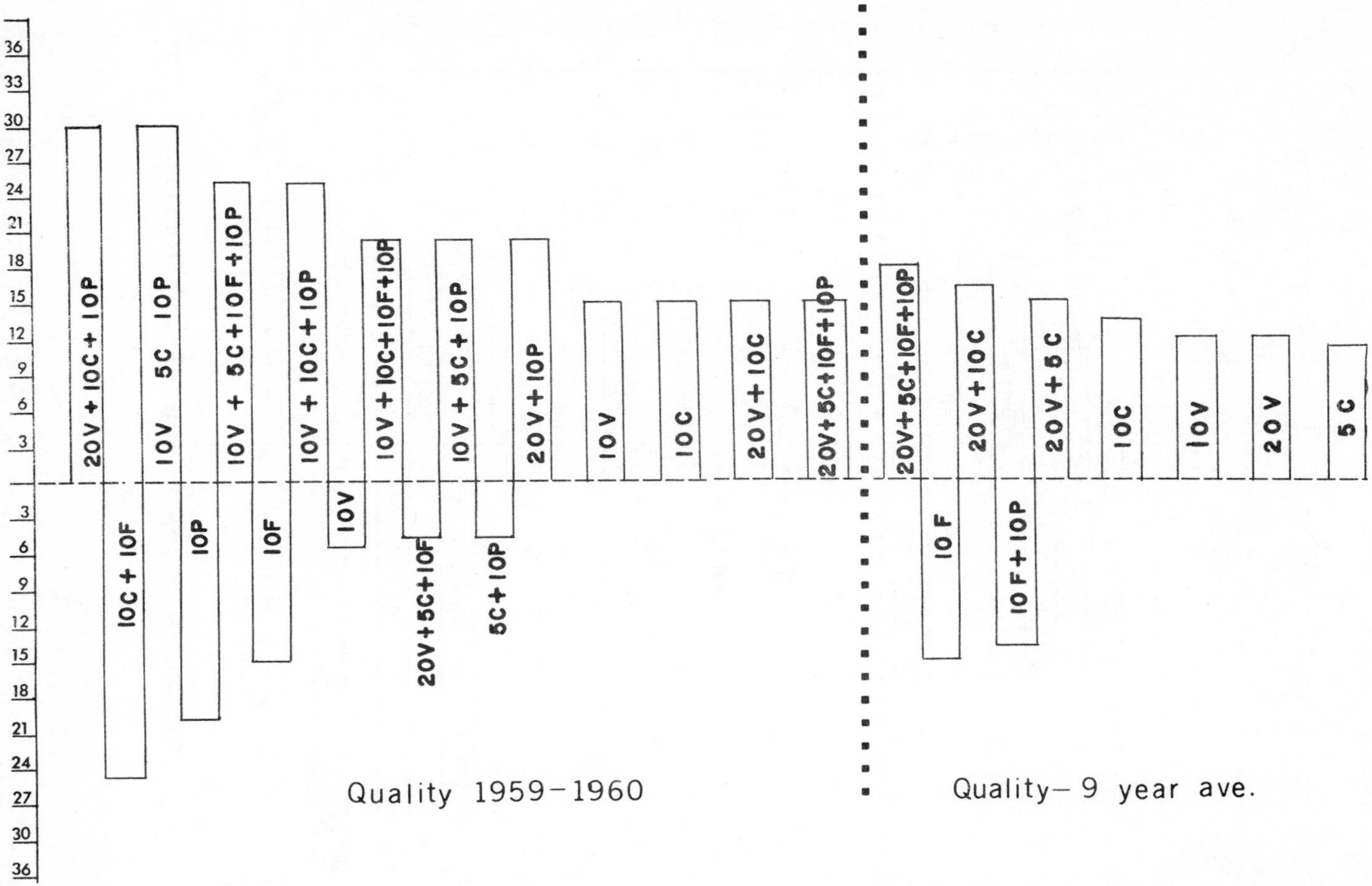

36
33
30
27
24
21
18
15
12
9
6
3
3
6
9
12
15
18
21
24
27
30
36
20V + 10C + 10P
10C + 10F
10V 5C 10P
10P
10V + 5C+10F+10P
10F
10V + 10C+10P
10V
10V+10C+10F+10P
20V+5C+10F
10V + 5C + 10P
5C+10P
20V+10P
10V
10C
20V+10C
20V+5C+10F+10P
Quality 1959-1960
20V+5C+10F+10P
10F
20V+10C
10F+10P
20V+5C
10C
10V
20V
5C
Quality- 9 year ave.

Figure 2: quality ratings of turfgrass grown on various experimental materials

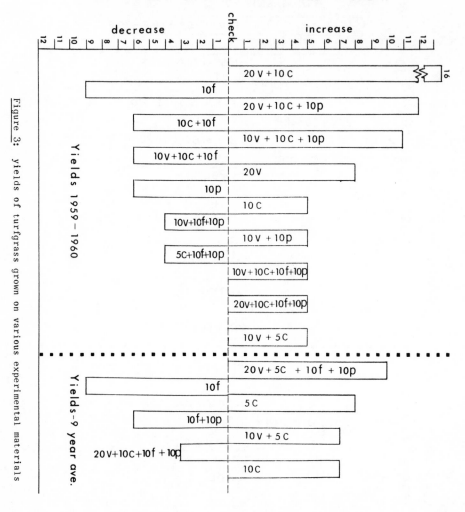

PERCENTAGE CHANGE — COMPARED TO CHECK

decrease   check   increase

12 11 10 9 8 7 6 5 4 3 2 1   1 2 3 4 5 6 7 8 9 10 11 12

Yields 1959 – 1960

20 V + 10 C   16

10f

20 V + 10 C + 10p

10C + 10f

10 V + 10 C + 10p

10v + 10C + 10f

20V

10p

10 C

10v+10f+10p

10 V + 10p

5C+10f+10p

10v + 10C + 10f + 10p

20v+10C+10f+10p

10 V + 5 C

Yields – 9 year ave.

20 v + 5C + 10f + 10p

10f

5 C

10f+10p

10 V + 5 C

20 V+10C+10f + 10p

10 C

Figure 3:   yields of turfgrass grown on various experimental materials

156

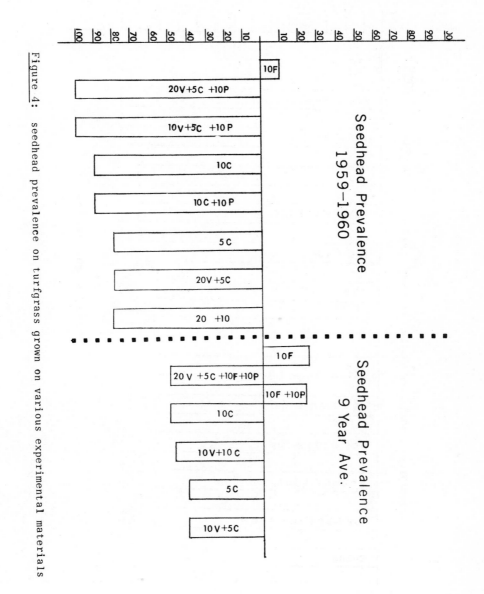

Figure 4: seedhead prevalence on turfgrass grown on various experimental materials

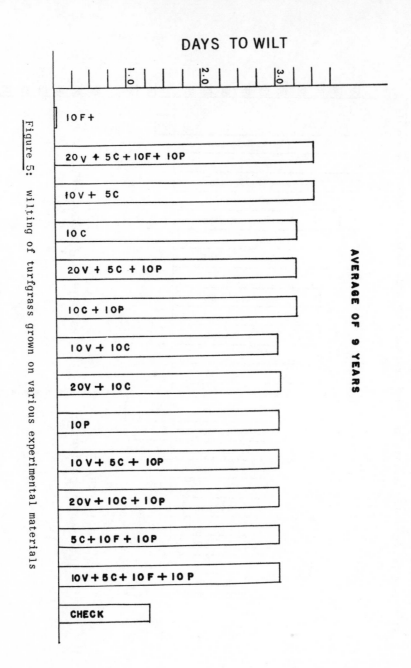

Figure 5: wilting of turfgrass grown on various experimental materials

SOIL MODIFICATION FOR TRAFFIC TOLERANCE

Ray A. Keen, Ph.D.,

Kansas State University, Manhattan, Kansas, U.S.A.

SUMMARY

The problem of soil compaction under traffic has long been studied and well described. Fine sands have most of the characteristics of a traffic-tolerant growing medium.

Research shows that 85-100% sand mixtures provide excellent substrates for growing Agrostis spp. but the surface is easily modified by the addition of materials used in good management. Dilution with sand of the fines and turf residues that accumulate on the surface, must be a continual uniform process to avoid layering and other problems. In practice this produces a springy "fibre" rather than a suffocating "thatch".

The results of traffic and compaction on soil have been reported in detail, including loss of pore space, layering, anaerobic decomposition of organic fractions, death of roots, high CO_2 content, low oxygen supplying ability, and poor playing surface.

The work of Lunt in California and Kunze in Texas left the problem of which grade of sand, and how much of the silt present in all prairie soils, should be used in construction of athletic fields and golf greens for turf. Various combinations of materials had been used in the past - local soil plus peat; equal parts by volume of peat, sand and soil; pea gravel with sufficient soil and peat to fill the voids, etc. All were failing to provide a good substrate for turf under ever-increasing traffic.

Two local sands were chosen for experimental work. One was a white angular sand of glacial origin from the Blue River with the bulk of the particles 1 mm in diameter. The second was a brown silicon sand with rounded particles 0.25-0.5 mm in diameter known locally as "blow", "wash-back" or "quick sand" from the Kansas River.

Each sand was combined with soil and peat to give mixtures of 65%, 75%, 85%, 90% and 100% sand by volume in the original mix. Mechanical analysis determined the actual sand content somewhat higher because of a very fine sand present in the silt loam soil. These mixtures, in 1 m strips, were randomized in 3 replications to build a green 20 x 30 m. Mixture depth was 30 cm before settling. It was placed on a gravel blanket 10 cm thick.

Five bentgrasses (Agrostis spp.) in 2 replications were planted at right angles to the mixes. With careful management good turf was produced under putting traffic, on all plots. The turf on the coarser sand was too liable to drought and was hard to keep alive in winter, but was satisfactory on 85 to 90% sand. The fine sand gave good results in the pure sand plots and the turf of all grasses did very well on it at 85% and 90% sand. When allowed to die without irrigation, the turf on the low sand mixtures survived longest but had the least roots under traffic and irrigation.

In the light of these results 18 greens, a putting clock and a nursery were built using blow sand taken from the property. The unwashed sand contained about 2% silt and clay. Hypnum peat 2.5 cm in depth was added to the surface and tilled into the top 5-7 cm. Penncross bentgrass (<u>Agrostis palustris</u> Huds.) was seeded 16 September. These greens have given excellent service under heavy traffic and wet conditions that took all other courses out of play for 10 to 30 days. Irrigation water is no problem on this course in the river valley.

A serious problem has been the blowing dust of this region that magnified the universal problem on all courses of adding fine materials to the surface of traffic-tolerant mixtures. In addition to the airborne materials many materials are added that are of clay or silt texture. These, with the plant residues, tend to seal the surface under high moisture and traffic. They need constant and regular dilution with sand to keep the profile uniform.

Sands vary from source to source. Soil physicists should take another long hard look at the sand fraction of mixtures. Sand is the only economic material that retains pore space under traffic. When the playing surface is covered with fine materials and spongy turf residues, sand must be added in sufficient amounts to dilute the "thatch" from an impervious, choking blanket into a springy, traffic-tolerant "fibre". When the athlete enters the arena he should have sand under foot; it has performed well since Roman times.

REFERENCES

KUNZE, R. J. (1957) The effects of compaction on different golf green
   solid mixtures. USGA Journal and Turf Management <u>10</u>, 6, 24.

LUNT, O. R. (1956) Minimizing compaction in putting greens. USGA Journal
   and Turf Management <u>9</u>, 5, 25.

PAIR, J., and KEEN, R. A. (1962) Comparing percentages of greens mixtures.
   USGA Journal and Turf Management <u>15</u>, 3, 26.

WILSON, C. G. (1969) The correct sand for a putting green. The Golf
   Superintendent <u>37</u>, 1, 52.

TURFGRASS SOIL MODIFICATION WITH SINTERED FLY ASH *

J. C. Patterson, Jr.,

West Virginia University, Morgantown, W. Virginia,   U.S.A.

and

P. R. Henderlong, †

Associate Professor of Agronomy, The Ohio State University and The Ohio
Agricultural Research and Development Center, Columbus, Ohio,
U.S.A.

SUMMARY

Field and laboratory studies were conducted to evaluate the feasibility
of utilising sintered fly ash as a soil modifier. Sintered fly ash was
applied in 13 different particle size and rate combinations to a poorly drained
established turfgrass area. Incorporation of sintered fly ash with the upper
6 in. (15 cm) of soil generally increased water infiltration and movement in
the treated layer, and overall soil drainage. The increased intake is likely
to improve aeration, reduce soil compaction, and improve root penetration and
growth, thus developing a more vigorous and dense turf or sod cover. The
addition of sintered fly ash did not alter the textural classification of the
original silt loam soil. The data suggested that sintered fly ash readily
absorbs large quantities of water. However, the absorbed water appeared to
be retained less tightly by the soil modified with sintered fly ash than by
the unmodified soil during periods of high moisture tension as indicated by
the soil moisture, moisture tension and infiltration data.

INTRODUCTION

In many of the highly industrialised nations throughout the world, there
is growing concern with respect to the increasing accumulation of great
quantities of industrial waste materials. These accumulated waste materials
not only detract aesthetically from the immediate environment but are also
potential health hazards. Among such industrial waste materials is fly ash
or flue ash, a solid waste by-product from pulverized-coal-fired power plants.
Disposal of this material is commonly done by dumping in the sea or other large
bodies of water, on hillsides, in sluice ponds, and in mountain valleys. All
of these methods are rather costly for the producer. Brackett (1) reported
that 20 million tons of fly ash were produced in the United States in 1965 and
that an estimated 40 million tons will be produced in the U.S. by 1980.
The Northern European countries were effectively utilising from 30-50 percent
of the fly ash produced in their countries in 1965, whereas the United States
was utilising only 3 percent of its production.

---

*   Contribution from the West Virginia University Agricultural Experiment
     Station. Published with the approval of the Director of the West Virginia
     University Agricultural Experiment Station as Scientific Paper No. 1074.

†   Formerly Assistant Professor and Assistant Agronomist, Department of
     Agronomy and Genetics, West Virginia University.

Figure 1:   samples of fly ash

    left -   raw fly ash
    centre - sintered fly ash: smaller aggregate (< 4.71 - > 1.41 mm)
    right -   "   "   " : larger aggregate (< 9.51 - > 4.71 mm)

The Bureau of Mines, U.S. Department of the Interior, has conducted various studies aimed at developing commercial uses of fly ash. A product resulting from some of these studies was a light-weight aggregate material for use in concrete blocks and light-weight concrete. The light-weight aggregate was produced by pelletizing and sintering the raw fly ash. This light-weight fly ash aggregate (Figure 1) appeared to exhibit many characteristics similar to calcined clays and expanded shale materials which are commonly used as soil amendments or modifiers for intensively used turfgrass areas.

Soils supporting turfgrass or sports turf are frequently subjected to conditions that enhance soil compaction or decrease porosity. Soil amendments are commonly used to improve, maintain, or stabilize soil physical properties such as internal drainage, infiltration, aeration, porosity, surface resiliency, moisture availability and resistance to compaction (13). The overall objectives in the use of soil amendments are (1) development and maintenance of the soil physical properties to provide a more favourable environment for turfgrass growth, and (2) increased use of, or play on, the turf throughout the year.

Materials commonly used as soil amendments include various types of peat, lignified wood, calcined clay, calcined diatomite, expanded shales, sewage sludge, animal manures, many different types and grades of sand, and sawdust. The benefits from the use of various soil modifiers, i.e. increased aggregation, water infiltration and percolation, reduced surface runoff, improved hydraulic conductivity and decreased soil compaction, have been well documented by Hendrick and Mowery (7), Taylor and Martin (17), Shoop (14) and many other workers.

The cost of the commonly used soil modifiers is extremely variable, as shown by the following:

Modifier	Approximate cost/English ton (1016 kg) (In U.S. dollars)
Calcined clay	64.00
Calcined diatomite	40.00
Expanded shale	8.35
Coarse silica sand	3.50

For sintered fly ash, however, the cost is not well established to date. Estimates suggest the cost would range from $4 to $6 per ton.

In view of the apparent feasibility and potential use of sintered fly ash for turfgrass soil modification, a cooperative research project was initiated to evaluate this potential use. The project involved both field and laboratory methods to accomplish the objectives.

Fly Ash Composition and Properties

Raw fly ash, varying from acidic to alkaline in reaction, is composed of many elements. The concentration of these elements, however, varies greatly in different ashes according to the geological history of the coal, the location of the coal seam with respect to other strata, and other factors. Limited amounts of calcium, phosphorus, magnesium, iron and other elements have been found in raw fly ash (3) (Table 1). Raw fly ash is deficient in the macronutrient nitrogen and often potassium (4, 8, 10), but contains many essential micronutrients. An overabundance of some micronutrients, however, presents the possibility of phytotoxicity. Boron is particularly abundant in raw fly ash (9, 10). Phytotoxic levels of manganese and the non-essential element aluminium (10, 12) are also quite possible. Holliday (9) suggested that neither manganese nor aluminium were the primary causes of phytotoxicity of

Table 1: fly ash analysis

Element	% dry weight
Calcium	1.000
Magnesium	0.360
Potassium	1.740
Phosphorus	0.132
Cobalt	0.005
Molybdenum	0.007
Boron	0.008
Manganese	0.021
Aluminium	14.100
Iron	9.940

Table 2: water infiltration rate of a soil modified with sintered fly ash compared to the unmodified soil

Elapsed time (min.)	(hrs.)	Undisturbed control Average accumulated intake (in)	Intake rate (in./hr.)	33% mixture * Average accumulated intake (in.)	Intake rate (in./hr.)
0	0.000	0.00	--	0.00	--
1	0.017	0.53	31.18	0.50	29.40
3	0.050	0.98	19.60	1.10	22.02
5	0.083	1.12	13.49	1.70	20.48
10	0.167	1.35	8.08	3.08	18.43
20	0.333	1.50	4.50	5.16	15.48
45	0.750	1.60	2.13	9.64	12.85
60	1.000	1.63	1.63	12.64	12.64
90	1.500	1.67	1.13	16.24	10.83
120	2.000	1.70	0.85	19.08	9.54
150	2.500	1.76	0.70	23.17	9.26
180	3.000	1.82	0.61	25.79	8.60
210	3.500	1.86	0.53	28.64	8.02
240	4.000	1.93	0.48	31.71	7.93
270	4.500	2.02	0.45	34.23	7.62
300	5.000	2.09	0.42	39.98	7.20

* 50% 4.71 - 1.41 mm and 50% 9.51 - 4.71 mm.

raw fly ash. The high temperature sintering process converts many of the
potentially phytotoxic elements into more tightly bonded and essentially
unavailable compounds. Cope (5) reported that the soluble salt content may be
initially high but decreased with weathering. He also reported that the
cation exchange capacity of raw fly ash is low, ranging from 2 to 4 meq./100 g.

The physical properties of raw fly ash, like the chemical ones, vary
with the source of the coal. The hydraulic conductivity of raw fly ash is
somewhat lower than that of its soil counterpart; thus it affords more moisture
retention and retards quick run-off (3). Sintered fly ash, because of its
porous structure, should facilitate moisture movement through the surface soil.
Bredakis (3) reported the hydraulic conductivity to be 0.27 in. per hour which
is much lower than that of a fine sandy loam. Cope (5) found it to be 1.25 in.
per hour into dry raw fly ash, and 0.20 in. per hour into wet raw fly ash.
Moisture content at 1/3 atmosphere tension (field capacity) is 40-50% of the
dry weight of the raw fly ash (10). Bulk density of raw fly ash has been found
to be about 1.13 g/cu cm. The specific surface area has been reported to range
from 2,000 to 4,500 sq cm/g (5).

Raw fly ash consists predominantly of particles more than 200 μ in
diameter (12) and is therefore texturally similar to a very fine sandy loam (3).
Sintered fly ash, on the other hand, is classified as similar to coarse sand
and gravel, which may make it more attractive as a soil conditioner.

METHODS AND MATERIALS

Raw fly ash from a local electric power plant was pelletized on a
revolving disc, sintered on a travelling grate at temperatures of 1080° to
1650°C,then crushed to break up any clinkers. The aggregate was graded into
the required sizes and transported to the experimental field site. The
established sod, primarily Poa pratensis L., Festuca rubra L., and Trifolium
repens L.,was cut at 4 cm with a mechanical sod cutter and rolled to the edge
of each respective plot. The exposed soil was rotary-tilled to a depth of
15 cm. The sintered fly ash was added in amounts equal to 14, 25 and 33% by
volume and mixed thoroughly to the 15 cm depth. The plot areas were then
smoothed and the original sod replaced. Two unmodified treatments were
included in the field site; one was treated identically to the above plots
but no sintered fly ash was added, the other remained undisturbed. These two
treatments, hereafter, will be referred to as the check (Ck) and undisturbed
control (Uc), respectively.

Moisture tension characteristics were determined for the various soil-
sintered fly ash mixes in the laboratory using the pressure membrane method (2).
Soil moisture data, both per cent and total, were determined as outlined by
Black et al. (2).

A double ring infiltrometer was used to determine water infiltration
rates (6, 15, 16). The outer ring was 61 cm and the inner ring 25 cm in
diameter. Soil samples were taken immediately before and after each infiltration determination for total moisture content.

RESULTS AND DISCUSSION

Soil moisture

The soil moisture percentage at the 0-7.5 cm depth was essentially the
same for the fly ash treatments and the two unmodified treatments (Uc and Ck)
under high or favourable moisture conditions (Figure 2-A). The soil moisture

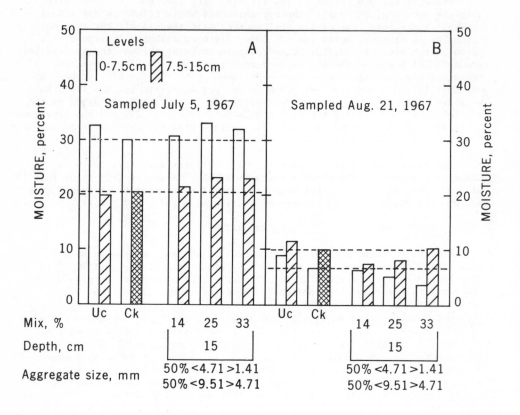

Figure 2: effect of sintered fly ash treatment on soil moisture content, under high (A) and low (B) moisture conditions

percentage at the 7.5-15 cm depth, however, was slightly higher for the modified soils under the same high moisture conditions. Under periods of low moisture conditions, or high moisture stress (Figure 2-B), the addition of sintered fly ash decreased the soil moisture percentage at the 0-7.5 cm depth. The actual measured soil moisture at the 7.5-15 cm depth for the undisturbed control (Uc) and check (Ck) treatments was 11% and 10% respectively; whereas the soils modified with 14, 25 and 33% fly ash showed moisture percentages of 7.6, 8.2 and 10.2 respectively (Figure 2-B). This suggests that the mixture of soil and fly ash held more water in the low tension range than the original soil, but less in the high tension range. Thus, the water is held with less force under low tension and would more readily be lost from the soil surface (0-7.5 cm) under conditions conducive to high evapotranspiration losses or readily move to a lower root zone depth.

The laboratory moisture tension data agree with the above suggestion. The soil moisture at 1/3 atmosphere tension was 27% for the original unmodified soil, but 25, 22.2 and 22% for the 14, 25 and 33% mixtures (Figure 3).

Therefore, it is thought that the sintered fly ash tends to absorb moisture rather rapidly. In addition, the absorbed water is retained less tightly and released more readily from the sintered fly ash aggregates. The data further suggest that the water in the 0-7.5 cm rootzone was readily released and moved downward into the 7.5-15 cm rootzone (Figure 4).

Water infiltration

The infiltration rates for the 14% modification treatment were not greatly different from those in the unmodified soils. The average intake rate for the undisturbed control (Uc) was 0.42 in. (1.07 cm) per hour after 5 hours (Table 2). The average intake rate for the 33% treatment was 7.2 in. (18.3 cm) per hour after 5 hours. This rate was nearly 17 times greater than the rate for the undisturbed control.

The data indicate that the accumulated intake and the intake rates of the soil-sintered fly ash mixtures were greatly increased compared with the undisturbed control (Uc). Using the classification suggested by Kohnke (11), the intake rates were as follows (larger S.F.A. = 9.51 - 4.71 mm aggregate: smaller S.F.A. 4.71 - 1.41 mm aggregate):-

A. moderately slow -   undisturbed control
                          14% mixture with smaller S.F.A.
                          14% mixture with larger S.F.A.

B. moderate -   14% mixture with 50% smaller and 50% larger
                             S.F.A.
                          33% mixture with smaller S.F.A.

C. moderately rapid -   33% mixture with larger S.F.A.

D. rapid -   33% mixture with 50% smaller and 50% larger
                             S.F.A.

The accumulated intake was variable but tended to increase with increased volumes of sintered fly ash incorporated. In all cases the trend for the average accumulated intake and intake rate was as follows (listed in increasing order of infiltration):

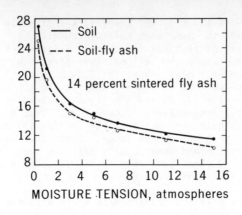

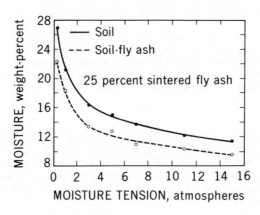

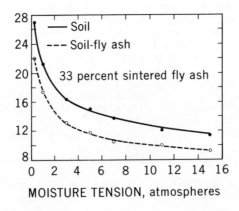

Figure 3: moisture curves for soils containing 14, 25 and 33% of the 50:50 mixture of smaller and larger sintered fly ash

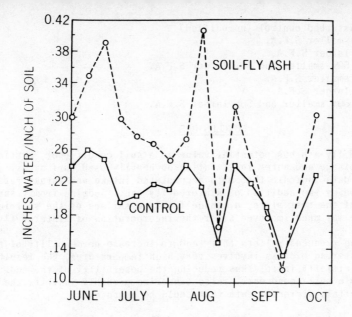

Figure 4: seasonal changes in total water content of the 7.5 - 15 cm rootzone (1967 data): comparison of control and soil containing 33% of the 50:50 mixture of smaller and larger sintered fly ash

1. Undisturbed control (unmodified)
2. 14% smaller S.F.A.
3. 14% larger S.F.A.
4. 14% 50% smaller and 50% larger S.F.A.
5. 33% smaller S.F.A.
6. 33% larger S.F.A.
7. 33% 50% smaller and 50% larger S.F.A.

CONCLUSIONS

Sintered fly ash has potential value as a soil conditioner, particularly to assist drainage and water infiltration on heavily used turf areas. The infiltration data indicate that both accumulated intake and intake rates were increased by the addition of sintered fly ash. Judging from visual comparisons of the test plots, drainage from the surface of the soil into the root zone was much improved after the incorporation of sintered fly ash.

Sintering produces pellets that tend to increase permeability of the soil. Since the sintering process involves very high temperatures, the resulting material is initially inert, thus reducing the possibility of the addition of any undesirable soil amendments. Also sintering probably inhibits the excess release of certain micronutrients that could be phytotoxic.

The most attractive aspect of sintered fly ash is that it compares very favourably, both economically and physically, with other soil amendments and soil conditioners.

ACKNOWLEDGEMENTS

This research was supported in part by the Morgantown Coal Research Center of the Bureau of Mines, U.S. Department of the Interior. Figures 2, 3 and 4 were supplied by the Bureau of Mines, U.S. Department of the Interior. Financial support from the National Ash Association Inc., Washington, D.C., for partial travel expenses for the International Turfgrass Research Conference is hereby acknowledged.

REFERENCES

1. BRACKETT, C. E. (1967) Availability, quality and present utilization of fly ash. Fly Ash Utilization Proceedings. U.S. Dept. of Interior, Bureau of Mines I.C. 8348. pp. 16-36.

2. BLACK, C. A., EVANS, D. D., WHITE, J. L., EMSINGER, L. E., and CLARKE, F. E. (1965) "Water Capacity". Methods of Soil Analysis, Part 1. Am. Soc. Agron., Inc., Monograph No. 9, Madison, Wisc. 770 p. See pp. 279-285.

3. BREDAKIS, E. J. (1966) Stabilization of fly ash by means of vegetation and its possible use as a soil amendment. Final Report. Department of Plant and Soil Science, University of Massachusetts, Amherst, Mass., pp. 1-18.

4. BREDAKIS, E., and PAGE, H. (1965) Can fly ash support plant life? Electrical World 165, 17, 31.

5. COPE, F. (1961) Agronomic value of power station waste ash. Ph.D. Thesis , University of Leeds, West Riding, Yorkshire.

6. HAISE, H. R., DONNAN, W. W., PHELAN, J. T., LAWHON, L. F., and SHOCKLEY, D. G. (1965) The use of cylinder infiltrometers to determine the intake characteristics of irrigated soils.: U.S.D.A.-A.R.S-Soil Conserv. Ser. 41, 7, 1.

7. HENDRICK, R. M., and MOWERY, D. T. (1952) Effect of synthetic polyelectrolytes on aggregation, aeration and waste relationships in soils. Soil Sci. 73, 427.

8. HODGSON, D. R., and HOLLIDAY, R. (1966) The agronomic properties of pulverized fuel ash. Chemy. Ind. 20, 785.

9. HOLLIDAY, R. (1958) Plant growth on fly ash. Nature 181, 1079.

10. JONES, L. H., and LEWIS, A. V. (1960) Weathering of fly ash. Nature 108, 400.

11. KOHNKE, H. (1968) Soil Water. p. 30 In Soil Physics. McGraw-Hill Book Co., New York.

12. REES, W. J., and SIDRAK, G. H. (1956) Plant nutrition on fly ash. Pl. Soil 8, 141.

13. SHOOP, G. J. (1968) Soil mixtures for golf course greens. Proc. 1967 W. Va. Turfgrass Conference. West Virginia Univ. Agric. Exp. Stn. Misc. Pub. 5, pp. 27-33.

14. SHOOP, G. J. (1968) The effects of various coarse textured material and peat on the physical properties of Hagerstown soil for turfgrass production. Ph.D. Thesis. Pennsylvania State Univ., University Park, Pa.

15. SWARTZENDRUBER, D., and OLSON, T.C. (1961) Sand-model study of buffer effects in the double-ring infiltrometer. Soil Sci. Soc. Am. 25, 5.

16. SWARTZENDRUBER, D., and OLSON, T.C. (1961) Model study of the double-ring infiltrometer as affected by depth of wetting and particle size. Soil Sci. 92, 219.

17. TAYLOR, G.S., and MARTIN, W.P. (1953) Effect of soil-aggregating chemicals on soils. Agric. Engng. 34, 550.

CELLULAR POLYSTYRENE IN THE PREPARATION OF GRASS PLAYING FIELDS

B. Werminghausen,

B.A.S.F., Limburgerhof, West Germany

SUMMARY

A description is given of the properties of flakes of cellular polystyrene, and recommendations made for their possible use in different soil types.

The turf of grassed playing fields is continually at risk. The surface compaction caused by running players can hinder or even prevent the passage of water and air; rainwater cannot penetrate into the subsoil, and the surface soil can become waterlogged. Soil with a good structure is permeable to water, permitting it to be stored and available to encourage growth. If the structure breaks down, a non-permeable compacted layer can be formed: this gradually causes the grass to die off and to be eventually worn away from the playing surface.

For this reason when grass playing fields are laid out it is usual to lighten the soil with peat and sand, especially if the soil is heavy or has been compacted by the passage of heavy machines; drainage must also be provided by field drains and gravel, cinders, etc. The same lightening and improved drainage can however be achieved by the use of Styromull (Registered Trade Mark.)

Styromull consists of flakes of cellular polystyrene. It is used on its own as a filter material for field drains, and to lighten heavy soil. It can be used mixed with compost, peat, sewage sludge, etc., to improve the aeration and water permeability of soils.

The flakes are 4-12 mm across, and the bulk density is 14-22 kg/cu m. Since the material is based on polystyrene it is sterile, has no effects on plants, and does not rot. It is compressible: a pressure of 0.2 kgf/sq cm (corresponding to the pressure of the overlying earth at a depth of 1 m) reduced the volume of loose flakes by about half. The volume is partially recoverable when the stress is removed.

The permeability of loosely packed Styromull can be expressed by Darcy's law: the flow of water through a layer of thickness d and area A under a pressure equivalent to a head of water of height h is

$$Q = k \, (hA / d)$$

If centimetre-gram-second units are used, the numerical values of k vary between 1.8 and 0.1 as the degree of compression of the material varies between 0% and 50%. The permeability of flakes thus corresponds to that of fine gravel or sand with particle sizes between 3 mm and 0.6 mm.

The topsoil of a playing field is not only the bed for the turf; it also contributes to the quality of the playing surface and its resistance to wear. It must withstand repeated loads, so that the ground does not become compacted and retains a sound porous structure. It has been found in practice that admixture with something such as Styromull, which keeps the soil open and imparts a degree of resilience, improves the quality of the playing surface. Recommendations for the application of cellular polystyrene are given in the following sections.

172

Treatment of topsoil

(a) Light soils

Sandy soils are quite permeable enough, and overall introduction of flakes
would reduce water retention still further, leading to scorching in dry
periods. However the material can be used in heavily stressed areas, for
instance in the penalty areas, to increase the elasticity of the soil and to
prevent surface caking. The proportion of Styromull required is 10-15% by
volume.

(b) Medium soils

Medium loams are sufficiently permeable in the normal way, but are liable
to become compacted by trampling or the passage of heavy machines. The topsoil should therefore be mixed with 15-20% flakes of cellular polystyrene by
volume.

(c) Heavy soils

Heavy loams and clays are not ideal for sports ground because they drain
badly and are easily compacted. They must be lightened considerably and
made more springy: 20-30% flakes by volume is recommended.

Treatment of subsoil

(a) If the subsoil is already permeable it is necessary only to break up the
hard pan to ensure that water can drain unimpeded from the improved topsoil.

(b) If the subsoil drains badly it is necessary to provide artificial drainage.
Piped or unpiped drains can be used. The latter are filled with coarse filter
material, and can consist of mole drains filled with Styromull. However, a
deep drainage trench with a narrow rectangular section is better than a
cylindrical drain with a cross-section of the same area. It has three advantages: the peripheral surface is increased (by 30% if the drainage trench is
three times as deep as it is wide): a slotted drainage trench cuts through
impermeable layers above the bottom of the drain and the fall need not be so
accurate.

The Styromull-filled drainage slot is an excellent means of getting
surplus water down through impermeable layers, and it can also be used for
lateral drainage if the fall is adequate and the distances involved are not too
great. It thus constitutes an additional drainage element that can be used
as well as piped drains and ditches.

Method of use

After the area has been levelled any drainage channels required are dug.
Immediately behind the digging implement a chute fed from a hopper leads flakes
into the channel: the depth to which the channel is filled is controlled by
a restrictor fitted to the chute. The channels, which are normally 8-10 cm
wide, can be made at any desired interval, but an interval of 1 m is normal.

The topsoil is then relaid and covered with a layer of cellular polystyrene.
This is thoroughly mixed with the topsoil; the amount required will depend on
the depth to which the implement can work. It may be a disc harrow or an
agricultural rotary cultivator: (small cultivators rotating at high speed are
unsuitable). Such machines might work to a depth of 15 cm, so that a 4 cm

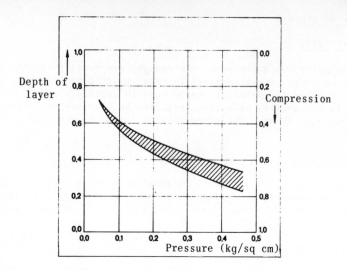

Figure 1:   compression of Styromull

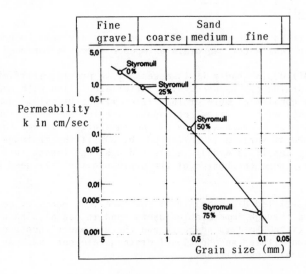

Figure 2:   Darcy permeability constant for mineral earth without clay, and for Styromull at room temperature with the percentage compressions shown

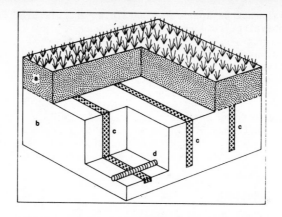

Figure 3: drainage system for a grassed playing field
(a) top soil; (b) subsoil; (c) Styromull – filled
slit drain; (d) flexible drain pipe

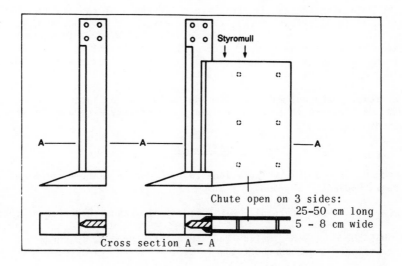

Figure 4: subsoiling share modified (on right) to fill slit drain
with Styromull

layer of material must be applied to obtain a 25% mixture. A 4 cm layer of flakes is equivalent to 4 cu m/100 sq m.

It is not always possible to work in all the Styromull required in one stage. For instance, if 5 cu m/100 sq m are to be mixed in, it is best to plough in a layer 3 cm thick to a depth of 15-18 cm, then to apply a 2 cm layer and work this in with a harrow.

As an example of how much material would be used, a field of area 8000 sq m whose heavy soil requires 25% flakes worked into a depth of 15 cm, would need 320 cu m for the topsoil. If drains are required and these are 10 cm wide, 30 cm deep, and spaced at intervals of 1 m, the additional Styromull required is 240 cu m.

Advantages and disadvantages

Styromull has the following advantages compared with other mineral or organic materials for improving the soil. Firstly, unlike most organic materials it does not rot, and stays permanently in the soil. Secondly, although it is as permeable as gravel, sand, or slag, it is resilient and does not permit heavy soils to bake hard: it keeps the soil open and the ground springy. Thirdly, it is very light and easy to transport and handle.

Its main disadvantage is the extreme lightness of the flakes, which make it difficult to distribute evenly on windy days. It can, however, be prevented from blowing about by wetting it with solutions of mineral fertilizers, or by mixing it with sewage sludge, etc. This is essential only when small areas have to be treated or when the field is in a built-up area and wind-blown material would be regarded as a nuisance.

Styromull does not make the playing surface more liable to damage by studded boots unless it is used in quantities greatly exceeding those recommended.

REFERENCES

KNOBLOCH, H. (1964) Die Melioration nasser Böden in allgemeiner Sicht. Wass. Boden 16, 12, 403.

KNOBLOCH, H. (1966) Styromull, ein Filterstoff. Wass. Boden 18, 12, 415.

WERMINGHAUSEN, B. (1965) Welche Bedeutung hat Styromull in Landschafts-gartenbau. Neue Landschaft 10, 7, 275.

WERMINGHAUSEN, B. (1967) Styromull/Styropor für den Bau von Sportanlagen und Gehwegen. Neue Landschaft 12, 9, 472.

WERMINGHAUSEN, B. (1968) Neue Möglichkeiten der Bodenverbesserung bei der Anlage von Rasensportflächen. SB 67, Sportstättenbau und Bäderanlagen 2, 2, 230.

DISCUSSION

SOIL MODIFICATION TECHNIQUES

J. F. Shoulders (Virginia, U.S.A.)

What species and mixtures did Dr. Janson use to obtain establishment of turf adequate for play in four weeks?

L. E. Janson (Sweden)

We have used a seeds mixture of <u>Poa pratensis</u> and a turf type of <u>Phleum bertolonii</u>. The mixture is basically Weibull's "Kick Off Special".

R. W. Miller (Ohio, U.S.A.)

If the period of play in Sweden started in September rather than in early spring would Dr. Janson alter his soil modification procedures?

L. E. Janson (Sweden)

I see no reason for altering my modification system. We are not just dealing with a spring problem, as the football season lasts from April to September, but the same construction methods would apply for winter football.

B. Langvad (Sweden)

Yes, we consider that this method of improvement is effective not only in spring, but at other times as well.

J. R. Watson (Minnesota, U.S.A.)

What is the effect of winter desiccation on high sand mixes? In Minnesota, we find that turfgrass plants are severely desiccated on such soil mixtures.

B. Langvad (Sweden)

We find much better winter resistance on soils with high sand content, than on wetter soils. Grasses survive best when they are dry, as for example on the roof of a building.

PROBLEMS OF FIELD STUDIES ON SOIL MIXES

P. E. Rieke (Michigan, U.S.A.)

In my experience with soil modification studies under field conditions, different mixes vary greatly in their requirements for frequency and rate of application of water and nitrogen. It is very time-consuming and difficult to provide optimum water and nitrogen for each soil mix separately. For example, if we irrigate for the water needs of a very sandy mix, soils high in clay will be overwatered. I would like to ask Dr. Keen if he attempted to consider these widely variable requirements for water and nitrogen in his field studies.

R. A. Keen (Kansas, U.S.A.)

We have not been troubled with nutrition or water problems. Those golf clubs that can afford the U.S.G.A. mix can afford good watering systems. Nitrogen release studies at Kansas State University show good nutrition for

4-6 weeks from urea, activated sludge or urea-formaldehyde, with little difference between sources. The picture is complicated by dust, soot and other "fallout" from the air that is universal in occurrence. This tends to seal the surface of a sandy soil mix but will help the cation exchange capacity if it is incorporated or diluted with top-dressing, especially so if the thatch is breaking down rapidly. In the Pittsburg district of Kansas, this fallout amounts to 18 tons per sq. mile per week. We have built greens from pure sand, with a little peat, and they have successfully withstood very heavy rain.

J. H. Madison (California, U.S.A.)

I am concerned because in the laboratory we are very careful to mix ingredients of modified soils thoroughly, but in the field mixing is often not thorough. Rototiller mixing has been shown in slides. When we examine soils in which the rototiller has been used to incorporate amendments, we find there has not been uniform mixing but the creation of channels of amendment. This results in a field performance quite different from that predicted by laboratory results.

DRAINAGE EFFECTS OF LARGE PARTICLES OF SINTERED FLY ASH

W. A. Adams (U.K.)

Our experience at Aberystwyth is in agreement with the first four contributors in this section, namely that in order to improve soil drainage, particle sizes in the range of 150μ-250 μ diameter are most efficient. Even so, the quantity required to produce a significant effect on soil drainage under "good mix" conditions is high (60-65% of total by weight). I should be pleased therefore if Dr. Henderlong could suggest reasons why he was able to obtain an improvement in soil drainage with 33% by volume of relatively large particles of sintered fly ash.

P, R. Henderlong (Ohio, U.S.A.)

The soil on which this study with sintered fly ash was conducted is not a typical soil for a desirable turfgrass root zone. The soil was actually a sub-soil (B horizon) material due to excavation and landscaping or grading around new buildings. The original material was an extremely heavy clay with very poor or restricted internal drainage, and a bulk density of 1.8 g/cu cm at the 3-6 in. level.

It may appear rather like "putting marbles into porridge": however, the sintered fly ash aggregate used in this study, although rather large in particle size, is actually extremely porous and absorbs water rather readily. Four different rates of fly ash application were used in this study ranging from 7 to 33% by volume. In general the only rate that greatly improved water infiltration was the 33% rate.

SESSION 2B: NUTRITION AND FERTILIZERS

(Chairman: Mr. B. Langvad)

SLOW RELEASE NITROGEN FERTILIZERS ON TURF

R. E. Engel,

Research Professor in Turfgrass Management, Department of Soils and Crops,
College of Agriculture and Environmental Science, Rutgers University,
New Brunswick, New Jersey 08903, U.S.A.

SUMMARY

The slow-release nitrogen carriers are described, with their advantages
for turf use. In particular, information is given on ureaformaldehydes and
on carriers in which a protective material delays the nitrogen from entering
the soil solution. The practical problems in using slow-release nitrogen
carriers are discussed, and areas suggested for future investigation.

Of all turf nutrients, nitrogen receives the most attention. It is the
most commonly deficient nutrient; it is used abundantly by plants; and it
has profound effects on both success and failure of the turfgrass plant.
Control of nitrogen availability is of great importance, and it is theorized
that slow-release N carriers should prove helpful by spreading the nitrogen
response over a longer period of time. A slow-release nitrogen turfgrass
fertilizer is defined as a nitrogen carrier that gives a delayed plant
response because the nitrogen is not in a form usable by the plant, or it is
protected from entering the soil solution.

CLASSIFICATION OF THE NITROGEN CARRIERS USED ON TURF

Many classifications of nitrogen carriers are used. The simple categories
of quick-release and slow-release are most practical. Examples of quick-
release are the simple inorganics such as ammonium sulphate, sodium nitrate,
ammonium nitrate, etc. Quick-release organic N carriers are exemplified by
urea and some of the smallest ureaformaldehyde molecules. Among the slow-
release types are the natural organics such as activated sewerage sludge,
cottonseed meal, fish scrap, tankage, and castor bean. Metal ammonium
phosphates are inorganics that have a slow-release nitrogen effect. Urea-
formaldehyde is one of the more recent slow-release types. This latter group
can include soluble quick-acting types of molecules or long chain molecules
that give very slow release. Ureaform, the best-known type, is a mixture of
types that range from soluble to the very slow-release molecules. Among the
newer slow-release types are those which prevent a form of quick-acting nitrogen
from entering the soil solution by encapsulating or impregnating the nitrogen
with a protective material.

REASONS FOR USING SLOW-RELEASE NITROGEN CARRIERS

In turf culture, spreading the growth of turf over a long period of time
is commonly desired, rather than development of maximum peaks of available
nitrogen as is often preferred in many types of field crop production. This is
the major theoretical basis for their use. Slow-release materials are not
leached as readily when used on very porous sandy soils with low organic
matter content. This characteristic is commonly accepted and was illustrated
in turfgrass research by Bredakis and Steckel (1963). Practical advantages of
slow-release nitrogen are: (1) less danger of turfgrass injury than from
fertilizers with high salt index, and (2) better retention of physical

condition in storage. Theoretical disadvantages of slow-release fertilizers are: (1) nitrogen release when the grass of concern is dormant, (2) their inability to give maximum concentrated growth thrust on occasions when maximum growth rate is desired, or (3) their prolonged delay of nitrogen release when growing temperatures commonly range below 16°C.

PERFORMANCE OF SLOW-RELEASE NITROGEN CARRIERS

Numerous tests have been made to give information on the potential of slow-release nitrogen carriers. Clark, Gaddy, and Jacob (1951) worked with a variety of natural organics. On an average, 39% of the insoluble nitrogen was converted to the nitrate form after 15 weeks as compared with 81% for ammonium sulphate. Availability of nitrogen from the insoluble materials was highest in the 4% nitrogen grades. Other ingredients seemed to influence the results. Probably the most characteristic feature of natural organics is their variability in total nitrogen and its release. Some include useful amounts of other nutrients. The iron response of some activated sewerage sludges is an example. It is generally expected that the major portion of nitrogen release from natural organics occurs during a period of 4 to 8 weeks of moderately warm and moist conditions. In areas with milder winters, when air temperatures of 0-10°C occur, enough nitrogen may be released from late fall or early winter applications to stimulate grass growth. However, applications in spring on cold soils often give no significant nitrogen response of the turf until there is an accumulation of 16-21°C days. The use of natural organics as a source of nitrogen will continue, because such by-products will always exist.

The ureaformaldehydes as nitrogen carriers are rather new and are an interesting slow-release group. Methylene diurea, the simplest form of one molecule of formaldehyde plus urea (a molecule which is found in ureaform) was reported by Hays (1966) to delay its release of nitrogen as compared with urea. Unpublished data of the New Jersey Agricultural Experiment Station did not show any significant difference in rate of turfgrass response between these two components. The stimulation of grass growth by dimethylene triurea (the next largest size of molecule of ureaformaldehyde) classifies it nearer to quick-release than slow-release. Trimethylenetetraurea and a low solubility fraction of ureaform showed definite slow-release characteristics. Two commercial preparations of ureaform in the same test appeared to have a slow-release component. It is generally held that ureaforms have a component that releases little nitrogen in the first 3 or 4 months and tends to spread its release over a period of 1 to 2 years (Hays, 1966). Samples taken from the surface of sod fertilized for 3 years with ureaform at the New Jersey Station had higher total N than those receiving quick-release nitrogen or natural organic nitrogen carriers. This component of slower release ureaform poses two questions. First, does nitrogen release occur in excess of the turf needs on occasions? Unreported data from the New Jersey Agricultural Experiment Station show excessive growth stimulation and turf injury three to four weeks after treatment with 8 lb. of ureaform N per 1000 sq. ft. (ca. 4 kg/100 sq m). Some reports claim that available nitrogen excesses do not occur with moderate totals of ureaform or ureaform plus other carriers. The second question concerns the availability of this long-lasting fraction in subsequent seasons. Data reported by Escritt and Legg (1968) showed no significant growth response of turf from this theorized cumulation after 6 years.

Coated ammonium sulphate showed slow release nitrogen characteristics on Kentucky bluegrass (Poa pratensis L.) as reported by Dahnke et al. (1963). Work by Horn in 1967 with this type of carrier on bermudagrass (Cynodon spp.) gave turf quality that compared with a similar treatment of ureaform. Urea impregnated into low-melting hydrocarbons gave a delayed release of nitrogen when applied to bentgrass (Agrostis spp.) turf in work of Dunn and Engel (1966). Also, metal ammonium phosphates give a slow release of nitrogen. A greater assortment of slow-release nitrogen carriers should be available in the future.

THE FUTURE OF SLOW-RELEASE NITROGEN CARRIERS

There is a function and a desire for slow-release nitrogen in turfgrass production. Certainly it is a method of adding some additional nitrogen per individual application without causing burn or lushness. The non-professional grower desires this type of nitrogen fertilizer to minimize the number of applications. Some turf areas that are difficult to fertilize might benefit from slow-release nitrogen, and others such as bentgrass greens can benefit from the light, infrequent use of slow-release nitrogen fertilizer in hot weather. As indicated, slow-release nitrogen is not appropriate when a large and sudden growth rate increase is needed. This is especially true when the weather and soil are cold.

Several important questions about slow-release nitrogen need answers. First, efficiency in terms of total growth and growth rate stimulation is generally low. The former seems contradictory when the great potential for leaching of the quick-acting types is considered. In the case of natural organics, inability of materials to release the last 1½% of their nitrogen is inherent (Ensminger and Pearson, 1950) and can be a major cause of low nitrogen return. The inefficiency of ureaform was emphasized in work reported separately by Daniel (1958) and Davis (1965), where a total of 60% or more of ureaform nitrogen was required to give turf response equal to other fertilizers. The prolonged resistance to decomposition by the larger, very complex ureaform molecules might account for part of their inefficiency. Also it may be inherent that slow-release nitrogen carriers are inefficient in terms of plant response because they spread the nitrogen release into less efficient growth periods.

What is the agronomic significance of slow-release nitrogen from these slow-reacting carriers? If a surge of growth within the early weeks after application is not needed, slow-release nitrogen has the distinct value of avoiding nuisance peaks of growth. However, realizing a predictable major growth increase with most materials after 60 days does not appear common. The contrast in delayed growth response from slow- and quick-acting nitrogen carriers is minimized in some cases because the quick-acting nitrogen is not lost promptly from the soil by leaching. Major quantities of ammonium can be held in association with clays or other colloidal material. Also, a very active microorganism population can utilize large portions of a quick-acting nitrogen which may reduce leaching. This causes the quick-reacting nitrogen to serve similarly to ammonia released from slow-reacting nitrogen fertilizer.

Total nitrogen in the ordinary soil is estimated at 1,500-3,000 lb/ac. (1,700-3,400 kg/ha). This is largely in the soil organic matter. Some of this can be in the form of plant residues, but more specific information on the nature of soil nitrogen is limited (McLaren and Peterson, 1950). Three-dimensional polymeric components of bakelite type occur, while bound amino-acids comprise 20-40% of the nitrogen in most surface soils, according to Bremner (1965). Much of the organic matter occurs in water-stable aggregates of clay-metal-organic matter complexes. Many of the microbial cells are not attacked by proteolytic enzymes that can degrade intracellular substances rapidly (Bremner, 1965). Bartholomew (1965) considers microbially produced organic nitrogen more resistant to decomposition. Possibly there is an association of microbial protein with non-protein materials resulting from the decomposition. Are some of these aromatic? Possibly these may be polyphenols produced by microbes or fragments of residues. These complicated aspects of soil organic matter cannot be measured with present research techniques. Yet, it is known that the more complex nitrogen forms decompose in the soil. If they did not, vast quantities of nitrogen would accumulate. Unfortunately, the complicated behaviour of soil organic matter and its nitrogen prevent the understanding of a number of important aspects of slow-release nitrogen in turf culture.

While complete understanding of soil nitrogen is not conceivable presently, much can be done to increase efficiency of both slow- and quick-release forms. Favourable pH, oxygen supply, adequate energy material, temperature and nutrient balance might encourage a better supply of nitrogen from the soil and fertilizer applications. With deficiencies of these conditions, nitrogen release can be very poor. Information is needed on total nitrogen in the soil, conditions that favour more uniform release of nitrogen for turfgrasses, seasonal availability of soil nitrogen, and seasonal needs of the grasses. Denitrification should be studied under turfgrass conditions. Allison (1966) classifies this action as second only to leaching as a cause of nitrogen loss to agricultural soils. Current nitrogen carriers should be better known. Nitrogen is nitrogen to the plant, but it is oversimplification to say that all nitrogen carriers influence the turf similarly. The study of slow-release nitrogen as related to soil nitrogen dynamics is a great challenge.

REFERENCES

ALLISON, F. E. (1966) The fate of nitrogen applied to soils. Adv. Agron. 18, 243.

BARTHOLOMEW, W. V. (1965) Mineralization and immobilization of nitrogen in the decomposition of plant and animal residues. Agron. Monogr. 10, 293.

BREDAKIS, E. J., and STECKEL, J. E. (1963) Leachable nitrogen from soils incubated with turfgrass fertilizers. Agron. J. 55, 145.

BREMNER, J. M. (1965) Organic nitrogen in soils. Agron. Monogr. 10, pp. 97, 123, 136.

CLARK, K. G., GADDY, V. L., and JACOB, K. D. (1951) Availability of water-insoluble nitrogen in mixed fertilizers. Agron. J. 43, 57.

DAHNKE, W. C., ATTOE, O. J. ENGELBERT, L. E., and GROSKOPP, M. D. (1963) Controlling release of fertilizer constituents by means of coatings and capsules. Agron. J. 55, 3, 242.

DANIEL, W. H. (1958) Nitrogen applied to bentgrass turf. Golfdom 32, 50.

DAVIS, R. R. (1965) Forms of nitrogen for fertilizing Kentucky bluegrass in Ohio. Golf Course Reptr. 33, 42.

DUNN, J. H., and ENGEL, R. E. (1966) Bentgrass turf growth response to urea nitrogen impregnated on hydrocarbons and vermiculite carriers. New Jersey agric. Exp. Stn. Bull. 816, 22.

ENSMINGER, L. E., and PEARSON, R. W. (1950) Adv. Agron. 2, 90.

ESCRITT, J. R., and LEGG, D. C.(1968) Gradual release nitrogen fertilizer for use on fine turf. J. Sports Turf Res. Inst. 44, 66.

HAYS, J. T. (1966) Nitrogen fertilization of turfgrasses. Hercules
    Agricultural Chemicals Technical Information Bulletin A1-105.

HORN, G. C. (1967) Comparison of N sources for Tifgreen bermudagrass.
    Florida Turfgrass Association 14, 1.

McLAREN, A. D., and PETERSON, G. H. (1965) Physical chemistry and biological
    chemistry of clay mineral organic nitrogen complexes. Agron. Monogr.
    10, 280.

MUSSER, H. B., and DUICH, J. M. (1958) Response of creeping bentgrass
    putting green turf to ureaform compounds and other nitrogen fertilizers.
    J. Am. Soc. Agron. 50, 381.

FERTILIZER TRIALS AT BINGLEY

J. R. Escritt and D. C. Legg,

The Sports Turf Research Institute, Bingley, Yorkshire, U.K.

SUMMARY

Fertilizer trials, carried out at the Sports Turf Research Institute over a period of thirty years, have shown that the performance of turf is influenced not only by the amounts of plant nutrients given but also by the form in which they are applied and that season of application influences the long term effects of some fertilizers.

INTRODUCTION

As with other perennial crops, management practices in one year can have a considerable influence on the performance of turf in succeeding years. Observations made over the comparatively short period of, say, one season can therefore be misleading. Fertilizer treatment has important long-term as well as short-term effects and the former are only revealed with the passage of time. Indeed some of the effects, such as disease incidence, influx of weeds, and surface softness, often fail to be related to the fertilizer treatment and are attributed instead to other factors. Clearly other factors such as mowing practices may also influence the effects mentioned but quite often fertilizer treatment plays an outstanding part.

On the experiment ground at Bingley there have been several long-term trials on the use of different kinds of fertilizers to supply the three main plant foods and the results from these trials have been remarkably consistent. It is appreciated that the results apply to one centre with one type of soil but the general picture revealed is supported by practical experience and is consistent with that obtained by other workers e.g. at the Rhode Island Agricultural Experiment Station (1).

LONG-TERM FERTILIZER TRIALS UNDERTAKEN

Long-term field trials at Bingley have included the following:

Trials A   1929 to 1968   Study of sulphate of ammonia, nitro-chalk, calcium nitrate, ammonium phosphate, sodium nitrate, urea, dried blood, Peruvian guano, superphosphate, bone meal and sulphate of potash on different fine grass swards (i.e. various Festuca and Agrostis spp.) Fertilizer was applied dry with a carrier of compost.

Trial B   1937 to 1963   A factorial examination of the effects of sulphate of ammonia, superphosphate, calcined sulphate of iron, carbonate of lime, compost and solid tine forking on fine turf. Fertilizer was applied dry without carrier.

Trial C   1939 to 1960   Comparison of dried poultry manure and sulphate of ammonia as sources of nitrogen for fine turf (sown with Festuca rubra L. ssp. commutata Gaud. and Agrostis tenuis Sibth.). Fertilizer was applied dry with compost as carrier.

Trial D   1939 to 1960   Comparison of sulphate of ammonia, dried poultry
                 manure, dried blood, hoof and horn meal and rape meal as sources
                 of nitrogen for fine turf. Fertilizer was applied dry with
                 compost as carrier.

Trial E   1948 to 1969   Study of sulphate of ammonia, sodium nitrate,
                 sulphate of ammonia plus dried blood, sulphate of ammonia plus
                 sodium nitrate, with and without different phosphatic materials
                 (superphosphate, bone meal and ground mineral phosphate), and
                 with and without carbonate of lime (to regulate pH) on general
                 sports field turf. Fertilizers were applied dry with compost as
                 carrier.

Trial F   1948 to 1969   Evaluation of the influence of season of
                 application (spring, autumn) on the effects obtained from
                 sulphate of ammonia, hoof and horn meal, nitrate of soda and
                 dried blood on fine turf, also from mixtures of pairs of these.
                 Phosphate and potash were given throughout and all fertilizers
                 were applied dry with sand as carrier.

Trial G   1931 to 1967   Comparison of various nitrogenous fertilizers
                 (including ammonium phosphate) with and without calcined sulphate
                 of iron, these being applied to mown-down pasture turf (compost
                 as carrier).

Trials H   1959 to 1968: Study of gradual release nitrogenous fertilizers:-

                 1.   Trials with urea formaldehyde fertilizers (3,4)

                 2.   Yield and performance trials comparing urea formaldehyde
                      fertilizer with sulphate of ammonia, dried blood and hoof
                      and horn meal (4,5)

                 3.   Observations on effects of high rates of urea formaldehyde and
                      sulphate of ammonia on the occurrence of Fusarium nivale (Fr.)
                      Ces. (5)

                 4.   Comparison of the effects of urea formaldehyde and sulphate
                      of ammonia, dried blood and hoof and horn meal on turf
                      quality (5)

                 5.   Yield and performance trial with gradual release nitrogen
                      materials - urea formaldehyde (powder and granular), Magamp,
                      urea/paraffin wax, crotodur, mixture of sulphate of
                      ammonia with dried blood and hoof and horn meal. (6)

                 All treatments in Trials H were applied without carrier.

RATES AND TIMES OF FERTILIZER APPLICATION

     The amounts of nitrogen, phosphorus and potash applied per annum have
varied in the different trials. Typically, trial plots have received nitrogen
equivalent to ½ oz. sulphate of ammonia per sq. yd. (17 g/sq m) in spring
(e.g. end of April) and late summer (end of August) with supplementary dressings
as considered necessary in the light of growth. Usually this has meant about
four such dressings in all, equivalent to 2 oz. sulphate of ammonia per sq. yd.
(68 g/sq m) but in some years more or less has been given. 2 oz. sulphate
of ammonia per sq. yd. is equivalent to 120 lb. nitrogen per acre (135 kg/ha or
2.8 lb. per 1,000 sq. ft.)

In the trial with poultry manure as a slow release N fertilizer
(Trial C) the poultry manure was applied in dressings equivalent to multiples
of ½ oz. sulphate of ammonia per sq. yd. and similar considerations apply
to the trials with urea formaldehyde,etc. (Trials H).

In trials C, D and F the basal treatment with phosphate and potash was
given to all plots,using a mixture of superphosphate, bone meal and sulphate
of potash once a year in the spring. In trial A phosphorus and potash formed
part of the experimental treatments; in trial B and E phosphorus formed part
of the experimental treatment but no potash was applied. Turf in trial G
received nitrogen only,except for that treated with ammonium phosphate.

RESULTS OF TRIALS

Mown turf required regular fertilizer treatment and of the three main
plant foods commonly supplied in fertilizers the order of importance seems to
be (1) nitrogen, (2) phosphorus and (3) potassium. Turf receiving only
nitrogen persisted many years as good turf; turf receiving nitrogen and
phosphorus remained satisfactory even longer but it was over twenty years
before plots receiving potash showed superiority over those receiving no potash
and this was in the form of drought resistance. "No nitrogen" plots,
particularly those receiving phosphate and potash, usually became subject to
invasion by Trifolium repens L.

Trial A.

Sulphate of ammonia and other ammonium salts contributed to soil acidity,
discouraged annual meadow-grass (Poa annua L.),disease, weeds and earthworms,
and produced firm, dry surface conditions. The various nitrates led to weedy,
wormy turf prone to Fusarium nivale and containing annual meadow-grass. Urea
produced lush turf with much annual meadow-grass and prone to F. nivale but it
had comparatively little effect on weeds and worms. The organic treatments
(guano, dried blood, bone meal) produced swards with much annual meadow-grass
and prone to disease and to weed and worm invasion. Phosphate and potash
contributed to drought resistance but it was over twenty years before the
benefits of the potash were seen. In the later years over-acidity, particularly
on the ammonia plots,led to lack of vigour and poor drought resistance so that
it became necessary to lime.

Trial B.

Sulphate of ammonia kept out weeds and worms and F. nivale but reduced
soil pH, available phosphate and moisture retention. Superphosphate directly
or indirectly helped to keep out moss. Calcined sulphate of iron decreased
weeds but, although burning out moss on application, in the long term it
increased the amount of moss. It had little effect on soil pH. Lime increased
weeds, worms, soil moisture, pH and available phosphate but decreased moss.
The main value of the small amounts of compost used was to decrease fertilizer
scorch (as compared to those plots not receiving compost). Forking decreased
moss, increased moisture and, perhaps surprisingly, increased worm activity.

Trial C.

The dried poultry manure used was not a very satisfactory fertilizer for
turf and showed poor slow release action. With increase of soil pH there was
marked incidence of weeds especially pearlwort (Sagina procumbens L.) which was
particularly prominent until bone meal was omitted from the basal dressing.

Trial D.

    All the organic materials produced a soft (easily damaged) turf which
became very weedy (especially with pearlwort). In the early years bone meal
was included in the basal phosphate and potash dressing given and is thought
to have contributed to the deterioration of the organic plots. The organic
treatments also encouraged earthworm activity, hoof and horn meal less so than
the other treatments.

Trial E.

    The trial was sown down with a general sports ground mixture including
Lolium perenne L. but with mowing at 7/16 in. (11 mm) the sward gradually
reverted to Agrostis spp. and annual meadow-grass with some patches of Yorkshire
fog (Holcus lanatus L.). The best playing surface (firm and dry in wet
weather and weed-free), has been produced by the sulphate of ammonia/super-
phosphate treatment, especially when the pH has not been allowed to drop too
far. Dried blood and nitrate of soda have produced soft easily damaged surface
conditions and increased annual meadow-grass, but the turf has shown a better
colour, particularly in drought. Bone meal has had similar effects on the
turf to those produced by dried blood and nitrate of soda and the worst turf
in this trial from the wear point of view is that receiving nitrate of soda
and bone meal. It is interesting to note that clear indications of these
effects were to be seen in the first season, e.g. visiting groundsmen were
able to pick out firm or soft plots in the autumn of the first year.

Trial F.

    The fertilizer applied in the spring has had more effect on the type and
quality of the turf than that applied in the autumn. Thus turf receiving
sulphate of ammonia in the spring and dried blood in the autumn resembles
turf receiving sulphate of ammonia throughout the year, while turf receiving
dried blood in the spring and sulphate of ammonia in the autumn resembles turf
treated regularly with dried blood. Combinations of sulphate of ammonia and
one of the other nitrogenous fertilizers avoid the extreme effects of either
on its own.

Trial G.

    Sulphate of ammonia had a considerable effect in producing a fine weed-
free Festuca/Agrostis sward from the original mixed pasture turf but turf
treated with nitro-chalk, nitrate of soda or dried blood was decidedly weedy
and calcium cynamide increased the weed population considerably. Calcined
sulphate of iron had a marked effect on the weed population, offsetting to a
considerable extent the weed-encouraging effect of the treatments other than
sulphate of ammonia and ammonium phosphate. Sulphate of iron helped these
latter materials produce a good turf in a shorter period of time but continued
use led to turf lacking vigour and drought resistance.

Trials H.

    Urea formaldehyde fertilizer has not yet shown itself very suitable for
use on turf. Only part of the nitrogen seems to become available and this
quite rapidly (as with sulphate of ammonia). The effect on turf quality seems
similar to that of natural organics, i.e. some tendency to encourage weeds,
disease and earthworms. The other slow release nitrogenous materials used have
also been disappointing.

DISCUSSION

The trials described have been very much of an applied nature, being attempts to find the most suitable rates and combinations of available fertilizers to produce under British conditions the results required (i.e. turf suitable for the purpose intended) with minimum expenditure on labour and materials. Obviously many points come into this reckoning, including:-

1. Ability of the turf to withstand wear.
2. Amount of growth to be mown off.
3. Density.
4. Invasion by weeds (including weed grasses).
5. Disease susceptibility (original turf grasses and invading grasses).
6. Incidence of pests (especially surface casting earthworms).
7. Colour.
8. Drought resistance.
9. Winter hardiness.
10. Fibre formation (mat or thatch).
11. Direct scorch by fertilizer.
12. Physical suitability and miscibility of fertilizers.
13. Duration of effects of fertilizer.
14. Effects on soil conditions.
15. Cost of treatment.

Assessment of these points is not always capable of easy statistical measurement on an experiment ground! It would seem that a period of 3 to 5 years is the minimum necessary to obtain a reasonable assessment of the long-term effects of fertilizer treatments, though clear indications may be given in the first year

The trials have shown up quite clearly that the form in which the main plant foods are applied has a considerable influence on the quality and performance of the turf produced. As regards nitrogen regular use of sulphate of ammonia has shown decided advantages in discouraging weeds, pests and disease, and providing a firm, dry surface, but has also caused over-acidity, excess fibre production and poor drought resistance. On the other hand organic nitrogen fertilizers (including urea formaldehyde) and fertilizers leaving an alkaline residue have produced soft, easily damaged turf prone to invasion by weeds (and weed grasses), earthworms and to attacks of disease (particularly F. nivale) though the turf has been less susceptible to drought and less fibrous. Super-phosphate has generally proved more satisfactory than bone meal for supplying phosphate. From these trials no information on the best form of potash is revealed but in British practice there seems little problem here - sulphate or muriate of potash are commonly used and both seem satisfactory. Sulphate of iron has been shown to have marked disadvantages as well as some advantages but in practice is still quite popular and probably over-used.

Control of pH is obviously an important factor and here species preferences need to be taken into account as well as other aspects. Over-acidity causes difficulties but high pH's also cause decided problems. In practice, as in some trials, correction of over-acidity by liming results in the immediate production of a high surface pH (even though only light dressings of lime are given) and consequently difficulties with disease, earthworms and weeds.

The relationship shown between season of application and fertilizer treatment as regards the long-term effect of treatment are very interesting and may well have useful practical implications.

It can be claimed with some justice that the results of the trials described

189

are limited in value because of the fact that in all cases the final turf has been mainly a mixture of bentgrass and annual meadow-grass, the proportions depending on the treatment. In some cases this has been due to the original grasses used and in the remainder the position has been very much affected by the heights of cut. It is however worth noting that in variety trials at the Institute it has been normal to maintain pure swards of several varieties of <u>Lolium perenne</u> with treatments based on sulphate of ammonia, superphosphate and sulphate or muriate of potash so long as the height of cut was maintained at 1 in. (2.5 cm): lowering the height to ¾ in. (1.9 cm) has been necessary to show differences between varieties.

It would seem that there is need for a great deal more research on turf nutrition (both basic and applied) bearing in mind any special needs of different species and varieties as well as user requirements, management practices (e.g. removal or non-removal of cuttings) and environmental factors. More information like that given by Bradshaw (7) would assist greatly. Information on the reasons for some of the effects, e.g. moisture retention, would be very useful indeed and a whole new field may be opened up by the modern tendency to turn to "artificial" soils. Selection of suitable fertilizers to maintain a desirable pH would be very useful.

REFERENCES

1. SKOGLEY, C. R. (1967) Turfgrass fertilizer research at Rhode Island Agricultural Experiment Station. J. Sports Turf Res. Inst. 43, 34.

2. ESCRITT, J. R., and LIDGATE, H. J. (1964) Report on fertilizer trials. J. Sports Turf Res. Inst. 40, 7.

3. ESCRITT, J. R. (1961) Report on yield trials with urea-formaldehyde resins. - 1961. J. Sports Turf Res. Inst. 10, 37, 290.

4. ESCRITT, J. R., and LIDGATE, H. J. (1962) An investigation of the suitability of a urea-formaldehyde fertilizer product for use on turf. J. Sports Turf Res. Inst. 10, 38, 385.

5. ESCRITT, J. R., and LIDGATE, H. J. (1965) Further report on the suitability of a urea-formaldehyde fertilizer product for use on turf. J. Sports Turf Res. Inst. 41, 5.

6. ESCRITT, J. R., and LEGG, D. C. (1968) Gradual release nitrogen fertilizers for use on fine turf. J. Sports Turf Res. Inst. 44, 66.

7. BRADSHAW, A. D. (1962) Turf grass species and soil fertility. J. Sports Turf Res. Inst. 10, 38, 372.

NITROGEN NUTRITION OF TURFGRASSES

R. E. Schmidt,

Virginia Polytechnic Institute, Blacksburg, Virginia,
U.S.A.

SUMMARY

Ecological phenomena must be considered in formulating nitrogen nutritional programmes for turfgrasses. Seasonal effect on nitrogen metabolism is dependent upon the carbohydrate status of the grass. If grass carbohydrate reserves are reduced, nitrogen assimilation decreases.

Nitrogen fertilization of cool-season grasses during fall and winter increases colour, carbohydrate reserves and root growth. This has been attributed to the increased net photosynthesis during mild days during winter and fall. Nitrogen fertilization during early spring stimulates top growth at the expense of the carbohydrate reserves and root development. It appears that for best year-round turfgrass vigour, nitrogen fertilization should coincide with natural carbohydrate reserve build-up and root development.

In formulating a nitrogen nutrition programme for turfgrasses, all environmental phenomena must be considered. For example, bermudagrasses do well in the semi-tropics and bentgrasses are adapted to the temperate regions. This discussion will be limited to the general observations of nitrogen nutrition of those grasses that are mainly used within the temperate region (the cool-season grasses).

Ecological factors, both natural and imposed, influence chemical reactions within a plant. Symptoms of bad nitrogen fertilization management may be noticeable only after the turf has undergone stresses. It has been observed on the author's research plots that Poa pratensis L. recovery from summer drought was influenced by timing of nitrogen fertilization. Plots receiving 6 lb. nitrogen per 1000 sq. ft. (ca. 3 kg/100 sq m) were much slower to recover when 2/3 of the nitrogen was applied in the spring than when 2/3 was applied in the fall.

Normally, under soil conditions, nitrate is the principal source of nitrogen utilized by higher plants; it may be absorbed into the plant, reduced to ammonia, and then incorporated into amino-acids and proteins for plant growth and structure. In order for nitrates to be reduced, enzymatic reactions must occur which require the reduced forms of nicotinamide adenine dinucleotide ($NADH_2$) or nicotinamide adenine dinucleotide phosphate ($NADPH_2$). These reductants are formed upon the metabolism (oxidation) of carbohydrates. Thus, nitrogen and carbohydrate metabolism are interacting and therefore nitrogen nutrition cannot be discussed without directly or indirectly including carbohydrate metabolism behaviour.

In glycolysis and the tri-carboxylic acid cycle, one molecule of glucose yields 38 molecules of adenosine triphosphate (ATP) in carbohydrate respiration (4). ATP is an essential co-factor in plant growth processes. Under high temperatures, inhibitors may be formed preventing ATP production. This loss of energy appears to be especially true with high nitrogen and warm temperatures.

Both nitrogen assimilation and carbohydrate metabolism are influenced by environmental factors such as moisture, pH, light, temperature, and nitrogen concentration.

Soil acidity influences nitrogen metabolism in several ways; for example nitrate uptake increases with pH to about pH 6, then decreases with further pH increase (18, 11).

Nitrogen assimilation is dependent upon the carbohydrate reserves that supply the partially oxidized sugars (organic keto-acids) required for amino-acid formation. Carbohydrates also furnish the substrate for respiratory release of energy (9). With an increase in light intensity, metabolic co-factors such as ATP and $NADH_2$ (6), carbon dioxide fixation (16) and nitrate uptake (5, 3) increase.

The rate of nitrate and ammonium ion absorption has been shown to increase with their external concentrations up to a certain point (10). Nitrogen-starved plants high in carbohydrates absorb nitrate more rapidly than those grasses previously fertilized with nitrogen (19). The rate of nitrogen assimilation in the plant may act in regulating nitrogen absorption (11).

Increases in temperature generally increase nitrate uptake (18, 10). However, nitrate reductase increases with temperature only to a certain point, after which it decreases (3). Temperature also affects photosynthesis and respiration thus influencing photophosphorylation and oxidative phosphorylation processes. When temperature is increased, CO_2 fixation increases to a point (then decreases with further temperature rise): respiration is stimulated: and oxidative phosphorylation (ATP formation) is increased, thus enhancing nitrogen assimilation (9) and carbohydrate utilization (16). If respiration increases so that carbohydrate reserves are used faster than CO_2 can be fixed, there will be less partially oxidized sugar (organic acids) available for amino-acid production, the provision of respiratory substrate, and the subsequent release of energy. This is what appears to limit cool-season grass growth when large amounts of nitrogen are made available during periods of high temperature.

Cool-season grasses preconditioned to maintain high carbohydrate content are better able to stand heat stresses. Bentgrass grown for 45 days at $32^{\circ}C$ was seriously injured with heavy nitrogen fertilization (16) but bentgrass that was preconditioned for 45 days at 24 and $13^{\circ}C$ did not show injury when switched to $32^{\circ}C$ and fertilized with heavy nitrogen.

In formulating a nitrogen nutritional programme one must consider seasonal root and top growth development, carbohydrate accumulation, and extreme temperature stresses. Bentgrass under almost uniform nitrogen supply has been shown to yield the most foliage in early spring followed by a sharp decline (12). In late spring, foliage yields increased again, but then declined as hot weather persisted in July and August. Top growth did not increase with the approach of lower temperatures in the fall, but in fact continued to decrease, with the lowest yields given in October.

Underground seasonal growth of cool-season grasses differs somewhat from the top growth. Hanson and Juska (7) showed that roots and rhizomes of Kentucky bluegrass increased from December to May with much less root development thereafter. This agrees with the findings of other workers (17, 14).

Results obtained in Virginia showed that carbohydrates of bentgrasses increased from fall to spring and then decreased at about the time that the flush of spring top growth occurred(15). Carbohydrates remained low during the summer months. High nitrogen fertility generally increased top growth and decreased root development and carbohydrates (8). However, late fall and winter nitrogen applications applied to cool-season grasses have increased roots and rhizomes (7). The increased underground plant development appears to be contingent upon the increase of chlorophyll associated with increased nitrogen fertilization and sufficient mild days during the late fall and winter to favour photosynthesis. Powell et al. (13, 14) reported that winter nitrogen applications on bentgrass increased carbohydrate reserves and root growth because the associated low respiration enhanced net photosynthesis.

Root growth of cool-season grasses is favoured over foliage growth at a low temperature (1). This, combined with a high carbohydrate reserve and an adequate nitrogen supply, enhances root development and should enable plants to have more vigour during summer stress (16). On the other hand, nitrogen application immediately prior to or during the spring flush growth increases top growth at the apparent expense of root development and carbohydrate reserves (13). When excessive nitrogen is made available to the cool-season grass during periods conducive to rapid top growth, it stimulates respiration and lowers carbohydrate reserves (16), and thus offsets the root development initiated by late fall and winter fertilization (Table 1).

It appears that for best year-round turfgrass vigour, nitrogen fertilization should be programmed to conserve carbohydrates and enhance root development. Seasonal stresses and management practices within an ecological area must be considered in formulation of a nitrogen nutritional programme.

Table 1: winter and spring nitrogen fertilization influence on roots of Kentucky bluegrass grown in glass-sided box for 20 days in April

	Average number of roots along glass at 15 cm	
Nitrogen (kg/ha)	Winter N only	Winter N + 50 kg/ha N on 1 April
None	23	18
50 - Oct., Dec., Feb.	63	38
50 - Oct., Nov., Dec., Jan., Feb.	63	45
100 - Oct., Nov.	45	38

REFERENCES

1. BEARD, J. B. (1959) Microclimate and bentgrass roots. Proc. Midwest
    Regional Turf Found. and Purdue Univ. Turf Conf. p.23.

2. BEEVERS, L., and COOPER, J. P. (1964) Influence of temperature on
    growth and metabolism of ryegrass seedlings. II. Variation in
    metabolites. Crop Sci. 4, 143.

3. BEEVERS, L., SCHRADER, L. E., FLESHER, D., and HAGEMAN, R. H. (1965)
    The role of light and nitrate in the induction of nitrate reduction
    in radish cotyledons and maize seedlings. Plant Physiol. 40, 691.

4. BONNER, J., and VARNER, J. E. (1965) Plant Biochemistry, Academic Press,
    New York, New York. Pp. 214-229.

5. DERBYSHIRE, E., and STREET, H. E. (1964) Studies of the growth in
    culture of excised wheat roots. V. The influence of light on
    nitrate uptake and assimilation. Physiologia Pl. 17, 107.

6. EVANS, H. J., and NASON, A. (1953) Pyridine nucleotide-nitrate
    reductase extracts of higher plants. Pl. Physiol. 28, 233.

7. HANSON, A. A., and JUSKA, F. V. (1961) Winter root activity in Kentucky
    bluegrass (Poa pratensis L.) Agron. J. 53, 372.

8. HYLTON, L. O., Jnr., ULRICH, A., and CORRELIUS, D. R. (1965) Comparison
    of nitrogen constituents as indication of nitrogen status of Italian
    ryegrass and relation of top to root growth. Crop Sci. 5, 21.

9. KESSLER, E., (1964) Nitrate assimilation by plants. Ann. Rev. Pl.
    Physiol. 15, 57.

10. LYCKLAMA, J. C. (1963) The absorption of ammonium and nitrate by
    perennial ryegrass. Act. bot. neerl. 12, 361.

11. MINOTTI, P. L., CRAIG, D., and JECKSON, W. A. (1969) Nitrate uptake by
    wheat as influenced by ammonium and other cations. Crop Sci. 9, 9.

12. MUSSER, H. B., and DUICH, J. M. (1958) Response of creeping bentgrass
    putting green turf to ureaform compounds and other nitrogenous
    fertilizers. Agron. J. 50, 381.

13. POWELL, A. J., BLASER, R. E., and SCHMIDT, R. E. (1967) Effect of
    nitrogen on winter root growth of bentgrass. Agron. J. 59, 529.

14. POWELL, A. J., BLASER, R. E., and SCHMIDT, R. E. (1967) Physiological
    and colour aspects of turfgrass with fall and winter nitrogen. Agron.
    J. 59, 303.

15. SCHMIDT, R. E. (1965) Some physiological responses of two grasses as
    influenced by temperature, light, and nitrogen fertilization. Ph.D.
    Thesis, Virginia Polytechnic Institute, Univ. Microfilms No. 66-562.
    Ann Arbor, Mich. 117p.

16. SCHMIDT, R. E., and BLASER, R. E. (1967) Effect of temperature, light and nitrogen on growth and metabolism of 'Cohansey' bentgrass (Agrostis palustris Huds.) Crop Sci., 7, 447.

17. STUCKEY, I. H. (1941) Seasonal growth of grass roots. Am. J. Bot. 28, 486.

18. VAN DEN HONERT, T. H., and HOOYMANS, J. J. M. (1953) On the absorption of nitrate by maize in water culture. Act. bot. neerl. 4, 376.

19. WILLIS, A. J. (1951) Synthesis of amino acids in young roots of barley. Biochem. J. 49, 27.

TISSUE ANALYSES AS INDICATORS OF TURFGRASS NUTRITION

R. R. Davis,
Professor of Agronomy, Ohio Agricultural Research and Development Center and
Ohio State University, Wooster, Ohio, U.S.A.

SUMMARY

The direct reading emission spectrograph and automated equipment for nitrogen analysis have made possible the rapid analyses necessary for a successful plant analysis service. Sampling procedures and correlations with plant response have not yet been developed to the point of making tissue analysis a satisfactory guide for routine fertilizer recommendations for turfgrasses. In the hands of a skilled manager, tissue analysis can be a useful tool in diagnosing uncommon nutritional problems.

INTRODUCTION

The analyses of plant tissue for the purpose of diagnosing the nutritional status of the plant is not new. Hoffer (1926) and Thornton et al. (1939) were early advocates for the use of the tissue test as a guide for making fertilizer recommendations. The idea of going directly to the plant rather than testing soil to assess nutrient requirements is attractive since many complicated soil chemical reactions can be by-passed. However, as with soil tests, the results of plant analyses must be correlated with plant responses. The difficulty of obtaining sufficient data to establish this relationship is one of the principal factors limiting the use of plant analyses for turfgrasses.

The development of the direct reading emission spectrograph with computer read-out (Jones and Weaver 1967) and equipment for automated nitrogen analysis has made possible the rapid determinations necessary for a successful plant analysis service. A limited number of Land-grant Universities and several private laboratories in the United States offer a plant analysis service. A list of laboratories and the service they offer are given by Breth (1968).

A PLANT ANALYSIS PROGRAMME FOR TURFGRASSES?

Ohio and a few other states have a Plant Analysis programme for field crops, fruits, vegetables and some ornamentals. Jones (1967) has shown that it is essential to sample a given plant part at a specific stage of maturity for a plant analysis to be meaningful. For example, the ear leaf of Zea mays L. is sampled at the time of silking. Critical levels of the nutrient of interest must be established for each species at a specific stage of development. These critical levels are very difficult to establish for turfgrasses. Hylton et al (1964) reported the critical nitrate nitrogen level in blade one of Lolium multiflorum Lam. to be 1000 ppm in a nutrient culture experiment. Davis (1965) found total nitrogen in leaf clippings of well fertilised Poa pratensis L. to vary from 5.5% to 4.0% of the dry weight. The highest nitrogen level was in spring and early summer and the lowest level in late summer when moisture was deficient. Chapman (1966) reviews critical levels of essential elements for many crop plants including some grasses. Davis and Jones (1968) have recently discussed the prospects for a plant analysis programme for turfgrasses.

Table 1 illustrates one of the problems of using plant analysis to determine the nutrient status of P. pratensis, namely, the importance of time of sampling. The potassium content of clippings varies more with time of sampling than with levels of potash fertilization. Soil samples from these plots showed increasing potassium levels with increased fertilization and ranged from soil test values at a medium level to a very high level. Plots receiving no potassium fertilizer for eight years showed no evidence of potassium deficiency.

Another problem with spectrographic analysis of turfgrass clippings is the influence of a small quantity of unseen soil on the mineral content of the sample (Table 2). Close mowing and earthworm casts, topdressing or an uneven surface means a soil-contaminated sample. Certain elements (Al, Fe, Mn, Si) are dramatically increased by soil contamination while others (K, P) are apparently diluted by the presence of soil.

QUICK TISSUE TESTS

Quick tests of fresh turfgrass tissue are used by some turfgrass managers as a guide for their fertilizer programme. Wickstrom (1967) outlines the steps for using tissue testing in field diagnosis. The Purdue test (Ohlrogge 1952), Bray's nitrate test (Bray 1945) and Milsted's potassium test (Milsted 1950) are usually used for quick tissue tests. Quick tests have all the limitations of more sophisticated laboratory analyses except for time, and the additional limitation of much less precision. Their value depends on the knowledge and skill of the user.

Table 1: potassium content of P. pratensis clippings as influenced by fertilization and date of sampling

| K Fertilizer | % K in clippings (dry matter basis) | | | |
	25 May 1964	17 July 1964	28 Aug. 1964	18 Nov. 1964
No K	3.19	2.19	2.75	1.75
9.3 kg K/ha/year	3.21	2.25	2.82	1.84
46.5 kg K/ha/ 5 years	3.28	2.35	2.89	1.87
55.8 kg K/ha/year	3.47	2.37	2.75	1.89
279.0 kg K/ha/5 years	3.48	2.43	2.91	1.92

<u>Table 2</u>: the influence of cutting height (soil) on the spectrographic analysis of Merion <u>Poa pratensis</u>

% in dry weight - 13 October 1967

	K	P	Ca	Mg	Na	Si	N*
Mowed 19 mm	2.45	0.56	0.43	0.23	0.01	1.76	5.13
Mowed 38 mm	3.08	0.71	0.34	0.24	0.01	0.50	5.12

PPM in dry weight - 13 October 1967

	Mn	Fe	Bo	Cu	Zn	Al	Sr	Mo	Co
Mowed 19 mm	174	2474	6	11	52	2878	22	5	4
Mowed 38 mm	63	431	5	12	50	369	21	2	3

*Kjeldahl method

CONCLUSIONS

The present state of knowledge does not justify total reliance on tissue analyses as a guide for fertilizing turfgrasses. Many problems of time of sampling, plant parts to sample, sample contamination, and correlation of test results with grass response must be solved before this practice can be a precise and practical method of predicting nutrient requirements. In its present stage of development, tissue analysis can help a skilled turfgrass manager diagnose uncommon nutrition problems such as minor element deficiencies.

REFERENCES

BRAY, R. H. (1945) Nitrate test for soils and plant tissues. Soil Sci. 60, 219.

BRETH, S. A. (1968) Plant analysis. What it can do for you. Crops and Soils. April - May, 1968.

CHAPMAN, H. D. (Ed.) (1966) Diagnostic criteria for plants and soils. University of California, Division of Agricultural Sciences.

DAVIS, R. R., and JONES, J. B., Jnr. (1968) Prospects for a plant analysis programme for turfgrasses - problems and potential. Agron. Abstr. 1968, 58.

DAVIS, R. R. (1965) Forms of nitrogen for fertilizing Kentucky bluegrass in Ohio. Golf Course Reptr. 33, 5, 1.

HOFFER, G. N. (1926) Testing corn stalks chemically to aid in determining their plant food needs. Purdue agric. Exp. Stn. Bull. 298.

HYLTON, L. O., Jnr., WILLIAMS, D. E., ULRICH, A., and CORNELIUS, O. R. (1964) Critical nitrate levels for growth of Italian ryegrass. Crop Sci. 4, 16.

JONES, J. B., Jnr. (1967) Interpretation of plant analysis for several agronomic crops. In "Soil Testing and Plant Analysis. Plant Analysis Part 2". Soil Science Society of America Special Publication 2. Madison, Wisconsin.

JONES, J. B., Jnr., and WEAVER, C. R. (1967) Determination of mineral composition of plant tissue by direct reading emission spectroscopy. Proceedings of Pittsburgh Conference on Analytical Chemistry and Applied Spectroscopy.

MELSTED, S. W. (1950) A simplified field test for determining potassium in plant tissue. Better Crops with Plant Food 1, 14.

OHLROGGE, A. J. (1952) The Purdue soil and plant tissue tests. Purdue Agric. Exp. Stn. Bull. 584.

THORNTON, S. F., CONNER, S. D., and FRASER, R. R. (1939) The use of rapid chemical tests on soils and plants as aids in determining fertilizer needs. Purdue Univ. Agric. Exp. Stn. Circ. 204.

WICKSTROM, G. A. (1967) Use of tissue testing in field diagnosis. In "Soil Testing and Plant Analysis. Plant Analysis Part II". Soil Science Society of America Special Publication 2, Madison, Wisconsin.

R. Hansen,

Institut für Stauden und Gehölze, Staatl. Lehr- und Forschungsanstalt für
Gartenbau, Weihenstephan, West Germany

SUMMARY

Fertilizer trials since 1961 at Weihenstephan have compared organic and
mineral fertilizers, and slow-acting and quick-acting nitrogen fertilizers.
Results are given in terms of turf appearance and quality, and weed and turfgrass population. Trials were also made on the effects of deficiencies and
different proportions of N, P and K, which showed the over-riding importance
of N. Large-scale trials of commercial lawn fertilizers are briefly reviewed,
but for various reasons it is not valid to classify fertilizers according to
efficiency or cost per unit.

Since 1961 various turf fertilizer trials have been running at
Weihenstephan concerned with questions relating to the influence of individual
nutrients and nutrient proportions, and also with fertilizer formulations. The
high buffer capacity of the heavy loam soils caused, during the first year's
investigation, limited and inexact results. With the raising of the nitrogen
content from 17 to 25 g N / sq m during the next two years results were obtained,
after a further four years, which could be properly evaluated. The first
results were obtained from the various investigations with organic and inorganic
and slow-acting and quick-acting fertilizers.

1.   THE EFFECTS OF ORGANIC AND MINERAL FERTILIZERS ON THE SWARD

Triplicate fertilizer trials were made to compare a complete organic
fertilizer (Kama-Orka) with a pure mineral fertilizer mixture (sulphate of
ammonia, superphosphate and sulphate of potash in the proportions 10N;   9P:
13K) and the same mixture with a peat carrier equivalent in organic matter to
Kama-Orka. The mineral fertilizer mixture was applied in four equal portions,
whilst 2/3 of the organic fertilizer were given in autumn and 1/3 was given
in spring. The clear results from subsequent observations were as follows:-

(a) On average, turf receiving organic fertilizer was brighter green than
    turf receiving equal amounts of nitrogen in the mixture, whether purely
    mineral or mineral with peat carrier.

(b) As expected, the organic fertilizer caused insignificant colour
    fluctuations, in marked contrast to the mineral fertilizer.

(c) An essential distinction is shown in effect on the weed population.
    Mineral fertilizer plots showed a continuous weed decrease and after
    four years there was a very small weed population, whilst the organic
    fertilizer plots showed a marked increase in Bellis perennis L.
    Estimations of the areas taken up by patches of Bellis were, on average:-

Organic fertilizer	1.75 sq m
Mineral fertilizer	0.07 sq m
Mineral fertilizer + peat	0.15 sq m

Similar relationships obtained with less frequent weeds (Taraxacum
officinale Weber and Plantago spp.). Doubtless this weed suppression was

related to the acidifying effect of the fertilizer mixture, particularly
the proportion of sulphate of ammonia, and not to the effect of mineral
fertilizer as such.

(d)   Another direct result of the acidifying action of the mineral fer-
      tilizer was a change in sward composition from a mixture relatively
      rich in species to a sward consisting predominantly of Agrostis spp.
      Only Holcus lanatus L.,which had invaded the sward in patches, per-
      sisted and spread further.

(e)   With the change to an Agrostis sward, susceptibility to snow mould
      increased and was particularly apparent in the after-winter colour.

(f)   A particular disadvantage of the mineral fertilizer treatment was
      the increased danger from scorch, which did not occur with normal
      applications of the completely organic fertilizer.

2.   COMPARISON OF SLOW-ACTING AND QUICK-ACTING NITROGEN FERTILIZERS

With the development of synthetic organic nitrogen fertilizers giving slow
nitrogen delivery the question has existed for ten years as to how far these
simplify matters, by requiring only one application, without attendant disadvantages. "Floranid" (based on Crotodur) was thought to meet these requirements.
A 10:5:5 mineral fertilizer mixture was compared at a rate of 25 g/sq m, applied
in 4 equal amounts, with "Floranid", given as a single application in the early
spring.

The following results were obtained:-

(a)   In contrast to the trial described in section 1, there was
      little colour difference between the treatments, particularly
      in wet years.

(b)   The slow-acting power of the Crotodur fertilizer decreased in
      mid-summer, and in dry cool springs action was relatively slow
      in starting.

(c)   As opposed to the mineral fertilizer, high rates of application
      of Floranid gave no damage.

(d)   A disadvantage as compared to the acidifying mineral fertilizer, was
      the lack of weed suppression. The average of replicates showed
      Bellis patches occupying 3.98 sq m in plots receiving "Floranid", but
      only 0.03 sq m with the other treatment.

(e)   Continuous uniform delivery of nitrogen from "Floranid" depends
      closely on the weather; observations showed that the total yearly
      application is best divided into two doses.

3.   NUTRITIONAL DEFICIENCY TRIALS

These trials, complementing the trials on proportions of nutrients, were
mainly planned to elucidate the influence of the main individual nutrients
(N, P and K) on the quality and composition of swards. The trials included
treatments from which one or two of these nutrients were omitted, and others
in which double doses were given. Five years' investigations gave the following
results, relating particularly to weed population and colour:-

(a) By comparison with P & K, N had the greatest influence on the
     quality and composition of sward; effects on colour were
     particularly marked.

(b) Lack of N increased weed population twenty-fold as compared
     with balanced NPK fertilizing (1:1:1) and caused a striking
     decrease in colour intensity. The balance between Poa trivialis L.
     and Poa annua L. tipped in favour of the former; the percentage
     of Lolium spp. was much decreased.

(c) Lack of P and lack of K were similar in effect. They gave, on
     the whole, a somewhat higher weed population than balanced NPK
     fertilizer.

(d) Double N applications led to the total disappearance of weeds.
     The number of grass species was decreased, Poa trivialis and
     Festuca rubra L. being depressed and Lolium perenne L. and Poa
     annua favoured. The high tolerance of soluble salts by the two
     species doubtless played a big role in this. A luxuriant leafy
     growth and the lack of sward-thickening species (Agrostis, Poa
     trivialis) gave a more open sward.

(e) Doubling the P & K applications, on the contrary, gave a clear
     increase in weeds and some grasses (Poa trivialis and Festuca rubra).

(f) Application of N alone, without P & K, allowed slight weed
     growth, whilst Poa trivialis predominated among the grasses.

(g) Application of P or K alone, without N, caused a substantial
     increase in weed infestation, up to 50% of the turf surface.

4. NUTRIENT-PROPORTION TTRIALS

Provided that the amount of N is the same, different proportions of the
other nutrients showed, even after 6 years on heavy clay loam, very little
influence on the condition and composition of the swards. A high dose of N,
as sulphate of ammonia, gave a hard wearing fairly uniform sward, with Poa
annua predominating and practically no weeds. Present findings show Lolium
perenne taking second place, N - P and N - K ratios of 1:0.75 giving optimum
development, and departures from these proportions causing decreases.

5. LARGE-SCALE TRIALS OF COMMERCIAL LAWN FERTILIZERS

Between 1965 and 1968 the Turf Research Association (Gesellschaft für
Rasenforschung) undertook replicated large-scale fertilizer trials in 4 places
in Germany with the object of testing the effect of commercial turf fertilizers.
A unit of 21g N/sq m was selected to give a uniform basis for comparison of the
different fertilizers. Assessment of density, uniformity, colour and weeds
was undertaken once a month during the growing period, together with assessment
of overall appearance and sward development. Generally the results were as
follows:-

(a) As expected, results confirm the distinctive differences between
     the effects of organic and mineral fertilizers, particularly those
     of an acidifying nature, already seen in trials described in
     Sections 1 & 2. Because of the great difference between fertilizers
     a general evaluation according to groups cannot be made.

(b) Very low percentage fertilizers (1-3% N) with high organic matter are exceptional and should be avoided for turf use during the growing period.

(c) High percentage natural and synthetic organic fertilizers containing high proportions of nitrogen are as effective as those with balanced N, P & K. This showed itself ultimately in the weed population, giving similar results to the nutrient deficiency trials described in Section 3.

(d) Equivalent amounts of nitrogen per unit area were given in all trials but in spite of this the various organic fertilizers gave much reduced nitrogen effects, particularly with regard to colour and vigour, as compared with mineral fertilizers. The cause must be sought in the different availabilities of nitrogen in organic combinations.

(e) Classification of fertilizers on the basis of appraisal scores is possible, but must be avoided as the conditions vary from case to case. Very effective mineral fertilizers, for example, have a marked influence on turf composition, favour many diseases and scorch the turf. On the other hand, weak organic fertilizers can be very useful on good turf surfaces, particularly when completely even application is impossible.

(f) Though equivalent nitrogen was used in the trials no information can be accordingly given concerning price and values. Computation of costs per kg nitrogen is indeed possible, but as mentioned in (d) above, has no direct relation to the results. Regard must be paid to the long-lasting effect of many relatively expensive fertilizers. Cheaper fertilizers may be good value, or their reduced effectiveness may be a drawback.

POTASSIUM FERTILIZERS FOR TIFWAY BERMUDAGRASS

G. C. Horn,
Professor of Ornamental Horticulture and Turf, University of Florida, Gainesville, Florida, U.S.A.

SUMMARY

The results are given from the first six years of a comparison of various potash treatments (seven sources of potash at different rates) on Tifway bermudagrass.

INTRODUCTION

Potassium is one of the elements necessary for the growth of turfgrasses. Unlike the other essential elements required in the growth of grasses, potassium does not become an integral part of the chemical structure of grasses but is very necessary as a "catalyst" or "activator" for several vital biochemical functions.

Literature is abundant on the indirect effects of the lack of potassium on turfgrasses. A reduction in the potassium available to turfgrasses will reduce yield and quality, decrease drought resistance, increase susceptibility to certain diseases, decrease sugar and protein content, increase respiration rate, reduce turgor of cells, etc.

The role of potassium as an enzyme activator for the enzyme pyruvic kinase necessary for formation of pyruvic acid has been clearly established. This element is vital to the normal flow of metabolites in many growth reactions. This important function regulates the rate of chlorophyll formation indirectly.

Potassium has been shown to increase the leaf area of grasses and speed up the intake of CO_2, both important in chlorophyll production. It is known to be essential to the formation and movement of sugar and to the formation of proteins in grasses. While the literature is abundant on the role of potassium in grasses, little can be found on exactly how much potassium should be applied, how frequently or which source is best to use.

EXPERIMENTAL METHODS AND MATERIALS

To determine the best source of potassium, also to determine the best rate and frequency to use, an experiment was started on a block of Tifway bermudagrass (Cynodon hybrid) at the Horticultural Unit of the Florida Agricultural Experiment Station in March, 1961. Sources of potash used included KCl, K_2CO_3, K_2SO_4, KNO_3, $CaK_2P_2O_7$, FN-500 (K-Frit) and green sand. The first 4 sources are all water soluble sources and the last three are mostly water insoluble sources. Enriched Hybro-Tite was substituted for green sand in 1965. Rates of potash applications used were 2½, 5 and 10 lb. K per 1,000 sq. ft. (ca. 1.2, 2.5 and 5.0 kg/100 sq m). These rates were compared with several check plots that received no K. Two frequencies of application (all in one application, and the total split into four equal applications) were used. Rates, sources and frequencies of K applications were in factorial combinations. Treatments were assigned in a randomized block design and replicated 3 times. The experimental unit was a block of turf 6 ft. by 9 ft. l(1.8 x 2.7m).

The soil was an Arredondo loamy fine sand, a soil with a phosphatic limestone origin. During establishment the turf received only ammonium nitrate every other week at the rate of 1 lb. N per 1000 sq. ft. per application (0.5 kg/100 sq m). Prior to planting the bermudagrass, superphosphate was rototilled into the upper 4 in. (10 cm) of soil at the rate of 2 lb. P per 1,000 sq. ft. (1 kg/100 sq m). None has been added since.

Potash treatments were started 1 March 1961 and were applied by hand each time.

The routine annual maintenance programme consisted of monthly applications of nitrogen at the rate of 1 lb. N per 1000 sq. ft. applied in March through October. From 1961 through 1965 the source of nitrogen was ammonium nitrate. From 1966 on, each plot was split into two plots 3 ft. by 9 ft.; one half received 1 lb. N per 1000 sq. ft. per month in the form of ammonium nitrate and the other half received ammonium sulphate at the same rate.

The plots were mowed twice weekly and clippings removed each time. Starting in March the mowing height was 1/2 in. (13 mm) and this height was gradually increased to 3/4 in. (19 mm) by October. During February of each year each plot was severely "verticut" and scalped to the soil level. Insects were controlled as needed. A nematicide was applied each year.

Yields were taken 4 times per year for the first few years. Appearance ratings were made monthly, usually 2 weeks after the application of nitrogen. The rating scale was from 1 (very poor turf) to 9 (excellent turf).

Representative soil samples were taken periodically during the experiment.

RESULTS AND DISCUSSION

The first part of this discussion is based on results prior to 1965 and the second part on those from 1966 and 1967. During 1965 the experiment was redesigned in an effort to examine the sulphur relationship that was suspected.

Yields(Table 1). Yield data were taken in the first 4 years and thereafter responses were based on appearance ratings. Significant yield increases were obtained during 1961 and 1962 in plots that received K_2CO_3 and K_2SO_4. During 1963 and 1964 this difference was highly significant. The other soluble sources of K, namely KCl and KNO_3, did not produce yields significantly different from the plots that received no potash. In Florida, KCl is the source used in over 90% of mixed fertilizers and is the most used source where only potash is needed. Insoluble sources of potash resulted in yields that were no better than where no potash was applied.

Potash composition (Table 2). Potash percentages varied from about 1% to 2%. In a few instances the K concentration in bermudagrass increased to over 2%. Most of the plots that received potash produced bermudagrass with higher percentages of K than the checks. In general, the soluble sources of K resulted in higher percentages of K in tissue than insoluble sources of K. Percent K in bermudagrass tissue would be of little value in measuring a K source response but would be of value in determining if K was limiting growth. Comparison of % K in Table 2 with average appearance ratings in Table 4 indicates that visual ratings gave a better indication of K response than % K determinations.

Soil potash (Table 3). The table contains soil test results collected at the end of each treatment year. With the exception of green sand, all sources of K used in the experiment resulted in increased levels of acid ammonium acetate extractable K found in the soils. It was also learnt that the level of extractable K found in the soil was not a good indication of the K available to the bermudagrass. After 4 years, no accumulation of available K was found in the soils, even where 10 lb. K per 1000 sq. ft. per year were applied.

Appearance ratings (Table 4). The appearance of a turfgrass, to a trained eye, gives a better evaluation of response to potash than either yields or % K determination in tissue or soil. These appearance ratings are averages of two or more raters. The superiority of K_2CO_3 and K_2SO_4 are clearly shown in Table 4. Appearance of plots receiving KCl and KNO_3 was much better than % of K in tissue or soil would indicate.

The experiment was changed during 1965 in that the plots were split with both ammonium sulphate and ammonium nitrate being the sources of N. The addition of the extra sulphur in the form of ammonium sulphate resulted in a significant increase in the 1966 and 1967 responses to both KCl and KNO_3. The insoluble sources of K were still unaffected (Table 4).

Throughout the experiment, 2.5 lb. K were as good as higher rates of K regardless of N source (Table 5). The same results were obtained in the earlier part of the experiment. It was interesting to find that 2.5 lb. K applied as K_2CO_2 were better than 5 or 10 lb. K applied as K_2SO_4 (Table 6).

The effects of source of N on K response in appearance ratings are shown in Table 7. Appearance ratings were better, where ammmonium sulphate was the source of N, for all sources of K except K-frit. The checks were unaffected by source of N.

Infection by dollarspot fungus (Sclerotinia homoeocarpa F. T. Bennett) was found to be related to rate of K, source of K and frequency of application. (Tables 8, 9 & 10). Also source of N is related to incidence of dollarspot fungus.

Throughout the experiment, and under the conditions of this experiment, one application of potash was as good as splitting the total into 4 equal applications (Table 11).

This experiment is to continue with some major changes in treatment.

Table 1: average annual yields per plot (g/14 sq. ft.) of Tifway bermudagrass treated with various sources of potash

Source of potash	1961	1962	1963	1964
KCl	17.2	15.7	18.0	15.0
K_2CO_3	19.0*	20.7*	26.5**	30.1**
K_2SO_4	20.9*	22.9*	26.1**	24.2**
KNO_3	16.5	13.6	19.3	16.5
$CaK_2P_2O_7$	14.5	13.8	16.8	14.2
K-Frit	16.2	15.0	17.4	15.1
Green sand	17.3	16.5	19.7	15.0
Check	16.7	15.7	17.9	15.5

* Significant at 5% level of probability
** Significant at 1% level of probability

Table 2: average % K in Tifway bermudagrass clippings (oven-dry basis) treated with various sources of potash

Source of potash	1961	1962	1963	1964
KCl	1.30	1.44	1.36	1.30
K_2CO_3	1.29	1.34	1.65	1.75
K_2SO_4	1.30	1.41	1.55	1.50
KNO_3	1.33	1.32	1.30	1.20
$CaK_2P_2O_7$	1.29	1.40	1.19	1.12
K-Frit	1.29	1.20	1.15	1.10
Green sand	1.15	1.10	1.05	1.06
Check	1.10	1.10	1.01	1.00

Table 3: acid ammonium acetate soluble K (ppm) found in soil at end of each year's treatment

Source of potash	1961	1962	1963	1964
KCl	72	53	58	60
K_2CO_3	63	48	57	55
K_2SO_4	59	51	57	55
KNO_3	86	56	61	75
$CaK_2P_2O_7$	116	58	77	65
K-Frit	73	63	75	66
Green sand	35	20	22	19
Check	33	16	21	14

Source of potash	1961 AN	1962 AN	1963 AN	1964 AN	1966 AN	1966 AS	1967 AN	1967 AS
KCl	5.8	5.4	5.6	5.4	5.3	6.6	5.5	6.9
K_2CO_3	8.0	7.5	8.2	7.5	7.4	7.6	7.8	8.3
K_2SO_4	7.1	7.1	7.2	7.0	7.1	7.4	7.8	8.2
KNO_3	5.8	5.9	5.7	5.3	5.4	6.8	5.9	7.3
$CaK_2P_2O_7$	5.7	5.4	4.9	4.9	4.6	4.7	4.5	4.8
K-Frit	5.6	5.3	4.9	4.8	4.8	4.6	4.6	4.6
Green sand (1961-64)	5.3	5.0	4.5	4.7				
Enr. Hybro-Tite (1966-67)					5.1	5.3	5.0	5.4
Check	5.5	5.3	4.8	4.7	4.6	4.6	4.6	4.6

AN = Ammonium nitrate
AS = Ammonium sulphate

Table 5: effects of rates of application of potash and different sources of nitrogen on the average appearance rating of Tifway bermudagrass during 1966 and 1967

Rate of potash lb. per 1000 sq. ft.	1966 Ammonium nitrate	1966 Ammonium sulphate	1967 Ammonium nitrate	1967 Ammonium sulphate
0	4.6	4.6	4.6	4.6
2.5	5.7	6.1	5.8	6.2
5.0	5.8	6.5	5.9	6.6
10.0	5.8	6.2	5.9	6.3
LSD for rates:	5% = 0.51 1% = 0.80		5% = 0.60 1% = 0.90	

Table 6: effects of two nitrogen sources on appearance ratings of Tifway bermudagrass treated with various sources of potash at 3 rates during the 1966-1967 season

Source of Potash	Rate of Potash (lb. per 1000 sq. ft.)							
	0	2.5	5.0	10.0	0	2.5	5.0	10.0
				Source of nitrogen				
			Ammonium nitrate				Ammonium sulphate	
KCl	4.5	5.5	5.7	5.6	4.5	6.7	8.0	7.2
K_2CO_3	4.6	8.0	8.3	8.5	4.6	8.5	8.5	8.6
K_2SO_4	4.5	7.8	8.0	8.2	4.8	8.3	8.3	8.0
KNO_3	4.8	5.5	5.8	5.5	4.8	6.8	8.2	7.2
$CaK_2P_2O_7$	4.5	4.6	4.6	4.5	4.6	4.6	4.8	4.6
K-Frit	4.5	4.6	4.6	4.6	4.5	4.7	4.6	4.5
Enr. Hybro-Tite	4.5	5.0	5.5	5.3	4.5	5.3	5.8	5.5
Checks	4.6	4.6	4.6	4.6	4.6	4.6	4.6	4.6

LSD for rates of K: 5% = 0.71   LSD for source of N: 5% = 0.43
                    1% = 1.23   1% = 0.78
                                     LSD for source of K: 5% = 0.51
                                                     1% = 0.80

Table 7: effects of two nitrogen sources on appearance ratings of Tifway bermudagrass treated with various sources of potash during 1966-1967 season

Source of potash	Source of nitrogen	
	Ammonium nitrate	Ammonium sulphate
KCl	5.33	6.60
K_2CO_3	7.35	7.55
K_2SO_4	7.13	7.35
KNO_3	5.40	6.75
$CaK_2P_2O_7$	4.55	4.65
K-Frit	4.83	4.55
Enr. Hybro-Tite	5.08	5.28
Checks	4.60	4.60

LSD for source of K: 5% = 0.51   LSD for source of N: 5% = 0.43
                       1% = 0.80   1% = 0.78

Table 8: the effects of potash sources and rates on the incidence of
dollarspot fungus in Tifway bermudagrass (25 May 1967)
Rating Scale: 1 = severely infested: 9 = no damage

Source of potash	One application per year Rates of K (lb. per 1000 sq. ft.)			Four applications per year Rates of K (lb. per 1000 sq. ft.)		
	2.5	5.0	10.0	2.5	5.0	10.0
KCl	4.6	6.0	4.0	5.3	5.6	5.3
K_2CO_3	4.3	5.0	6.0	4.3	3.0	4.3
K_2SO_4	4.7	5.6	5.0	4.3	4.6	4.6
KNO_3	6.0	6.6	7.3	5.6	4.6	5.0
$CaK_2P_2O_7$	4.7	4.3	4.3	3.7	5.0	5.0
K-Frit	6.0	3.7	4.0	4.3	3.3	5.3
Enr. Hybro-Tite	5.7	7.0	8.7	5.0	5.3	5.3
Checks	4.1	4.1	4.1	4.1	4.1	4.1

Table 9: the effects of applying potash in one application or four equal
applications on the incidence of dollarspot fungus on Tifway
bermudagrass (25 May 1967). Rating scale: 1 = severely infested:
9 = no damage)

Source of potash	Number of applications 1	4
KCl	4.9 NS	5.4*
K_2CO_3	5.1*	3.8 NS
K_2SO_4	5.0*	4.5 NS
KNO_3	6.6**	5.1*
$CaK_2P_2O_7$	4.4 NS	4.6 NS
K-Frit	4.6 NS	4.3 NS
Enr. Hybro-Tite	7.1**	5.2*
Checks	4.1	4.1

LSD between sources
* 5% = 0.90
** 1% = 1.60

LSD between number of applications
* 5% = 0.75
** 1% = 1.25

Table 10: the effects of applying sulphur (as ammonium sulphate) on the incidence of dollarspot fungus on Tifway bermudagrass (25 May 1967). Rating scale: 1 = severely infested: 9 = no damage

Source of nitrogen	All potash treatments
Ammonium nitrate	4.17
Ammonium sulphate	5.40**

LSD 5% = 0.80
    1% = 1.20

Table 11: average appearance ratings of Tifway bermudagrass with potash applied all in one application or split into four equal applications

	Times per year applied	
All K treatments	1	4
	3.13	3.26

LSD 5% = 0.37   NSD
    1% = 0.51

SOIL pH FOR TURFGRASSES

P. E. Rieke,

Soil Science Dept., Michigan State University, East Lansing, Michigan, U.S.A

SUMMARY

Soil pH affects several important physical, chemical, and biological properties of the soil. Under intensively managed turfgrass conditions with liberal irrigation, extensive leaching of bases may occur. This can lead to acid soil conditions, especially when high rates of strongly acidifying nitrogen carriers, such as ammonium sulphate, are being used. This can result in reduced availability of some nutrients and toxic levels of other nutrients.

Water quality is an important factor in maintaining soil pH levels. When water contains appreciable quantities of calcium and magnesium, a gradual increase in pH is observed with increasing levels of exchangeable calcium and magnesium in the soil, and leaching of soil potassium. The degree of leaching of potassium is increased when high rates of nitrogen are used under irrigated conditions.

Attempts to acidify highly alkaline soils under established turf must be approached cautiously. Elemental sulphur caused decreases in soil pH with the greatest change in acidity occurring in the surface layer of soil. Injury to turfgrass can result if excess amounts are used. When evaluating acidification or liming treatments, soil samples should be obtained from the surface 1-2 cm as well as from lower depths for adequate interpretation.

As early as 1900 (28) the value of liming an acid soil was reported to have increased growth of several grasses. Before the development of selective weed control chemicals, soils were often kept acid to control weeds (10). This technique is still used in some places on acid-tolerant turfgrasses such as browntop bentgrass (Agrostis tenuis Sibth.), and Chewings fescue (Festuca rubra L. ssp. commutata Gaud.) (26).

INFLUENCE ON SOILS

Soil pH influences chemical, physical, and biological properties of a soil. Figure 1 illustrates the effect of pH on nutrient availability. Nitrogen availability from organic sources is reduced under acid or highly alkaline conditions. This is due in large part to the susceptibility to extreme pH values of the soil micro-organisms involved in nitrification, ammonification, nitrogen fixation, and other organic matter transformations (13). The autotrophic organisms primarily responsible for nitrification, Nitrobacter spp., are especially sensitive to acid soils as pointed out by Cornfield (4). He found that in soils incubated in the laboratory, ammonium accumulated in acid soils while nitrate accumulated in neutral or alkaline soils.

Soil pH influences phosphorus availability by affecting the solubility of phosphorus compounds which predominate at a given pH. Solubility of the phosphate depends on the degree of acidity and the kind of soil (2). The pH also affects phosphorus and sulphur availability through its influence on microbial activity.

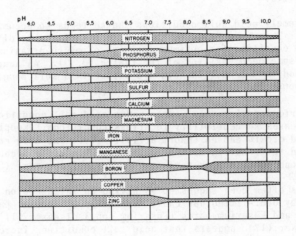

Figure 1: General relationship of pH to the availability of plant nutrients
in the soil: the wider the bar, the more available is the nutrient
(adapted from Truog (25))

Iron, manganese, copper and zinc can often be deficient on highly alkaline soils. Iron is most frequently limiting under turf conditions. On the other hand, manganese and aluminium can occur at toxic levels on extremely acid soils although they can be easily reduced by liming. Molybdenum deficiency also occurs on acid soils (13).

Calcium and magnesium availability are normally directly related to pH since these bases replace the acid hydrogen ions on the cation exchange sites when pH is raised. Calcium has received particular attention because of its influence on maintaining the integrity of the plant root in selective nutrient absorption (13).

Lime additions to acid soils, especially those with appreciable quantities of clay, tend to improve physical conditions of the soil (21, 24). For example, liming has been observed to result in higher soil moisture content (8, 16). This has been attributed to better water penetration as a result of improved soil structure (27). Heavy thatching on an acid soil may however limit water penetration to some degree. Excessive soil acidity contributes to limited root growth, particularly lack of root hairs, and leads to increased drought susceptibility (17).

Under extremely acid soil conditions thatch tends to accumulate more rapidly (7, 9). This is considered to be a result of the acidity providing an unfavourable condition for optimum activity of micro-organisms which would normally cause some decomposition of the thatch (8, 9). An annual application of lime was found to decrease the organic matter in a soil plug, suggesting increased decomposition of the thatch layer (8).

Reduced turfgrass vigour is common under acid soil conditions (17, 21) leading to increased susceptibility to stress conditions. Keeping a soil acid will reduce weed growth and earthworm activity (7). The acid condition leads to fine-textured turf, but pH must be carefully maintained because a small decrease in pH can lead to weak turf or even loss of the turf (26).

Soil pH has often been suggested as having an influence on disease activity. High pH caused by over-liming has caused increased Ophiobolus patch (Ophiobolus graminis Sacc.) and Fusarium patch (Fusarium spp.) diseases (11,12). On the other hand, Musser (17) suggests that acid soil conditions increase the activity of dollarspot (Sclerotinia homoeocarpa F.T.Bennett), brownpatch (Rhizoctonia solani Kuhn), and snowmould (Typhula itoana Imai and Fusarium nivale (Fr.) Ces.). Couch (5, 6) observed in greenhouse and controlled chamber studies that the effect of pH on turfgrass susceptibility to a number of pathogens is influenced considerably by other factors, such as nutrient levels and moisture stress. He suggests that perhaps the most important aspect of soil pH is the influence on production of new vegetation in order to overcome disease activity.

Nitrogen fertilization has a major influence on soil pH. Pierre (19) established lime requirement values for the various acid-forming nitrogen carriers. Ammonium sulphate has been widely used for acidifying turfgrass soils (23). Other carriers have less acidifying tendencies (20). Wolcott et al (29) compared several carriers and found the following order of decreasing acidification under field crop conditions: $(NH_4)_2SO_4 > NH_4Cl > NH_4NO_3 =$ Urea $>$ Ureaform $> Ca(NO_3)_2 > NaNO_3$.

MEASUREMENT OF pH

Most pH values reported in North America are measured in a soil-water slurry, while in Europe soil-salt solution slurry measurements are more common. The pH values determined in the salt solution are normally lower than for soil-water suspensions, depending on the soil and the type and concentration of salt (3). pH values reported in this paper are based on soil-water suspension determinations.

THE pH PREFERENCES OF TURFGRASSES

Kentucky bluegrass (Poa pratensis L.) requires a near neutral soil for optimum growth while the bentgrasses and fescues can adapt to more acid conditions (10, 23). The latter grasses however grow better at pH 6.5 than 4.5 (15). Redtop (Agrostis alba L.) is quite tolerant of acid soils (22) while Zoysiagrass (Zoysia spp.) prefers near neutral soils (14). Nutritional levels can affect pH responses of turfgrass as well (22). The general pH preferences for several turfgrasses are shown in Table 1.

EFFECTS OF IRRIGATION

Irrigation and natural precipitation cause leaching of bases, thus contributing to acid soils. Under intensively managed sports turf conditions with liberal irrigation, appreciable leaching will take place, particularly on sandy soils. Changes in pH may occur rapidly under these conditions.

Water source is also an important factor. Many sources of water in central and western North America contain appreciable levels of bases. This is reflected in the data in Table 2. Merion Kentucky bluegrass was seeded on Grayling sand in 1963, in a co-operative study with J.B. Beard. Half the plots were irrigated beginning in 1964; the other half were unirrigated until 1967 and 1968, when irrigation was applied on both plot areas. The continued use of irrigation water high in calcium and magnesium carbonates and bicarbonates caused increases in exchangeable calcium and magnesium, increases in pH, and increased leaching of potassium.

Table 1: the pH preferences of turfgrasses (Adapted from Musser) (17)

Turfgrass	pH preference
Kentucky bluegrass (Poa pratensis L.)	6.0 - 7.7
Annual bluegrass (Poa annua L.)	5.1 - 7.7
Canada bluegrass (Poa compressa L.)	5.6 - 7.7
Rough bluegrass (Poa trivialis L.)	5.8 - 7.7
Bentgrasses (Agrostis spp.)	5.4 - 7.6
Buffalograss (Buchloe dactyloides (Nutt.) Engelm.)	6.1 - 8.7
Redtop (Agrostis alba L.)	5.1 - 7.6
Creeping red fescue (Festuca rubra L. ssp. rubra)	5.4 - 7.6
Chewings fescue (Festuca rubra L. ssp. commutata Gaud.)	5.4 - 7.6
Tall fescue (Festuca arundinacea Schreb.)	5.4 - 7.6
Centipedegrass (Eremochloa ophiuroides (Munro) Hack.)	4.0 - 5.1
Bermudagrass (Cynodon dactylon (L.) Pers.)	5.1 - 7.1
Carpetgrass (Axonopus affinis Chase)	4.7 - 7.1
Crested wheatgrass (Agropyron cristatum (L.) Gaertn.)	6.1 - 8.7
Gramagrasses (Bouteloua spp.)	6.1 - 8.7
Ryegrasses (Lolium spp.)	5.5 - 8.1
St. Augustinegrass (Stenotaphrum secundatum (Walt.) Kuntze)	6.1 - 8.1

influence of irrigation water on soil tests of Grayling Sand
(samples taken from 0-10 cm depth)

Moisture regime	pH	Exchangeable cations (ppm*)		
Unirrigated		K	Ca	Mg
1966	6.4	128	815	30
1967	6.4	51	597	49
1968	6.6	45	526	39
Irrigated				
1966	7.2	44	1197	86
1967	7.2	47	780	74
1968	7.3	20	832	80

* Extracted with neutral normal ammonium acetate, determined on flame photometer.

Nitrogen applications also influenced pH and exchangeable bases on this soil as illustrated in Table 3. Nitrogen, particularly on the irrigated plots with the higher nitrogen rate, caused a decrease in pH, and a marked reduction in soil potassium tests at all soil depths. These data agree with results obtained by Abruna et al (1) and Pearson et al (18) who reported extensive reduction of potassium in the 0-45 cm depth on a sandy loam soil. Heavy nitrogen applications on pasture soils caused extremely acid conditions in the subsoil where liming would not be feasible. However, they found a combination of liming, heavy nitrogen applications, and leaching provided a means of replenishing the base supply of the subsoil.

SOIL ACIDIFICATION

Acidification of established turfgrass soils can not only be accomplished by the use of acidifying nitrogen fertilizers, but aluminium sulphate, iron sulphate, and elemental sulphur can also be used (21). Care must be used in utilizing these materials to prevent over-acidification and loss of turf. Data in Table 4 show the effect of elemental sulphur on soil pH of a sandy loam tee soil. The sulphur was applied in June 1967. Soil tests were obtained from the 0-10 cm depth in October 1967 and 1968. The sulphur treatments continued to acidify the soil throughout 1968.

Application of sulphur should be restricted to small quantities to prevent injury to the turf. Optimum rates for specific soils should be based on the amount of free carbonates, the cation exchange capacity of the soil, and soil pH.

The danger of using acidifying materials on established turf is the abrupt change in pH of the surface layer. Data in Table 5 show this for samples obtained from the plots described for Table 4. For example, in 1968 the highest sulphur rate had caused a pH of 5.4 in the 0-5 cm layer (Table 5) while the 0-10 cm pH was 6.4 (Table 4). In addition, there was some loss of bentgrass on the plots treated with the highest dose (29.3 kg) indicating that the surface

cm of soil may have been much more acid even than the 0-5 cm sample.
There was also some reduction in pH at the lower sampling depths with the
high rate of sulphur application.

Table 3:   influence of irrigation and nitrogen application on soil
           tests of Grayling Sand, 1968

Treatment			pH	Exchangeable cations (ppm*)		
				K	Ca	Mg
Moisture regime	Nitrogen rate (kg/100 sq m)	Depth of sample (cm)				
Irrigated	None	0-5	7.5	33	832	69
		10-15	7.3	51	534	50
		20-25	7.3	65	322	52
Unirrigated	None	0-5	6.5	110	576	43
		10-15	6.0	68	322	18
		20-25	6.2	64	406	18
Irrigated	5.9	0-5	7.2	22	833	79
		10-15	6.9	19	406	40
		20-25	6.9	33	406	40
Unirrigated	2.9	0-5	6.4	44	661	50
		10-15	6.2	41	322	18
		20-25	6.2	48	322	18

* Extracted with neutral normal ammonium acetate, determined on flame photometer.

Table 4:   influence of elemental sulphur applied on sandy loam soil
           in June 1967

Sulphur application rate (kg/100 sq m)	pH of 0-10 cm layer	
	1967	1968
0	7.3	7.3
4.9	7.3	7.3
9.8	7.2	7.2
14.6	7.1	7.0
19.5	7.0	6.8
24.4	7.0	6.6
29.3	6.7	6.4

Table 5: influence of elemental sulphur and depth of sampling on the pH of a sandy loam soil

| Depth of sampling, cm | Sulphur applied (kg/100 sq m) | | | | | |
| | 0 | | 9.8 | | 29.3 | |
	1967	1968	1967	1968	1967	1968
0-5	7.2	7.3	7.1	7.1	6.2	5.4
5-10	7.4	7.3	7.3	7.3	7.1	6.9
10-15	7.4	7.4	7.4	7.4	7.2	7.2
15-20	7.5	7.4	7.4	7.4	7.2	7.2

These data show the importance of shallow sampling under established turf conditions when testing soils for evaluation of pH change either by acidification or liming.

CONCLUSIONS

Control of soil pH is important because of its effects on physical, chemical, and biological properties of the soil. Extensive use of acid-forming nitrogen fertilizers and liberal irrigation cause accelerated leaching of bases and soil acidification. Liming can be used to counteract this action.

In some situations soil pH is raised with the use of alkaline irrigation water. Leaching of potassium is increased under these conditions, especially on sandy soils.

Attempts to acidify soil under established turf must be carried out carefully. Excessive applications of elemental sulphur can lead to over-acidification of the soil surface and loss of turf. Depth of sampling soil is important in evaluation of liming or acidification treatments.

REFERENCES

1. ABRUNA, F., PEARSON, R.W., and ELKINS, C.B. (1958)
Quantitative evaluation of soil reaction and base status changes resulting
from field application of residually acid-forming nitrogen fertilizers.
Proc. Soil Sci. Soc. Am. 22, 539.

2. ADAMS, F., and PEARSON, R.W. (1967) Crop response to lime in the
southern United States and Puerto Rico. In "Soil acidity and liming".
R.W. Pearson and F. Adams, editors. Am. Soc. Agron. Monogr. 12, 161.

3. COLEMAN, N.T., and THOMAS, G.W. (1967) The basic chemistry of soil acidity.
In "Soil acidity and liming". R.W. Pearson and F. Adams, editors.
Am. Soc. Agron. Monogr. 12, 1.

4. CORNFIELD, A.H. (1952) The mineralization of the nitrogen of soils during
incubation: influence of pH, total nitrogen, and organic carbon contents.
J. Sci. Fd. Agric. 3, 343.

5. COUCH, H.B. (1962) Diseases of turfgrasses. Reinhold Publishing Co.
New York, 1.

6. COUCH, H.B. (1966) Relationship between soil moisture, nutrition, and
severity of turfgrass diseases. J. Sports Turf Res. Inst. 42, 54.

7. DAWSON, R.B., and GREIG, R. (1933) Report on results of research work
carried out in connection with soil acidity and the use of sulphate of
ammonia as a fertilizer for putting greens and fairways. Jour. Bd. of Green.
Res. 3, 9, 65.

8. ENGEL, R.E., and ALDERFER, R.B. (1967) The effect of cultivation, top-
dressing, lime, nitrogen and wetting agent on thatch development in ¼-inch
bentgrass turf over a ten-year period. Rutgers agr. Exp. Stn. Bull. 818, 32.

9. ESCRITT, J.R., and LIDGATE, H. J.(1964) Report on fertilizer trials.
J. Sports Turf Res. Inst. 40, 7.

10. GARNER, E.S., and DAMON, S.C. (1929) The persistence of certain lawn
grasses as affected by fertilization and competition.
Rhode Island agr. Exp. Stn. Bull. 217, 1.

11. GOSS, R.L. (1967) Some effects on soil pH and calcium levels from
fertilizer applications on soil producing putting green turf.
J. Sports Turf Res. Inst. 43, 23.

12. JACKSON, N, and HOWARD, F.L. (1966) Fungi as agents of turfgrass disease.
J. Sports Turf Res. Inst. 42, 9.

13. JACKSON, W.A. (1967) Physiological effects of soil acidity. In "Soil
acidity and liming". R.W. Pearson and F. Adams, editors. Am. Soc. Agron.
Monogr. 12, 43.

14. JUSKA, F.V. (1959) Response of Meyer Zoysia to lime and fertilizer treatments.
Agron. J. 51, 81.

15. JUSKA, F.V., HANSON, A.A., and ERICKSON, C.J. (1965) Effects of phosphorus
and other treatments on the development of red fescue, Merion and Common
Kentucky bluegrass. Agron. J. 57, 75.

16. LONGNECKER, T.C., and SPRAGUE, H.B. (1940) Rate of penetration of lime in soils under permanent grass. Soil Sci. 50, 277.

17. MUSSER, H.B. (1962) Turf Management. McGraw-Hill Book Co. New York 1.

18. PEARSON, R.W., ABRUNA, F., and VINCENTE-CHANDLER, J. (1962) Effect of lime and nitrogen applications on downward movement of calcium and magnesium in two humid tropical soils of Puerto Rico. Soil Sci. 93, 77.

19. PIERRE, W.H. (1928) Nitrogenous fertilizers and soil acidity: I. Effect of various nitrogenous fertilizers on soil reaction. J. Am. Soc. Agron. 20, 254.

20. PIERRE, W.H. (1934) The equivalent acidity and basicity of fertilizers as determined by a newly proposed method. J. ass. off. agr. Chem. 17, 101.

21. ROBERTS, E.C. (1965) Why turfgrass responds to proper use of lime and sulphur compounds. Golf Course Reptr. 33, 4, 28.

22. SHOOP, G.J., BROOKS, C.R., BLASER, R.E., and THOMAS, G.W. (1961) Differential responses of grasses and legumes to liming and phosphorus fertilization. Agron. J. 53, 111.

23. SKOGLEY, C.R. (1967) Turfgrass fertilizer research at the Rhode Island agr. Exp. Stn. J. Sports Turf Res. Inst. 43, 34.

24. TIEDJENS, V. (1949) Understanding the use of lime in the soil. Golf Course Reptr. 17, 6, 7.

25. TRUOG, E. (1947) The liming of soils. In "Science in Farming". U.S. Dept. Agr. Yearbook of Agriculture, 1943-47, 566.

26. WALKER, C. (1962) Influence of acidity on sports turf texture. New Zealand Inst. for Turf Culture Newsletter 18, 18.

27. WALKER, C. (1966) The influence of trial plots on practical green-keeping. New Zealand Inst. for Turf Culture Newsletter 41, 2.

28. WHEELER, H.J., and TILLINGHAST, J.A. (1900) Effect of liming upon the relative yields and durability of grass and weeds. Rhode Island agr. Exp. Stn. Bull. 66, 1.

29. WOLCOTT, A.R., FOTH, H.D., DAVIS, J.F., and SHICKLUNA, J.C. (1965) Nitrogen carriers: I. Soil effects. Proc. Soil Sci. Soc. Am. 29, 405.

EFFECTS OF NITROGEN ON CARBOHYDRATE RESERVES

H. H. Williams (California, U.S.A)

What are the reasons for the reduction in carbohydrates in cool-season grasses as summer approaches?

R.E. Schmidt (Virginia, U.S.A.)

In Agrostis spp. and other cool-season grasses, the following processes occur:-

1. Increase in solubility of the permeable membranes, resulting in increased uptake of nitrate. This is associated with increased nitrogen metabolism, utilizing carbohydrate in amino-acid synthesis.

2. Respiration rate increases, using carbohydrate in energy production for growth.

Through these processes, carbohydrate is used faster than it is being formed by photosynthesis.

R.W. Schery (Ohio, U.S.A.)

The newer varieties of Poa pratensis L. have been selected under conditions of relatively high fertility and are better adapted to summer fertilization than the older American varieties and most European ones. Even if hot weather fertilization is of doubtful benefit to these new varieties or even damages them slightly, it damages competing species or weed grasses even more, and so improves the total turf condition.

G.C. Horn (Florida, U.S.A.)

Has Dr. Schmidt done any work on the reaction to fertilizer in warm-season turfgrasses?

R.E. Schmidt (Virginia, U.S.A.)

Warm-season turfgrasses are different from cool-season turfgrasses. Warm-season grasses accumulate carbohydrate in July and August. This, therefore, requires a wholly different approach to nitrogen fertilization. Differences between species are greater than between varieties.

SLOW RELEASE NITROGEN FERTILIZERS

W.H. Daniel (Indiana, U.S.A.)

There is some very promising current research on the application to seed-beds of very coarse particles of IBDU (isobutydiene diurea) of 5 to 10 mm size, or even larger, for long-term nitrogen release by gradual hydrolysis over more than 2 years. Obviously, heavy initial applications can be made. Particles of 2 mm gave one year's supply.

SEED-BED FERTILIZER APPLICATIONS ON SAND

E.W. Schweizer (Switzerland)

What is the optimum rate of seed-bed application of NPK fertilizers on pure sand, to provide maximum speed of establishment with no damage from salt concentration or poor root development?

W.H. Bengeyfield (California, U.S.A.)

On U.S.G.A. mixes, if the soil composition is satisfactory, fertilization is of secondary importance compared to choice of species and variety. Rate of fertilization must depend on irrigation and drainage. For bentgrass greens, the general rule is 1 lb./1,000 sq. ft., (ca. 0.5 kg/100 sq m) of N per month of the growing season. For bluegrass, the rate is less.

G.C. Horn (Florida, U.S.A.)

For fertilization of Tifgreen bermudagrass on a sandy soil, we use ½ lb. N/1,000 sq. ft. (ca. 250g/100 sq m) applied every week throughout the year. When 1 lb. N per week was given results were satisfactory for nine months but then potassium was needed. Phosphate requirements should be based on a soil test. Potassium should be applied at 8-12 lb./1,000 sq. ft. (ca. 4.0 - 6.0 kg/100 sq m) of K_2O per year.

R.E. Engel (New Jersey, U.S.A.)

On a sandy soil, we apply in the seed-bed 3 lb./1,000 sq. ft. (ca. 1.5 kg/100 sq m) of N in an NPK fertilizer. The purpose is simply to provide adequate stimulation, without attempting to satisfy long term nutritional needs through initial large applications. We expect the initial dose to last 3 to 4 months and thereafter we rely on fresh applications as sandy soils do not retain fertility long.

B. Langvad (Sweden)

In construction we use 3 tons/ha (10 kg/100 sq m) of complete fertilizer (21:7:14) with 2/3 of the nitrogen as ureaformaldehyde and 1/3 as ammonium nitrate. On raw areas, we use 12 - 14 kg/100 sq m, incorporated to 10 - 15 cm. On roadside embankments there is no incorporation.

R.W. Miller (Ohio, U.S.A.)

If levels of P & K are considered adequate we in Ohio recommend giving at establishment 1.4 kg/100 sq m of N, 1.8 kg of P and 0.9 kg of K.

R.A. Keen (Kansas, U.S.A.)

Urea and sludge giving N at 2 and 4 lb./1,000 sq. ft. (ca. 1 and 2 kg/ 100 sq m) and ureaform giving N at 2, 4, 8 and 16 lb./1,000 sq. ft. (ca. 1, 2, 4 and 8 kg/100 sq m) gave no decrease in newly seeded Agrostis stolonifera L. stands and gave greatly increased growth compared with later surface applications which burned the grass at 4 lb./1,000 sq. ft. (ca. 2 kg/100 sq m) of N in the case of urea and sludge, although ureaform was very safe.

P.E. Rieke (Michigan, U.S.A.)

We are afraid to use more than 2 lb./1,000 sq. ft. (ca. 1 kg/100 sq m) of N for fear of reducing germination. Potassium, as KCl, has also done this. We therefore recommend doses of 2 lb. N and a maximum of 2 lb. K, incorporated and worked in, and followed by supplemental dressings.

J.R. Escritt (U.K.)

Is it as easy as some people claim, to deal with minor element deficiencies on pure sand?

<u>R.E. Engel (New Jersey, U.S.A.)</u>

Most golf superintendents like to use some natural organics, and these may partly remedy deficiencies of minor elements.

<u>J.H. Madison (California, U.S.A.)</u>

The content of minor elements in sand varies. As quartz is a most resistant material, fine sands are high in quartz and low in other minerals. Orthoclase in sand can supply some potassium to bents but not to bluegrasses. Olivine and serpentine supply iron and magnesium; vermiculite supplies magnesium and perhaps some potassium. Seaside sands are deficient in sulphur and this must be supplied. In general, organic amendments may help to supply minor elements. Single superphosphate, potassium sulphate and dolomitic limestone can be used to supply the first year's nutrition exclusive of nitrogen and iron. Precise formulations are given in the University of California Bulletin No. 23, which deals with sand and peat mixes for container growing.

LIMING LAWNS

<u>C. Eisele (West Germany)</u>

U.S. literature often refers to liming lawns. Is this necessary?

<u>G.C. Horn (Florida, U.S.A.)</u>

In Florida, where many soils are acid sands and receive high rates of nitrogen, especially from ammoniacal sources, liming is essential and soil tests are made each year.

<u>W.H. Daniel (Indiana, U.S.A.)</u>

In Indiana, only about 10% of lawns need liming. Irrigation with hard water reduces the need on established lawns.

<u>R.A. Keen (Kansas, U.S.A.)</u>

In the central U.S. we must use lime on acid soils (pH below 6.2) to establish and keep <u>Poa pratensis</u> L. No lime is necessary on <u>Agrostis</u> spp., <u>Festuca</u> <u>rubra</u> L. and <u>Cynodon</u> <u>dactylon</u> (L.) Pers. Lime is detrimental to <u>Zoysia</u> <u>japonica</u> Steud.

<u>R.R. Davis (Ohio, U.S.A.)</u>

In Ohio, some soils are derived from limestone and do not need lime. Some soils of eastern Ohio are acid and need lime for the best growth of <u>Poa</u> <u>pratensis</u>. As a rule of thumb, when pH is below 5.5, lime is recommended.

SOIL pH AND ITS EFFECT ON PLANT NUTRIENTS

<u>W.H. Daniel (Indiana, U.S.A.)</u>

In comment on Dr. Rieke's paper, we have found that a golf course superintendent can in one year, by giving or withholding potassium, change the level of available potassium in the soil by one step, e.g. from low to medium or from high to medium.

<u>R.L. Morris (U.K.)</u>

I should like to ask Dr. Rieke whether it would not be better to use sulphate of ammonia and sulphate of iron to lower pH rather than sulphur, particularly as there would be a nutritional benefit.

P.E. Rieke(Michigan, U.S.A.)

Of course sulphate of iron or even aluminium sulphate can be used to acidify an alkaline soil. If iron deficiency is the reason for acidifying the soil, sulphate of iron would provide for this need as well. But it is only safe to use sulphates at considerably lower rates than elemental sulphur. This would extend the time over which pH change can be achieved. At present we are recommending elemental sulphur at a rate of 10 kg/100 sq m. Higher rates may cause turf injury. Repeat applications will be needed but pH change should be checked periodically.

J.R. Escritt (U.K.)

There are two points here:

1. If it is desired to lower pH, elemental sulphur is useful and is in fact so used in Europe.

2. If it is desired only to increase soil sulphur, surely it is better to use sulphates which have much less effect on soil pH.

SESSION 3A: TEMPERATURE AND SOIL WARMING

(Chairman: Ir. G. J. Ruychaver)

WINTER INJURY OF TURFGRASSES*

James B. Beard,

Dept. of Crop and Soil Science, Michigan State University, East Lansing, Michigan, U.S.A.

SUMMARY

The winter injury discussions in this paper are limited to the effects of direct low temperature kill. The other two major causes of winter injury are low temperature fungi and winter desiccation. Two distinct types of symptoms are associated with low temperature kill of turfgrasses. One type involves the immediate kill of the entire plant which is completely dead at the time of spring thaw. The second type involves a differential low temperature kill of the root crown tissue and subsequent desiccation of the shoots. Relative low temperature hardiness of turfgrasses varies through the season, with late winter and early spring being most critical in terms of minimum hardiness to low temperature. Cultural factors which stimulate growth and cause a reduction in hardiness will result in increased low temperature kill: the most important of such factors are excessive nitrogen, a deficiency of potassium, a close cutting height, or inadequate surface and internal soil drainage. Winter injury of turfgrasses is frequently associated with ice and snow accumulations. However, research to date indicates that the commonly used perennial turfgrass species can tolerate up to sixty days of ice coverage without damage. Under Michigan conditions direct low temperature kill of turfs which are in a high state of hydration is a more significant cause of winter injury than the effects of toxic accumulations under an ice cover. The relative low temperature hardiness of fourteen hardened cool season turfgrass species is presented.

INTRODUCTION

The actual temperature of a turfgrass plant or its individual parts is determined by the surrounding environment. Temperatures of the below-ground portions of the plant are usually identical with the adjacent soil temperatures, while the above-ground parts tend to follow the air temperature. The greatest temperature extremes usually occur at the surface of the turf and are moderated with increasing distance above and below the turfgrass surface (4). The actual soil-air temperatures will vary with latitude, altitude, topography, season of the year and time of day.

The temperature at which a particular process occurs at the highest rate is referred to as the optimum temperature. The optimum temperature will vary depending on (a) the age of the plant, (b) the stage of development, (c) the specific plant organ involved, (d) the physiological condition of the plant, (e) the duration of the temperature exposure and (f) the variation in other environmental factors. Because so many factors influence the optimum temperature it should be considered as a range rather than a specific fixed temperature.

* Contribution from the Michigan Agricultural Experiment Station, East Lansing, Michigan, as Paper No. 4995.

Turfgrasses having a temperature optimum for growth in the range of 15 to 24°C are commonly referred to as cool-season turfgrasses while species with an optimum temperature range of from 27 to 35°C are called warm-season turfgrasses. The optimum temperature for maximum growth is not necessarily synonymous with the optimum temperature for turfgrass quality. The optimum temperature for growth is usually higher than that for turfgrass quality. Also, the optimum temperature for shoot growth is generally higher than the optimum temperature for root growth. In general, it is more important to have optimum temperatures for root growth of turfgrasses than for shoot growth.

Turfgrasses growing in the optimum temperature range will have increased nutrient and water-holding requirements as well as requiring more frequent mowing. As temperatures are increased or decreased from the optimum range the various metabolic processes within the plant are slowed. The net result is a general reduction in the growth which continues until, at a certain point, growth actually ceases.

LOW TEMPERATURE STRESS

Direct low temperature kill is a problem in both warm-season and cool-season turfgrass species. Low temperature stress is a major factor affecting the northern limits of adaptation of warm-season turfgrass species. Low temperature kill, winter desiccation and low temperature fungi are the three major causes of winter injury to turfgrasses. The following sections will be devoted to a discussion of low temperature kill and related phenomena.

At temperatures below the minimum for growth the turfgrass plant becomes semi-dormant. However, respiration and photosynthesis continue in cool-season turfgrasses even at temperatures below 5°C.

If temperatures become sufficiently low, direct low temperature kill occurs. The low temperature injury may involve ice crystal formation of an intra-cellular or extracellular nature.

Intracellular freezing is usually a non-equilibrium process which results in the explosive growth of ice crystals in tissues having a high hydration level. These large ice crystals cause mechanical disruption of the tissue of the protoplasm and the eventual death of the tissue.

Equilibrium freezing processes involve extracellular ice formation in which the living protoplasts may or may not be injured. During equilibrium freezing there is a redistribution of water from within the cells to the extracellular regions because of the lower vapour pressure of the extracellular ice. If this extracellular ice formation continues for a sufficient length of time actual frost desiccation of the protoplasm may occur. Associated with the phenomena is a contraction of the protoplasm. With extreme dehydration the protoplasm becomes brittle and is subjected to extreme tensions during contraction which can result in actual mechanical damage of the protoplasm.

LOW TEMPERATURE HARDINESS

The ability of a turfgrass plant to survive an unfavourable internal low temperature stress is referred to as low temperature hardiness. With the advent of cooler temperatures during the late fall period, certain morphological and physiological changes occur in the turfgrass plant which result in low tempera-ture hardening prior to the occurrence of low temperatures. The growth rate of the turfgrass plant is slowed and eventually ceases, the plant becomes darker green, smaller in size, reduced in leaf area, and more prostrate in growth habit with a lower tissue hydration level (19). During this hardening period there is an accumulation of carbohydrates. Enzymes are activated which convert the insoluble carbohydrates to soluble sugars which accumulate in the vacuole and cause an increase in the osmotic potential (13, 16). There are also changes which occur in the protoplasmic proteins which result in an increased capability to bind water (12, 15). As a result of these physiological changes there is a significant reduction in the water content of the protoplasm which enables the plant tissues to achieve a maximum level of low temperature hardiness (8, 13). A period of approximately three to four weeks at temperatures below 7°C are required for cool-season turfgrasses to achieve maximum low temperature hardiness (13).

A reduced cell size is correlated with increased low temperature hardiness. Studies have shown that, in the crown meristematic area of annual bluegrass (Poa annua L.) the larger cells in the lower portion which are responsible for initiating new roots are injured much more readily than the small cells in the upper portion of the crown which are responsible for initiating shoot growth (9). In addition, young tissues are more low temperature hardy than old tissues (3). Leaf or root kill by low temperatures is not critical as long as the meristematic area of the crown is not injured. These root and leaf tissues can be readily replaced by the initiation of new growth from the crown meristem area. However, should injury occur to the crown meristem area serious loss of turf will occur (9).

Environmental influences

The relative low temperature hardiness achieved by a turfgrass plant is influenced by the environment. The first prerequisite for introducing hardiness is low average daily air and soil temperatures. Actively growing plants generally have a minimum level of low temperature hardiness (8).

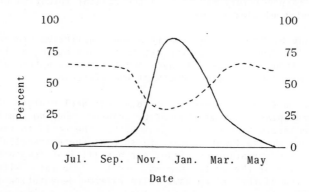

Figure 1: variation in the low temperature hardiness (——) and crown tissue hydration level (- - -) of Toronto creeping bentgrass (Agrostis palustris Huds.) during a typical winter season at East Lansing, Michigan

The hardiness level varies over the winter period (Figure 1). Maximum low temperature hardiness generally occurs during December or early January. There is a slight reduction in hardiness in February followed by a very drastic reduction in March and April. This decline in hardiness over the winter period is also associated with an increase in the crown hydration level (8). The minimum level of low temperature hardiness occurs in late winter and early spring. Thus, low temperature injury of turfgrasses is most likely to occur during this period, especially if the crown tissues contain a high water content. Thawing winter snows and the associated standing water, especially if the soil is frozen, will accentuate the increase in crown hydration level at this time and increase the likelihood of low temperature injury should temperatures decline to below $-6^{\circ}C$.

Cultural factors

Any cultural practice which stimulates growth will cause a reduction in hardiness and an increase in the susceptibility to kill by low temperature. Thus, excessive nitrogen fertilization, irrigation or any similar cultural practice which tends to stimulate growth in late fall will result in a reduction in low temperature hardiness (1, 3, 10, 12, 13, 14, 17, 21). In contrast to the nitrogen response, higher potassium levels result in improved low temperature hardiness (1, 10). Actually, it is not just a low nitrogen level or a high potassium level that is critical in maximum low temperature hardiness but the interrelationship or balance between the two nutrients (10). A fertilization ratio of 2 to 1 or 3 to 1 nitrogen to potassium has resulted in maximum low temperature hardiness of Kentucky bluegrass (Poa pratensis L.) under Michigan conditions.

Mowing height also affects low temperature hardiness (21, 23). Low temperature kill of Kentucky bluegrass was substantially increased at cutting heights below 3.8 cm (10).

Low temperature kill of turfgrasses is frequently associated with standing water. Proper surface and internal drainage are important factors influencing the crown hydration level of the turfgrass plant and the resulting susceptibility to low temperature kill. Proper surface contouring will ensure rapid removal of excess water. Adequate non-capillary pore space in the soil and a well-designed tile system will ensure the most effective and rapid removal of excess water from within the soil.

Turfgrass species influenced

The low temperature hardiness of turfgrass species varies greatly (Table 1). The warm-season species are usually more susceptible to low temperature kill than the cool-season species. There is also a great range of variability among the cool-season varieties (2, 3, 8, 11, 12, 16, 18, 20, 21, 22).

Controlled climate chamber studies at Michigan State University showed creeping bentgrass (Agrostis palustris Huds.) and rough bluegrass (Poa trivialis L.) had superior low temperature hardiness (8). Other cool-season turfgrasses possessing an acceptable level of low temperature hardiness included Kentucky bluegrass (Poa pratensis L.), colonial bentgrass (Agrostis tenuis Sibth.), and timothy (Phleum pratense L.). Intermediate in hardiness were annual bluegrass (Poa annua L.) and red fescue (Festuca rubra L.), while tall fescue (Festuca arundinacea Schreb.), perennial ryegrass (Lolium perenne L.) and Italian ryegrass (Lolium multiflorum Lam.) had inferior hardiness levels along with the warm-season turfgrass species.

Table 1: the relative low temperature hardiness of fourteen hardened turfgrasses

Relative low temperature hardiness	Turfgrass species
Excellent	Rough bluegrass Creeping bentgrass
Good	Timothy Kentucky bluegrass Canada bluegrass Crested wheatgrass Colonial bentgrass Redtop
Intermediate	Annual bluegrass Red fescue Tall fescue Meadow fescue
Poor	Perennial ryegrass
Very poor	Annual ryegrass

Varietal differences in low temperature hardiness are also evident (8, 22). The relative low temperature hardiness of several commonly used creeping bentgrass cultivars and one colonial bentgrass are shown in Table 2. Similar varietal differences have been evident in the Kentucky bluegrasses and ryegrasses.

LOW TEMPERATURE KILL SYMPTOMS

Two distinct types of symptoms are associated with low temperature kill of turfgrasses. The first type involves immediate kill of the entire turfgrass plant including the meristematic tissues. In this situation, the turf is completely dead at the time of spring thaw.

The second type involves a differential low temperature kill of the crown tissue. Basically, the temperature becomes low enough to kill the lower portion of the crown tissue but not the upper portion (9, 21). As a result the root system and meristematic tissues capable of initiating new roots are killed whereas the above-ground portion of the plant is uninjured at the time of spring thaw. As warmer temperatures occur, growth and transpiration are stimulated and death of the turfgrass plant usually occurs immediately. The shoot tissues die of desiccation because there is no root system present to absorb moisture for replacement of the water lost through transpiration. Atmospheric desiccation is the secondary cause of death with the original cause being differential low temperature kill of the turfgrass crowns which probably occurred during the late winter or early spring period.

ICE AND SNOW COVERS

Ice and snow accumulations sometimes persist for an extended period during the winter. The possibility exists under these conditions that a dense ice cover could impair gaseous diffusion processes to the extent that the turf-grass plant is injured due to either (a) suffocation caused by a lack of oxygen necessary for respiration or (b) direct kill caused by toxic gases which accumulate under the ice cover. Evidence to date suggests that the latter is the more likely cause of injury attributed to ice sheets. However, extensive field and controlled climate chamber studies at Michigan State University have failed to confirm that ice covers themselves are a major cause of turfgrass winter injury (5, 6, 7). Most turfgrass species are relatively tolerant to extended periods of ice cover of up to sixty days (Figure 2). Species differences in tolerance are evident, with annual bluegrass being more suscept-ible than Kentucky bluegrass or bentgrass. Bentgrass has survived continuous ice cover for as long as 150 days at -3°C.

Table 2: percentage low temperature survival of turfgrasses sampled 5 Dec., 1963

Grass	Percent crown moisture	Temperature treatment ($^{\circ}$F. and $^{\circ}$C.)							
		25 -4	20 -6.7	15 -9.4	10 -12.2	5 -15	0 -17.8	-5 -20.4	-10 -23.2
Creeping bentgrass									
Toronto	61.3	100	100	100	100	100	99	98	97
Cohansey	64.5	100	100	100	100	100	100	99	98
Washington	61.0	100	100	100	100	100	100	98	94
Seaside	62.2	100	100	100	100	100	99	97	67
Penncross	55.5	100	100	100	100	97	93	90	75
Congressional ..	54.0	100	100	100	99	97	93	87	67
Colonial bentgrass									
Astoria	66.1	100	100	100	99	94	71	30	7
Redtop	55.0	100	97	90	78	70	60	47	27
Rough bluegrass ..	72.1	100	100	100	100	100	99	96	76
Kentucky bluegrass									
Merion	76.6	100	100	100	100	96	79	50	32
Kenblue	77.9	100	100	100	100	91	65	15	2
Newport	73.2	100	100	100	98	85	65	4	1
Annual bluegrass .	79.8	100	100	100	100	95	31	8	3
Creeping red fescue									
Pennlawn	78.0	100	100	97	90	63	17	4	0
Tall fescue									
Kentucky 31	74.1	100	100	100	83	40	27	5	3
Alta	77.4	100	100	98	72	33	22	4	0
Perennial ryegrass									
Norlea	79.3	100	100	100	100	71	4	1	0
Common	81.1	100	100	98	78	13	0	0	0
Italian ryegrass .	85.5	83	68	17	3	0	0	0	0

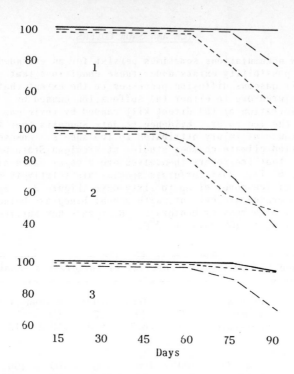

Figure 2: percent survival of hardened Toronto creeping
bentgrass, common Kentucky bluegrass, and annual
bluegrass:

——— Bentgrass
— — Kent. Bluegrass
- - - - Annual Bluegrass

1. After being flooded, then frozen and held at
    -4°C for intervals up to 90 days.
2. After being frozen, then layered with ice and
    , held at -4°C for intervals up to 90 days.
3. After being frozen, then layered with ice over
    snow and held at -4°C for intervals up to 90 days.

Ice removal

A question frequently arises as to whether the ice and snow covers should
be removed, particularly from greens and teés of golf courses. Basically, this
is a sound practice in the United States although the reason for removal may be
different from what most turfgrass laymen think. Complete removal of an ice
or snow cover may subject the turf to winter desiccation injury. Actually,
there is no urgency in the removal of an ice and snow cover during the initial
sixty days unless a thaw is imminent. Probably more injury to turfgrasses is
caused by the increased crown hydration effect associated with standing water
when the ice and snow thaws than by the direct effect of the ice cover causing
an accumulation of toxic gases and kill of the grass plant. Kill of the plant
is highly likely if the hydrated crowns which have stood in water during the
thaw period are subjected to low temperature stress of below -6°C. Thus the
removal of an ice or snow cover is essentially a means of "mechanical draining"
of water from the green. If and when an ice and snow cover is removed, approximately one-half to one-quarter inch of cover should be left on the green in
order to avoid winter atmospheric desiccation problems. Research to date at
Michigan State University indicates that, under the climatic conditions found
in Michigan, direct low temperature kill of turfgrass plants which are in a
high state of hydration is a much more significant cause of winter injury than
the direct effects of toxic accumulation.

232

<u>REFERENCES</u>

1. ADAMS, W.E., and TWERSKY, M. (1959) Effect of soil fertility on winter killing of Coastal bermudagrass. Agron. J. <u>52</u>, 325.

2. ARAKERI, H.R., and SCHMID, A.R. (1949) Cold resistance of various legumes and grasses in early stages of growth. Agron. J. <u>41</u>, 182.

3. BAKER, H.K., and DAVID, G.L. (1963) Winter damage to grass. Agriculture <u>70</u>, 8, 380.

4. BEARD, J.B. (1959) The growth and development of <u>Agrostis palustris</u> roots as influenced by certain environmental factors. M.S.Thesis, Purdue University. 1.

5. BEARD,J.B. (1964) Effects of ice, snow and water covers on Kentucky bluegrass, annual bluegrass, and creeping bentgrass. Crop Sci. <u>4</u>, 638.

6. BEARD, J.B. (1965) Effects of ice covers in the field on two perennial grasses. Crop Sci. <u>5</u>, 139.

7. BEARD, J.B. (1965) Bentgrass (<u>Agrostis</u> spp.) varietal tolerance to ice cover injury. Agron. J. <u>57</u>, 513.

8. BEARD, J.B. (1966) Direct low temperature injury of nineteen turfgrasses. Quart. Bull. Michigan agric. Exp. Stn. <u>48</u>, 3, 377.

9. BEARD, J.B., and OLIEN, C.R. (1963) Low temperature injury in the lower portion of <u>Poa annua</u> L. crowns. Crop Sci. <u>3</u>, 362.

10. BEARD, J.B., and RIEKE, P.E. (1966) The influence of nitrogen, potassium and cutting height on the low temperature survival of grasses. Agron. Abstr. 1966, 34.

11 BERGGREN, F. (1952) MRTF turf researcher freeze-tests zoysia. Midwest Turf News and Research. <u>6</u>, 3, 3.

12. CARROLL, J.C. (1943) Effects of drought, temperature, and nitrogen on turf grasses. Pl. Physiol. <u>18,</u> 19.

13. CARROLL, J.C., and WELTON, F.A. (1939) Effect of heavy and late applications of nitrogenous fertilizer on the cold resistance of Kentucky bluegrass. Pl. Physiol. <u>14</u>, 297.

14. CORDUKES, W.E., WILNER, J, and ROTHWELL, V.T. (1966) The evaluation of cold and drought stress of turfgrasses by electrolytic and ninhydrin methods. Can. J. Pl. Sci. <u>46</u>, 337.

15. DAVIS, D.L., and GILBERT, W.B. (1967) Changes in the soluble protein fractions during cold acclimation of bermudagrass. Agron. Abstr. 1967, 50.

16. HODGSON, H. J. (1964) Performance of turfgrass varieties in the subarctic. Agron. Abstr. 1964, 101.

17. LAWRENCE, T. (1963) The influence of fertilizer on the winter survival of intermediate wheatgrass following a long period of drought. J. Br. Grassld. Soc. <u>18</u>, 292.

18. MILLER, R.W. (1966) The effect of certain management practices on the botanical composition and winter injury of turf containing a mixture of Kentucky bluegrass (Poa pratensis L.) and tall fescue (Festuca arundinacea Schreb.). 7th Illinois Turfgrass Conference Proceedings. 7, 39.

19. NITTLER, L.W., and KENNY, T.J. (1967) Response of seedlings of Festuca rubra varieties to environmental conditions. Crop Sci. 7, 463.

20. ROGLER, G.A. (1943) Response of geographical strains of grasses to low temperatures. J. Am. Soc. Agron. 35, 7, 547.

21. VORST, J.J. (1966) The effects of certain management practices on winter injury to turf containing a mixture of Kentucky bluegrass (Poa pratensis L.) and tall fescue (Festuca arundinacea Schreb.). M.S. Thesis. Ohio State University. 1.

22. YLIMAKI, A. (1962) The effect of snow cover on temperature conditions in the soil and overwintering of field crops. Annls. agric. fenn. 1, 192.

23. ANON. (1952) Factors affecting winter survival of bermuda grass. Golf Course Reptr. 20, 4, 7.

SOIL WARMING IN NORTH AMERICA

W. H. Daniel,

Dept. of Agronomy, Purdue University, Lafayette, Indiana, U.S.A.

SUMMARY

Earlier work on soil warming under turf reported from England prompted the initial U.S.A. work in 1963. Expansion of research into nine locations within Arizona, Texas, Indiana, Minnesota, Maryland and Missouri has provided a basis for current information which is reviewed. Details of some U.S. installations are given in an appendix.

One way of reducing the natural seasonal limitations on outdoor sports turf use is soil warming. Already turf managers add fertilizers to force growth, even on cool soils, and provide irrigation to cool the soil and force growth during dry periods. With soil warming both the root zone and plant can be affected. Thus turf heating is another aid in the management of high quality turf. It can help to melt snow; improve playing quality by keeping the soil unfrozen, which favours water penetration; and keep turf growing slowly.

Barrett and Daniel conducted trials in four locations, including 40 sub-plots, during 1963-69. They tested six types of heating cables, and studied spacing distance, depth and heat input with and without covers. As a result, the fundamental requirements have been determined and described. The exact design of a warming system, however, will depend on extent of use, time of need, purpose of warming, cost and availability of power, and grass species and varieties used. Further, the day-to-day management and the use of the area drastically affect the benefits of the system.

In the U.S. it is desired to start heating early enough in the autumn to maintain active growth as long as the area is used. For Poa pratensis L., temperatures above 8^{0}C seem adequate. Mechanised plastic covers for regular night use can greatly increase the assurance of growth. In general, temperatures in the Midwestern U.S. drop from 15 August until 15 January; hold steady for about 30 days; then gradually rise from 20 February to July. Protective soil warming needs to start about 1 October, as soil temperatures at 1 in. (2.5 cm) depth approach 12^{0}C. Table 1 illustrates how warming modified soil temperatures in one trial.

During the trial soil temperatures at 15 cm depth were stabilised at 15^{0}C with less than 1^{0}C variation during winter. Power was needed 71% of the time at 100 W/sq m. The normal growth produced under the various treatments was clipped, and by comparison with the treatment giving the most heat, the others showed a decline in growth rate (Table 2).

The stabilisation of heat supply in the soil is illustrated by Table 3, where the heat loss in depth shows the characteristic pattern of a heat "sump".

Table 1: monthly average soil temperatures (^{o}C) at 3 cm in sports turf

Heat applied when air under 5°C and soil under 15°C	1964		1965		
	Nov.	Dec.	Jan.	Feb.	Mar.
100 W/sq m	12	8	8	8	8
50 W/sq m	10	7	6	7	7
Unheated	1	0	0	0	1
Air at 1.5 m	5	-2	-6	-6	-3

Table 2: relative amounts of clippings and number of days with frozen soil surface, on warmed areas, Purdue, 1964

Treatment		Relative amounts of dry clippings			Number of days on which soil surface was frozen at 8.0 a.m.			
Watts	Hours per day	9 Jan.	12 Feb.	6 Mar.	Jan	Feb.	Mar.	Total
50	24	100	70	30	4	0	0	4
100	24	90	100	100	0	0	0	0
100	7	60	30	10	6	1	2	9
50	7	60	30	20	10	7	2	19
25	24	95	30	20	11	1	0	12
0	0	5	10	10	24	19	7	50

Table 3: temperatures at 8.0 a.m. 29 January 1964 during cold open weather (Air temperature - 10°C)

Depth (cm)	Warming treatment		
	100 W/sq m	25W/sq m	No heat
0	3	0	-2
2	7	1	0
15	15	4	2
30	16	7	3
60	15	7	4
90	14	10	5

G.F. McBee in Texas conducted tests on keeping bermudagrass (<u>Cynodon</u> spp.) green during occasional frost periods in southern Texas; but the leaf was more affected by air temperature around it than by soil temperature under it. Earlier, Baltensperger in Arizona had tried to force bermudagrass to grow during the winter, removing frost-damaged leaves by mowing as damage occurred. Without protective covers to raise the interface of heat, soil warming was inadequate alone. Radiant heat lamps have been discussed as a way to protect leaves at low air temperatures.

In the work of Barrett and Daniel at Purdue University soil freezing during winter was eliminated with cable spacings up to 18 in. apart (46 cm). Thermostats only 1 in. deep in the soil did not give adequate warning of changing weather although they adequately defined the heat reserve in the soil. Air thermostats exposed to free air movement and shaded at a 1.5 m height were the best indicators of heat need.

In Minnesota, D.W. White and James Watson considered snow removal techniques and power requirements for keeping soil unfrozen.

Dense turf with medium thatch is nearly equal to a plastic cover in reducing heat loss. If the main bulk of snow is quickly removed by mechanical means then that remaining in the leaf blade zone can easily be melted. The threshold temperature for snow melt effectiveness is about 10^0C when winds are less than 10 miles per hour. As experienced elsewhere, coverings placed over the snow increased the rate of melting, and uniform water penetration improved later playing quality.

Felix Juska confirmed observations on slow growth even on unfrozen soil.

Le Beau of Canada, working towards the reduction of wintertime desiccation and snow mould (<u>Fusarium nivale</u> (Fr.) Ces. and <u>Typhula</u> spp.) found that if surface soil temperatures were kept just above freezing, at $1-2^0C$, disease did not develop, provided that the soil absorbed free water promptly. This confirms outside observations that poor drainage, even temporarily caused by frozen soil, can contribute to snow mould development. Based on this work, some golf greens at Banff, Canada, have soil warming systems in them for springtime use.

Freeborg found that the threshold value for active growth of <u>Zoysia</u> spp., about 12^0C at soil surface, was difficult to maintain unless turf was covered. The interface between air temperature and soil temperature was usually below the blades, so this limited turf response. In Busch Stadium, however, it was possible in March and April with plastic covers to force the greening up of sodded <u>Zoysia</u> well before it would occur normally.

Powered field covers, such as are available in Sweden, offer much promise to improve the performance of turf over a soil warming system. Porous root zones, which permit rapid water infiltration, and semi-insulated clear plastic field covers, with or without holes for air and water exchange, also promise further advances.

REFERENCES

1. ANON. (1951) Electrical soil warming as an anti-frost measure for sports turf. J. Sports Turf Res. Inst. 8, 27, 25.

2. BARRETT, J.R., Jnr., and DANIEL, W.H. (1965) Electrically warmed soils for sports turfs - second progress report. Midwest Turf News & Research No. 33.

3. BARRETT, J.R., Jnr., and DANIEL, W.H. (1966) Turf heating with electric cable. Agric. Engng. 47, 10, 526.

4. DANIEL, W.H., BARRETT, J.R., Jnr., and COOMBS, L.H. (1964) Electrically warmed soils for sports turfs - a progress report. Midwest Turf News & Research No. 28.

5. ESCRITT, J.R. (1954) Electrical soil warming as an anti-frost measure for sports turf - a further report. J. Sports Turf Res. Inst. 8, 30, 354.

6. ESCRITT, J.R. (1959) Electrical soil warming as an anti-frost measure for sports turf - a further report. J. Sports Turf Res. Inst. 10, 35, 29.

7. FREEBORG, R. and DANIEL, W.H. (1967) Improving the stadium field. Proceeding Midwest Regional Turf Conference: 43.

8. McCULLOUGH, C. (1967) Electric greens. The Greenmaster III: 10, 1, 10.

APPENDIX: NOTES ON SOME INSTALLATIONS IN THE U.S.A.

Falcon Stadium at the U.S. Air Force Academy, Colorado, had the first heating system for football turf for college use. Fifty-five polyvinyl chloride insulated cables each 450 m long were buried 15 cm deep into bare soil at 30 cm intervals before sodding in 1966. Each cable has a braided copper grounding jacket and is protected by a 40-ampere, single pole 277-volt breaker. The system operates from a 3-phase, four wire 277/480 volt sub-station with a load of 429 kW, equal to 65 W/sq. ft. or 50 W/sq m.

The centre and two side zones each have a remote sensing bulb placed 3 cm into the soil, which is in series with an air thermostat at 1.5 m in a shaded position.

From 1 September to 30 November 1967 the centre zone was heated. On 14 November the heated turf was greener and more dense, so the outside zones were heated for the remainder of the use season.

Busch Stadium in St. Louis, Missouri, was the first multisport profes- sional stadium to have heated turf in the U.S. Forty-nine PVC insulated cables, varying from 600 m to 900 m in length, were spaced 30 cm apart into existing turf in August 1966. The total length of cable was 115,000 ft. or 33,000 m, giving a combined load of 529 kW at 4.5 W/sq. ft. or 90 W/sq m.

Two centre zones include the football area and baseball infield and centre field; these are flanked by two outside zones extending to moveable bleachers. A normal year's use starts about 1 April and includes 80 baseball games, plus warm-ups and home team practice. Soccer has been added as 16 scheduled games plus warm-ups. Then overlapping in August and extending into mid-December are 12 or more professional football games. In addition, from 10 September the football team also has daily practice (50 players). Therefore, the entire turf is completely worn out by the end of the season, in spite of high mowing, auto- matic soil sensing irrigation, aerification, top dressing and maximum soil warming.

Originally in the spring of 1966 a mixture of Zoysia and new varieties of Poa pratensis L. were sodded. In 1966-7 winter Meyer zoysiagrass (Zoysia japon- ica Steud.) was sodded; before 1968 use Tifway bermudagrass (Cynodon hybrid) was sodded, and before 1969 use Tifway was sodded and heavily over-seeded with Lolium perenne L. and Poa pratensis. Although warming has been at a maximum each autumn, excessive turf wear is accepted as normal. It is cheaper to re-sod than to maintain separate suburban practice fields for the football team.

Turf heating is used to force growth in spring after sodding and covering with plastic, thus giving green turf on the opening date. Soil heating has permitted overwinter renovation and re-sodding with the usual labour force. In general, the maximum heat that can be produced has been used each autumn to provide the most benefit to turf and players.

Lambeau Field at Green Day, Wisconsin, is used for professional football only, but in a very severe climate. Forty-eight Vulkene insulated cables with braided copper ground, also covered with Vulkene, totals 730 kW for 73,000 sq. ft., or 100 W/sq m.

The installation cost less than $100,000 and a proposed energy use of 1,000,000 kW at   1-1.5/W for the 3 month period from 15 September to 15 December is expected.

In 1967, all practice fields had frozen by 20 November and from then on daily practice was on the heated stadium. For a game on 17 December the field was in excellent playing condition although at 7.0 a.m. the air temperature was - 24°C and it was -20°C when play began. Even during the NFL championship game on 31 December 1967 a 15 miles per hour wind and a temperature of -25°C during the game did not freeze the soil surface where a double layer cover had been previously used.

SOIL WARMING IN THE UNITED KINGDOM

J. R. Escritt,

Director, The Sports Turf Research Institute, Bingley, Yorkshire, U.K.

SUMMARY

The first electrical soil warming trials were carried out at Bingley in the winter of 1947/48 and the last recorded trials were completed in the winter of 1959/60. The aim was to provide unfrozen turf for sport using turf in the winter in Britain (e.g. soccer, rugby football, greyhound racing, etc.) and the trials led to the practical recommendation that using off-peak loading an input of 10 W/sq. ft. (108 W/sq m) should be allowed for a minimum period of 30 hours through wires 6 in. (15 cm) deep and 6-9 in. (15-22.5 cm) apart. Severe frosts are relatively rare in much of Britain and only a few installations exist, the oldest being at Murrayfield, Edinburgh, the home of the Scottish Rugby Football Union, and this installation has performed satisfactorily for ten winters.

The value of covers with or without underground heating has also been investigated.

DESCRIPTION OF TRIALS AND RESULTS

The first experimental plots were provided with special galvanised steel wires fed through transformers with low voltage electricity since this procedure allowed the testing of different electrical loadings with the same installation. The wires were fed into the ground by a small home-made mole-plough. After three winters' observations on these trials it was reported (1) that soil warming provided a practical solution to the problem, an input of 10 W/sq. ft. (108 W/sq m) being suggested. Cover was shown to reduce the amount of heat required and, in all trials, the excellent insulating value of straw was clearly shown. Under British conditions it has been considered that use of underground heating and use of insulating covers are alternative rather than complementary procedures.

Since much of the cost of underground heating systems lies in capital equipment and a heavy irregular load is unpopular with the electricity supply authorities, trials were next instituted to try and get successful results with lower loadings used for the total number of "off-peak" hours available and it was suggested (2), that not less than 6 W/sq. ft. (65 W/sq m) should be considered even where supply difficulties occurred and that it would be best to stick to 10 W/sq. ft. (108 W/sq m). With regular warming, 9 in. (23 cm) spacing of 6 in. (15 cm) deep wires was satisfactory but 12 in. (30 cm) spacings resulted in occasional hard strips. In this particular series of trials attention was drawn to the effects of a porous drainage layer below the top soil. This restricted heat transfer so that without heat the surface was more likely to freeze but with heat temperatures rose higher. It was also recorded that prevention of freezing facilitated drainage in some conditions.

Trials were carried out for a further six years with insulated cables at mains voltage in some plots and with supply controlled by thermostats in the surface. Again attention was paid to achieving success with lower electricity loadings but again it was recommended that 10 W/sq. ft (108 W/sq m) was the best loading (3).

241

It was noted that although the soil warming installations were used merely for producing unfrozen pitches they did in fact result in earlier spring growth. It was also observed that snow (itself a good insulator) did not stay long on heated pitches.

PRACTICAL INSTALLATIONS

In S.T.R.I. trials warming wires and cables were installed by a small home-made mole-plough type of implement but when the first practical soil warming installation was made (1958) a full sized implement did not exist and the heating cables were laid by hand during ground reconstruction. Unfortunately drainage troubles arose and became associated with the soil warming which may in part account for the relatively few installations which exist in Britain. (Other reasons are to be found in making stands comfortable and getting spectators to the ground in bad weather!) The warming cables are at present not in this pitch and the oldest installation in Britain is Scottish Rugby Union's football pitch at Murrayfield, Edinburgh. Here the heating cable wires were installed by the David Brown mole-plough type of implement and have so far served ten winters with an average cost per winter of £1,000 - £1,500. In the south of England the famous Arsenal Soccer Club spends only £50 - £150 per season (£10 per night) but consider it well worthwhile. The Leeds Rugby League Club have had soil heating since 1963 and their average cost is about £1,000 per season (just under 200,000 kWh). All these installations are controlled by surface thermostats but at the Arsenal Football Club there is an air thermostat also. In each case economies are effected by switching off altogether for short periods during the winter when important matches are not imminent.

Several dog-racing tracks are known to have installed underground heating but there is no information about these installations available to the author.

REFERENCES

1.   ANON (1951) Electrical soil warming as an anti-frost measure for sports turf. J. Sports Turf Res. Inst., 8, 27, 25.

2.   ESCRITT, J.R. (1959) Electrical soil warming as an anti-frost measure for sports turf - a further report. J. Sports Turf Res. Inst., 10, 35, 29.

3.   ESCRITT, J.R. (1954) Electrical soil warming as an anti-frost measure for sports turf - a further report. J. Sports Turf Res. Inst., 8, 30, 354.

THEORETICAL INVESTIGATION OF ARTIFICIAL HEATING OF THE TOP SOIL

Lars-Eric Janson,

V.B.B., Stockholm, Sweden

SUMMARY

The heat transfer from an artificial heating system below the ground surface is mathematically dealt with. By studying the relationship between power output, soil and air temperatures, thermal conductivity and moisture content of the top soil it has been possible to verify experimentally the equations given.

INTRODUCTION

During the years 1964-66 the author carried out on behalf of the Swedish Football Association a number of experimental and theoretical investigations to determine the possibilities of prolonging the growing period of turfgrasses by artificial means. Experimental studies were being conducted at the same time at Weibullsholm, Landskrona, under the supervision of Bjarne Langvad. When the experiments were completed a basis had been established for the dimensioning of heated football grounds. These studies have been described in detail by L-E. Janson and B. Langvad (2). An account of the reconstruction of Solna Football Stadium ground is given in a booklet issued by the Swedish Football Association (1).

Experimental areas were established for the investigation at Solna Football Stadium and Weibullsholm. The areas were equipped with various types of heating systems at various depths below the ground surface. Variation of the heating made it possible to determine what is necessary for early growth. Studies have also been made of various principles for constructing football grounds, as well as the heat insulation and reduction of evaporation provided by plastic sheeting. The investigation has also included various types of turfgrasses.

In addition to the experimental investigation the problem of heat transfer from an underground system has been studied in mathematical terms. By measuring in the course of the heating experiments such dependent quantities as power output, soil and air temperatures, heat conductivity, moisture content and depth of ground frost, it has proved possible to verify the deduced equations. In this way it has been demonstrated that experience gained from experiments in one place can be transferred in the form of calculations applicable to another place without it being necessary to conduct another experiment there.

HEAT TRANSFER FROM HEAT SOURCES LOCATED BELOW THE GROUND SURFACE

The heat transfer from a circular heat source of infinite length located at the depth h under the ground surface can be studied mathematically. The easiest way of doing so is to study a heat source located in an infinite solid. Subsequently, a negative heat source is introduced in accordance with the common method, this source being inverted in relation to the first and having the ground surface as symmetry axis.

The following expression for the temperature field surrounding an individual heat source may thus be deduced:-

$$(\vartheta_{x,y} - \vartheta_h) = \frac{q_e}{4\pi\lambda} \ln \frac{y^2 + (h + x)^2}{y^2 + (h - x)^2} \qquad \text{(equation 1)}$$

where

$\vartheta_{x,y}$ = temperature at the point x,y

ϑ_h = temperature at the depth h, with no influence from the heat source

q_e = power output of the heat source in W/m

λ = thermal conductivity of the material surrounding the heat source in W/m°C

x,y = rectangular co-ordinates in accordance with figure 1.

The temperature on the outside of the heat source, ϑ_u, is obtained if x = h and y = r is inserted in equation 1, where r is the radius of the heat source. If this is slight in relation to h the following equation is obtained:-

$$(\vartheta_u - \vartheta_h) = \frac{q_e}{2\pi\lambda} \ln \frac{2h}{r} \qquad \text{(equation 2)}$$

If there are several heat sources in the ground, and in the special case a large number of heat sources located parallel at the same level and at the same distance, L, from one another, the temperature field in the ground can be described by applying the principle of superposition. Thus each heat source is regarded as a separate heat-generating system. The temperature at the point x,y is obtained as the sum of the temperature-raising effect of each heat source on the point in question, thus obtaining:-

$$\sum(\vartheta_{x,y} - \vartheta_h) = \frac{q_e}{4\pi\lambda} \left[\ln \frac{y^2 + (h + x)^2}{y^2 + (h - x)^2} \right.$$

$$+ \ln \frac{(L - y)^2 + (h + x)^2}{(L - y)^2 + (h - x)^2} \quad + \ln \frac{(L + y)^2 + (h + x)^2}{(L + y)^2 + (h - x)^2}$$

$$+ \ln \frac{(2L - y)^2 + (h + x)^2}{(2L - y)^2 + (h - x)^2} \quad + \ln \frac{(2L + y)^2 + (h + x)^2}{(2L + y)^2 + (h - x)^2}$$

$$+ \ldots\ldots \left. \right] \qquad \text{(equation 3)}$$

The temperature on the outside of the heat source is obtained by inserting x = h and y = r in equation 3 to give:-

$$\sum(\vartheta_u - \vartheta_h) = \frac{q_e}{2\pi\lambda} \left[\ln \frac{2h}{r} + \ln(1 + 4M) + \right.$$

$$\ln(1 + M) + \ln(1 + \tfrac{4}{9}M) + \ln(1 + \tfrac{4}{16}M) + \ldots\ldots \left. \right] \qquad \text{(equation 4)}$$

where $M = (h/L)^2$.

By development of functions in series and neglecting terms of higher order, equation 4 can be transformed to:-

$$(\vartheta_u - \vartheta_h) = \frac{q_e}{2\lambda} \; 2\frac{h}{L} + \ln \frac{L}{2\pi r} \qquad \text{(equation 5)}$$

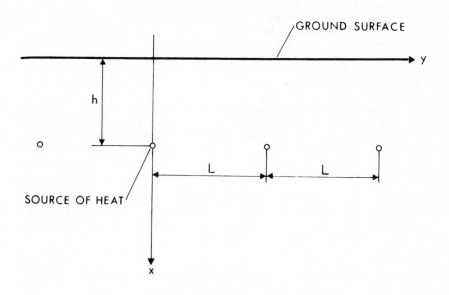

Figure 1: location of heating system

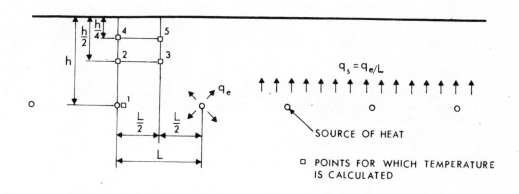

Figure 2: points for which temperature is calculated

245

It follows from the equations that for a constant value for q_e, the temperature of the heat source increases with an increased value of h. If instead of q_e, Lq_s is introduced, where q_s stands for the power output per unit of area of the heat source range, it follows that if q_s is kept constant, the temperature of the heat source also increases with an increased value of L.

In the special task of attaining, with the aid of heat sources, a certain growth temperature in the root zone of the grass, it is of great importance to select the correct relationship between q_s, L and h. For the determination of q_s as a function of the geographical situation of the plant, regard is paid to the local climate by a suitable choice of ϑ_h. In addition to the economic requirements of the problem, to give a balance between the cost of construction and the cost of operation, steps must be taken to ensure that the temperature of the root zone is maintained as even as possible. A difference in temperature of 1 to 2^0C between a point immediately above a heat source and a point between two heat sources can be sufficient to cause obvious difference of growth. During the winter, when it is desirable with regard to the frost-heaving risk to restrict frost penetration by intermittent operation of the heating system, it is also important that the heat sources should be located so as to prevent frost from penetrating in the intervening areas.

Figure 2 shows five points for which temperature co-efficients in accordance with the equations given above have been calculated for the two cases L = h and L = 2h. In addition it has been assumed that q_s = 50 W/sq m, $\vartheta_h = 0^0$C constant throughout the whole soil, λ = 0.93 W/m^{0}C and h = 0.15 m.

Figure 3 shows the calculated temperatures, both for h = L = 0.15 m and h = L = 0.30 m. In Figure 4 the corresponding values have been given for h = L/2 = 0.15 m and h = L/2 = 0.30 m.

The Figures indicate that the temperature on the surface of the heat source increases with increased depth h and increased distance L. On the other hand, the temperature of the root zone (here shown symbolically at the 7.5 cm level under the ground surface) is not thereby raised but remains even and constant so long as h/L = 1. When h/L = 0.5 the temperature of the root zone is more uneven, and between the heat sources it is lower than for h/L = 1. If h/L falls below 0.5 conditions become still more unfavourable.

In order to obtain an even temperature in the root zone, h/L should thus lie between 0.5 and 1. Furthermore, h should not be deeper than strictly necessary, since the temperature of the heat sources increases with the depth. If electric cables are chosen as heat sources, it should be borne in mind that their life expectancy is shorter at high temperatures than at low. If hot water pipes are used instead, it can very often prove difficult with existing boiler equipment to achieve the necessary temperatures for outgoing water if the pipe system is deep underground.

The temperature distribution described above refers to the case where the soil temperatures, when the soil is unaffected by the heating system, are everywhere the same. This is, however, very seldom the case. During the spring the surface of the soil receives heat even from above. For this purpose the temperature distribution described above may be combined with the natural temperature distribution in the soil. It then becomes necessary to choose the actual value for ϑ_h. If, thus, the natural temperature distribution assumes an appearance like that shown in Figure 5, the temperature values given in Figure 5 are obtained by combining the influence of the artificial heat sources, in accordance with Figure 3, and the soil, acting as two separate heat-generating systems.

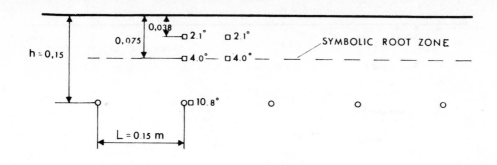

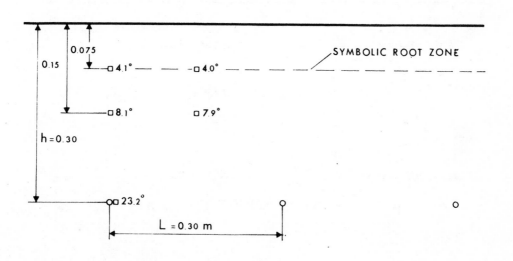

Figure 3: calculated soil temperatures for h = L = 0.15 and 0.30 m
($\vartheta_h = 0^0$C and q_s = 50 W/sq m)

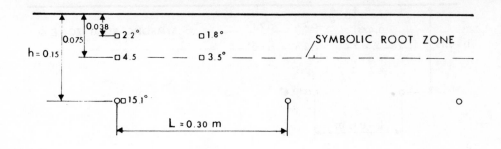

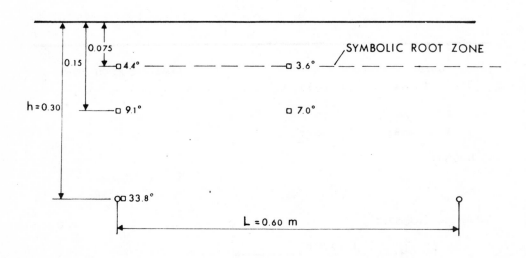

Figure 4: calculated soil temperatures for $h = \frac{1}{2}L = 0.15$ and 0.30m $(\vartheta_h = 0^\circ C$ and $q_s = 50$ W/sq m$)$

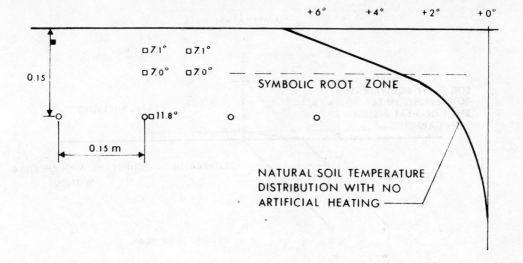

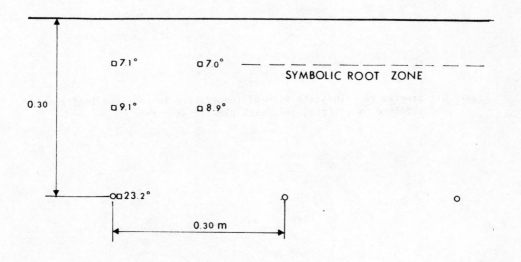

<u>Figure 5</u>:   calculated soil temperatures based on the natural temperature
distribution in the soil on a spring day (q_s = 50 W/sq m)

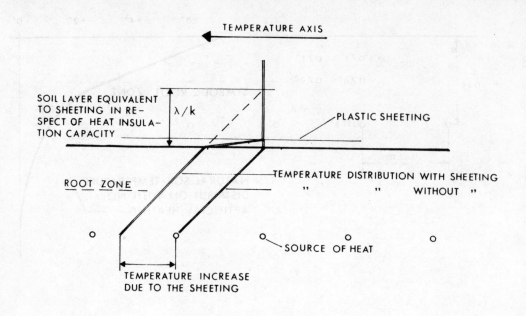

In the unsteady state the heat capacity of the soil layer above the heating system acquires significance. Thus the temperature of the root zone rises as h grows shorter, when the soil receives heat from above. On the other hand the conditions are reversed when the ground surface is losing heat.

The special case which arises when the ground surface is covered by plastic sheeting or other insulating coat can also be treated theoretically. For this purpose it is simplest to assume that the insulating coat (which can also consist of a layer of turf with a lower thermal conductivity than the soil round the heat source) may be replaced with a soil thickness, λ/k, of equivalent value from the point of view of thermal conductivity. As before, λ stands for the thermal conductivity of the soil and k for the heat transmission coefficient for the plastic sheeting in combination with the air space it encloses. As shown in outline in Figure 6, this gives the same result as if the heating system were located at a greater depth than is actually the case. From this it follows that the temperature of the heat source for one and the same power output rises. In the same way the temperature in the root zone and on the surface of the soil rises; uniformly, in the steady state.

In order to obtain this higher temperature in the root zone without an insulating coat, the effect of the heat source must be increased, usually to a considerable degree. This is connected with the fact that the plastic sheeting provides a wind shelter for the turf grass, which thereby acquires a far better heat insulation than is the case without such protection.

REFERENCES

1. JANSON, L-E. (1967) A longer football season. The Swedish Football Association, Solna, 1967. (Reprinted in English 1969)

2. JANSON, L-E., and LANGVAD, B. (1968) Prolongation of the growing season for sport turfgrasses by means of artificial heating of the root zone. Weibulls Grastips, Landskrona, Sweden, 1968.

3. JANSON, L-E. (1969) Artificial heating of sports fields. Proc. I.A.K.S. Congress, Cologne, May 1969.

SOIL HEATING UNDER SPORTS TURF IN SWEDEN

Bjarne Langvad, M.Sc.,

W. Weibull A.B., Landskrona, Sweden

SUMMARY

Soil heating under sports turf is now common in Sweden. Theoretical and practical investigations have shown that in the Stockholm area, for example, a ground can be ready for play in spring six weeks earlier with soil heating than it would otherwise be. An essential prerequisite is construction according to the sandbed method, which is described in detail. Types of heating systems and the use of plastic sheeting as a necessary adjunct to soil heating are described, and costs given.

INTRODUCTION

Heating of the soil under sports turf has become common practice in Sweden. This is a result of collaboration over a number of years between Dr. Lars-Erik Janson at Vattenbyggnadsbyrån and the writer. The theoretical and experimental parts of the work have been carried out in collaboration with Swedish sports authorities, who have also shared the costs of the same. The investigation has shown that it is possible, if heating is begun on 1 March, to get fresh green turf fit for play by 1 April in the Stockholm area. This is six weeks earlier than normal. The prerequisite for this, however, is that the ground has been constructed according to the sandbed method with a very thin topsoil layer on the surface and that hardy grass species and varieties are used. It is also possible to use the same area for winter and summer sports if the ground is constructed in the above-mentioned way and the cooling system used in reverse for heating up the turf. With the help of underground heating and plastic sheeting, it is possible in less than four weeks to transform the ice-rink into freshly growing turf.

The aim of the studies and research work done in Sweden with soil heating under sports turf has been to study the possibility of creating favourable conditions for early growth of turf grass with the help of artificial heating of turf during winter and spring. This would allow more games to be played during the season and training by the players to start early on a frost-free and green ground. The results of the research done in Sweden have been published by Janson and Langvad (1968).

The number of stadia with heating equipment is increasing every year. The following grounds have been constructed on modern principles:-

1. Nya Ullevi, Gothenburg (electric heating system)
2. Valhalla Stadium, Gothenburg (electric heating system)
3. Football Stadium, Solna (electric heating system)
4. Värendsvallen, Växjö (warm water in plastic pipes)
5. South Stadium, Stockholm (solution of brine)
6. Högslätten Stadium, Härnösand (electric heating system)
7. Jägersro Horse Racing Stadium (warm water in plastic pipes)

Of these, Nya Ullevi, the Football Stadium at Solna and the South Stadium in Stockholm are equipped with machines that can handle plastic sheeting.

The following stadia are due to be built or reconstructed:-

1. Stockholm Stadium (with electric heating system)
2. Karlstad Stadium (with electric heating system)
3. Jönköping Stadium (with electric heating system)
4. Billingehus Stadium (solution of brine)
5. Eyravallen, Örebro (electric heating system)
6. Idrottsparken, Copenhagen (electric heating system)

CONSTRUCTION OF FOOTBALL GROUNDS

Irrespective of whether it is attempted to prolong the growth period by artificial means or not, a football field can be constructed in a way that is optimal for grass growth. In establishing suitable principles of construction, it is essential to take into account both geohydrological and phytobiological considerations. In the first place, it is known that if football grounds do not drain rapidly after rain, there is exceptional wear and tear which gives rise to considerable damage to the turf. The best resistance to abrasion is provided by a rather dry turf in full growth. The prerequisite for rapid drainage is that the top layer of soil should have good permeability for water. One must not, however, aim at excessive permeability, since the capacity to retain water is necessary. In this connection, it has proved ideal to make the top layer of fine sand mixed with peat mould, the latter functioning as a water retainer.

If such a material is chosen instead of soil for the root zone of the grass one gets a deep root system, since water, air and nourishment are allowed to penetrate well into the surface layer. In this way, one gets grass that is drought resistant during the growing period. Further, one gains the advantage that the root zone is not waterlogged but is well aerated in the winter, thus affording favourable conditions for winter hardiness in the grass. Early in the spring, when the earth is frozen, a dry soil means that the thawing out takes place quickly and that melt water from the surface can easily be drained off downwards. It is thus possible to avoid surplus water, which causes lack of oxygen in the soil.

This construction of the ground which allows the surplus ground water in the spring to be drained off, also creates favourable conditions for a long growing period. Optimal conditions are obtained if in this situation one supplements the ground heat in the spring by means of an artificial heating system in the root zone.

The drainage of football grounds should be so arranged that the capacity of the drainage system corresponds to the amount of precipitation which the permeability of the chosen soil will allow to penetrate the densest layer of soil occurring above the drainage system. In a correctly constructed football field the densest layer is the grass-grown top soil, which must rest direct on a free-draining sandy material. This latter must then in its turn be in connection, either directly or via a free-draining filling of sand, with the drainage system.

If the natural soil consists of good draining material such as sand, this will in itself constitute the drainage system. If, on the other hand, the natural soil is denser than the soil of the top layer, drainage of the sand or gravel bed must be effected by a collecting drainage conduit running round the ground and connected with a run-off. The drainage of the sand bed is made more effective by installing at the bottom branch conduits running transversely across the ground and connected with the collecting conduit. It should, however, be pointed out that this is not absolutely necessary if the sand bed is thick and has a particularly good draining capacity. But this last-mentioned condition is difficult to fulfil, and in many cases natural variations in the composition of the sand may result in local sealing of the sand bed. Thus a more certain result is attained with drainage pipes in good contact with the overlying layer of sand. For every kind of soil there is a recognised connection between the grain particle curves of the top layers and the distance between the drainage conduits.

The following construction method is now recommended and used extensively in Scandinavia.

Stage I

1.1 Grade the ground after marking out. It must be 20 cm higher in the middle along its length.

Stage II

2.1 Drain the ground transversely. The pipe trenches must be at 4 m centres and the depth 20 cm. The breadth of the trenches should be the same as the depth. Use perforated plastic piping 5 cm in diameter. The piping should be laid hard up against one edge of the trench.

2.2 Fill the trenches with coarse gravel (2-8 mm) up to the level of the ground. The drainage may also be done after the addition of the gravel bed.

2.3 Harrow between the trenches with a rigid-tined cultivator to a depth of 10 cm, but be careful of the trenches. This is done to loosen the packed soil after the heavy grading machines and lorries.

Stage III

3.1 Add sand (0.02 - 4 mm) in an even thick layer (15-20 cm). The sand must be driven in from the sides, preferably with a caterpillar tractor. Wheel tracks or caterpillar tracks are successively removed with the cultivator.

3.2 Add fertilizer to the sand bed, e.g. 3 tons of Super Gramino with Peraform (21:7:14). By harrowing or rotavating the fertilizer is well mixed with the sand to a depth of 10 cm.

3.3 The sand bed is levelled to a tolerance of $\pm$ 3 cm.

Stage IV

4.1 Add top soil to a thickness of 5 cm. This consists of 60 per cent by volume of sand and 40 per cent by volume of peat mould. This mixture must be well mixed with a rotavator or in a cement mixer. The peat mould must be thoroughly moistened. The top soil is transported to the sand bed with a light caterpillar tractor.

4.2 Fertilize the top soil with 1 ton Super Gramino with Peraform which is cultivated in to a depth of 5 cm.

4.3 Produce a fine tilth by hand raking, so that all unevennesses are eliminated.

4.4 Sow with "Kick-off Special" grass seed mixture (80% Poa pratensis L. Merion and Sydsport, 20% Phleum bertolonii DC Evergreen) at 2.5 kg per 100 sq m. The sowing is best done with a Lawn Beauty grass seed and manure spreader, or with a Lawnmaker machine. Sowing may also be done by hand, but the job must in this case by done by one who is accustomed to it.

4.5 The grass seed is best worked in with a grid roller or by light raking. The soil does not afterwards need to be rolled, even though it would stand up well to it.

This method has proved to give the foundation in which the grass flourishes and develops best. The turf becomes tough and always gives the players dry ground. The pitch never develops drainage problems even in persistently rainy weather. Moreover, the turf grass is more winter-hardy, as there is no surplus of water in the upper layer of the soil. As the grass can develop a deep root system and a big root volume, the turf becomes resistant to drought. The benefits of heating the soil will also be improved, as clearly demonstrated by Janson (1969). The method is as a rule considerably cheaper than traditional construction methods.

TYPES OF HEATING SYSTEM

To supply the requisite amount of heat to the root zone of the grass the alternatives are either a system of pipes with circulating liquid or heating with electric cables. The choice between liquid circulation and heating with electric power is in the main a question of the cost of the power. For heating with electric power to be profitable, the cost should not exceed 3 öre/kWh. Furthermore, electric power should already be installed for other equipment with heavy power consumption, such as flood lighting, so that there need be no extra power charge for the heating installation of the football ground. Electric heating has a number of technical advantages that ought not to be under-estimated, such as the even emission of a constant amount of heat along the source of heat; no risk of freezing; easily managed plant, and low maintenance costs.

The temperature limit for grass growth is 6^{0}C for Phleum bertolonii and 8^{0}C for Poa pratensis in the root zone down to 6 cm deep. The optimum temperature for the same species is $12-16^{0}$C. If the temperature is to exceed the minimum, there must be a definite relationship between the position of the heating system and the heat conducting capacity of the kind of soil material. Janson (1969) deals with this subject.

Both electric cables and polythene pipes can easily be ploughed mechanically into the soil with modern machines.

USE OF PLASTIC SHEETING WITH HEATING SYSTEMS

Economic exploitation of the possibilities of a heating system presupposes that the ground can be covered with plastic sheeting. The investigations at the Football Stadium in Solna showed that the soil temperature that was obtained with 61 W/sq m without sheeting was also attained with only 25 W/sq m if the surface of the ground was covered with sheeting. This shows the importance of sheeting as a retainer of heat. It has, however, also proved necessary to cover the turf with sheeting for the sake of the moisture balance between soil and air. With the sheeting one gets a necessary protection against evaporation, so

that the air in the leaf zone is saturated with moisture. It has been possible
to demonstrate clearly the effect of a plastic covering from the phytobiological
point of view, both in experiments with models and in full scale operation.

The sheeting can also protect the ground from heavy precipitation, especially in the autumn, so that a further important cost-saving aid in the management
of the grounds is obtained. A turf which is left to rest in winter in not too
badly worn a condition will also acquire greater winter hardiness, and growth
will start quicker in the spring.

In general it may be said that an arrangement for covering with plastic
sheeting gives a higher degree of utilization and lower maintenance costs for a
ground. A necessary prerequisite is to have a place available for a cylinder
arrangement of the type used in the Football Stadium, and arrangements must be
made for the disposal of the water collecting on the sheet. This may be most
simply effected by a trench with crushed rock bedding and with drainage contact
to wells along the short sides of the grounds to receive the water escaping at
the sides when the sheeting is rolled up.

The plastic sheeting must be transparent and UV-stabilised, and have a
thickness of 0.15 mm. A suitable size for the sheeting is 80 x 110 sq m, rolled
on a 112 m long steel cylinder of diameter 0.5 m. The cylinder is driven with
two electric motors, one at each short end of the ground.

When the sheeting is not being used it must be protected against sunlight
and heat, and should therefore be stored in a closed space along one of the
long sides of the field.

COSTS OF LAYING OUT AND OPERATION

The costs of laying out a completely satisfactory football field constructed
according to the sand bed method, amounts to about 15-25 Swedish crowns per
sq m. This cost is of course reduced in cases where the existing grounds are
already well drained and built up with sandy soil.

For a normal electric heating system in the root zone, the cost is at present about 12-15 crowns per sq m. In the future it will probably be possible to
reduce this cost. To this must be added tne cost for the plastic sheeting cover.
For the plastic sheeting itself the cost is between 7,000 and 14,000 crowns, with
a trend towards the lower price, and for the rolling-up device about 40,000 crowns,
or in all, for plastic sheeting and cylinder about 50,000 crowns. For the storing
of the plastic sheeting cylinder about 10,000 crowns should be set aside.

The operating costs for the heating will of course depend on the cost of
power, and how this varies during the heating up period. On the assumption that
the first match of the season is played on 15 April on green turf, the heating
must in Central Sweden and under normal climatic conditions be continued up to
the beginning of May. During this latter period, however, the thermostatic
control of the system will turn off the heat during the day. This means that
the effective heating period is about one and a half months during the season.
With power costing 3 öre/kWh one thus gets an operating cost for the heating
system of about 6-12,000 Swedish crowns, depending on the latitude and winter
temperature.

If instead it is desired to have green turf ready for training matches as
early as the end of March, the clearing of snow and the heating must be begun

about 15 February in the Stockholm area and the operating cost will be doubled. As play can be begun on a dried out turf in full growth at the start of the series, the wear and tear will be appreciably reduced. The maintenance normally required on conventional football grounds in the central and northern parts of Sweden in order to get the ground fit for play again between the early spring matches is considerable. By creating early growth of grass with bottom heating one may expect this type of maintenance cost to be reduced by amounts similar to the cost of the electric power for the cheaper operating alternative.

REFERENCES

1.   JANSON, L.E., and LANGVAD, B. (1968) Prolongation of the growing season for sports turf grasses by means of artificial heating of the root zone. Weibulls Grästips 1968.

2.   JANSON, L.E. (1969) Theoretical investigation of artificial heating of the top soil. (Preceding paper in these Proceedings.)

PERFORMANCE OF SOME KENTUCKY BLUEGRASSES UNDER HIGH TEMPERATURES

T.L. Watschke and R.E. Schmidt,

Virginia Polytechnic Institute, Blacksburg, Virginia, U.S.A.

SUMMARY

Nitrate-nitrogen absorption, nitrate-nitrogen content, and carbohydrate content were important factors in correlation with high temperature tolerance of five cultivars of Poa pratensis. Cultivars having the
best root and foliar growth under warm temperature regimes had higher
carbohydrate levels, lower nitrate-nitrogen absorption, and lower foliar
nitrate-nitrogen than the varieties that had poor growth.

Kentucky bluegrass (Poa pratensis L.) has a broad genetic constitution.
Consequently, different Kentucky bluegrass cultivars vary in their adaptability
to adverse environmental conditions. Many Kentucky bluegrasses have been
released in the last decade (2) for fine turf purposes, but the selection of
these cultivars has been made without attempting to match them with their areas
of best adaptation.

Temperature is one of the most critical environmental factors influencing
Kentucky bluegrass growth and survival. The interaction of temperature and
nitrogen fertility affects Kentucky bluegrass metabolism. Carbohydrate metabolism, which influences Kentucky bluegrass tolerance to environmental stresses,
is particularly affected. The degree of influence that temperature and nitrogen
level have on a particular cultivar depends on its origin and carbohydrate status
(3).

Externally supplied nitrogen combines primarily with alpha keto-acids
(alpha keto-glutaric acid) which are products of carbohydrate metabolism to
form amino-acids. Different sequences of amino-acids constitute proteins which
are essential for plant growth (1).

It is feasible that a plant rapidly absorbing nitrogen could deplete the
available carbohydrate supply. Theoretically, plants having low nitrogen
absorption during periods of high temperature stress could conserve carbohydrate.
High temperatures result in high respiratory rates; consequently, plants with
high carbohydrate content best support growth at higher temperatures (3).

To test this hypothesis, the performance of five Kentucky bluegrass cultivars was measured under three temperature regimes at two nitrogen rates in the
authors' growth environmental laboratory. Results indicated that cultivar
origin, nitrate-nitrogen absorption, nitrate-nitrogen content, and carbohydrate
status are important parameters to consider in attempting to explain differences
in tolerance of high temperatures.

The five cultivars, selected on origin, were: Nugget (a selection from
Alaska), 124 and 110 (selections from coastal Virginia), Pennstar (a release by
the Pennsylvania State University), and Kenblue certified common Kentucky bluegrass (from Kentucky).

In the two cooler regimes ($18^{o}C$ light - $10^{o}C$ dark and $27^{o}C$ light - $18^{o}C$
dark) both foliage and roots of all cultivars grew relatively well. The high
nitrogen treatment induced more foliar and less root production than the low
nitrogen rate in all cultivars in the two cooler ranges. The nitrate-nitrogen

258

content was highest in the coolest regime. The carbohydrate status of all cultivars was relatively the same, except Nugget which had a trend toward lower carbohydrate content in the 27-18°C regime.

In the high temperature regime (35° - 20°C), drastic reductions in both foliar and root production of all cultivars occurred. Kenblue and the two cultivars selected from areas with high temperatures (110 and 124) tended to have the best foliar and root production. Nugget and Pennstar, selected from cool areas, performed very poorly in this temperature regime. The three cultivars that yielded the best had higher carbohydrate levels, lower nitrate-nitrogen absorption, and lower foliar nitrate-nitrogen than the two which performed poorly. It appears that a cultivar having low nitrate-nitrogen absorption and relatively high carbohydrate content has the ability to tolerate temperature stresses better than one not possessing these characteristics.

Increased respiration at high temperatures may reduce the carbohydrate supply of poorly performing cultivars. Some of the energy in the form of ATP (adenosine triphosphate) realized from the high respiratory activity may be involved in the "active" absorption of ions, particularly nitrate-nitrogen. This is supported by the fact that those cultivars having poor growth at high temperatures also had high nitrate-nitrogen absorption and nitrate content.

The cultivars having relatively better growth at high temperatures had lower nitrate-nitrogen absorption and higher carbohydrate contents. The energy obtained from the respiration of these cultivars may be used in metabolic processes manifested by increased foliar and root production rather than the "active" absorption of nitrate-nitrogen.

REFERENCES

1. BONNER, J., and VARNER, J.E. (1965) Plant Biochemistry, Academic Press, New York, New York. Pp. 214-229.

2. HANSON, A.A. (1965) Grass varieties in the United States. U.S.D.A. Handbook 170. Pp. 82-85.

3. YOUNGNER, V.B., and NUDGE, F.V. (1968) Growth and carbohydrate storage of three Poa pratensis L. strains as influenced by temperature. Crop Sci. 8, 455.

DISCUSSION

WINTER INJURY

R.W. Miller (Ohio, U.S.A.)

I should like to ask Dr. Beard whether low temperature injury at higher moisture levels is due to increased hydration or lower concentrations of solutes?

J.B. Beard (Michigan, U.S.A.)

Many changes are associated with the hardening process. The basic mechanism of low temperature injury involves ice crystal formation. The type and size of crystals are important. Solutes will have an effect, but cell water content is one of the most critical factors.

H. Vos (Netherlands)

Is there a good correlation between artificial results and natural conditions, since the pattern of freezing in the two situations is different?

J.B. Beard (Michigan, U.S.A.)

Field observations have confirmed results from controlled climate chambers.

W.B. Gilbert (North Carolina, U.S.A.)

The effect of freezing plants of Tifdwarf and Tifgreen bermudagrass (Cynodon hybrids) in the cold chamber is very closely correlated with results in the field when plants freeze normally. There are similar results when the roots and shoots are both frozen simultaneously in the chamber, and when the plant is frozen from the top downwards in the field.

D.T.A. Aldrich (U.K.)

Can Dr. Beard say what is the highest nitrogen level which can be used without giving winter injury in Michigan, assuming an adequate balance between potassium and nitrogen?

J.B. Beard (Michigan, U.S.A.)

It depends on species. The nitrogen level is not critical with Agrostis palustris Huds., but it is with Poa annua L. and Poa pratensis L. For varieties which have a high nitrogen requirement, e.g. Merion, do not exceed 6 lb./1,000 sq. ft. (ca. 3 kg/100 sq m) per year on loam soils. More important, avoid high levels in the fall hardening period, to prevent forced shoot growth which leads to low temperature kill.

R.W. Miller (Ohio, U.S.A.)

In studies conducted with mixtures of Festuca arundinacea Schreb. and Poa pratensis, winter kill of Festuca arundinacea was increased when about 2.4 kg/100 sq m of nitrogen were applied, compared with application rates of 1.2 and 0.6 kg/100 sq m. No differential winter killing of Poa pratensis was observed at these rates.

HIGH TEMPERATURE RESPONSES

H.H. Williams (California, U.S.A.)

We have found that syringing Poa pratensis under control of a moisture sensing device has reduced moisture stress at high temperatures.

J.A. Simmons (Ohio, U.S.A.)

Can Dr. Schmidt say if the performance of the better cultivars of Poa pratensis under high temperatures is due to less uptake of nitrates or to better assimilation of nitrates by the plant?

R.E. Schmidt (Virginia, U.S.A.)

Our work indicates that cultivars that have high nitrate uptake during warm weather decrease the carbohydrate content, which reduces the substrate available for respiration and other metabolic processes. Those grasses with the lowest nitrate uptake conserve carbohydrates, permitting ample energy substrate for a longer duration.

J.B. Beard (Michigan, U.S.A.)

Our work indicates that carbohydrate exhaustion is not the only potential factor in high temperature growth stoppage or reduction. Under certain conditions, a blockage in protein synthesis can be a critical limiting factor.

W.A. Adams (U.K.)

Is there any specific metabolic information which may help to account for the poor performance of the cultivar Nugget at high temperatures? For example, is the increase in respiration rate greater than the increase in the rate of photosynthesis?

J.B. Beard (Michigan, U.S.A.)

We have only studied differences between species, not between varieties. In Agrostis palustris Huds. (variety Toronto), respiration increased up to 45^0C. Photosynthesis also increased, but only up to 40^0C. Leaf growth started to decline at 30^0C. Provided that light and carbon dioxide are not limiting, the ratio of photosynthesis to respiration remained at 6 to 1. This work was done on pre-conditioned plants, using a manometer. It will be reported in "Crop Science".

SOIL HEATING

G.G. Fisher (U.K.)

Would Mr. Langvad give an opinion on the use of warm air as a source of heat under winter sports pitches.

B. Langvad (Sweden)

We have tried this, blowing warm air through perforated plastic pipes. Although theoretically it can be used, it is not effective in practice. The air temperature falls so fast that it is difficult to obtain even soil temperatures. The fall in temperature is linear, and you could get interesting information in this way on the temperatures at which grass grows. It does not appear possible to design a practical system for use with stadium turf.

<u>J.P. van der Horst (Netherlands)</u>

Are any discussions going on in Sweden to increase the number of fields with heating systems, for example to provide all the 1st and 2nd division teams with these?

<u>B. Langvad (Sweden)</u>

The Swedish Football Association wants to lengthen the playing season. The plans for the 1970's provide for all 1st and 2nd division stadia to have equal turf standards, which will mean that in the next five years about 20-30 stadia will need to instal heating systems and plastic rollers.

<u>H.H. Williams (California, U.S.A.)</u>

Heating <u>Cynodon</u> turf for winter colour with electric cables has shown promise for southern Californian conditions in studies at the Los Angeles State and County Arboretum, Arcadia.

SESSION 3B: LIGHT AND SHADING

(Chairman: Ir. G. J. Ruychaver)

RESPONSES OF VARIOUS TURFGRASSES TO

CERTAIN LIGHT SPECTRA MODIFICATIONS

G.R. McVey, E.W. Mayer and J.A. Simmons,

Research Agronomists, O.M. Scott & Sons, Marysville, Ohio, U.S.A.

SUMMARY

Windsor Kentucky bluegrass (Poa pratensis L.), Tifgreen bermudagrass
(Cynodon dactylon L.) and C-26 fescue (Festuca ovina var. duriuscula(L.)
Koch) were grown under different light-transmitting plastic panels in field
plots during the years 1964-1967. Each year modifications were made in the
test system and plant material to reflect previous findings. The acrylic
plastic units tested included the blue (410-510 mμ), green (500-560 mμ) and grey
(390-760 mμ) transmitting units with light quantity levels of equal transmittance, ranging from 18 to 74% of the full sunlight. Mature turfgrass
sod and seedlings grown under blue acrylic plastic were darker green, of
better quality and elongated at a slower rate that turf grown in grey
transmitted sunlight of comparable light intensity. These differences
were most evident at transmittance levels below 60%. The minimum light
quantity for acceptable Tifgreen bermudagrass and Windsor Kentucky bluegrass should exceed 40 to 50% of the full sunlight if they are grown under
blue transmitting plastic and should exceed 60-70% if grown under grey
transmitted sunlight.

REVIEW OF THE LITERATURE

The trend in recent years in the United States is to enclose athletic
fields, swimming pools and other areas used for outdoor activities. A controlled
environment provides uniform playing conditions, spectator and player comfort and
game scheduling which is not affected by inclement weather conditions. The
selection of light transmitting barriers must take into consideration the spectator, player, turfgrass requirements and engineering aspects such as aesthetic
factors, glare, optimum light quality and quantity and minimum infra-red energy
input.

The effects of light quality on plant growth and development have been
reported widely on dicotyledonous plants, but published information is limited
for monocotyledonous plants (1,2, 3 & 4). Ashton (1) stated that maximum increase
in fresh weight of oats occurs in the red and blue region of the spectrum with
only a slight increase in the yellow and green region. Datta and Dunn (2) also
reported that yields for mustard and tomato seedlings were greatest under red
light followed closely by blue at equal foot candles. Miller and Miller (11)
suggested that blue light regulates cell elongation by regulating an auxin
system.

Expansion of leaf blades of pea and bean was retarded 50 and 85% in the
blue and green portion of the spectrum respectively, according to Went (16).

Frank (5) reported that at equal irradiances a narrow band in the blue at
about 455 mμ is most effective in inducing chlorophyll formation in oat seedlings, a broad wave band in the orange red (620 to 600 mμ) being the second most
effective. Hoover (8) investigated the effect of different wave lengths upon

the rate of photosynthesis in wheat plants. Using equal but low intensities
he found maximum photosynthesis occurred at a wave length of 665 mμ (red) and
a secondary maximum of 440 mμ in the blue.

This study was designed to develop information on the selection of
transparent barriers used in covering turf areas such as athletic fields.
The specific objective was to determine the optimum light quality and quantity
for maintaining quality turf.

EXPERIMENTAL MATERIALS AND METHODS

The initial study in 1964 was designed to evaluate the effect of various
regions within the visible spectrum on Windsor Kentucky bluegrass (<u>Poa</u>
<u>pratensis</u> L.). Pigmented acrylic plastic units* (90 x 180 cm) were mounted on
metal frames 30.5 cm (12 in.) above the turf. The turf was clipped weekly at
38 mm (1.5 inches), watered once per week to assure optimum soil moisture and
fertilized monthly with the equivalent of 0.44 kg of nitrogen per 100 sq m
(0.9 lb/1,000 sq. ft.) in a fertilizer with a 23-3-6 ratio of N, P_2O_5 and K_2O.

In 1965 a similar test system was utilized but the individual acrylic
plastic units were 180 x 180 cm. A comparable maintenance programme was followed
as in 1964. Only plastic units transmitting in the blue and green regions of
the visible spectrum were included.

In the 1966-1967 studies the turf was grown in 15.2 x 20.3 cm (6 x 8 in.)
plastic pots or in 7.5 cm diameter styrofoam cups. The turf was placed under
55.3 x 55.3 cm (20 x 20 in.) acrylic plastic sheets 0.42 mm (0.187 in.) thick.
The acrylic sheets were suspended 15.2 cm (6 in.) above the turf and the pot
placed 55.3 cm (20 in.) above the ground level on a rack to assure good air
movement around the pot. A 15.2 cm (6 in.) opaque black drop cloth was hung
around each acrylic plastic unit to reduce incident light.

Plant material was selected which varied in physiological age and genetic
characteristics. Established sod of Windsor Kentucky bluegrass was used on
site for the 1964 and 1965 test. In 1966 two year old sod of Windsor bluegrass
and Tifgreen bermudagrass (<u>Cynodon dactylon</u> L.) were used as the source material.
In 1967 five week old seedlings of Windsor Kentucky bluegrass and C-26 fescue
(<u>Festuca ovina</u> var. <u>duriuscula</u> (L.) Koch) were grown in 75 mm diameter (3 in.)
containers. A 3/1 Sloan silty clay loam/sand mixture was utilized for the
growing media. In all pot culture tests the turf received a fertilizer with a
23-7-7 N-P_2O_5 - K_2O ratio, to a total of 1.75 kg of nitrogen per 100 sq m for
the bluegrass and bermudagrass and 1.30 kg of nitrogen per 100 sq m for the
fescue. The turf was cut weekly at 38 mm and watered as needed to assure quality
turf.

Turf responses were measured by both quantitative and qualitative observations. Colour, quality and density were based on subjective rating (10-9 denoting
excellent colour, 8-7 good and 6-5-4 poor colour). Turf quality was ranked using
a comparable scale, but 8, 7 and 6 were considered good, fair and poor turf
quality respectively. Density was based on the thickness of the cover and
expressed as per cent. Leaf growth and clipping fresh weights were recorded
above the mowing height (38 mm).

---

* Plexiglas G; Compliments of Rohm and Haas, Independence Mall West,
  Philadelphia, Pennsylvania.

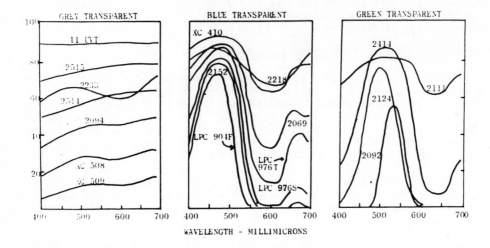

Figure 1: spectrophotometric curves of grey, blue and green transparent acrylic plastics

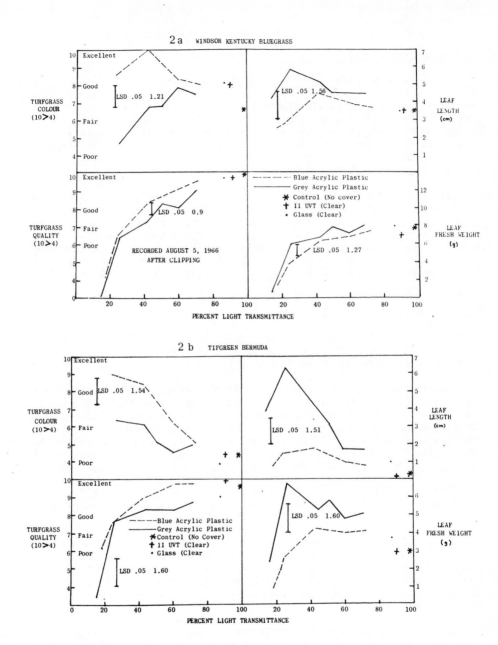

2 a WINDSOR KENTUCKY BLUEGRASS

TURFGRASS COLOUR (10>4)

TURFGRASS QUALITY (10>4)

LEAF LENGTH (cm)

LEAF FRESH WEIGHT (g)

RECORDED AUGUST 5, 1966 AFTER CLIPPING

LSD .05 1.21
LSD .05 1.56
LSD .05 0.9
LSD .05 1.27

– – – Blue Acrylic Plastic
—— Grey Acrylic Plastic
✳ Control (No cover)
✝ II UVT (Clear)
• Glass (Clear)

PERCENT LIGHT TRANSMITTANCE

2 b TIFGREEN BERMUDA

TURFGRASS COLOUR (10>4)

TURFGRASS QUALITY (10>4)

LEAF LENGTH (cm)

LEAF FRESH WEIGHT (g)

LSD .05 1.54
LSD .05 1.51
LSD .05 1.60
LSD .05 1.60

– – – Blue Acrylic Plastic
—— Grey Acrylic Plastic
✳ Control (No Cover)
✝ II UVT (Clear)
• Glass (Clear)

PERCENT LIGHT TRANSMITTANCE

Figure 2: turfgrass colour and quality, and leaf length and fresh weight, of Windsor Kentucky bluegrass and Tifgreen bermudagrass grown in blue and grey transmitted sunlight

267

The spectrophotometric curve and percent transmittance of the various acrylic plastic panels evaluated are shown in Figure 1.

RESULTS

Established Sod - 1964 test system

Ten plastic barriers representing 10 regions within the visible spectrum were evaluated in the initial study. One barrier was superior to all others at low levels of light intensity (Table 1). Windsor bluegrass covered with blue acrylic plastic (23% transmittance) was superior in colour, density and quality to turf grown under green light at a comparable transmittance level. These results suggested further evaluation of the blue region of the spectrum.

Established Sod - 1965 test system

To further define the role of the blue spectrum on turf development a wider range of light transmittance levels in the blue and green region of the spectrum was studied. As shown in Table 2 the blue region of the spectrum produced a turf superior in quality, colour and clipping production and exhibited less injury than turf maintained in the green spectrum. This difference was evident at low light intensities (20-30% transmittance). At light intensities greater than 55% the blue and green regions did not greatly alter turf performance.

Newly Established Sod - 1966 test system

In 1966 the blue pigmented acrylic plastic was compared with a spectrally neutral grey filter using newly established sod plugs of Windsor bluegrass and Tifgreen bermudagrass grown in plastic pots.

Windsor bluegrass grown under blue acrylic plastic had a darker green colour, improved quality and produced less leaf growth and clipping yields than turf grown at a comparable light transmittance level under grey light (Figure 2a). In contrast Windsor grown in grey transmitted sunlight was equal or inferior to turf grown in full sun. The quality of the turf was good to excellent when the transmittance range in the grey fell between 50 and 71%. The rapid rate of leaf extension below 50% transmittance in the grey distracted from the turf quality.

These findings suggest that a Windsor Kentucky bluegrass turf of good quality, excellent colour and a slow rate of growth can be grown under a blue barrier transmitting 40 to 70% of the full sunlight.

Tifgreen bermudagrass performed in a similar way to Windsor bluegrass, the differences, however, being more pronounced (Figure 2b). Turf colour under the blue plastic barriers was significantly better than turf grown in full sun or under the grey acrylic plastic barriers at light intensities of 20 to 60% of full sunlight. Turf quality was good to excellent if the transmittance in the blue or grey exceeded 40%.

A striking difference in leaf growth and fresh weight was obtained for turf grown under the blue acrylic plastic as compared to the grey plastic. There was no significant increase in blade extension or fresh weight production when the bermudagrass was grown in blue transmitted sunlight of 18 to 74% transmittance as compared to turf grown in full sun. In contrast bermudagrass grown in grey transmitted sunlight elongated significantly faster at all levels of light intensity than turf grown in full sun or under blue acrylic plastic with 18-55% transmittance. The fresh weight production followed a similar pattern.

268

Table 1: effects of blue and green acrylic barriers on Windsor Kentucky
bluegrass performance

Barrier	Transmittance %	Colour (code)	Colour (10-1)	Height (cm)	Density %	Total fresh weight (g)	Injury (%)
No cover	100	-	7.7	6.0	93	95	0
Window glass	100	clear	8.0	6.5	79	115	0
2152	23	blue	9.3	8.3	85	125	10
2092	26	green	6.2	9.7	48	109	80

Table 2: effects of various acrylic plastic barriers on the performance of
Windsor Kentucky bluegrass

Barrier	Transmittance	Colour of Barrier	Injury (%)	Colour (10-1)	Dry weight (g)	Quality (10-1)
No cover	100		1.0	9.5	4.5	9.5
Window glass	100		1.0	10.0	5.5	9.5
2218	76	blue	1.0	10.0	5.0	9.5
2111	77	green	1.0	10.0	5.5	10.0
2069	55	blue	1.0	10.0	5.5	9.5
2414	60	green	1.0	10.0	4.0	9.0
2152	23	blue	5.5	9.5	4.5	9.5
2124	30	green	80.0	6.5	2.0	5.5
LSD .05			5.3	.7	2.0	3.0

Table 3: effects of blue and green acrylic barriers on the colour of Windsor
Kentucky bluegrass and C-26 fescue

Barrier	Transmittance (%)	Colour of Barrier	Colour (10-1) Windsor bluegrass	C-26 fescue
No cover	100	clear	7.7	7.3
11 uvt	90	clear	7.0	8.0
2218	74	blue	7.0	7.0
2515	71	grey	7.0	7.5
2069	60	blue	8.0	9.0
2233	60	grey	7.3	8.3
976 T	43	blue	9.0	10.0
2094	43	grey	6.7	8.0
976 S	24	blue	10.0	8.0
508	26	grey	6.7	7.3
904 F	18	blue	9.3	9.3
509	15	grey	6.3	7.0

Good to excellent Tifgreen bermudagrass can be grown under a blue plastic barrier with a transmittance rating greater than 40%. In contrast bermudagrass maintained under a grey acrylic plastic transmitting less than 60% of the full sunlight elongates more rapidly and would require more frequent mowing to maintain turf quality.

Seedling development - 1967 test system

The response of immature Windsor bluegrass and C-26 fescue plants followed a similar pattern as that realised with mature sod. As shown in Table 3, turf maintained under blue acrylic plastic exhibited superior colour to that maintained in grey transmitted sunlight when the level of transmittance was between 15 and 60% of the full sunlight. The differences were more striking at the lower levels of transmittance. The rate of shoot extension for C-26 and Windsor was much slower in the blue transmitted sunlight as compared to the grey light. The rate of elongation increased in a linear fashion with a decrease in light intensity. The turf grown under the grey barrier elongated approximately 2½ times faster than turf grown under blue barriers as the per cent transmittance was reduced.

DISCUSSION

The improved performance of turf grown in blue light as compared to turf grown under grey tinted acrylic plastic is supported directly in the literature. The reduced blade elongation in blue light is supported by observations made by Went (16) in 1941.

The darker green leaf colour in blue light and to a lesser degree in grey light as compared to turf grown in full sun may be a result of increased nitrogenous compounds in the plant tissue. Horvath (9) supports this concept in a recent finding where he demonstrated lower light intensities (12 to 50% of full sunlight) result in a higher proportion of nitrogen compounds in the tissue. At higher light intensities the formation of carbohydrates is dominant. The energy requirements for amino acid synthesis via 2-glyceric acid 3-phosphate and phospho-enol-pyruvate are not as high as that required for carbohydrate production. Zucker and Stinson (17) have reported that chloroplasts contain a large proportion of the protein in green leaves. In addition, nitrogen is a part of the chlorophyll molecule and is required for chlorophyll synthesis, as reported by Meyer, Anderson and Bohning (10).

In support of these findings it has been reported by Vernon and Avron (13) that blue light is required by plants to photosynthetically reduce NADP to NADPH which is required in the fixation of carbon dioxide.

McBee (12) also reported improved quality of FB-137 bermudagrass when grown under reduced light intensities.

It is of interest that the light transmitted through a tree canopy has a high percent of blue light and a low level of red light as compared to full sunlight (Gaskin, 6). In addition it has been reported by Robertson (7) that below 9 degrees the proportion of the blue light continues to increase as the sun sinks below the horizon. Cloud cover and heavy overcast during a thunderstorm increase the relative amounts of blue light. This would suggest that plants have maximum efficiency of utilization of blue light as a result of an evolutionary process.

These findings suggest that quality turfgrass can be grown under acrylic plastic barriers with greater than 40% transmittance in the blue region (410-510 mμ) of the spectrum. This region allows maximum input of the light quality found most important in plant development and reduces the input of infrared light which contributes to the refrigeration requirements of enclosed areas.

REFERENCES

1. ASHTON, F.M. (1965) Relationship between light and toxicity symptoms caused by atrazine and monuron. Weeds 13, 164.

2. DATTA, S.C.,and DUNN, S. (1959) Effects of light quality on herbicide toxicity to plants. Weeds 7, 55.

3. DUNN, S., and WENT, F.W. (1959). Influence of fluorescent light quality on growth and photosynthesis of tomatoes. Lloydia 22, 302.

4. FLINT, L.H., and MORELAND, C.F., (1942) A comparison of the effect of green light and red light on the simple leaf development of intact and decapitated bean plants. Pl. Physiol, 17, 677.

5. FRANK, S.R. (1946) The effectiveness of the spectrum in chlorophyll formation. J. Gen. Physiol. 29, 157.

6. GASKIN, T. (1964) Growing turfgrass in shade. Park Maintenance (Oct. issue).

7. ROBERTSON, G.W. (1967) The measurement of the spectral intensity of light. Greenhouse, Garden, Grass (Plant Research Institute) 6, 1, 7.

8. HOOVER, W.H. (1937) The dependence of carbon dioxide assimilation in a higher plant on wave length of radiation. Smithson. misc. Collns. 75, No. 21.

9. HORVATH, L., and SZASZ, K. (1965) Effect of light intensity on the metabolic pathways in photosynthesis. Nature Lond. 207, 546.

10. MEYER, B.S., ANDERSON, D.B., and BOHNING, R.H. (1963) Introduction to Plant Physiology. D. Van Nostrand Co., Inc., 184.

11. MILLER, J.H., and MILLER, P.M. (1965) The relationship between the promotion of elongation of fern protonemata by light and green growth substances. Am. J. Bot. 52, 871.

12. McBEE, G.G., and HOLT, E.C. (1966) Shade tolerance studies of bermudagrass and other turfgrasses. Agron. J. 58, 523.

13. VERNON, L.P., and AVRON, M. (1965) Photosynthesis. Ann. Rev. Biochem. 34, 271.

14. WASSINK, E.C., and STOLIYK, J.A.J. (1956) Effects of light quality on plant growth. Ann. Rev. Pl. Physiol. 7, 373.

15. WASSINK, E.C., DeLINT, P.J.A.L., and BENSINK, J. (1959) Some effects of high intensity irradiation of narrow spectral regions. Published in Photoperiodism and Related Phenomena in Plants and Animals, edited by R. B. Withrow. Publication No. 55 of the American Association for the Advancement of Science, Washington, D.C. 111.

16. WENT, F.W. (1941) Effects of light on stem and leaf growth. Am. J. Bot. 28, 83.

17. ZUCKER, M., and STENSON, H.T. (1962) Chloroplasts as the major protein bearing structure in Oenothera leaves. Archs. Biochem. Biophys. 96, 637.

TURFGRASS SHADE ADAPTATION*

Dr. James B. Beard,

Department of Crop and Soil Science, Michigan State University, East Lansing, Michigan, U.S.A.

SUMMARY

The mechanism of shade adaptation cannot be attributed to a single factor but is influenced by a complex of microclimatic, pathological and physiological responses. The primary factors are:-

(a)   reduced light intensity,

(b)   tree root competition for nutrients and water,

(c)   disease activity favoured by the microenvironment,

(d)   a more succulent, delicate leaf structure, and

(e)   reduction of shoot density, root growth and carbohydrate reserves.

Turfgrasses may fail under shaded conditions due to one or more of the first three factors. Evidence is presented which indicates that disease is of particular importance in turfgrass shade adaptation of cool-season species.

INTRODUCTION

Between 20 and 25% of the existing turfgrass areas are probably maintained under some degree of shade. In most cases the shading is attributed to a foliage canopy of trees, although a certain amount of shading is also associated with buildings and similar structures. The following discussion will relate primarily to shading by a tree canopy.

THE SHADE MICROENVIRONMENT

The plant's microenvironment is substantially altered by a tree canopy. Not only is the light intensity lowered but there are:-

(a)   a restriction in wind movement,

(b)   an increase in relative humidity,

(c)   a moderation of extremes in temperature, and

(d)   an increase in the carbon dioxide level (Table 1).

The moderation of temperature extremes in the shade is favourable for the growth of cool-season turfgrasses including red fescue (21). However, the restricted wind movement (11) and the increased relative humidity (10) result in a more favourable microenvironment for disease activity. Considerable modification

---

*   Contribution from the Michigan Agricultural Experiment Station, East Lansing, Michigan, as Paper No. 4994.

in light quality occurs under a deciduous tree canopy, whereas conifers act more as neutral filters (8, 15, 27). A so-called "green shade" is the most common under a deciduous tree canopy and is characterised by maximum reflection and transmission of the green, yellow and dark red regions of the visible spectrum with maximum absorption in the blue, orange and red (2, 15, 25). Thus, light under a deciduous tree canopy is depleted of the photosynthetically active wavelengths.

The reduced light intensity under a tree canopy results in certain growth and development responses by turfgrass plants. Basically, the low light intensity limits the photosynthetic capability of the turfgrass plant and results in a reduction of the carbohydrate reserve (1, 4, 7, 23, 24). The net effect is a decrease in shoot, root, rhizome and stolon growth. Generally, the reduction in root growth is greater than the reduction in shoot growth, which results in a lower root to shoot ratio (17, 18, 22, 28). Other effects associated with shaded conditions include:-

(a) thinner leaves and stems,

(b) longer internodes,

(c) reduced tillering and shoot density,

(d) a larger leaf area, and

(e) a higher tissue moisture content (9, 13, 14).

These latter factors result in a general deterioration in plant vigour and reduced resistance to heat, cold, drought, disease and wear stresses (16, 28, 30).

Table 1: a comparison of the microenvironments of an unirrigated red fescue turf in full sunlight and in dense shade* on a typical day in mid-August at East Lansing, Michigan

(* under an enclosed stand of mature sugar maples (Acer saccharum Mersh.)

Environmental factors	Full sunlight	Shade
Light intensity at 12 noon (ft. candles)	10,200	1,000
Total incident radiation (g cal/cm)	659	38
Average air temperature at 1 cm (^{o}C)	23	17
Average soil temperature at 15 cm (^{o}C)	22	16
Maximum air temperature at 1 cm (^{o}C)	36	23
Minimum air temperature at 1 cm (^{o}C)	11	12
Wind speed at 5 cm (12 noon) (miles per hour)	4	0
Per cent relative humidity at 5 cm (12 noon)	45	68
Atmospheric carbon dioxide at 1 cm (12 noon) (p.p.m.)	276	305
Duration of dew (hours)	12.5	0

FACTORS IN SHADE ADAPTATION

The mechanism of shade adaptation does not involve just a single factor but is influenced by a complex of microclimatic, pathological and physiological responses. These are mainly:-

(a) reduced light intensity under the tree canopy,

(b) tree root competition for nutrients and water,

(c) a microenvironment more favourable for disease activity,

(d) a more succulent, delicate leaf structure, and

(e) reduction of shoot density, root growth and carbohydrate reserves.

Turfgrasses may fail under shaded conditions due to lack of light; excessive tree root competition for water or nutrients; or increased activity of disease, in a favourable microenvironment, on insufficiently resistant varieties. The failure of turf under shaded conditions could be due to one factor or several combined. The following section indicates that disease is of particular importance in shade adaptation by cool-season species.

EXPERIMENTAL RESULTS

Studies were conducted at Michigan State University to study the mechanism involved in the adaptation of cool-season turfgrasses to shade (2). The experimental area used in the study was developed in a woodland composed of sugar maples (Acer saccharum Mersh.) 0.4 - 0.8 m in diameter. No tree root pruning was attempted other than in the surface 10 cm which was necessary in order to prepare an adequate seed bed. The trees provided a fairly uniform, dense shade throughout the experimental plot area. Measurements at one hour intervals from 7.0 a.m. to 7.0 p.m. showed that the light intensity under the tree canopy was only 5% of the incident sunlight. Plot size was 1.5 by 3 m with three replications arranged in a randomized block design. The sandy loam soil was limed to raise the pH to 6.0 and fertilized to provide adequate phosphorus and potassium levels in the seedbed. Seven cool-season turfgrass varieties were seeded alone and in eight combinations on 7 September 1961. All plots were seeded at a rate of 3,400,000 seeds per 100 sq m. The turfs were not irrigated at any time during the experiment and were mowed weekly at a 5 cm cutting height. Nitrogen was applied at a rate of 0.9 kg/100 sq m per year, half in early spring and the other half on 1 September. Fallen tree leaves were removed semi-weekly during the autumn period.

Results of the first four growing seasons are summarised. During the initial winter of 1961-62, tall fescue (Festuca arundinacea Schreb.) was severely injured by grey snow mould (Typhula spp.) while common and Norlea perennial ryegrass (Lolium perenne L.) exhibited over 65 per cent kill from low temperature stress (Table 2.) Through April 1962, rough bluegrass (Poa trivialis L.), Pennlawn red fescue (Festuca rubra L.), common Kentucky bluegrass (Poa pratensis L.) and Merion Kentucky bluegrass ranked high in turfgrass quality. In late May, 1962, Pennlawn red fescue was severely attacked by leafspot (Helminthosporium sativum PKB) resulting in over 90 per cent thinning of the turf. A gradual build-up in powdery mildew (Erysiphe graminis P.C.) also occurred in early May 1962, in both Merion and common Kentucky bluegrass. As a result, these two species were 95 per cent thinned by August 1962. Rough bluegrass performed

Table 2: the 1962 seasonal turfgrass performance ratings of seven turfgrasses grown under 5% of incident sunlight

Turfgrass	Turfgrass quality ratings (1 - best; 9 - poorest)									
	2 Apr.	30 Apr.	15 May	12 June	22 June	5 July	30 July	17 Aug.	11 Sep.	6 Nov.
Rough bluegrass	4.3	2.5	3.3	4.2	3.3	3.3	2.0	1.2	3.0	4.0
Pennlawn red fescue	2.3	5.0	4.7	7.3	7.3	7.0	7.3	7.0	8.3	8.5
Common perennial rye-grass	6.0	4.0	6.0	6.0	5.0	6.0	7.0	6.0	7.0	6.0
Kentucky 31 tall fescue	7.0	4.0	7.0	7.0	6.0	7.0	7.0	7.0	8.0	9.0
Norlea perennial ryegrass	5.0	4.0	4.0	6.0	5.0	6.0	7.0	7.0	8.0	8.0
Common Kentucky bluegrass	2.7	6.8	8.0	9.0	8.7	8.7	8.7	8.3	9.0	9.0
Merion Kentucky bluegrass	2.0	6.0	7.0	6.0	8.0	9.0	9.0	9.0	9.0	9.0

Table 3: turfgrass quality ratings and shoot density of seven turfgrasses grown under 5% of incident sunlight

Turfgrass	Shoot density count*		Turfgrass quality rating+		
	1962	1964	1962	1963	1964
Pennlawn red fescue	25	34	6.5	5.4	4.3
Rough bluegrass	54	44	3.2	4.9	5.8
Common perennial ryegrass	23	10	5.9	5.3	7.0
Kentucky 31 tall fescue	18	10	6.8	7.0	7.3
Common Kentucky bluegrass	15	4	7.9	6.7	8.1
Norlea perennial ryegrass	10	1	6.0	6.7	8.7
Merion Kentucky bluegrass	10	0	7.4	9.0	9.0
LSD 5%	11.5	14.5	0.8	1.0	1.8

* Shoots per 80 sq cm; counts made the second week in October

+ 1 - best; 9 - poorest (Average of the monthly seasonal ratings).

exceptionally well throughout the 1962 growing season, particularly in view of the droughty conditions that existed. Tall fescue and the two perennial ryegrasses showed no significant recovery from the snow mould and low temperature injury which occurred during the winter of 1961-62.

A surprising degree of recovery was noted in the red fescue turf during the spring of 1963, specially considering the severe thinning by leafspot which had taken place in 1962. In contrast, Merion and common Kentucky bluegrasses showed little or no recovery from the powdery mildew damage.

During the summer of 1963, Helminthosporium leafspot occurred again on the red fescue, but the attack was not as severe as in 1962. In late July, 1963, the rough bluegrass was severely thinned by Helminthosporium species. The lower ratings of the rough bluegrass plots in 1963 are a result of this severe disease injury.

In the spring of 1964, good recovery of the red fescue was again noted, but the Kentucky bluegrasses, tall fescue and ryegrasses continued to perform poorly throughout the season (Table 3). Rough bluegrass recovered considerably from the severe thinning of July 1963. A slight, but minor, incidence of leafspot was noted in the red fescue and rough bluegrass during the 1964 season.

Throughout the three years of observation, the turfgrass mixtures performed similarly to the dominant grass component or components (Table 4). During the initial year, those mixtures containing rough bluegrass ranked highest, whereas in subsequent years those mixtures containing predominantly red fescue showed marked improvement. Mixtures containing predominantly Kentucky bluegrass, tall fescue, or perennial ryegrass performed poorly. Species composition data presented in Table 4 show that where common Kentucky bluegrass was included with either red fescue or rough bluegrass, the latter two species predominated. In the 50-50 red fescue-rough bluegrass mixture, red fescue was dominant in a 2 to 1 ratio. In Kentucky bluegrass or rough bluegrass mixtures with red fescue, the rough bluegrass persisted as a much higher proportion of the stand than did Kentucky bluegrass. In the mixture containing equal numbers of red fescue, rough bluegrass, and common Kentucky bluegrass seed, the red fescue and rough bluegrass persisted in about equal percentages, while the Kentucky bluegrass was reduced by two-thirds.

Comparison of Tables 3 and 4 shows that after three years, the 33-33-33 mixture of red fescue, rough bluegrass and Kentucky bluegrass was higher in density than any one of the grass components planted alone.

Table 4: species composition, shoot density counts, and turfgrass quality ratings of eight turfgrass mixtures grown under 5% of incident sunlight

Turfgrass mixture*	Composition %		Shoot density counts***		Turf quality ratings (1-best; 9-poorest)****		
	Original seed**	Plants on 10/10/64	1962	1964	1962	1963	1964
F-K	50-50	86-14	16	39	6.8	6.4	3.9
F-K	75-25	91-9	22	41	7.0	5.5	4.4
F-K	25-75	92-8	27	33	6.2	6.0	4.6
F-R	50-50	68-32	48	35	3.3	5.6	5.5
K-R	50-50	17-83	56	22	3.3	5.0	5.5
F-K-P	33-33-33	63-11-26	23	30	6.5	5.6	5.6
F-K-R	33-33-33	45-12-43	46	59	3.9	5.2	5.7
K-T	50-50	32-68	16	19	6.9	5.2	5.8
LSD 5%			11.5	14.5	0.8	1.0	1.8
DR 5%			13.2	16.6	0.9	1.1	2.0

* F-Pennlawn red fescue; K-Common Kentucky bluegrass; R-Rough bluegrass;
  P-Common perennial ryegrass; T-Kentucky 31 tall fescue.
** Based on seed numbers.
*** Shoots per 80 sq cm, counted 2nd week October.
**** Average of the seasonal ratings.

The most significant observation in this study is the prominence of disease in influencing the adaptation of turfgrasses to shade. It was the microenvironment favourable to disease under shaded conditions and the lack of disease resistance in the turfgrass cultivars that resulted in the severe disease problem. Powdery mildew caused complete kill of the Kentucky bluegrasses when planted as a pure stand, with no recovery observed in later years, although the Kentucky bluegrass was able to persist when included in a mixture with other species. Pennlawn red fescue was severely injured by Helminthosporium leafspot in 1962, but recovered in subsequent years. The reduction in the seriousness of Helminthosporium leaf-spot attack in each succeeding year indicates that the leafspot-susceptible strains in the red fescue community were killed and the more tolerant strains were persisting and increasing. The reduction in Helminthosporium leafspot severity in each succeeding year is particularly significant, since the leafspot infection on red fescue grown on an adjacent area in full sunlight was actually more serious in 1963 and 1964 than in 1962. The rough bluegrass performed satisfactorily during the 1962 growing season and through July 1963. This was of interest since no irrigation was provided, and a serious drought occurred during this period. Thus, rough bluegrass was able to persist and produce an adequate turf under droughty conditions when shaded. It appears that heat, as well as drought, is a key factor in the deterioration of red fescue on unshaded, droughty sites.

The modified microenvironment of shade, including a higher relative humidity and reduced light intensity, produced succulent, delicate tissues and encouraged disease activity. (There is some evidence that disease response also plays a role in the adaptation of warm-season turfgrass species.)

Reduced light intensities resulted in a decrease in turf shoot density and turfgrass quality. But if disease attacks had not occurred, the turf would have been adequate for the adverse shade condition although certainly not as high in quality as an unshaded turf. Moisture deficiencies were common throughout the study due to severe tree root competition, lack of precipitation, and low water-holding capacity of the soil. Moisture stress, however, was not the key factor affecting the extremely poor performance of some turfgrasses in this study, since turfgrass deterioration was directly correlated with the time of disease incidence. If normal precipitation had occurred, improved fall recovery from disease injury would have been expected.

The value of mixing turfgrass species is of particular interest. In 1964 several mixtures had higher shoot densities than any one component of that mixture seeded alone. This suggests that mixtures function in reducing the severity of disease on any one specific turfgrass species contained in the mixture.

ADAPTATION OF SPECIES TO SHADE

Considerable variation has been observed in the shade adaptation of warm-season and cool-season turfgrass species. (2, 3, 5, 6, 12, 19, 20, 26, 29). A composite summary of turfgrass shade adaptation is presented in Table 5. Since disease is a major factor in shade adaptation, the development of disease-resistant cultivars, such as improved cultivars of Kentucky bluegrass resistant to powdery mildew, could result in a realignment of certain cultivars within the various shade adaptation categories. The rankings shown in Table 5 are based on the cultivars of each species now commercially available.

On the evidence of the limited data on species tolerance to shade, red fescue is the turfgrass to be preferred in the cool-humid climatic region. No comparisons between the bentgrasses and red fescue have been reported, but if diseases are controlled the bentgrasses should provide adequate turf under shaded conditions, although lower in quality than that produced in full sunlight. Among the warm-season turfgrasses, St. Augustinegrass is generally reported to be superior under shaded conditions, with the Zoysia species also exhibiting fairly good adaptation. For turfgrass cultivars to perform well under shaded conditions, they must possess improved disease tolerance. Characteristics such as growth habit and ability to capture and convert light energy into chemical energy at various wavelengths are also involved in shade adaptation, but disease resistance is currently the key limiting factor which must be resolved.

Table 5: the relative adaptation to severe shade of eighteen commonly used turfgrasses

	Excellent	Good	Intermediate	Poor
Cool-season turfgrasses	Red fescue	Rough bluegrass	Colonial bentgrass	Kentucky bluegrass
	Velvet bentgrass	Creeping bentgrass	Redtop	
		Tall fescue	Perennial ryegrass	
			Meadow fescue	
Warm-season turfgrasses	St. Augustine grass	Zoysia-grass	Centipede-grass	Buffalograss
	Manilagrass		Carpet-grass	Bermudagrass

REFERENCES

1. ALBERDA, T. (1957) The effects of cutting, light intensity and night temperatures on growth and soluble carbohydrate content of Lolium perenne L. Pl. Soil 8, 199.

2. BEARD, J.B. (1965) Factors in the adaptation of turfgrasses to shade. Agron. J. 57, 5, 457.

3. BEARD, J.B. (1967) Shade grasses and maintenance. 38th Int. Turfgrass Conf. Proc. 39.

4. BLACKMAN, G.E., and TEMPLEMAN, W.G. (1940) The interaction of light intensity and nitrogen supply in the growth and metabolism of grasses and clover (Trifolium repens.) IV. The relation of light intensity and nitrogen supply to the protein metabolism of the leaves of grasses. Ann. Bot. N.S. IV, 15, 533.

5. BURTON, G.W. (1956) Lawn grasses for the south. Plants and Gardens 12, 2, 156.

6. BURTON, G.W., and DEAL, E.E. (1962) Shade studies on southern grasses. Golf Course Reptr. 30, 8, 26.

7. BURTON, G.W., JACKSON, J.E., and KNOX, F.E. (1959) The influence of light reduction upon the production, persistence and chemical composition of coastal Bermudagrass, Cynodon dactylon. Agron. J. 51, 9, 537.

8. COOMBE, D.E. (1957) The spectral composition of shade light in woodlands. J. Ecol. 45, 823.

9. DAUBENMIRE, R.F. (1959) Plants and environment. Wiley, New York. 1.

10. DENMEAD, O.T. (1964) Evaporative sources and apparent diffusivities in a forest canopy. J. appl. Meteorology 3, 383.

11. FONS, W.L. (1940) Influence of forest cover on wind velocity. J. For. 38, 481.

12. HUFFINE, W.W. (1963) Grasses. Turfgrass Research, Oklahoma State University 2.

13. JUSKA, F.V. (1963) Shade tolerance of bentgrasses. Golf Course Reptr., 31, 2, 28.

14. JUSKA, F.V., HANSON, A.A., and HOVIN, A.W. (1969) Kentucky 31 tall fescue - a shade tolerant turfgrass. Weeds, Trees and Turf 8, 1, 34.

15. KNUCHEL, H. (1924) Spektrophotometrische Untersuchungen in walde. Mitt. schweiz. Centralanst. Forst. Versuch. 11, 1.

16. LUCANUS, R., MITCHELL, K.J., PRITCHARD, G.G., and CALDER, D.M. (1960) Factors influencing survival of strains of ryegrass during the summer. N. Z. Jl. agric. Res. 3, 185.

17. MITCHELL, K.J. (1954) Influence of light and temperature on growth of ryegrass (Lolium spp.) III. Pattern and rate of tissue formation. Physiologia Pl. 7, 51.

18. MITCHELL, K.J. (1955) Growth of pasture species. II. Perennial ryegrass (Lolium perenne), cocksfoot (Dactylis glomerata) and paspalum (Paspalum dilatatum). N.Z.Jl. Sci. Technol. Sect. A. 37, 1, 8.

19. McBEE, G.G. (1969) Association of certain variations in light quality with the performance of selected turfgrasses. Crop Sci. 9, 14.

20. McBEE, G.G., and HOLT, E.C. (1966) Shade tolerance studies on Bermuda-grass and other turfgrasses. Agron. J. 58, 523.

21. McGINNIES, W.J. (1966) Effects of shade on the survival of crested wheat-grass seedlings. Crop Sci. 6, 482.

22. REID, M.E. (1933) Effects of shade on the growth of velvet bent and metropolitan creeping bent. Bull. USGA. Green Section. 13, 131.

23. SCHMIDT, R.E. (1965) Some physiological responses of two grasses as influenced by temperature, light and nitrogen fertilisation. Ph.D. Thesis. Virginia Polytechnic Institute, 1.

24. SCHMIDT, R.E., and BLASER, R.E. (1967) Effect of temperature, light and nitrogen on growth and metabolism of 'Cohansey' bentgrass (Agrostis palustris Huds.) Crop Sci. 7, 447.

25. SHULL, C.A. (1929) A spectrophotometric study of reflection of light from leaf surfaces. Bot. Gaz. 87, 5, 583.

26. STURKIE, D.G., and FISHER, H.S. (1942) The planting and maintenance of lawns. Alabama agric. Exp. Stn. Circ. 85, 1.

27. VEZINA, P.E., and BOULTER, D.W.K. (1966) The spectral composition of near ultraviolet and visible radiation beneath forest canopies. Can. J. Bot. 44, 1267.

28. WHITCOMB, C.E. (1968) Grass and tree root relationships. Proc. Florida Turfgrass Mgmt. Conf., 16, 46.

29. YOUNGNER, V.B., and KIMBALL, M.H. (1962) Zoysiagrass for lawns. California Turfgrass Culture 12, 3, 23.

30. ANON. (1967) Grass thrives under Plexiglas sheets. Florist and Nursery Exchange 147, 16.

SHADE TOLERANT TURFGRASSES

OF THE UNITED STATES AND SOUTHERN CANADA

Glen M. Wood,

Associate Professor, Department of Plant and Soil Science. University of
Vermont Agricultural Experiment Station, Burlington, Vermont, 05401, U.S.A.

SUMMARY

The long-accepted shade turfgrasses adapted to the U.S. and southern
Canada are briefly discussed. Reference is also made to more recent research
pertaining to these species. Vermont short-duration growth chamber and
field techniques for evaluating turfgrasses for shade tolerance, together
with results obtained, are briefly presented. Emphasis is placed on
cultivars of Festuca rubra L. and Poa pratensis L., although several other
cool-season turfgrasses are included.

LITERATURE REVIEW

Most turfgrasses will thrive under some degree of shading but few will
tolerate severe light restriction without serious thinning or loss of stand. A
few genera and species have come to be accepted as possessing appreciable
natural shade tolerance. Among the perennial cool-season turfgrasses the most
noteworthy with respect to shade tolerance are Festuca rubra L. (red fescue)
(1, 2, 8, 12, 15, 16) and two of its forms, ssp. commutata Gaud. (Chewings
fescue) (8, 12, 15, 16) and the less known var. heterophylla (Lam.) Mut.
(shade fescue) (7). Festuca arundinacea Schreb. (tall fescue), cultivar Kentucky
31, produced unsatisfactory turf and was inferior to red fescue and other turfgrasses in dense natural shade under Michigan conditions (2) but in Maryland,
under artificial shade, Kentucky 31 was superior (10). In the Michigan tests
Lolium perenne L. (perennial ryegrass) also produced unsatisfactory turf in shade.

Poa trivialis L. (roughstalk bluegrass) is another cool-season perennial
accepted for its shade tolerance (1, 2, 8, 12, 13, 15, 16). Poa nemoralis L.
(wood bluegrass) although adapted to Europe, northeastern United States, and
southeastern Canada, is commonly planted in shade only by European lawn makers (13).
Poa annua L. (annual bluegrass) is considered quite shade-tolerant and able to
survive and produce viable seed under lower light intensity than any other turfgrass grown in northwestern United States (5). Poa compressa L. (Canada bluegrass),
which is described by Musser (12) as growing well in shade, is, like Poa pratensis
L. (Kentucky bluegrass), generally not considered a shade-tolerant species.

Three bentgrasses are commonly used for cool-season perennial turf:
Agrostis tenuis Sibth., Agrostis palustris Huds., and Agrostis canina L. Most
authorities fail to mention shade tolerance as a characteristic of any of these.
Pool (13) lists both A. tenuis and A. stolonifera L. (a species closely related to
A. palustris) as being unsuitable for shade, but does describe A. canina as doing
well in shade. Reid (14) found A. canina to be superior in shade tolerance to
A. palustris, cultivar Metropolitan. Variation in relative shade tolerance has
been shown within species for cultivars of Agrostis palustris (4,9).

A perennial warm-season turfgrass demonstrating considerable shade tolerance is Stenotaphrum secundatum (Walt.) Kuntze (St. Augustine grass) (3, 6, 8, 12, 15, 16, 17). Other perennial warm-season species described as shade tolerant are Zoysia matrella (L.) Merr. (Manila grass) (3, 6, 8, 12, 15, 16, 17); Zoysia japonica Steud. (Japanese lawn grass) (12, 15, 16, 17); Zoysia tenuifolia Willd. 2 x Trin.(Mascarene grass) (15, 16, 17); and Zoysia japonica x Zoysia tenuifolia Willd. 2 x Trin. (Emerald Zoysia) (6, 15, 16, 17). Zoysia japonica cultivar Meyer was found to be generally unsatisfactory when grown under artificial shade (11). Some shade tolerance has been credited to Paspalum notatum Flugge (bahiagrass) (17) but most authorities do not list shade tolerance as a characteristic of this species. Of the other important warm-season perennial grasses grown for turf, Axonopus affinis Chase (carpetgrass), Eremochloa ophiuroides (Munro) Hack. (centipedegrass), and Cynodon spp. (bermudagrass), the Cynodon spp. are considered the poorest for shade sites (12, 15, 16, 17). However one selection of Cynodon spp., No-Mow (FB137), surpassed Stenotaphrum secundatum in shade tolerance and exhibited exceptional tolerance to low light intensity under artificial shading (11).

VERMONT STUDIES TO DETERMINE SHADE TOLERANCE

Much of the success or failure of turf seedings in shade may be determined during the early weeks of development. It is during this time, when endosperm nourishment runs out, that seedlings must use the available light to manufacture food. If seedlings survive this period successfully they may be considered potentially shade-tolerant. Of course, this potential may be eliminated later by disease or other environmental factors. Short-term tests, covering an 8-week period, and utilizing replicated pots of grasses, were used to screen large numbers of turfgrasses rapidly for shade tolerance in the growth chamber and field (18). Because Poa pratensis is the leading turfgrass in most of the United States and because there is a great need among turfgrowers for selections of this species that can tolerate shade, emphasis was placed on evaluating genetic materials of Poa pratensis for shade tolerance. Comparisons with cultivars of Festuca rubra were made because of its known shade tolerance and the need for more shade-tolerant fescues. Eight fescue cultivars and 8 bluegrass cultivars (7 Poa pratensis and 1 Poa trivialis) grown in the growth chamber at four light levels (3,000, 1,500, 500 and 230 ft.-c.) were compared for production of root dry weight (Table 1). The superiority of most of the cultivars of Festuca rubra over those of Poa pratensis was established at the 500 ft.-c. level. At 230 ft.-c., Golfrood red fescue was ranked higher than all of the other turfgrasses, as measured in terms of production of root dry matter. All fescue cultivars, except one, produced significantly more root dry matter at the lowest light level than did the bluegrasses. An explanation for the poor performance of Poa trivialis in the growth chamber was not evident. Dry matter production of tops was compared in the field, under natural deciduous shade, which permitted entrance of approximately 5% of incident sunlight during tree leaf-out. Fifty-seven cultivars of Poa pratensis, 1 Poa compressa, 1 lot of Poa trivialis, 18 cultivars of Festuca rubra, 1 of Festuca ovina var. duriuscula (L.) Koch, 5 of Agrostis tenuis Sibth., 2 of Agrostis palustris Huds., and 1 of Agrostis canina L. were evaluated in this field test.

As in the growth chamber the superiority of Festuca rubra over the other species was evident. Golfrood, the best Festuca rubra cultivar in the growth chamber test, produced over 5 times more tops (turf) dry matter in the field than the lowest Festuca rubra selection, Alaska station. Poa trivialis ranked 5th in the field test and produced significantly more dry matter than 3 of the red fescues and all of the 57 cultivars of Poa pratensis except one, P-7, an experimental selection from New Jersey. All of the Agrostis species did poorly, as did the one cultivar of Festuca ovina var. duriuscula and the Poa compressa.

Table 1: root production by Poa trivialis and cultivars of Poa pratensis and Festuca rubra from seed to eight weeks under four light levels in growth chamber

3,000 ft.-c.		1,500 ft.-c.		500 ft.-c.		230 ft.-c.	
Turfgrass*	Mean dry wt.** per pot (g)	Turfgrass	Mean dry wt. per pot (g)	Turfgrass	Mean dry wt. per pot (g)	Turfgrass	Mean dry wt. per pot (g)
ILLAHEE	2.602 a	CHEWINGS	.974 a	CHEWINGS	.391 a	GOLFROOD	.364 a
JAMESTOWN	2.358 ab	JAMESTOWN	.945 ab	GOLFROOD	.357 ab	PENNLAWN	.291 b
Windsor	2.095 a-c	OLDS	.893 a-c	DOMESTIC	.348 ab	JAMESTOWN	.289 b
GOLFROOD	2.049 bc	Windsor	.881 a-c	PENNLAWN	.329 a-c	CHEWINGS	.284 b
Poa trivialis	1.951 bc	Geary	.875 a-c	ILLAHEE	.323 a-c	OLDS	.284 b
CHEWINGS	1.854 bc	ILLAHEE	.865 a-c	JAMESTOWN	.299 b-d	RAINIER	.263 bc
Prato	1.851 bc	GOLFROOD	.826 a-d	OLDS	.291 b-d	DOMESTIC	.263 bc
PENNLAWN	1.797 c	PENNLAWN	.819 a-d	Geary	.282 b-d	ILLAHEE	.202 cd
Delta	1.782 c	Prato	.784 a-d	Park	.275 b-d	Windsor	.152 de
Geary	1.753 c	Delta	.777 a-d	Prato	.259 cd	Geary	.139 de
Park	1.700 cd	Park	.744 b-e	Delta	.259 cd	Park	.131 e
DOMESTIC	1.666 cd	DOMESTIC	.720 c-f	Poa trivialis	.258 cd	Delta	.122 e
OLDS	1.650 cd	A34	.699 c-f	RAINIER	.258 cd	Prato	.112 e
RAINIER	1.587 cd	Domestic	.629 d-f	A34	.228 d	A34	.104 e
A34	1.311 d	Poa trivialis	.620 d-f	Windsor	.226 d	Domestic	.102 e
Domestic	1.214 d	RAINIER	.535 f	Domestic	.215 d	Poa trivialis	.095 e

285

*Festuca rubra cultivars and selections are given in capitals for identification and to show distribution at various light levels.

**Means within light levels followed by the same letter are not significantly different (0.05 level of probability) by Duncan's multiple range test.

Table 2: turf production by turfgrasses under natural shade from seed to eight weeks at 5% of incident sunlight (Sources shown in brackets, according to key at foot of Table)

Turfgrass	Mean dry wt. per pot* (g)	Turfgrass	Mean dry wt. per pot (g)
Festuca rubra Golfrood	1.449 a	Poa pratensis Windsor	.194 j-q
Festuca rubra Ruby	1.220 ab	" " Prato	.194 j-q
" " Domestic	1.049 bc	" " K-128 (PSU)	.193 j-q
" " N-88 (NK)	.973 b-d	" " Fylking	.192 j-q
Poa trivialis	.781 c-e	" " Pennstar	.183 k-q
Festuca rubra ssp. commutata N2-72 (NK)	.719 c-f	" " K-141 (PSU)	.179 k-q
Festuca rubra Syn. 1-64 (AAES)	.711 c-f	" " K-149 (PSU)	.177 k-q
Festuca rubra ssp. commutata (Chewings)	.693 d-f	" " K-139 (PSU)	.168 k-q
Festuca rubra Duraturf	.642 d-g	" " K-145 (PSU)	.168 k-q
" " N2-71 (NK)	.630 d-h	Poa compressa Domestic	.167 k-q
" " Arctared (AAES)	.620 e-i	Poa pratensis K-135 (PSU)	.167 k-q
" " Illahee	.611 e-i	" " Park	.159 k-q
" " Highlight	.539 e-j	" " K-127 (PSU)	.158 k-q
" " Pennlawn	.533 e-j	" " Troy	.158 k-q
" " Jamestown	.503 e-k	" " Geary	.154 k-q
" " Sioux	.455 e-l	" " Delft	.145 l-q
Poa pratensis P-7 (NJ)	.442 e-m	" " K-124 (PSU)	.145 l-q
Festuca rubra Olds	.424 f-n	" " K-138 (PSU)	.143 l-q
Poa pratensis Beltsville 117 (ARS)	.418 f-o	" " Merion	.135 l-q
" " N1-51 (NK)	.406 f-o	Agrostis tenuis Highland	.133 l-q
" " 412 (AAES)	.400 f-o	Poa pratensis K-122 (PSU)	.125 l-q
Festuca rubra Rainier	.383 f-p	" " K-137 (PSU)	.119 l-q
Poa pratensis P-3 (NJ)	.383 f-p	" " Delta	.118 l-q
" " P-1 (NJ)	.333 g-q	" " K-146 (PSU)	.115 l-q
" " Newport	.315 g-q	" " K-121 (PSU)	.115 l-q
" " Cougar	.292 h-q	" " Nudwarf	.106 l-q
" " K-109 (PSU)	.289 h-q	" " K-107	.105 m-q
Festuca rubra Alaska Station (AAES)	.273 i-q	" " K-125	.097 m-q
Agrostis palustris Seaside	.255 j-q	" " K-106	.094 m-q
Poa pratensis A34 (W)	.255 j-q	" " K-116 (PSU)	.093 m-q
" " P-6 (NJ)	.254 j-q	" " K-126 (PSU)	.093 m-q
" " P-5 (NJ)	.241 j-q	" " K-123	.076 n-q
" " Nugget (AAES)	.236 j-q	" " K-144	.072 o-q
" " Anheuser dwarf	.232 j-q	" " K-108	.070 o-q
" " Belturf (ARS)	.225 j-q	Agrostis palustris Penncross	.069 o-q
" " K-142 (PSU)	.225 j-q	Poa pratensis K-111 (PSU)	.069 o-q
" " K-148 (PSU)	.209 j-q	Festuca ovina var. duriuscula Durahard	.068 o-q
" " K-136 (PSU)	.207 j-q	Poa pratensis K-143 (PSU)	.043 pq
" " K-147 (PSU)	.207 j-q	Agrostis tenuis Holfior	.034 pq
" " Arboretum	.206 j-q	Poa pratensis Domestic	.034 pq
" " K-140 (PSU)	.200 j-q	Agrostis tenuis Exeter	.022 q
" " K-1 (51) (PSU)	.198 j-q	" " Domestic	.021 q
		Agrostis palustris Smaragd	.010 q
		Agrostis canina Kingstown	.010 q

*Means followed by the same letter are not significantly different (0.05 level of probability) by Duncan's multiple range test.

Key to abbreviations in Table 2:

ARS - Agricultural Research Service, Beltsville.
AAES - Alaska Agricultural Experiment Station.
NK   - Northrup, King & Co.
NJ   - New Jersey Agricultural Experiment Station.
PSU - Pennsylvania State University.
W   - Warrens Turf Nursery.

Short-duration growth chamber and field techniques as described were considered feasible methods for conducting preliminary screening evaluations for shade tolerance in turfgrasses. The field technique was found to offer more promise than the growth chamber because of the natural environment and much larger number of grasses that could be evaluated at one time. Details of these experiments are given in the original publication (18).

REFERENCES

1.   BEARD, J.B. (1965) Factors in the adaptation of turfgrasses to shade. Agron. J. 57, 457.

2.   BEARD, J.B. (1967) Shade grasses and maintenance. Proc. 38th Int. Turfgrass Conf. Golf Course Superintendent Association of America, Washington, D.C.

3.   BURTON, G.W., and DEAL, E.E. (1962) Shade studies on southern grasses. Golf Course Reptr. 30, 8, 26.

4.   GASKIN, T. (1964) Growing turfgrass in shade. Park Maintenance, 17, 10, 90.

5.   GOSS, R.L. (1964) The Ecology of Poa annua (annual bluegrass). Proc. 18th Ann. Northwest Turfgrass Conf., Burnsby, British Columbia.

6.   HANSON, A.A. (1965) Grass varieties in the United States. U.S.D.A. Agr. Handbook No. 170.

7.   HITCHCOCK, A.S. (1957) Manual of the Grasses of the United States, 2nd Edn. U.S.D.A. Misc. Publ. No. 200.

8.   HOOVER, M.M., HEIN, M.A., DAYTON, W.A., and ERLANSON, C.O. (1948) The Main grasses for farm and home. In "Grass". U.S.D.A. Yearbook of Agriculture. Washington, D.C.

9.   JUSKA, F.V. (1963) Shade tolerance of bentgrasses. Golf Course Reptr. 31, 2, 28.

10. JUSKA, F.V., HANSON, A.A., and HOVIN, A.W. (1969) Kentucky 31 tall fescue - a shade tolerant turfgrass. Weeds, Trees and Turf 8, 1, 34.

11. McBEE, G.G., and HOLT, E.C. (1966) Shade tolerance studies on bermudagrass and other turfgrasses. Agron. J. 58, 523.

12. MUSSER, H. (1962) Turf Management. McGraw Hill Book Co. Inc., New York.

13. POOL, R.J. (1948) Marching with the grasses. Univ. of Nebraska Press, Lincoln.

14. REID, M.E. (1933) Effect of shade on the growth of velvet bent and Metropolitan creeping bent. Bull. U.S.G.A. Green Sect. 13, 131.

15. SCHERY, R.W. (1961) The Lawn Book. The Macmillan Co. New York, N.Y.

16. WISE, L.N. (1961) The Lawn Book. Bowen Press Inc., Decatur, Ga.

17. WILSON, F. (1961) A comparison of lawn grasses for Florida. Florida agric. Ext. Serv. Circ. 210.

18. WOOD, G.M. (1969) Evaluating turfgrasses for shade tolerance. Agron. J. 61, (in press).

DISCUSSION

SHADE TOLERANCE STUDIES

H. Vos (Netherlands)

What was the natural botanical composition of the grasses under the sugar maples on the site described by Dr. Beard? Was there *Festuca rubra* L.?

J.B. Beard (Michigan, U.S.A.)

A dense upper canopy of 60 cm diameter sugar maples (*Acer* spp.) was present as well as an understory of small dense shrubs. The soil was covered with an 8 cm thick mantle of dead, partially decomposed deciduous leaves. I should like to ask Dr. Wood about his data showing the growth of Seaside bent (*Agrostis palustris* Huds.) to be superior to that of Kingstown velvet bent (*Agrostis canina* L.) The limited literature available indicates that *Agrostis canina* is superior. Do you attribute the responses observed in your data to difference in species or cultivar?

G.M. Wood (Vermont, U.S.A.)

The Kingstown cultivar of *Agrostis canina* was the only cultivar tested and so I cannot comment on other cultivars of this species.

P. Boeker (West Germany)

How often was it necessary to mow turf in the shade in comparison with turf in full sunshine?

J.B. Beard (Michigan, U.S.A.)

We mowed once a week at 6 cm, which was higher than the normal mowing height for the grasses we were using.

G.M. Wood (Vermont, U.S.A.)

In my work mowing was not necessary in the studies which only lasted for 8 weeks from seeding. Where the grasses were grown for 1 year, mowing at 3 in. (7.5 cm) was necessary at intervals of approximately 2 weeks during periods when there was no tree leaf canopy. Mowing intensity was related to the amount of light received by the plots, and intervals between mowing were longer when there was a full leaf canopy.

R.E. Engel (New Jersey, U.S.A.)

There is a definite need to classify micro-climates in shade studies. Great differences in shade environments exist and data will appear to conflict unless there is information on these differences.

Since shading reduces the root system and no irrigation was used in Dr. Beard's study, is it possible that the turfgrasses, with their roots in the top 1½ in. (4 cm) suffered serious drought injury?

J.B. Beard (Michigan, U.S.A.)

No tree root pruning was done on the experimental area discussed in the paper other than the removal of surface roots to permit soil preparation and seeding. The root system of the turfgrass species used in the experiments was substantially reduced due to the minimal light intensity and associated deficiency in carbohydrates. Moisture stress was evident at times during the study but was not the major cause of differences in persistence of various turfgrass species under the shade conditions. The lack of disease-resistant cultivars and a more favourable microclimate for disease were the primary limiting factors.

A.R. Woolhouse (Steward, S.T.R.I.,U.K.)

Did Dr. Wood make any attempt to adjust the red-far red balance in his growth chambers to be comparable to that in natural shade?

G.M. Wood (Vermont, U.S.A.)

No attempt was made to modify light quality in the growth chamber. Cool white fluorescent and incandescent light was used as recommended by the manufacturer of the growth chamber, and excellent grass growth was obtained at the highest light intensity. This subject and possible modification of light quality is discussed in my article, "Evaluating turfgrasses for shade tolerance," which appeared in the May-June 1969 issue of the Agronomy Journal.

SESSION 3C: WATER AND IRRIGATION

(Chairman: Ir. G. J. Ruychaver)

RELATIONSHIPS BETWEEN TURFGRASS AND SOIL UNDER IRRIGATION

John H. Madison,

Associate Professor of Environmental Horticulture, Department of Environmental
Horticulture, University of California, Davis, California, U.S.A.

SUMMARY

Fine particles largely determine capillary characteristics of mixed
soils. In thin turf soils with compacted surfaces and underlying drainage
layers, water wets the profile under capillary tension, then saturates from
the interface. A perched water table remains after drainage. When elevations change, low spots become the "bottom" from which tension heads are
measured, and where outflow occurs. Tension heads at higher elevations prevent soil saturation and reduce available water, which is used while low
areas remain saturated by water moving in the profile. Uniform growing
conditions do not obtain. Amendments can increase available water at
higher elevations to increase uniformity of growing conditions.

Golf, bowling and tennis greens, football fields, cricket pitches and such
play areas usually have several common soil profile characteristics. First:
either the root zone has been amended and modified, or the area is underlain
with cinders or drain rock so an interface with a perched water table is usually
present. Secondly, the surface is compacted. As a result infiltration through
the surface is less than the conductivity through the root zone. Discussion in
this paper will be limited to soil characterized by this interface and compacted
surface.

This paper first reviews a paper on soil modification by Bodman and
Constantin that is not as generally well known as it should be; and, secondly,
reviews the process of water entry into the soil, its behaviour at an interface,
and its drainage from the soil.

The paper of Bodman and Constantin (2) provides basic principles to anyone
contemplating soil modification. The paper gives excellent curves for compact-
ability of mixes at various water contents; for water release from compacted and
uncompacted mixes; and for frequency distribution of pores of various sizes.
It describes work with particles of two sizes, done first with glass beads and
sand, then extended to soils. Certain assumptions are made: that all mixtures
are thoroughly compacted; that the particles in each phase are uniform; that
mixing does not alter particle characteristics; that phases differ in size by at
least an order of magnitude; and so on. Each phase consists of solid particles
and voids. Considering only solid particles, the experimental condition consists
of taking one unit volume of solid matter and varying its composition from 100%
of the coarse particle phase, through all combinations, to 100% of the fine phase.
This is illustrated in Figure 1a. The question is to know the amount of voids
(pore space, porosity) associated with the mixed phases at each point.

The mixture can first be considered theoretically, using Figure 1 b. With
100% coarse particles, the total volume can be defined as $(1 + V_c)$, consisting of
the solid volume (1) plus the volume of voids (V_c). If the volume of solids is
decreased by 5% (or 10%, etc.) the void and total volume is also decreased by 5%.
If the 5% of coarse particles is now replaced by 5% of fine particles, the fine
particles sift down into the voids between the coarse particles. The solid volume is brought back to the original amount (1) without changing the total volume,

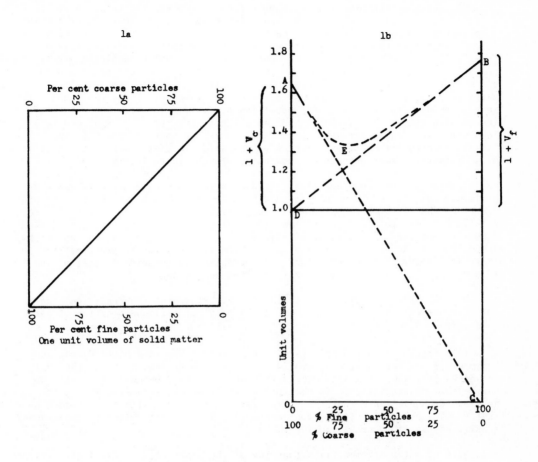

Figure 1: solid and void space with mixtures of two particle sizes

    1a. Unit solid space divided between various mixtures of coarse
        and fine particles

    1b. Line AC shows initial direction of change in void space with decreas-
        ing proportion of coarse particles, and BD the same for fine
        particles: the point E shows the theoretical (at intersection) and
        practical (on curve) point of minimum void volume (After Bodman and
        Constantin)

which remains at 5% less. On this basis we can draw the line AC indicating the theoretical direction total volume will take as coarse particles are replaced with fine particles.

Beginning at the other end with 100% fine particles, the total volume is $(1 + V_f)$, unity plus voids among the fine particles. Taking away 10% of the solid also removes 10% of the voids and the volume is decreased 10%. Adding back 10% coarse particles, the coarse particles fit into the matrix of fine. They add their solid volume back to the mix. But because the coarse particles are surrounded by fine and do not touch they do not contribute to the void space and the void space remains reduced by 10%. Hence as composition changes from 100% fine particles, the total volume begins to follow the line BD. These two lines intersect at point E and this is the composition of minimum volume. When theory is tested with mixtures of uniform sand and uniform glass beads or sand and soil the theoretical curve is essentially realised except that the point of intersection is smeared into a curve. Extent of deviation is affected by lack of uniformity of particle size and shape, and failure to obtain perfect mixing.

This work shows that additions of sand to soil decrease porosity and make a mixture less suited to plant growth unless we add so much sand that it is about 85-90% of the mixture. It also shows that pores in sand become rapidly filled with relatively small additions of silt and clay, a percentage that many washed sands already contain. This is widely known from experience, but the author has found that if the above theoretical discussion is presented to practical horticulturists, many of them understand and appreciate the problem of soil mixing to a degree that far surpasses their previous understanding.

Without soil compaction the above does not represent the conditions that obtain. However, where compaction is not a problem, soil modification is not likely to be needed or attempted.

Infiltration into the soil is characterized in Figure 2 after Bodman and Coleman (1). Entering water is moved under capillary tension and as the soil is wetted it reaches a moisture condition about halfway between the moisture equivalent and saturation. In the special soils under discussion it may be assumed for convenience that the soil layer is 35 cm deep with an interface at that depth. When the wetting front meets the interface the water is still under tension and fails to cross the interface.

Rate of water movement is a function of the distance, the tension difference over that distance, and the area cross-section of the conducting channels. Conduction is along paths where water is already present. When paths are thin layers of tightly held water, cross sectional areas are small and movement is slow. Principal water movement is in capillary channels. At the drainage interface where soil contacts sand, cinders, or other coarse materials, capillary channels are relatively infrequent and movement is along thin surface layers and is essentially nil so long as there is any tension in the upper soil layer. Only after tensions are satisfied and a pressure head exists do capillary menisci become convex. The water flows from the soil to the drainage layers. As soon as there is no longer a head and tension exists, capillary menisci become concave and movement into the drainage layer ceases. A perched water table remains at the interface with the tension on the soil water approximately zero at the interface. Golf superintendents have complained of poor greens drainage for generations without appreciating that thin soil layers above drainage materials tend to remain near saturation. Appreciation of the problem has resulted largely from repeated exposure of turf audiences to the movie prepared by W.H. Gardner of the University of Washington entitled "How Water Moves in the Soil" (3).

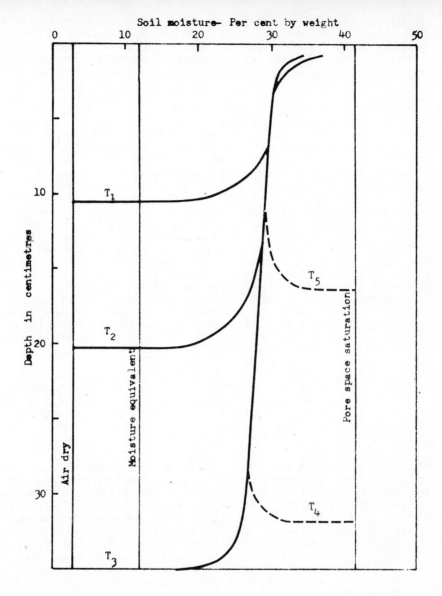

Figure 2:   soil wetting with time (soil wets at tensions between the moisture
equivalent and saturation: under putting green conditions with a
drainage interface, wetting to saturation occurs from the interface back to the surface)   (After Bodman and Coleman)

To return to the wetting front, when water reaches the interface, it does not move across but remains in the soil layer and the soil layer continues to fill from the bottom up. The compacted layer at the surface promotes this behaviour. At some point before the soil is completely saturated, tension due to gravity balances the remaining capillary tension and drainage begins.

The above describes wetting of soils in a laboratory column. It also describes wetting of a tennis or bowling green. On a putting green, however, there are contours. How do changes in elevation affect this picture? The question was raised in the author's mind by the early turf worker J.D. Wilson (6). He studied soil moisture by means of soil points, ceramic cones which were dried, inserted into the soil for one hour then weighed to determine the amount of water they had taken up. He always got low values on hillsides, even after long gentle rains that produced no runoff. This raised a question. On a soil 30 cm deep which changes elevation 100 cm across a 10 m green, is the tension on the soil water at the high point 30 cm of water or is it 130 cm of water? It is the latter. Having determined that, water movement into a contoured green can be described. Figure 3 illustrates four cases. In 3a, stabilised soil is placed over a subgrade of low permeability. With precipitation, wetting begins as described. By the time the wetting front reaches the interface, water movement has begun to develop a lateral component in response to the tension gradient (5). The wetted but unsaturated soil begins to wet from the lower corner. At some point the gravity head is greater than the residual tension in the soil at end B, and water begins to flow from the soil at end A. In time a steady state condition develops depending on soil conductivity and precipitation rate (5). Outflow develops at the lower end of the grade, the upper end remains unsaturated and precipitation continues to enter under tension.

This condition has been observed in greens where outflow from the surface begins after about 5 minutes of sprinkler irrigation. By the time outflow stops, tension has removed most of the available water from the high spots. In the low area grass grows in soil that is always saturated, at the high end in soil that is never saturated. In other instances, outflow has developed a pressure head sufficient to lift sod at the low end. The effect was of an artesian well.

Figure 3b illustrates the same situation but with drain rock and tile. A similar pattern develops except that outflow is from the bottom; a lesser volume becomes saturated at the lower end; and most of the soil is under some tension at all times, even during precipitation. In as much as the same pattern of flow would result if there were only tile with no drain rock the question may be asked "Does improved aeration result from use of drain rock?" Because of compaction and settling dust, the mean pore size of the surface soil is smaller. It often happens that the surface millimetre contains no noncapillary pores, and remains saturated at capillary tensions equal or greater than those developing between irrigations. If the surface is thus sealed by a saturated layer, drain rock could serve to aerate the soil.

Figure 3c shows conditions with a sand filter over rock. If this represents a level tennis green, there are two possibilities. If the green has a compacted surface with only capillary pores, the filter bed will remain saturated following irrigation and will remain saturated until airflow channels develop (4). In this instance the rootzone will be sandwiched between two saturated layers, the surface millimetre and the filter, and so the drain rock is of no value as a source of air. If the soil is of stabilised particles that maintain a degree of porosity in the surface, air will enter, the filter bed will drain, and aeration from the filter bed will be possible but will not be needed. If the area is sloped the condition will be as in Figure 3b with the filter bed saturated at the low spot, but drained at higher elevations because of tensions due to gravity.

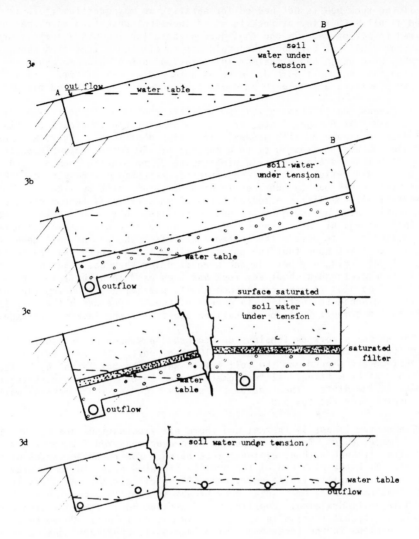

Figure 3: moisture conditions in greens which change elevation

3a. When the green is underlain with layers of low conductivity, precipitation results in a steady state condition with saturation and outflow at low elevations, and tension at high elevations

3b. With drainage below, outflow is into the drain

3c. On level greens, rootzones may lie between saturated surface and filter layers, so filter bed does not promote aeration

3d. Frequent small drains can replace drainage layers

If the rock bed is not needed for aeration we may question if it is needed at all. Four in. of rock is an engineering convention which has been elevated to scripture. On one roof garden where loading was a serious problem, the author could not persuade the engineers to eliminate rock even though the soil they were using had a maximum infiltration rate of 0.25 mm/hour. At the same time the engineers were draining an acre and a half of turf with a 2% fall and were providing a single 10 cm drain to remove all anticipated run-off.

In greens construction a maximum infiltration rate of about 4 cm per hour is desirable. At a higher rate, greens are susceptible to drought. This can be handled as in Figure 3d with greens either sloped or level. No rock is needed but drains should be from 60 cm to a maximum of 150 cm on centres because of the shallow layer drained. Drain pipe can be 27 mm plastic (nominal 3/4 in. - US) with one consideration. In new construction, settling may result in back flow. Debris will settle out in subsided lengths of tile. With subsidence of 30 mm a 100 mm tile will be little effected but a 27 mm drain will become clogged. Hence while small drains are adequate to handle the flow they should have a good positive fall throughout their length. It is also well to use a sheet of plastic under the modified soil to divide the rootzone soil from the parent soil beneath, as there is the likelihood that the parent soil will contribute tension to the surface layer during dry periods and keep it drier than was planned. At present, plastic tube drainage without any rock has been used in a sufficient number of turfed roof gardens to give confidence in its performance. During the coming year it is planned to instal it in greens of the 3a type where the soil is stabilised, and meets USGA specifications except for the lack of drainage.

The author's work on tensions due to grade has been conducted in a box, 500 cm long, 10 cm wide and containing 10 cm of soil. The soil is prepared, the tensiometers placed and the soil wetted while the box is in the horizontal position. After wetting, all tensiometers read zero. As one end is jacked up, response is immediate. The tensiometer at the high end reads tension while water drains from the low end.

The system is not isothermal and there are fluctuations due to the diurnal wave of temperature. To date responses have been measured for sands and silty loam soils with and without drainage rock below. The response varies with the material. With the high end of the profile elevated about 100 cm medium sand begins to lose capillary continuity near 100 mb of tension. As a result some of the tensiometers become isolated by breaks in capillary continuity while the low end is still draining. Equilibrium of tension head with elevation occurs in about 72 hours, but tension in the upper end may go to over 600 mb before any tension develops in the lower end. With loam soil, capillary continuity is preserved through the soil profile and tensions reach values corresponding to their elevation head in about 72 hours.

To date only drying cycles have been measured, but the apparatus is being prepared to measure tensions under wetting cycles as well.

The foregoing has two principal implications. The first is that grass is not grown under uniform conditions on contoured greens. The second is that present research could lead to modifying soils to reduce such differences.

On contoured greens there are apt to be areas of grass growing in soil that is continually saturated. Grass in other areas grows on soil that is perhaps never saturated. It is a familiar fact that high spots are dry spots. Over the years this has been attributed principally to "exposure to drying winds" and secondly to surface run-off from high areas that increases wetting of other areas.

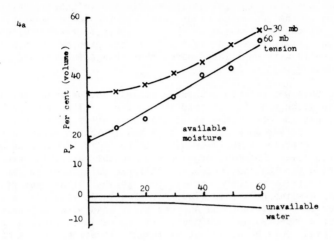

4a

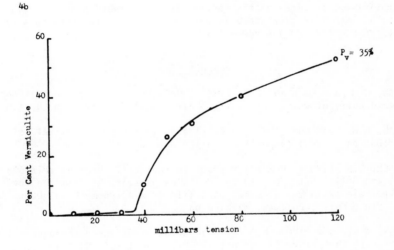

4b

Figure 4: Antioch river sand modified with expanded vermiculite

4a. Available water at 0-30 and 60 centibars tension with various percentages of vermiculite, and unavailable water left at PWP

4b. Amount of vermiculite needed in sand to give equal amounts of available water starting from different soil water tensions

(Data from work supported by funds from Turfgrass Adaptive Research Programme, Northern California)

With water stress on the high spots, these are often areas that suffer loss of grass during temperature extremes in both winter and summer. Low saturated spots also suffer and are often initial points of disease infection. With uniform soil, tension of the saturated areas cannot be reduced without killing turf on high areas, nor can the tension on the high spots be lowered without drowning grass on low spots. To provide relief from this problem it is necessary to construct greens soils with capillary spaces that change in size and number with changes in elevation.

One approach to this would be to set grade stakes, add an amendment at a depth proportional to grade and till it into the rootzone. The amendment would be added at rates to provide equal amounts of available water at all elevations. Of materials that could be added, work at Florida has indicated expanded vermiculite and colloidal phosphate as suitable minerals to increase water-holding capacity of sand-based soils. Of many organic and mineral materials which have been examined, expanded vermiculite increases available soil water to the greatest extent. Other properties militate against its use, but it has nevertheless been chosen to illustrate the points in Figure 4. Figure 4a illustrates increased availability of water in a mixture of an Antioch river sand with increasing amounts of expanded vermiculite added as an amendment. In Figure 4b is plotted the percent vermiculite that would be needed at different elevations so the mixture would have 35 volume per cent of available moisture at equilibrium with gravity following irrigation.

Successful applications of the theory presented would provide turfgrass managers with freedom to grow grass in a range of irrigation intervals of their choice; a freedom they do not now enjoy.

REFERENCES

1. BODMAN, G.B., and COLEMAN, E.A. (1943) Moisture and energy conditions during downward entry of water into soils. Proc. Soil Sci. Soc. Am. 8, 116.

2. BODMAN, G.B., and CONSTANTIN, G.K. (1965) Influence of particle size distribution in soil compaction. Hilgardia 36, 15, 567.

3. GARDNER, W.H. (1968) How water moves in the soil. Reprint reissued from Crops and Soils, Oct. Nov. 1962. Contains photographs from the movie which is available as 16 mm. 27 min. sound film from Agronomy Club, Dept. Agron., Wash. State Univ., Pullman, Washington.

4. NELSON, W.L., and BAVER, L.D. (1940) Movement of water through soil in relation to the nature of the pores. Proc. Soil Sci. Soc. Am. 5, 69.

5. WHISLER, F.D. (1969) Analyzing steady-state flow with an electric analogue. Soil Sci. Soc. Proc. 33, 19.

6. WILSON, J.D. (1927) The measurement and interpretation of the water supplying power of the soil with special reference to lawn grasses and some other plants. Pl. Physiol. 2, 386.

PREVENTION AND CONTROL OF DESICCATION ON GOLF GREENS

J.R. Watson,

Director of Marketing, Toro Manufacturing Corporation, Minneapolis, Minnesota, 55420, U.S.A.

SUMMARY

Golf greens are subject to varying degrees of mechanical and physiological winter injury. Damage may result from desiccation, disease, low temperature, and under certain conditions, suffocation, traffic and heaving. Desiccation and disease, alone and in combination, are probably responsible for more damage to golf greens in the high middle latitudes than any other natural phenomenon. Disease may be controlled and to a large extent prevented by the properly timed application of an appropriate fungicide. Desiccation occurs primarily on high, exposed and windswept areas of greens. In some cases the soil may not contain adequate supplies of moisture prior to freezing and in many cases soil moisture is lost by sublimation during the winter months. In either case, desiccation is especially critical when the soil has a low moisture content or when it is partially or completely frozen and temperature in the microclimate is high enough to stimulate growth activity (respiration and transpiration). Studies were initiated in the fall of 1958 at the Toro Research and Development Center to investigate the effectiveness of various covers to prevent desiccation. Since that time a number of materials have been tested. They include various thicknesses and colours of polyethylene, saran shade cloth, excelsior, wood fibres, wood pulp, fibreglass and polyester fibres. Most have been effective in preventing desiccation and in stimulating early uniform growth. In addition, many have proved to be of value in the establishment of late fall and early spring plantings.

INTRODUCTION

In the late fall, winter and early spring, golf greens may be damaged by one or more types of mechanical or physiological injury. The degree of injury will vary from year to year and is dependent, in part, on the vagaries of weather. In some years, if climatic and environmental conditions are good, little, if any, damage may occur. In other years, only slight variation in one or more macro-climatic or micro-climatic factors may cause severe winter injury. The uncertainty involved in predicting weather and the certainty of damage during adverse winters would seem to dictate the importance of using preventive measures when possible.

A brief review of the major types of winter injury may be worthwhile as a basis for establishing the role of desiccation and the importance of preventive techniques.

TYPES OF WINTER INJURY

1. Mechanical

Mechanical injury to established greens most often results from traffic on frosted or partially frozen grass. This may directly damage the grass either by causing cellular rupture or by attrition. Indirect damage to turf, often at a later date, may be due to the increase in soil compaction resulting from traffic on partially frozen soil (17 & 18).

Heaving, a second form of mechanical damage, may injure immature, late planted or poorly established seedlings. It is seldom a factor on established turf.

Mechanical damage from traffic may be prevented by controlling, eliminating, or diverting play. When this cannot be done, budgets must be adjusted to provide for corrective measures.

Heaving may be prevented by planting at an earlier date - 4 to 6 weeks before the first killing frost - and by careful seedbed preparation. When heaving does occur, a light early rolling may save some of the plants.

2. Physiological

Physiological damage suffered by turfgrass during this period is usually referred to as "winter kill". Most such injury is the result of desiccation, disease or low temperatures (3, 5, 6, 7, 10, 15). Under certain conditions oxygen suffocation, toxic accumulations under ice sheets and leaching of vital cellular constituents may also cause winter injury (3 & 6).

(a) Disease

Winter disease on putting greens is caused primarily by _Fusarium nivale_ (Fr.) Ces., _Typhula itoana_ Imai, and an unidentified low temperature basidiomycete (10 & 13). Damage from snow mould is particularly severe in years when snow accumulates and remains prior to the soil freezing up. Fungicides are available for use in preventing disease development. If used properly and at the correct time, they are effective (9 & 14). Lebeau (9) presents data to show that temperature regulation in combination with the application of fungicides will practically ensure protection against psychrophylic pathogens. Winter disease may be especially devastating when it occurs in combination with desiccation.

(b) Low temperature kill

Species, cultivar, winter hardiness and tissue hydration are factors influencing the severity of direct low temperature kill (2, 4 & 12). For any single species the frost killing temperature varies within a wide range and depends upon the degree or state of hardiness obtaining at any given time. Fluctuating temperatures in late winter and early spring are often damaging, because of the stimulation of growth when temperature is high with resultant damage if it drops rapidly or if it remains low for extended periods. Beard (2) attributes this increased susceptibility to a higher minimum temperature to an increase in tissue, especially crown, hydration under such conditions.

Low temperature kill may be modified by certain cultural techniques, including late fall watering to insure an adequate soil supply prior to freeze up, proper fertilization and an increase in height of cut. Hanson and Juska (8) and Powell et al (11) have shown that late fall fertilization is effective for the development and growth of root systems. These studies were conducted in Maryland and Virginia. Both states have a moderate winter climate, hence the results may not apply in those areas with more severe winters. An increase in height of cut in the fall with its attendant increase in carbohydrate production and storage may result in a deeper root system and will provide more cover or insulation for crown tissue.

302

(c) Desiccation

The greatest degree of injury from desiccation seems to occur in late winter and early spring. Greens affected most are those located on high and exposed sites subject to excessive wind movement. In years when snow cover is light, desiccation is particularly damaging. Damage from desiccation is more prevalent in the sub-humid, semi-arid areas of the upper middle latitudes. For example, in the North American continent the Plains States and the Prairie Provinces of Canada usually experience most winter kill of this type. However, winter kill from desiccation is by no means confined to these areas. From year to year damage may occur in all sections of Canada and the United States other than the Gulf Coast and the south-west.

In the cool, cold, sub-humid and semi-arid climates where winter play does not occur, golf course superintendents employ several techniques to prevent desiccation. Snow is an excellent insulator and if it can be trapped or held on the green, damage from desiccation will be minimized. Strategic placement of snow fences and brush piled on the green are effective techniques for trapping snow. Various types of organic mulches are sometimes placed on greens. These provide insulation and conserve moisture as well as preventing sublimation. In some cases, water is hauled to the greens in tanks. Application of relatively small amounts of water at a critical period of stress is most effective. This technique may be used in areas when limited or restricted winter play is permitted.

INVESTIGATIONS ON PREVENTING DESICCATION

The techniques just described pointed to the need for procedures and materials to prevent desiccation. Studies were initiated in 1958 at the Toro Research and Development Center to investigate the effectiveness of various materials (15). Since that date a number of products have been tested and used at different locations (1, 16, & 18). Many have proved to be of value as protective agents, but the microclimate created under the blankets is highly conducive to development of snow mould and therefore preventive treatments are essential if covers or blankets are to be used.

The studies have clearly shown the value of protective covers as a safeguard against desiccation. Most of them stimulate early uniform growth which, if properly maintained, will permit play at an earlier date. The uniformity of growth may be attributed to the insulating as well as the moisture retention properties of the products.

Clear 4 mil polyethylene (Polyfilm: Dow Chemical trade name) was one of the first materials tested. It was compared with a black 5 cm polyethylene blanket insulated with wood fibres (Cell-U-Mat: Conwed trade name). Thermocouples were installed at soil depths of 5, 10 and 15 cm, and at 7.5 and 15 cm above the soil surface. Little variation occurred in the temperatures recorded at the three depths until approximately mid-March. Temperatures of the unprotected plots reached a minimum of $-16^{\circ}C$ at the 5 cm level on 5 January. On that date, temperatures at the 5 cm level were $-12^{\circ}C$ under the Polyfilm and $-8^{\circ}C$ under Cell-U-Mat. Atmospheric temperatures of $-21^{\circ}C$ were recorded at the 5 cm level and $-23^{\circ}C$ at the 15 cm level on the same date.

Both materials were effective in preventing desiccation when temperatures were above freezing. Substantial amounts of water condensed each night on the soil side of the Polyfilm.

Since the early test, various colours and thicknesses of polyethylene and blankets of excelsior, fibreglass, processed wood pulp, polyester fibres and saran shade cloth have been evaluated. Comments on these different materials are made below.

1.   Polyethylene

Differences in thickness and density of polyethylenes made no appreciable difference to their "greenhouse" qualities. The major consideration is that of sufficient strength to withstand heavy stress (high wind) conditions and the tracking of animals. Four and six mil low density and two mil high density materials all met satisfactorily the requirements of sufficient strength.

Colour difference was more pronounced. Clear and green were comparable in their effect on amount and colour of growth. Red produced about the same amount of growth as the other two, but the grass colour was more chlorotic, indicating either a reduction in intensity of transmitted light, or absorption or reflection of a part of the spectrum critical to chlorophyll synthesis. Opaque white covers produced substantially slower growth. When greening did occur (some two weeks later than under the clear film) colour and general appearance were excellent. The slower growth was caused by the high reflectivity and low transmissibility of the material, which reduced the energy transmission.

The major disadvantages associated with the use of polyethylene are the difficulty of holding it in place and the maintenance of the grass when the covers are removed.

2.   Wood fibres & pulps

These materials, such as Precision Pak, (American Excelsior Trademark), an excelsior blanket, and several experimental blankets from Conwed Corporation, are effective in preventing desiccation and in modifying temperature fluctuations. They are of an open mesh nature and are easy to hold in place. The strength of the pulp blankets depends on the chemical binder used. Some require very close spacing of staples to avoid tear.

3.   Synthetic fibres

These products - Famcomat (American Air Filter Corporation Trademark) a fibreglass blanket; Viskon Aire (Chicopee Mills Trademark) a polyester fibre; and Lumite (Chicopee Mills Trademark) a saran shade cloth - provide protection against desiccation, and they all stimulate early growth, but not to an equal degree. Like the wood fibres, these open mesh materials do not cause the excessive heat build-up in late winter and early spring that polyethylene does. Also, they are easy to hold in place and are not subject to displacement by high wind. The saran shade cloth, irrespective of colour or density, is easier to handle and to hold in place than is polyethylene.

Like polyethylene, however, these materials will not trap or hold light snow; wind blows it off very easily. Thus, during years when snowfall is light or absent, the degree of protection provided is a function of the density and to an extent the colour. Under the conditions studied, saran cloths providing 36% and 64% shade are too open and are not effective against desiccation. The condition of the turf is similar to, and in some cases, worse than that on unprotected plots. Complete (100%) shade cloth in blue and in tan was effective in 1967-68 (a year with heavy snow cover) but ineffective in 1964-65 (a year of light snow cover).

TECHNIQUES FOR SUCCESSFUL USE OF PROTECTIVE MATERIALS

Time of placement of the covers is critical. Generally the blankets should not be put down until the grass is "hardened off" and has gone dormant, in late November or early December. Favourable results have been obtained by later placement in February, but there is the possibility of damage prior to this time if snow cover is light.

Time of removal in the spring is also critical. When covers are removed too soon, early growth stimulation does not take place. When they are left on too long, excessive growth will result and temperatures may reach levels high enough to either scald or burn the tall grass. In addition, maintenance is more difficult if the putting green grass is permitted to grow to an abnormal height.

The micro-environment created under the blankets and covers is highly conducive to disease development, especially activity of snow mould. Thus when covers are used it is mandatory that the greens be treated with a fungicide prior to their placement.

Maintenance practices after removal of the covers are essentially the same as for unprotected areas. There are two possible exceptions. Additional fertilizer to replace the nutrients removed by the accelerated growth may be required, and special care must be taken to avoid removing too much leaf growth at the first mowing.

Despite the fact that there are certain problems associated with use of the covers and blankets, results amply justify their application and use wherever winter kill, especially desiccation, periodically damages or destroys turf on golf greens.

The principles of protection and growth stimulation offer interesting possibilities in other areas. They have been used successfully to protect late fall and early spring plantings and may be used to stimulate early growth in nurseries and related facilities.

REFERENCES

1. BALTENSPERGER, A.A. (1961) Prolonged winter greenness of Bermudagrass by use of plastic covers and electric soil warming. Pub., Department of Agronomy, University of Arizona.

2. BEARD, J.B. (1964 a) Effects of ice, snow and water covers on Kentucky bluegrass, annual bluegrass and creeping bentgrass. Crop. Sci. 4, 638.

3. BEARD, J.B. (1964 b) Causal agents in winter injury of turfgrass and their relative importance. Agron. Abstr.

4. BEARD, J.B. (1966 a) Direct low temperature injury of nineteen turfgrasses. Michigan agric. Exp. Stn. Quart. Bull. 48, 3, 377.

5. BEARD, J.B. (1964 b) Winter injury. The Golf Superintendent, 34, 1, 1.

6. FERGUSON, M.H. (1964) Physiological mechanisms of winter injury to plants. Agron. Abstr.

7. GILBERT, W.E. (1965) Winter injury to Tifgreen - history and present status. Golf Course Reptr. 33, 7, 12.

8. HANSON, A.A., and JUSKA, F.V. (1961) Winter root activity in Kentucky bluegrass (Poa pratensis L.). Agron. J. 53, 372.

9. LEBEAU, J.G. (1964 a) Control of snow mould by regulating winter soil temperature. Phytopathology, 54, 6, 693.

10. LEBEAU, J.G. (1964 b) Pathology of winter - injured turfgrass. Agron. Abstr.

11. POWELL, A.J., BLASER, R.E., and SCHMIDT, R.E. (1967) Agron. J. 59, 529.

12. SIMINOVITCH, D. (1964) Winter hardiness in crop plants. Greenhouse, Garden, Grass (Plant Research Institute) 4, 4, -.

13. WATSON, J.R. (1956) Snow mould control. Golfdom 30, 10, -.

14. WATSON, J.R., and KOLB, J.L. (1956) Control of snow mould. Golf Course Reptr. 24, 7, -.

15. WATSON, J.R., KROLL, H., and WICKLUND, L. (1960) Protecting golf greens against winter kill. Golf Course Reptr. 28, 7, -.

16. WATSON, J.R., and WICKLUND, L. (1962) Plastic covers protect greens from winter damage. Golf Course Reptr. 30, 7, -.

17. WATSON, J.R. (1964) Methods of minimizing winter damage. Agron. Abstr.

18. WATSON, J.R. (1969) Winter protection of greens. Proc. 20th Ann. RCGA National Turfgrass Conf., Montreal, Quebec.

EFFICIENCY IN IRRIGATION

Wayne C. Morgan,

Kellogg Supply Inc. Wilmington, California, U.S.A.

SUMMARY

The various factors determining irrigation efficiency are discussed briefly. Examples are given of how tensiometers can be used to guide or control irrigation, and comparisons are made of water use and cost before and after the installation of tensiometers.

INTRODUCTION

Throughout the world, irrigation is the most important management practice in the culture of turfgrasses, yet most authorities will agree it is the one most often abused. As a chain is no stronger than its weakest link, experience and research have shown that efficiency in irrigation can only be realized when attention is paid to complete management programming. Principal factors to be considered in complete management programming for irrigation include frequency and duration of water application, reducing water run-off, uniform distribution of water from sprinklers, minimizing the detrimental effects of soil compaction by mechanical aerification, vertical mowing for thatch control, and the use of surfactants (soil pentrants) on hydrophobic soils.

FREQUENCY AND DURATION OF WATER APPLICATION

Field trials using tensiometers as a guide for determining the frequency and duration of water applications have shown the value of these instruments for this purpose, although their use is limited if there is neglect of the other factors in complete management programming for irrigation. If tensiometers are installed at two depths, the upper one can indicate how long irrigation frequency may be delayed and the lower one when the sprinklers should be run longer to replenish the water reservoir at the lower soil-root zone depths.

Special protective boxes have been designed so that tensiometers can be installed horizontally beneath the soil surface, avoiding interference with turf use and maintenance.

Tensiometers may be connected to automatic sprinkler controls or used as indicators of when and how to set the automatic controls. When they are used to override the automatic controllers, sprinklers will only be allowed to operate when the tensiometers signal that water is needed at one or other soil depth, according to pre-scheduled settings.

Results from several tests have shown that not only can stronger turf with deeper roots and less disease potential be produced, but savings of 40% - 80% in water use and costs have been achieved. These tests are described below.

EXAMPLES OF SUCCESSFUL USE OF TENSIOMETERS

One example of a successful tensiometer installation on a golf green (not attached to an automatic timing device) is at Whittier Narrows Golf Course

(owned by Los Angeles County Parks Department). Instruments were installed
at 2 in. and 5 in. depths in early June (5 cm and 13 cm). Before the tests
began, irrigation was scheduled for 15 minutes nightly. For the first seven
days after the tensiometers were installed, no water was applied to the green.
Frequency of irrigation for the remainder of June and July varied from one to
six day intervals. Length of irrigation varied from hand watering to five to
15 minutes.

A completely automatic tensiometer-controlled irrigation system was established near Sproul Hall on the campus of the University of California at
Los Angeles. Two tensiometers were installed in a location typical of the area,
one at a depth of 3 in. and the other at 8 in. (7.5 cm and 20 cm). The system
is regulated so that when either tensiometer indicates that water is needed,
the sprinklers operate at a predetermined time. Originally the sprinklers were
scheduled to run for two 15 minute periods during the night. When a sprinkler
can test was conducted, it was noticed that run-off water flowed into a surface
drain for some time after a fifteen minute watering. The controller was then
changed to allow only two seven minute waterings per night, whenever needed.

The number of irrigations is determined by the tensiometer which activates
the controller. The second irrigation will be applied only if insufficient
water has been applied to infiltrate to the desired soil depth.

The weather in September and October was extremely variable as there were
2 in. of rain over the three day period of 16 - 18 September, and five consecutive
days of temperatures over 100^{0}F (38^{0}C) starting 25 September. This was followed
by some cool, overcast periods. The irrigation frequencies and length of
irrigation varied according to different climatic conditions during this time, as
they have since the tests began. During March, problems with the controller arose
which caused excessive amounts of water to be applied.

A system similar to that at U.C.L.A. was installed on a Seaside bentgrass
golf green at the Deauville Country Club in Tarzana, California. Tensiometers
were placed at 2 in and 6 in. (5 cm and 15 cm) depths on the edge of this green.
When irrigation was needed, water was applied for 10 minutes each hour, until
enough water had been applied to reach to the depth of the tensiometer signal-
ling for water.

Information available from regular visits made to the green during the test
by the author and that supplied by the course superintendent showed that irrigation frequency in March, April and May varied from seven day intervals to daily
watering when temperatures rose above 38^{0}C. Length of irrigations varied from
10 minutes to 40 minutes.

The tensiometer installation at the Whittier Narrows Golf Club illustrated
how tensiometers can be beneficial even without completely controlled irrigation.
June and July irrigations according to previous practice would have resulted in
915 minutes or 83,265 gallons (ca. 380,000 1) of water being applied. (The
gallonage calculations are arrived at by multiplying the manufacturer's specified
output for the sprinklers by the number of sprinklers). With tensiometers as a
guide for scheduling frequency and duration of irrigation, only 160 minutes or
14,560 gallons (66,000 1) of water were applied. This is an 83% reduction in
water use. If a cost is assumed of $0.25 per 100 cubic feet (750 gallons: 3,400 1)
(these are the costs prevailing at a Southern California community and will be
used for illustration, although it is known that water costs may vary greatly)
the water costs from the normal practice on the green for the two months of June

308

and July would have been $22.80. With tensiometers being used, it was only $4.85.

Prior to the trials at U.C.L.A., irrigations were scheduled twice a week (15 minutes each setting) during the cool months (November to June) and three times a week from June to October. According to the manufacturer's specifications, output from the sprinklers covering the test area is 145 gallons (ca. 660 l) per minute at the pressure used. For the four months September to December, this means 630 minutes or 91,350 gallons (415,000 l) of water would have been applied; at the illustration costs described this would have cost $30.45. Under the completely automatic tensiometer-controlled system, only 270 minutes or 39,150 gallons (180,000 l) were applied, at a cost of $13.05. This represents about a 57% reduction in water use.

The information available for the irrigation on Green No. 4 at the Deauville Country Club from March to May is significant. Prior to this installation the watering schedule for the green had been approximately 35 minutes every other night. However, in cases of extreme heat and during the summer, water was applied every night with supplemental syringing during the day. At 35 minutes every other night, for the period mentioned, 26.5 hours of irrigation would have been applied. This represents 95,400 gallons of water at an approximate cost of $31.80, using the same illustration costs. Under the tensiometer-controlled system, only 16 hours or 57,600 gallons of water were used at a cost of $19.26. This means about a 40% reduction in water use (430,000 and 260,000 l).

The figures at Deauville become even more significant when it is realised that the tensiometers have since been changed to start irrigation at drier readings. The superintendent at Deauville has reported that after the first 5 to 6 weeks of completely automatic tensiometer-controlled irrigation, there had been a definite reduction of about 75 to 80% in hand watering required on this green in comparison to other nearby greens.

REDUCING WATER RUN-OFF

Water run-off can be reduced by the use of soil amendments which will allow better water penetration into and infiltration through soils. This has been shown from work done at the University of California, Riverside, and from trials at Forest Lawn Memorial Park, Hollywood Hills. Another method proving of considerable advantage is repeat cycling of water regulated by automatic controllers, such as the application of five minutes of water each hour throughout a given period.

UNIFORM DISTRIBUTION OF WATER FROM SPRINKLERS

Prabably the most universal problem facing turfgrass managers is the poor uniformity of water application from sprinklers. Sprinkler can tests show how this can be improved. By charting the water distribution in relation to where the sprinklers are located, determinations can then be made as to where correction must be made.

AERATION AND THATCH CONTROL

Trials have shown that mechanical aeration of turfgrass soils can significantly reduce irrigation requirements of turfgrasses besides developing deeper root systems. In one trial there was a 48% reduction in the number of irrigations required and 56% less water had to be applied. In one instance, deep aerification (3/4 in. diameter holes, on 4 in. centres, to a depth of 8 in.) done by hand with the holes backfilled with different soil mixes, resulted in the restoration of bentgrass golf and bowling greens that had been removed from use and were scheduled for rebuilding.

Programmes for removal and control of thatch by vertical mowing can be of substantial benefit in the irrigation management of turfgrasses. Efforts directed towards accomplishing this have shown how improved entry of water, and possibly oxygen also, into soils resulted in deeper rooting, and reduced irrigation requirements in both frequency and direction. Water-repellant soils are encountered throughout the world. Many demonstrations have shown how surfactants (soil penetrants) can often increase water movement through soils.

REFERENCES

1. MORGAN, W.C. (1962) Observations on turfgrass aeration and vertical mowing. California Turfgrass Culture, April.

2. MORGAN, W.C. (1964) Summer aeration helps turf growth. California Turfgrass Culture, July.

3. MORGAN, W.C. (1964) Sprinkler tests can help you. California Turfgrass Culture, October.

4. MORGAN, W.C., LETEY, J., and STOLZY, L.H. (1965) Turfgrass renovation by deep aerification. Agron. J. $\underline{57}$, 494.

5. MORGAN, W.C., and MARSH, A.W. (1965) Turfgrass irrigation by tensiometer-controlled system. California Agriculture, November.

REACTION OF TURFGRASSES TO WATERING

W. Skirde,

Rasenforschungsstelle, Institut für Grünlandwirtschaft und Futterbau,
Justus Liebig Universität, Giessen, West Germany.

SUMMARY

Watering turfgrasses has resulted in different reactions by various species and varieties. Although watering in dry periods improved the appearance of many grasses, there were varieties which were unaffected and others with special water requirements. Watering given sufficiently regularly during the whole summer to produce a fresh green appearance, caused in most grasses a strong invasion by shallow-rooting species. Marked differences were apparent among species and varieties; fodder types and types not well suited for turf were particularly susceptible to weed invasion.

Regular watering in drought reduces, in some important grasses, root mass and root penetration into deep soil layers, and causes in all grasses a loosened sward in autumn, apparent from the reduced weight of material in the sward. The content of water-soluble carbohydrate in the roots of all grasses was significantly higher under watering, but the above-ground parts showed little or no difference between watered and unwatered plots. The quantity of roots and sward material generally gave a good balance in the carbohydrate complex. Poa pratensis, Cynosurus cristatus and Lolium perenne showed over-compensation in favour of the unwatered plots.

It is concluded that watering should only be done to keep the sward alive, but not to the extent of trying to create a perfect appearance.

INTRODUCTION AND EXPERIMENTAL PROCEDURES

On the trial ground of the Turfgrass Research Station at Giessen (190 m above sea-level) the annual mean temperature is $8.5^{\circ}C$ and the average rainfall 620 mm a year. The long-term average monthly temperatures reach in July a maximum of $17.9^{\circ}C$ and a minimum in January of $\pm 0^{\circ}C$. The temperature in summer can reach 32 $-35^{\circ}C$ whereas temperatures in winter from -15° to $- 20^{\circ}C$ are not unusual.

The long-term average rainfall shows an even spread, although the months of June, July, August and December have a rather higher rainfall and especially February and March have comparatively little rain. In winter the precipitation is mostly as rain: the number of snowy days is on average low (5 to 10).

This weather pattern, with 8 - 10 rainy days per month, each giving 4 - 6 mm per day, and with good after-effects from winter moisture, should make turfgrass culture possible without additional watering. But Figure 1 shows that the weather in each year deviates considerably from the long-term mean, and there may be many periods without enough precipitation. This happened in 1967 in April, June and July, whereas in 1968 it was May which showed a rainfall deficit. Moreover, the benefit of natural precipitation is reduced by short heavy thunderstorms, when part of the rain runs off the soil surface (May 1967), or on the other hand when there is a large number of rainy days with only 0.2 - 3.0 mm per day (May 1968).

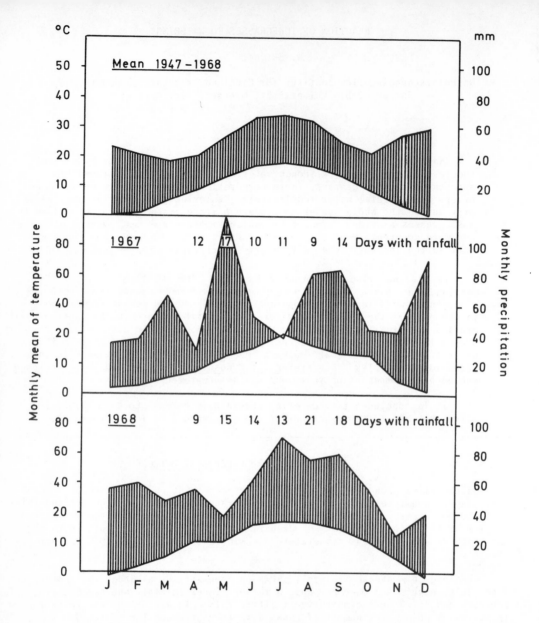

Figure 1:   climate of Giessen

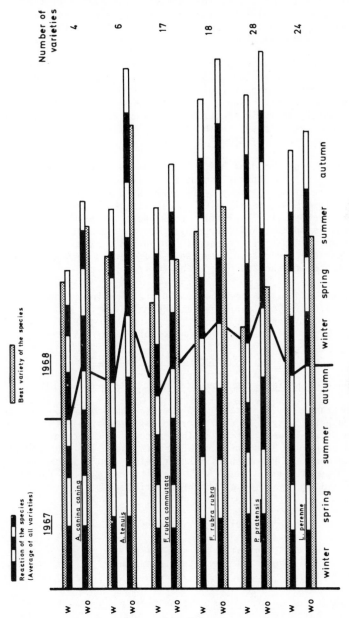

Figure 2: appearance of turfgrasses with (w) and without (wo) watering

Then the monthly rainfall amount of 30 - 40 mm, if it falls on soil previously dried out, will not be effective enough due to high temperature and wind evaporation, In such conditions an additional water supply is important to improve the appearance and to preserve the vitality of the grasses under extreme conditions. This leads to the question, how will the different turfgrass species and varieties react to watering, and what secondary effects will arise from giving adequate watering in dry periods with high temperatures and low humidity, because the watering only changes the water content of the soil.

The following results were obtained from the Giessen Collection of the world's turfgrasses (which includes 140 different varieties and selections), grown both in plots watered according to need and in plots not watered. The need for watering was assessed visually from the appearance of the grasses. To maintain a satisfactory sward in the trial year 1967 eight waterings were needed and in 1968 three waterings; in the long dry periods these were done every week, to provide 30 mm.

The experimental field of 3,200 sq m lies on a south-facing slope, so that a difference of soil conditions cannot be excluded. The non-watered plot is the upper part of the area, on stony heavy loamy sand that dries out easily, whereas the irrigated lower part is situated on alluvial soil and is naturally moister than the region above it. Therefore, when there is insufficient rainfall, extreme drought symptoms show very rapidly on the unwatered plot of a variety, while on the watered plot it is the aim to obtain a sward that shows the best possible appearance and colour. The soil differences between the watered and non-watered plots are checked by special control plots.

The following data are derived from plots sown in 1966 and regularly observed in 1967 and 1968, representing the main species and varieties of interest in west and central Europe. The plots were given 50 kg/ha N four times a year and a single spring dose of 50 kg/ha of PK fertiliser.

RESULTS AND DISCUSSION

(a) Appearance of turfgrasses, and differences between varieties

The appearance of the turfgrasses was ascertained by monthly observation, having regard particularly to dead sward constituents, but the colour intensity and invasion of weeds were not taken into account. The results of observations are recorded in Figure 2 as total values, with the short and long horizontal bars denoting good and bad results respectively. The diagram shows for the watered ("w") and the unwatered ("wo") plots the mean value for all varieties of a species and the reaction of the best variety.

The results can be summarised as follows:-

1. Of the six species, Agrostis canina L. ssp. canina and Festuca rubra L. ssp. commutata Gaud. showed the best turf appearance, in both the watered and the unwatered plots.

2. The varieties of Lolium perenne L. on average showed the smallest effect of watering. Agrostis tenuis Sibth., on the other hand, showed the greatest contrast between watered and unwatered plots, because without supplementary watering all varieties showed extraordinary damage under dry conditions, and showed a widespread discolouration that in the dry year 1967 covered up to 60% of the whole area; the effect of the long period of abnormal weather could be clearly seen to some extent even where watering was given.

314

3. Among the other species <u>Agrostis</u> <u>canina</u> <u>canina</u>, <u>Festuca</u> <u>rubra</u> <u>commutata</u> and <u>Poa</u> <u>pratensis</u> L. showed no marked differences between watered and unwatered plots, although differences were present.

4. Between the reaction of species to watering and the performance of the best varieties there is good correlation.

5. The difference between the average of all varieties of one species and the score for the best variety shows important differences in the quality of varieties. These differences are smaller in the real turfgrasses (<u>Agrostis</u> <u>canina</u> <u>canina</u>, <u>A</u>. <u>tenuis</u>, <u>Festuca</u> <u>rubra</u> <u>commutata</u>) than in the species that include fodder varieties as well as turf varieties (<u>Poa</u> <u>pratensis</u>, <u>Festuca</u> <u>rubra</u> L. ssp. <u>rubra</u>). Of course, even in the real turfgrasses, especially <u>Festuca</u> <u>rubra</u> <u>commutata</u>, there are also differences present.

It is not the purpose of this paper to describe the reaction of all the tested varieties of grass to watering and their behaviour during dry periods; reports of such investigations are given in the "Results and information on varieties" in the Giessen periodical "Rasen und Rasengräser". This paper, therefore, only deals with some special points that have arisen in the main turfgrasses and in pasture types of <u>Lolium</u> <u>perenne</u>. But consideration must be given separately to the immediate effects of watering in dry periods and to its long-term effect. The following varieties, even during the abnormal dry conditions of 1967, showed little or no reaction to watering:-

<u>Festuca rubra</u>	<u>Poa pratensis</u>
Oasis	Merion
Sceempter	St. 1000
HF1	Rocznovska
Bargena	
Novorubra	<u>Lolium perenne</u>
Agio	S23
Reptans	Kent
Sioux	
Golfrood	
St. 2000	

But at the end of the whole experimental period, there was a changed picture which includes the effects of watering.

<u>Festuca rubra</u>	<u>Lolium perenne</u>
Sceempter	Sceempter
Rasengold	NFG
Sioux	Combi
St. 2000	RvP pasture type
	S23
<u>Poa pratensis</u>	Kent
Prato	
St. 1000	
Rocznovska	

On the other hand, other varieties showed a special need for watering. This could be clearly seen in most fodder varieties of <u>Poa</u> <u>pratensis</u>: all varieties of <u>Agrostis</u> <u>tenuis</u>, <u>Cynosurus</u> <u>cristatus</u> L. and <u>Phleum</u> <u>pratense</u> L. (pasture type): and particularly on <u>Festuca</u> <u>rubra</u> Brabantia, <u>Poa</u> <u>pratensis</u> Baron and <u>Agrostis</u> <u>tenuis</u> Tracenta. There were other differences, but not so striking.

<u>Table 1</u>: effect of watering on weed population in the sward

Species	Variety	Weeds as percentage of the sward (22 October 1968)	
		With watering	Without watering
<u>Agrostis tenuis</u>	Tracenta	+	1
	Brabantia	+	1
	Holfior	2	1
	Bore	1	1
	Eko	1	1
	Highland Bent	3	1
<u>Festuca rubra</u> <u>commutata</u>	Highlight	4	0
	Barfalla	2	1
	Brabantia	3	+
	Golfrood	3	2
	Chewings	12	4
<u>F. ovina var.</u> <u>duriuscula</u>	Biljart	25	1
<u>F. rubra rubra</u>	Oasis	6	2
	Novorubra	9	9
	HF1	7	12
	Agio	17	20
	Commercial seed	55	40
<u>Poa pratensis</u>	Merion	5	2
	Baron	6	4
	Sydsport	2	1
	Arista	12	4
	Newport	45	17
	Commercial seed	87	52
<u>Lolium perenne</u>	Barenza	11	3
	Pelo	16	8
	RvP	10	3
	S 23	40	7
	Hay type	55	37
<u>Cynosurus</u> <u>cristatus</u>	Rocznovska	6	4
	Credo	4	2
	Commercial seed	17	14

+   Weeds present, but less than 1%

(b) Weed invasion

Although the temporary effect of watering during dry periods is to improve the appearance of grasses, their colour and their density, the consequences of additional watering must give rise to concern, unless extreme drought is likely to cause the death of the grass sward. This concern is based on the fact that a more or less optimum water supply during unchanging weather conditions not only forces the growth of plants to a point at which the sward comes naturally to a resting condition, but also it changes the soil structure and soil environment, through the permanent high soil water content and the continued beating of water drops, often large.

A good indicator of the changed growth conditions caused by watering is the weed invasion (weed population in % ground cover). As shown in Table 1 the weed invasion was, after two years, always greater among the plots that received watering than among those that did not, with the exception of three varieties of Festuca rubra rubra. There were, however, great differences between varieties in the amount of weed invasion. The outstanding turfgrass varieties showed under watering a very low weed invasion compared with varieties of less density or of greater susceptibility to diseases, or compared with commercial seed. The increase of weed population in the varieties with healthy and dense stands was always much less than in bad material. In the same way the differences between the species are noteworthy, as weed population shows up the density or lack of density in the sward.

The weed population (consisting mainly of Poa trivialis L., P. annua L., and Cerastium vulgatum L.) indicates that watering turf to the extent necessary to create and maintain an ideal turf appearance with adequate moisture, will promote the invasion of shallow-rooting aggressive weeds. Even the best grasses cannot completely oppose the competition induced by these changed conditions due to watering: many of them, even under frequent watering, are seriously endangered. Among them, Festuca ovina var. duriuscula (L.) Koch Biljart, which in the unwatered plots was almost free from weeds in spite of its poor appearance, was with watering invaded by weeds to the extent of 25% ground cover.

(c) Helminthosporium infestation on Poa pratensis

It is well known that there is a relationship between the type and moisture of the soil on one hand and susceptibility to disease on the other. In the watering trials at Giessen this was chiefly manifested on Poa pratensis but it was really clearly seen for the first time in winter 1968/69. This fact may be connected with the extraordinary weather pattern of the year 1968, that was characterised by dry periods in spring and heavy precipitation in mid-summer and early autumn. This meant that the soil of watered plots was almost continuously saturated from spring until winter, due at first to supplementary watering in April and May and then to the natural rain that began to fall very frequently from the end of July. Under these conditions there were extensive symptoms of infestation of Helminthosporium spp. on all varieties under watering, except on Merion, whereas in the preceding year such symptoms had only been seen on Sydsport, Arista and on the commercial seed plot. Also, the average of the tested varieties in the year 1967/68 did not show significant differences (Table 2).

(d) Roots

The formation and production of roots has long been a favourite subject of investigation both to elucidate particular problems of plant growth and for general physiological interest. The effect of water is to prevent the growth of roots if the soil water content is high; while a low water content will promote root growth.

317

Table 2: effect of watering on Helminthosporium infestation in Poa pratensis

| | % dead plants in the sward | | | |
| | 1967/68 | | 1968/69 | |
Variety	with watering	without watering	with watering	without watering
Merion	12	12	3	3
Baron	22	22	15	10
Sydsport	40	37	35	27
Arista	52	47	75	60
Newport	37	40	50	37
Commercial seed	80	77	75	65
Average of 28 varieties	51	50	55	44

318

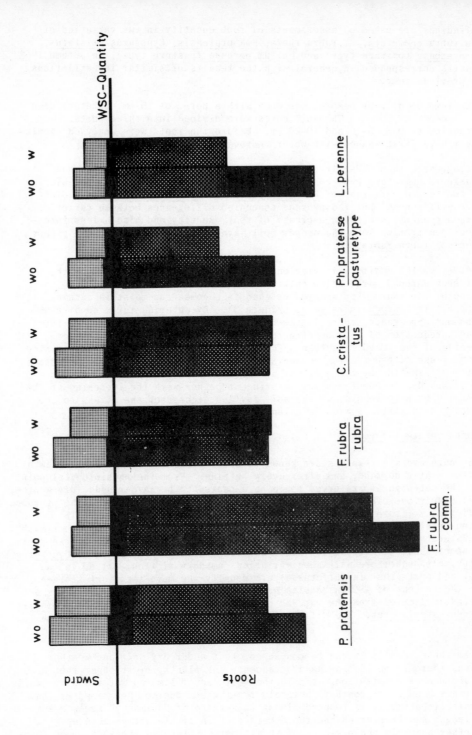

Figure 3: amounts of sward, roots and water-soluble carbohydrates (WSC) with (w) and without (wo) watering (dry matter g/175 sq cm)

These findings are based on assessments of root quantity in two varieties of
Festuca rubra commutata, F. rubra rubra, Poa pratensis, Cynosurus cristatus,
Phleum pratense (pasture type) and Lolium perenne (pasture type), in autumn 1968.
The results corresponded in general with the results of similar investigations
in the previous year.

The removal of root samples was done with a borer of 15 cm diameter, down
to a soil depth of 20 cm. The soil cores were divided into three parts,
corresponding to 0-5, 5-10 and 10-20 cm. Before the roots were analysed chemically they were first washed with water thoroughly.

It appeared that under irrigation Lolium perenne, Phleum pratense and
Festuca rubra commutata have considerably reduced amount of roots. The average
of the two tested varieties of F. rubra rubra and Cynosurus cristatus did not
indicate differences, but the average concealed differences between varieties.
There is a connection between decrease of root quantity and also a less intensive root penetration into the deeper soil layers of 5-10 and 10-20 cm, except
with Festuca rubra rubra.

Moreover, the additional water on all grasses led to a decrease in the
bulk of above-ground parts below cutting level. This reduction is due to the
loosening of the sward when watered or when it becomes too moist in autumn. It
was greatest in Festuca rubra rubra (Figure 3). By watering turf, to give an
ideal summer appearance, there is the risk of causing a decrease of root formation and a reduction of root penetration by the various grasses, which leads to
a loosening of the sward in autumn. The reduction of root quantity accompanied
by the decrease of penetration, especially into the deeper soil layers, reduces
the water utilization by the grasses; at the same time the reduction in above-
ground growth due to supplementary watering, together with the loosening of the
sward caused by waterlogging on the soil surface, increases the stress on the
turfgrass and facilitates weed invasion.

(e) Carbohydrate reserves

The carbohydrate reserves are known to be of great importance for regrowth,
both after winter dormancy and after every cutting. From the physiological point
of view the carbohydrate reserves could be expected to be larger under dry weather
and soil conditions, that permit only a limited plant growth, than in the presence
of sufficient moisture, when there is intensive growth of the plants. The
following results, however, do not agree with what has been said about root mass
in the literature. The content of water-soluble carbohydrates (WSC) in the roots
of all species was clearly higher under watering, with the exception of Cynosurus
cristatus, although there were some variations among varieties. Also, in the
above-ground parts that in turfgrasses are usually the more important storage
organs, the content of WSC in samples harvested from the unwatered plots was not
as high as in samples from the watered plots, with the exception of Poa pratensis
and Cynosurus cristatus. The differences, however, were very small, as shown in
Table 3.

From these results it can be concluded, that under dry soil and weather
conditions there is on the one hand a tendency for plants, by stronger root
growth and deeper penetration, to make the best use of limited water supply: while
on the other hand leaf growth is severely restricted, due to lack of water, and
photosynthetic activity is reduced almost to a state of "dormancy" because some
of the leaves had been dried and the others contain little active chlorophyll.
On the other hand, in the presence of sufficient moisture in the soil, root formation is not increased much, but leaf growth is promoted, with a big demand on
carbohydrate reserves. This would lead to a decrease of WSC-content if the

Table 3: effect of watering on carbohydrate reserves

| Species and Variety | % water soluble carbohydrates | | | | Quantity (g) of WSC in org. matter | |
| | Roots | | Sward | | | |
	with watering	without watering	with watering	without watering	with watering	without watering
Poa pratensis						
Merion	7.75	10.55	11.88	11.80	6.43	8.68
·Sydsport	7.90	5.42	6.12	8.42	5.14	6.10
St. 1000	10.25	6.20	8.92	10.07	7.41	6.12
Festuca rubra commutata						
Highlight	5.17	3.62	8.07	8.87	4.75	4.06
Brabantia	4.05	3.67	9.00	8.32	4.57	4.95
Festuca rubra rubra						
Sceempter	7.05	5.50	12.25	11.37	5.70	5.26
Novorubra	7.15	6.20	11.40	9.12	5.45	5.24
Cynosurus cristatus						
Credo	2.15	3.00	13.85	12.70	3.01	4.43
Rocznovska	1.90	2.67	9.92	12.32	2.71	3.54
Phleum pratense						
King	5.25	5.87	17.37	13.95	4.19	5.27
Sceempter	11.00	4.92	13.90	16.00	5.13	3.94
Lolium perenne						
Perma	4.62	2.37	14.12	9.37	2.98	2.76
Barenza	3.45	2.62	12.50	9.62	2.55	3.27

conditions for growth brought about by watering did not at the same time allow continuous photosynthetic activity, that raises again the level of carbohydrates.

If the total storage of reserve nutrients is taken into account - both the above-ground parts and the root mass - then it can be seen that the total carbohydrates are quite well balanced between "watered" and "unwatered" while there is even in Poa pratensis, Cynosurus cristatus and Lolium perenne an overcompensation in favour of the unwatered grasses (Figure 2). Thus in this pattern the roots can be considered firstly as a waterpump and secondly as a storage depot in conjunction with the above-ground parts below cutting level.

CONCLUSIONS

Although watering clearly improves the appearance of most turfgrasses in dry periods, excessive watering intended to guarantee a satisfactory green colour throughout the summer brings about undesirable after-effects and side-effects. Not only is there an invasion of shallow-rooting weeds, that become very aggressive in the permanently moist top soil, but there is also a marked decrease in root mass and root penetration into deeper soil, so that water up-take is impaired. On the other hand, in long dry periods, if no water is given, the percentage of WSC in the carbohydrate reserve complex decreases. Within the whole carbohydrate reserve complex, (consisting of the above-ground parts below cutting level and the underground parts, which develop into a large mass of organic material under dry conditions), there is an adjustment whereby even in Poa pratensis, Cynosurus cristatus and Lolium perenne there is a higher total of carbohydrates because of the mass of organic material and the WSC content.

From these results it can be concluded that in turfgrass culture in regions with continental weather patterns it is wrong in long dry periods to try to achieve an ideal turf appearance during the whole summer by frequent addition-al watering. It seems advisable to give water to swards which are in danger, but not advisable to water swards that are in good health. Nothing should be done to break the temporary physiological "dormancy" shown by grasses as a natural reaction to unfavourable conditions. To allow a poor appearance occasion-ally in this way will be compensated by a better general quality of the sward.

THE "PURR-WICK" ROOTZONE SYSTEM FOR

COMPACTED TURF AREAS

W. H. Daniel,

Purdue University, Lafayette, Indiana, U.S.A.

SUMMARY

A brief review is made of the various construction methods for turf areas receiving heavy use. The Purr-wick system is described, consisting of independently drained reservoir units, constructed over plastic sheeting in terraces to fit the contours. Advantages and disadvantages are listed.

There is more than one way to build a house, but a good house must do certain things. If the roof leaks, if the plumbing doesn't drain, if there is nowhere for storage it can be a poor house.

Turf rootzones can also be built in more than one way. A good rootzone for turf must do certain things - rapidly absorb water, have ample drainage, store nutrients and moisture, and anchor the turf for the use intended.

There are 10 ways to build, some good, some bad.

1. top soil on top soil, or -

2. top soil over fill subsoil (in both of these, compaction soon destroys structure at the surface).

3. as above, with sand and peat in the top 10-20 cm, to counter compaction.

4. as above, with field tile drainage and soil backfilling (not fast draining enough).

5. as above, but with fine gravel above tiles (faster drainage).

6. tiles under gravel under sand under a mix made offsite, after a preliminary laboratory test, of 75% sand, 15% peat and 10% soil by volume (U.S.G.A. method).

7. shallow rootzone method: plastic drains in a narrow trench, filled in with sand; layer of sand spread overall; peat added, with little if any soil; firmed and planted.

8. plastic under deeper sand; no reservoir pool, just zero tension.

9. Purr-Wick system of plastic in level steps.

10. Purr-Wick system with automatic float control subsurface irrigation.

System 7 is economical and simple to build. Excellent progress has been made with it. The Purr-Wick system is quite new, being first tested in 1966. The principles of the system can be adapted to serve sports grounds, golf tees and greens, roof and park gardens, planter boxes and other special uses.

The first part of the name "Purr-Wick" stands for the following points:-

P - Plastic (an impervious layer laid in level steps to follow the contours).

U - Under fine or medium size sands, forming a -

R - Reservoir, to conserve water for the -

R - Rootzone.

The "Wick" refers to the system's use of capillary action at low soil moisture tensions, or can be said to stand for "water in constant supply".

Construction

The system can be constructed above any firm subgrade with vertical outer edges, graded to the desired contours as a series of level steps. First, an impermeable underlayer of plastic is laid down, in 2 layers as a folded sheet, with the fold of one inserted into the split edge of another for sealing. The plastic layers should be shaped to match the surface design, in flat steps as needed. A stadium could all be one level, if the crown is less than 15 cm. A 10 cm ledge is needed before each step down to give uniform water reserves in each step.

For drainage above the underlay, 5 cm plastic pipes, with narrow slits in them, are laid and covered with sand coarser than the openings to make a filter. A seal must be made where each pipe is led through the vertical edge of the plastic. An adjustable outlet is made, to drain and regulate the water reserve. A removeable plug at the end of the pipe allows for complete drainage. An upturned T-piece provides a drain level for the regular water reserve. An upward extension of the outlet will provide a higher level if required.

In preparing the rootzone above the plastic, it is necessary to ensure filter action by putting coarser particles around drains. Then, to ensure wick action, fill with 30-50 cm of medium to fine sand (the finer 20% determines the action: particles above 0.4 mm do little work). A sieve (mechanical) analysis can define the depth needed. The sand must be kept moist while it is compacted. To make the users' surface (the top 3-4 cm) add peat or micas, using little or no soil and mixing into the sand. Finally, add nutrients, compact and plant.

Advantages of the Purr-Wick system

1. It gives maximum infiltration, and allows aerification through the users' surface into clean sand.

2. It allows specific construction standards, in ample detail.

3. It uses bulk raw materials, all work being done on site.

4. It can be made in wet weather.

5. Work can be done in fast sequence.

6. It gives the manager absolute water control.

7. It allows long periods between irrigation.

8. It stores nutrients as dilute solutions.

9. It conserves water to the maximum.

10. It gives uniformly moist playing conditions at all times.

Disadvantages

1. The system requires exact planning, and cautious and careful installation with the correct equipment (e.g. belts or a light wide-tread bulldozer to get sand on to plastic and over pipes).

2. It restricts modifications and some uses (e.g. no stakes into plastic).

3. It is different from conventional systems, e.g. there is no soil.

WINTER DESICCATION

D.T.A. Aldrich (U.K.)

Could Dr. Watson please comment on the use of irrigation in the autumn as a means of avoiding winter desiccation.

J.R. Watson (Minnesota, U.S.A.)

Moisture content should be adequate if possible (i.e. half to complete available water capacity). Moisture content must, however, relate to depth of roots, as they are frequently only 2.5 to 7.5 cm in depth. Moisture is easily removed from this soil layer by drying winds.

J.E. Howland (Nevada, U.S.A.)

In Ohio we had sod of Poa pratensis L. 1 in. (2.5 cm) thick on top of 6 in. (15 cm) of Portland Cement concrete and observed no desiccation injury in winter during 4 years with $-12^{\circ}C$ temperatures. The turf was fully exposed to sun with no protection from wind. Can Dr. Watson comment?

J.R. Watson (Minnesota, U.S.A.)

Climatic conditions in Ohio are substantially different from those in Minnesota. Ohio is further south, has higher temperatures, and has more protection from trees, compared with the open plains. Winter desiccation is a factor where rainfall is low (75 cm or less), there is no snow cover, the site is exposed to high wind movement, and soil temperatures are very low (frost depth of 1-2 m when there is no snow).

J.B. Beard (Michigan, U.S.A.)

We have studied winter protection and desiccation in growth chambers, and hope to develop covers to give protection against frost and wind.

SOILS CONSTRUCTED OVER PLASTIC SHEET FOR WATER REGULATION

V.I. Stewart (U.K.)

Can Dr. Daniel tell me the particle size of the dominant fine sand fraction (the finer 20%) which controls wick action in his sand mix?

W.H. Daniel (Indiana, U.S.A.)

Less than 20% of the finer fraction of sand seems to control the capillary action. Most sands are washed and this process, together with the source, determine the characteristics of the fine fraction.

J.A. Simmons (Ohio, U.S.A.)

What is the desired spacing of the plastic pipe supplying the water for the wick action described by Dr. Daniel?

W.H. Daniel (Indiana, U.S.A.)

A distance of 20 ft. (6 m) between pipes is adequate, provided there is time for gradual lateral movement of water.

R.E. Engel (New Jersey, U.S.A.)

What is the annual increment of roots in the sand rootzone medium?

W.H. Daniel (Indiana, U.S.A.)

The experiment has been in progress for 3 years. Most roots have accumulated in the top 2-3 in. (5-7 cm) but root depth has been the same in the two years in which we have measured it.

L.E. Janson (Sweden)

Some problems may arise with plastic sheeting permanently installed in the ground. During winter, when the ground surface is cooled down, there is a thermal moisture transfer from below, up to the soil surface. Under an imperm-eable layer like a plastic sheet, we would get an accumulation of water in the soil. If the soil is frost susceptible there is a risk of frost heaving processes. Has Dr. Daniel any observations on this subject?

W.H. Daniel (Indiana, U.S.A.)

There is no evidence of frost pushing up the plastic underlay, but this might occur if there were an extremely deep frost. Frost usually only penetrates 10-20 in. (25-50 cm), not below the depth of the plastic.

J.H. Madison (California, U.S.A.)

Dr. Janson's question is answered in the literature of highway research. In the winter thermally transferred water will condense on the underside of the impervious layer of concrete. Unless drainage is provided as a layer of rock, the concrete ends up floating on an unstable boggy layer. The same could happen on your athletic field if there were no drainage. At the end of winter the field could be floating on an unstable sub-layer.

TENSIOMETERS

P.E. Rieke (Michigan, U.S.A.)

Dr. Madison and Mr. Morgan have mentioned the use of tensiometers for determining irrigation requirements. Would they comment on the practical use of tensiometers on turf, particularly on sandy soils such as U.S.G.A. greens.

J.H. Madison (California, U.S.A.)

Tensiometers are good research and teaching instruments of high reliability in the range of 0-700 mb tension, which is in the range we use. As a practical control for irrigation there are problems with maintenance and in obtaining readings truly representative of the area. If the practical man reads and maintains the tensiometer daily he will soon learn that he can read the grass as well as he can read the instrument and will in time abandon use of the instrument.

W.C. Morgan (California, U.S.A.)

Tensiometers are only useful if there is a good distribution of water by the irrigation system. I use them for teaching greenkeepers water management.

D.C. Legg (Steward, S.T.R.I.,U.K.)

What are the best tensiometers?

W.C. Morgan (California, U.S.A.)

We use the Airometer. There are new ones made at Santa Barbara, which can be stuck into the ground, but I do not like these so much.

SESSION 4A: NEMATODES AND INSECTS

(Chairman: Mr. J.R. Escritt)

THE NEMATODE PARASITES OF WARM-SEASON TURFGRASSES

V. G. Perry,
Professor of Nematology,

&

G. C. Horn,
Professor of Ornamental Horticulture and Turf,

University of Florida, Gainesville, Florida, U.S.A.

SUMMARY

Zoysiagrass, fine textured bermudagrass, centipedegrass, St. August-inegrass and bahiagrass are severely affected by several types of plant parasitic nematodes. The severity and incidence of nematode diseases affect these grasses in the order given above, with zoysiagrass and bermudagrass being most damaged. Nematodes such as sting, lance, stubby-root, pseudo root-knot, root-knot, spiral, ring, and others damage warm-season grasses in this order. In a few cases other parasites such as cyst and root lesion nematodes bring about severe damage in localized areas and to certain grasses. General symptoms include abbreviated or shallow root systems, root necrosis and discoloration, paleness or chlorosis of foliage, sparseness of shoots, and failure to recover from the effects of winter, drought, etc. Control by chemical means is practiced in the southeastern United States. The nematicide DBCP (dibromochloropropane) has been used for the past 15 years with good results and is still the major chemical used for nematode control in home lawns and other non-commercial areas. Recently the organophosphates, Sarolex and Dasanit, have become standard nematicides for use on golf courses and other commercial areas.

INTRODUCTION

Shortly after World War II citizens of the United States found more time to devote to recreational activities and thus more efforts were expended to produce high quality turf. In Florida the numbers of golf courses expanded rapidly and this expansion is still evident today. More and more tourists began to visit Florida during the spring and summer; thus it became desirable to operate the golf courses on a twelve-month basis. Some of the fine textured bermudagrass varieties (Cynodon spp.) were introduced, obtained from the U.S. Department of Agriculture breeding programme at Tifton, Georgia, and golf course superintendents began to use them on golf greens. Many problems developed, especially during the warmer seasons, some of which could not be corrected by what were then considered good cultural practices for disease and insect control.

The senior author, in 1953, was contacted by the Superintendent of Mayfair Golf and Country Club in Sanford, Florida, and on examination found high populations of sting, stubby-root, and lance nematodes. With the cooperation of the superintendent, a nematode control experiment was initiated in 1953 on one green. This was apparently the first experiment designed to test nematicides for nematode control on turf. The soil fumigants D-D and ethylene dibromide were injected at normal rates to a depth of 4 in. (10 cm) on 12 in. (30 cm) centres. An experimental nematicide which later was named V-C 13 (75% a.i.) was surface-applied at a rate of 20 gal (90 1) as a drench. The experiment indicated that all materials gave excellent control of the parasitic nematodes and resulted in an outstanding growth response of the bermudagrass. This experiment then provided a basis for expanded research in Florida. It is now recognized that if high quality turf is to be produced in Florida, nematode control is necessary and most golf courses apply nematicides on a routine basis. The research results have been published by numerous authors, including the authors of this paper, in Volumes I - XVI of the Proceedings of the University of Florida Turf-Grass Management Conference (1). Each volume contains papers reporting the nematode problems encountered and their control.

Several other publications are worthy of mention. In 1962 Sledge (5) reported the occurrence and parasitism on St. Augustinegrass (Stenotaphrum secundatum (Walt.) Kuntze) of a species of Meloidogyne or root-knot nematode in Winter Haven, Florida. Later Sledge and Golden (6) described the species as Hypsoperine graminis and Esser (3) assigned the common name pseudo root-knot nematode. Several authors have added information so that the parasite is now recognized to be pathogenic to most warm-season turfgrasses and it is widespread in the southern U.S.A. DiEdwardo and Perry (2) described a cyst nematode Heterodera leuceilyma as a severe pathogen of St. Augustinegrass in Florida. Rhoades (4) reported on the pathogenicity of a stubby-root nematode, Trichodorus christiei Allen, and a sting nematode, Belonolaimus longicaudatus Rau, to St. Augustinegrass. Many other papers have contributed knowledge of the occurrence and control of parasitic nematodes on the warm-season grasses.

THE PARASITES

In most cases several nematode species occur together in turf. Frequently 10-15 species of parasites are found on one golf green or lawn. Thus the total effect on the plants is due to multiple attacks. In most cases, however, one or two species are most abundant and thus cause most of the damage. Judicious diagnoses can be arrived at only by consideration of the total population and interpretation of the pathogenic capabilities of the most abundant forms. The plant parasitic nematodes found most frequently in turf samples collected in Florida are listed in Table 1.

Ectoparasites

In Florida the great majority of the nematode damage on turfgrasses is due to feeding by the external parasites. These include the forms such as sting and stubby-root nematodes that feed while wholly external, primarily at root tips. Such forms as ring, sheath and sheathoid nematodes feed primarily from the exterior but they do at times become attached to or even embedded in roots. Lance and spiral nematodes feed primarily on older portion of roots by penetrating them so that the anterior portion of their bodies are within the roots; some specimens are completely within larger roots.

Most of the research into various aspects of the nematode problems in Florida has dealt primarily with the sting nematode and the resulting plant damage. This parasite is highly pathogenic to a long list of plant hosts, including most of the warm-season turfgrasses. Fortunately, it is relatively easy to control by chemical nematicides. Prior to widespread use of the nematicides the sting nematode was the most important nematode pathogen of turfgrasses in such plantings as golf greens, home lawns, etc.

Table 1: the major nematode parasites of warm-season turfgrasses arranged in descending order of their known importance in Florida

Common name	Scientific name	Mode of parasitism
Sting	Belonolaimus longicaudatus	Ectoparasite at root tips
Lance	Hoplolaimus galeatus	Ectoparasite away from root tips
Pseudo root-knot	Meloidogyne graminis	Sedentary endoparasite
Stubby root	Trichodorus christiei	Ectoparasite at root tips
Awl	Dolichodorus heterocephalus	Ectoparasite at root tips
Ring	Criconemoides spp.	Ectoparasites to endoparasites
Sheath	Hemicycliophora spp.	Ectoparasites
Sheathoid	Hemicriconemoides spp.	Ectoparasites
Spiral	Helicotylenchus spp.	Ectoparasite away from root tips
	Scutellonema spp.	" " " " "
	Peltamigratus spp.	" " " " "
Root-knot	Meloidogyne incognita	Sedentary endoparasite
Cyst	Heterodera leuceilyma	Sedentary endoparasite
Stubby root	Trichodorus spp.	Ectoparasites
Root lesion	Pratylenchus spp.	Migratory endoparasites
Stylet	Tylenchorhynchus spp.	Ectoparasites

In some cases, however, the annual use of minimal rates of certain nematicides has resulted in the reduction of sting nematode populations but there has been a corresponding increase in populations of lance nematodes. Sting nematodes are found only in soils with a high sand content and little clay or organic matter.

The awl nematode is also highly pathogenic to the warm-season turfgrasses but it is not found so frequently as most of the other parasites. Awl nematodes prefer the more moist soils, hence they are most frequently found in turf on lake-front properties and near water hazards on golf courses. Awl nematodes are found in soils with higher organic content than sting nematodes.

Grasses parasitized by either the sting or awl nematodes have very shallow, abbreviated and discoloured roots. Growth by the plants may be fair during periods of optimum weather but a rapid decline in the quality of turf begins soon after conditions become subnormal. It is impossible to maintain high quality of turf when moderate to high populations of these parasites are present, even though maximum care is given to the turf.

Stubby-root nematodes affect the grasses in much the same manner as sting nematodes but higher population levels are required for severe injury. These pests are widespread, but moderate to high population levels are found much less frequently than is the case for sting nematodes.

The lance nematode of most frequent occurrence at pathogenic levels in Florida is H. galeatus but others are found. This parasite is found even more frequently than is the sting nematode but it is somewhat less pathogenic. The nature of feeding on older portions of roots causes symptoms different from those caused by sting nematodes feeding at root tips. Roots parasitized by lance nematodes do penetrate the soil for several inches and fair root systems are produced even when population levels of the parasite are high. Nevertheless, the parasitism has been experimentally demonstrated to result in severe decline of turf, approaching that caused by the sting and awl nematodes. Spiral nematodes of various genera and species bring about a similar damage to turf but the extent of injury is less.

Ring, sheath and sheathoid nematodes are found with more frequency than other parasites in turf of the warm-season grasses. They are not so highly pathogenic as those discussed above but in many cases the population levels are so high that significant injury to turfgrasses results. Stylet nematodes are found in many turf areas but there is little evidence that they cause significant damage.

Endoparasites

Root-knot nematodes cause severe injury to turfgrasses in Florida and elsewhere. The pseudo root-knot nematode of turfgrasses is primarily a parasite of grasses and it is becoming an increasingly significant factor in the production of high quality turf. Common root-knot nematode species also attack the warm-season turfgrasses and cause decline. Some populations reproduce well on grass hosts and continue to produce injury from year to year. Other populations do not reproduce sufficiently to persist as major problems on grasses but when the turf is first established the indigenous parasites attack the roots to produce injury. The root galls on grass plants are small in comparison to those on other hosts but there is little correlation between extent of galling and extent of injury.

Cyst nematodes are found frequently in turf but most of them are parasites of clovers and other plants growing in the areas. The only species known to attack any of the warm-season turfgrasses is H. leuceilyma and St. Augustinegrass is the only known host. This species is highly pathogenic and difficult to control. The best control appears to be the use of grasses other than St. Augustine-grass.

Root lesion nematodes are known to be highly pathogenic to a wide range of hosts. Various species are found at frequent intervals in turf areas and undoubtedly some damage occurs on the grasses, but populations are usually low and, in most cases, the degree of injury is considered to be low.

Symptoms

The nematode parasites under discussion feed only upon the roots of the turfgrasses, and thus primary symptoms are expressed on the roots. Nematodes feed by puncturing individual cell walls with an oral stylet, which is a hollow tube of sclerotized material. Secretions from oesophageal glands are delivered to the plant cells under attack to help the parasite's penetration of cell walls and to bring about a partial pre-oral digestion of the food. These chemical secretions cause some interesting host responses such as production of "giant cells" and a cessation of mitosis. Generally they prove deleterious to the plant and may affect plant portions far removed from the point of feeding; for example the foliage is often chlorotic and stunted in growth. Thus it is generally assumed that nematode damage to host plants is of a biochemical nature. In some cases a low population level of certain nematode parasites may stimulate root production so that growth of the affected plants is actually increased.

The root symptoms are usually not distinctive. At first the roots are stunted in elongation but, with time and after invasion by secondary organisms, affected tissues become light or dark brown and eventually black. Many nematodes, if their population levels are sufficiently high, prevent root penetration into the soil deeper than 2 in. (5 cm). The grasses continually produce new roots which in turn are attacked and eventually destroyed. This results in a matting of roots near the soil surface and in order to maintain even fair turf it becomes necessary to irrigate and fertilize at frequent intervals. Then population levels of the parasites increase in the upper 2 in. of soil so that only poor turf can be produced even with the most intensive care.

The foliage of parasitized plants gradually takes on a pale green or yellowish appearance. Wilting occurs in sunlight even when the soil has an abundance of moisture. Then the turf becomes thin, allowing germination of seeds of undesirable grasses and broadleaf weeds. In midsummer these annual plants virtually cover turf areas that are severely affected by nematode parasites. Thus, in some cases the best herbicide is a good nematicide which provides conditions for the growth of healthy turfgrasses that can compete with the undesirable plants.

Nematode damage is almost always spotty in occurrence. Certain portions of a golf green or lawn show much more severe damage than others. This spotty appearance is believed to be due to one or more of several factors. First, populations of the parasites are seldom evenly distributed. Second, ecological factors and the abundance of other soil organisms influence nematode populations. Third, the plants in some locations exhibit more symptoms than those in other nearby locations, due perhaps to ecological influences on plant growth.

The different grasses are, of course, not affected in the same manner or to the same extent by the individual nematode parasites. Zoysiagrass (Zoysia spp.), bermudagrass and centipedegrass (Eremochloa ophiuroides (Munro) Hack.) are most severely injured by such parasites as sting, awl, lance, root-knot, and stubby-root nematodes. Varieties within these types of grasses are differently affected but little research data on these differences have been obtained. Bahiagrass (Paspalum notatum Flugge) is affected least by the more pathogenic nematodes but recently significant injury by sting and root-knot nematodes has been recorded from some locations.

Diagnosis of Nematode Problems

The symptoms discussed above are not sufficiently distinctive for diagnosis. The nematode parasites must be removed from the turf, identified and population levels estimated. Then a diagnosis may be based on numbers of nematodes, known pathogenicity to the particular grass and symptoms expressed by the grass. Thus, a proper diagnosis can only be made by a trained nematologist, preferably in consultation with a turf specialist.

The final evaluation of such situations should be postponed until nematode populations have been brought under control in a portion of the area and any turf responses noted. It is recommended that test application of control measures be made to areas as small as 4 sq. ft. Thus within a few weeks even homeowners can accurately determine the extent of nematode injury.

CONTROL

Most of the research on the turf nematode problems during the past 15 years has been directed toward control. The nematode species for the most part are the same as those that attack field crops and vegetables. Bionomics for the parasites have been studied and levels of pathogenicity, types of feeding, modes of injury and life cycles have been elucidated. Thus by using methods of nematode control considerable information has been gained concerning the host-parasite relationships of nematodes and grasses with a minimum of laboratory analysis. In addition excellent recommendations for control are now available.

At present control of the nematode problems of the warm-season turfgrasses can be obtained most effectively by chemical means. Other methods have generally proved inadequate due to the nature of the parasites and the cultural methods used on the grass hosts. The following chemicals are recommended in Florida as specified.

1.   Dibromochloropropane (DBCP) at a rate of 85 lb./ac. (95 kg/ha). Use the emulsifiable formulation only and drench with at least 10 parts of water to 1 part of the formulated chemical. Follow immediately with about ½ in. (12 mm) or more of irrigation. This material may be used on all types of areas but apply carefully to reduce the possibility of foliage burn. Do not apply when the soil is wet or when the sunshine is unusually hot.

2.   Sarolex (a special formulation of the pesticide diazinon) at a rate of 30 lb./ac. (33 kg/ha). The information given for DBCP applies to Sarolex also.

3.   Dasanit at a rate of 20 lb./ac. (22 kg/ha). This material is a highly toxic organo-phosphate pesticide and should be used on commercial areas only. For safety to humans, the granular formulation only should be used. Irrigate with a minimum of ½ in. water (12 mm) within a few hours, preferably immediately after application.

In areas where only the sting nematode is a significant factor in turf production the above rates may be reduced by 50%. The turf areas should be aerified prior to application to help the movement of chemicals into the soil. Research data indicates that the optimum amount of water for irrigation is 1 in. (25 mm). The irrigation should in all cases follow application immediately so as to minimize burn of the grasses, increase effects on the parasites and reduce the hazards to humans, domestic animals and wildlife.

Several other chemicals such as Mocap, Terracur, Furadan and Lannate show promise for use as nematicides on turf. Also several experimental compounds have proved effective in limited tests. Thus the nematode problems of the warm-season turfgrasses can be effectively controlled and quite possibly the ability to control them will be significantly increased within the'near future.

REFERENCES

1. Proc. Univ. Florida Turfgrass Mgmt. Conf. I - XVI, 1956-68.

2. DiEDWARDO, A.A., and PERRY, V.G. (1964) Heterodera leuceilyma n.sp. (Nemata: Heteroderidae) a severe pathogen of St. Augustinegrass in Florida. Fla. agric. Exp. Stn. Bull. 687 (Tech).

3. ESSER, R.P. (1964) Vernacular name for Hypsoperine graminis. Nematology Newsletter 10, 3, 17.

4. RHOADES, H.L. (1962) Effects of sting and stubby-root nematodes on St. Augustinegrass. Pl. Dis. Reptr. 46, 6, 424.

5. SLEDGE, E.B. (1962) Preliminary report on a Meloidogyne sp. parasite on grass in Florida. Pl. Dis. Reptr. 46, 2, 52.

6. SLEDGE, E.B., and GOLDEN, A.M. (1962) Hypsoperine graminis (Nematoda: Heteroderidae). A new genus and species of plant parasitic nematode. Proc. Helminthol. Soc. Wash. 31, 2, 83.

DISCUSSION

DISTRIBUTION AND SEVERITY OF NEMATODE DAMAGE

W.H. Daniel (Indiana, U.S.A.)

How often do nematodes need treatment?

G.C. Horn (Florida, U.S.A.)

At first we found that one treatment per year was effective but we now give two applications per year on very sandy soils in south Florida.

R.W. Schery (Ohio, U.S.A.)

How extensive is the nematode problem? Does it extend into the north? We have had no response from nematicides in Ohio.

G.C. Horn (Florida, U.S.A.)

Nematodes are a problem mainly in sandy soils. Tropical conditions cause a build-up to detrimental proportions, though the same organisms are found in lower numbers in other soils, and in colder climates.

P.E. Rieke (Michigan, U.S.A.)

In Michigan we consistently find small nematode populations in both mineral and organic soils under turf but the numbers are not considered great enough to cause significant injury to turf. This may support Dr. Horn's suggestion that in cooler regions soil temperatures are not high enough, for a sufficient period of time, to foster seriously large populations of nematodes.

G.C. Horn (Florida, U.S.A.)

Symptoms of nematode attack are more apparent when the grass is weakened for other reasons.

J.R. Escritt (U.K.)

The nematode problem is not recognized in the U.K. What is the situation in the Netherlands?

H. Vos (Netherlands)

I can give two examples of damage by nematodes in the Netherlands: one on a green on sandy soil in the Central Netherlands and one on a football field in the south east.

NEMATODE FOOD SOURCES

W.A. Adams (U.K.)

Are the nematodes causing plant damage entirely parasitic or are they partly saprophytic?

G.C. Horn (Florida, U.S.A.)

The nematodes I have described are parasitic. Many saprophytic nematodes occur, which are also, unfortunately, killed by nematicides.

V.I. Stewart (U.K.)

Have you experimental evidence of the obligate parasitic behaviour of the nematodes you describe? It could be that the relationship with low organic matter content has something to do with the lack of an alternative food source. Is the addition of organic matter helpful in avoiding nematode damage?

G.C. Horn (Florida, U.S.A.)

I have no information on this point but it does seem that organic fertilizers are better than inorganic, from this point of view.

SESSION 4B: DISEASES

(Chairman: Mr. J. R. Escritt)

DISEASES OF TURFGRASSES IN WARM-HUMID REGIONS

T. E. Freeman,

Professor of Plant Pathology, University of Florida, Gainesville,
Florida, U.S.A.

SUMMARY

There are fourteen diseases that commonly occur on the seven predominant grasses grown for turf purposes in warm-humid regions. In descending
order of their present importance, these diseases are caused by:
Rhizoctonia solani, Sclerotinia homoeocarpa, Helminthosporium spp., Pythium
aphanidermatum, Piricularia grisea, Puccinia spp., fleshy fungi, Rhizoctonia
and Pythium spp., Cercospora fusimaculans, Curvularia spp., Colletotrichum
graminicola, mosaic viruses, Ustilago spp., and slime moulds. The first
seven listed are the most important and have been studied the most extensively. Results of these studies have led to a better understanding of the
etiology, symptomology, epidemiology, and control of the important diseases
occurring on turfgrasses in warm-humid regions.

INTRODUCTION

In general, the diseases affecting grasses grown in warm-humid climates have
not received attention concomitant with their importance. In recent years, however,
considerable progress has been made, especially in the Southern United States,
towards a better understanding of these diseases. In this brief presentation
attention is drawn to the important turfgrass diseases encountered in this region
and some recent research results presented. Comments focus on diseases of
bermudagrass (Cynodon dactylon (L.) Pers.), centipedegrass (Eremochloa ophiuroides
(Munro) Hack.), St. Augustinegrass (Stenotaphrum secundatum (Walt.) Kuntze),
bahiagrass (Paspalum notatum Flugge), zoysiagrass (Zoysia spp.), carpetgrass
(Axonopus affinis Chase), and annual ryegrass (Lolium multiflorum Lam.). This
last species, although not one of the permanent warm-season grasses, is included
because of its extensive use during the winter months as a temporary overseeded
grass. The other six are the predominant turf species utilised in warm-humid
regions.

DISEASES

Excluding nematodes, there are over 100 diseases reported on grasses utilized
for turf purposes in warm-humid regions (11). Out of this large number only 14
occur with any degree of regularity in the United States. These diseases, along
with the host affected, are listed in Table 1. The first seven diseases listed
are the most important because they account for a majority of the annual damage
caused by diseases. Any one of the remaining seven, however, may cause considerable damage at any given time or location.

A complete list of the pathogenic organisms reported to occur on turfgrasses
in warm-humid regions, is given in Florida Agricultural Experiment Station
Bulletin 713, "Diseases of Southern Turfgrasses" (11). Since the publication of
this bulletin, three other disease-inciting organisms have been reported and thus
should be added to the list. They are: Polymyxa graminis Led. on bermudagrass
(3), Pythium myriotylum Drechsl. on ryegrass (15), and decline virus on St.
Augustinegrass (16).

Table 1: diseases that commonly occur in warm-humid regions and the primary grasses affected

Disease in descending order of importance	Causal agent	Grasses affected in descending order of susceptibility
1. Rhizoctonia brown patch	Rhizoctonia solani Kuhn	Carpetgrass St. Augustinegrass Ryegrass Centipedegrass Bermudagrass Bahiagrass
2. Dollar spot	Sclerotinia homoeocarpa F.T. Bennett	Bermudagrass Bahiagrass Zoysiagrass Ryegrass St. Augustinegrass Centipedegrass
3. Helminthosporium diseases	Helminthosporium spp.	Bermudagrass Ryegrass St. Augustinegrass
4. Pythium blight	Pythium aphanidermatum (Edson) Fitzpatrick	Ryegrass Bermudagrass
5. Piricularia leaf spot	Piricularia grisea (Cke.) Sacc.	St. Augustinegrass Centipedegrass Bermudagrass
6. Rust	Puccinia spp.	Ryegrass Zoysiagrass Bermudagrass St. Augustinegrass
7. Fairy ring	Fleshy fungi	All grasses
8. Seedling blight	Rhizoctonia spp. and Pythium spp.	Ryegrass Bahiagrass Bermudagrass Centipedegrass
9. Cercospora leaf spot	Cercospora fusimaculans Atk.	St. Augustinegrass
10. Curvularia fading out	Curvularia spp.	All grasses
11. Anthracnose	Colletotrichum graminicola (Ces.) Wils.	Centipedegrass Bahiagrass Ryegrass Bermudagrass
12. Mosaic	Virus	St. Augustinegrass Ryegrass
13. Smut diseases	Ustilago spp.	Bermudagrass St. Augustinegrass
14. Slime moulds	Primarily Physarum cinereum (Batsch) Pers.	All grasses

Most of the research has been concentrated on the first seven diseases listed in Table 1, with only a limited amount of effort expended on the remaining seven. By necessity almost all studies have been concerned with practical aspects, such as symptomology, etiology, epidemiology, and control. Only recently has a point been reached where some effort could be justified on the more basic aspects of the host-parasite relationships. The remainder of this paper touches briefly on some salient points derived from studies of diseases of warm-season grasses.

Rhizoctonia brown patch is the most serious disease on grasses in warm-humid regions. Symptoms of the disease on these grasses vary somewhat from the so-called classical ones described for cool-season grasses, For example, even though the grass is usually killed in a circular pattern, the "smoke ring" phase is seldom seen. In addition, R. solani may gradually thin the grass over a rather large area with no circular pattern discernible. Disease observations on fertility plots for a number of years revealed that R. solani more readily attacks grass in plots highly fertilized with a readily available source of nitrogen than that in plots receiving lower rates of the same nitrogen source. This is especially true with St. Augustinegrass and centipedegrass, but is less evident with the other warm-season species. Brown patch is most severe during periods when night temperatures are in the $18-20^{0}C$ range. Therefore, in certain areas of the warm-humid climatic region, brown patch can and does occur during any month of the year.

Fungicides recommended by the author for control of brown patch are:- PCNB; tetrachloroisopthalonitrile (Daconil 2787); the coordination product of zinc ion and maneb (Dithane M-45, Fore, and Manzate 200); thiram; and the various organic and inorganic mercury fungicides (13).

Sclerotinia dollar spot is another disease in which symptoms are different on certain warm-season grasses from those reported on cool-season grasses. This is especially true on coarse-textured grasses such as bahiagrass, where S. homoeocarpa kills the grass in a larger and more diffused area than is commonly associated with the disease. Bermudagrass, bahiagrass, and zoysiagrass are the most susceptible to dollar spot, although a high degree of variation in disease susceptibility occurs between varieties of these grasses. The bermudagrass varieties Ormond, Uganda, and Tifway are more susceptible than others, while Argentine bahiagrass and Meyer zoysiagrass are the most resistant varieties in these two species. Dollar spot is prevalent during periods of mild weather $(18-26^{0}C)$, but can occur throughout the summer months when the temperature is relatively warm. This is especially true in Florida where high temperature strains of the parasite have been isolated (5). Unlike brown patch, dollar spot on bermudagrass is retarded by high levels of a readily available nitrogen fertilizer (6). In fact this has become the accepted method of control on golf courses in Florida. The reason for this reduction in disease severity is not understood. However, it may be due to rapid recovery of the host as suggested by Couch (1). Endo (4) has suggested that there is a need by the parasite for a food base in senescing tissue present in poorly fertilized grass that is not present in highly fertilized grass. Some recent results (14) indicate that growth of S. homoeocarpa is inhibited by the amino-acid lysine. These results may have implications in explaining increased dollar spot resistance in grass highly fertilized with nitrogen.

Recent experiments on control methods (13) show that in addition to using nitrogen, tetrachloroisopthalonitrile (Daconil 2787) and the mercury fungicides are the most effective. Cadmium fungicides were not satisfactory for control of dollar spot in warm-humid regions.

Helminthosporium diseases are of primary importance on bermudagrass. In fact there are six different species of Helminthosporium that attack this grass. They are: H. cynodontis Marig., H. giganteum Heald and Wolf, H. rostratum Drechsl., H. spiciferum (Bain) Nicot, H. stenospilum Drechsl., and H. triseptatum Drechsl. At least five of these six fungi cause leaf spots of similar appearance (8). In extensive isolation studies it was determined that simultaneous infection of the grass by more than one species was a common occurrence (8). Differences exist between varieties of bermudagrass in susceptibility to infection by Helminthosporium spp. The Norrie variety is extremely susceptible to infection and is a good variety on which to evaluate control practices. Certain varieties of African origin, as well as common bermudagrass, are also extremely susceptible. Helminthosporium diseases cause severe damage to bermudagrass during periods when the nights are cool enough to retard growth and day temperatures are mild $(20-27^{0}C)$. The optimum temperature for infection by H. stenospilum is near $25^{0}C$, but some infection occurs over a wide range of temperatures $(20-30^{0}C)$. Although the optimum for infection by other species has not been determined, it is probably near this same temperature.

Partial control of Helminthosporium diseases can be obtained by using the newer bermudagrass varieties because they are, in general, more resistant. Tests have shown tetrachloroisopthalonitrile (Daconil 2787); the zinc ion-maneb products; and organic mercurials are the best fungicides for control of Helminthosporium diseases on bermudagrass (13).

Pythium blight is a devastating disease of overseeded grasses, especially ryegrass. Bermudagrass is also affected, but to a much lesser degree. This particular disease, although it occurs primarily on a cool-season overseed grass, is favoured by warm temperatures. In fact, the optimum for disease development is near $35^{0}C$, with negligible damage occurring below $20^{0}C$ (7). The fungus grows so rapidly, however, that the temperature needs to remain in a conducive range for only a short period during successive days. The length of this period is dependent upon the temperature, but may be as short as 2 hours when temperatures are near $35^{0}C$. Nutrition of the host may also affect the severity of Pythium blight. Results of recent studies in Florida indicate that high rates of nitrogen tend to reduce the severity of Pythium blight on grass.

Control of Pythium blight has been extremely difficult because of the rapidity with which the disease spreads, and to the lack of really effective fungicides. Until recently there was only one material on the market that provided a degree of control, p-dimethylaminobenzenediazo sodium sulfonate (Dexon). Recent tests by the author (12) have shown that two other materials control Pythium blight effectively. They are 5-ethoxy-3-trichloromethyl-1, 2, 4 thiodiazole (Kolan,Terrazole) and 1,4-dichloro-2, 5-dimethoxybenzene (Demosan).

Piricularia leaf spot or blast is a serious disease only on St. Augustinegrass. In fact, it is omnipresent on this grass during the warm rainy months, although not all plantings are affected equally. Varieties with yellow-green foliage are affected less severely than those with blue-green foliage. However, variation in disease severity also occurs within these two types due to fertility. The disease is favoured by high nitrogen fertilization. Increase in disease severity is correlated closely with increased nitrogen and free amino-acid content of leaves (9). Specific amino-acids affect germination of spores of P. grisea and, thus, may be of significance in the host-parasite relationship.

Almost all available turf fungicides will provide an acceptable degree of control of Piricularia leaf spot, but repeated weekly applications are necessary (12). Some relief from this situation may be on the horizon in the form of the benzimidazole compounds such as Benlate. A high degree of control with this fungicide has been obtained even when applications were spaced at monthly intervals (12).

Rust disease occurs on four of the grasses used for turf in warm-humid regions. Most of the recent interest, however, has centred on zoysiagrass rust caused by Puccinia zoysia Diet. Since this disease was first noted in the Western Hemisphere in 1965, it has spread to most zoysiagrass-growing areas. It is especially severe on the Meyer and Emerald varieties of zoysiagrass, while varieties of Z. matrella and Z. tenuifolia are less severely affected (10). This rust apparently is favoured by mild temperatures, since it thrives during such periods, but tends to diminish during warm months.

Experiments by the author have shown that zineb will adequately control rust on zoysiagrass. Because of the leaf characteristics of zoysiagrass, it is necessary to add a wetting agent to the spray mixture to achieve adequate coverage of the foliage.

Fairy rings are ranked as the seventh most important disorder of turfgrasses in warm-humid regions, yet studies of these disorders have been very limited. Although Type I rings as denoted by Couch (2) do occur, the Type II rings are the predominant type encountered in almost all warm-humid regions.

Many recommendations for fairy ring control on warm-season grasses call for the use of a liquid formulation of organic mercurial fungicide. However, these recommendations are extrapolated from recommendations for control of fairy ring in cool-season grasses. In Florida, rings are usually of Type II, and therefore a stepped-up watering and fertilization programme seems to reduce the disease problem.

Research effort on the diseases of turfgrasses grown in warm-humid regions has been less than that devoted to the elucidation of diseases of cool-season grasses. The total knowledge of diseases of warm-season grasses has now progressed to the point where it seems that the pressing practical problems have been solved, at least temporarily. Therefore, the future course should be directed toward basic studies to provide essential information on which lasting and effective control measures can be built.

REFERENCES

1. COUCH, H.B., and BLOOM, J.R. (1960) Influence of environment on diseases of turfgrasses. II. Effect of nutrition, pH, and soil moisture on Sclerotinia dollar spot. Phytopathology 50, 761.

2. COUCH, H.B. (1962) Diseases of turfgrasses. Reinhold Publishing Corp., New York. 289 pp.

3. DALE, J.L., and MURDOCH, C.L. (1969) Polymyxa infection on bermudagrass. Pl. Dis. Reptr. 53, 130.

4. ENDO, R.M. (1966) Control of dollar spot of turfgrass by nitrogen and its probable bases. Phytopathology 56, 877 (abstr.)

5. FREEMAN, T.E. (1959) Florida isolates of dollar spot fungus stand hot weather. Fla. agric. Exp. Stn. Rept. 4, 3, 3.

6. FREEMAN, T.E. (1960) Control of dollar spot by fertilization. Fla. agric. Exp. Stn. Rept. 5, 4, 17.

7. FREEMAN, T.E. (1960) Effects of temperature on cottony blight of ryegrass. Phytopathology 50, 570. (abstr.)

8. FREEMAN, T.E. (1964) Helminthosporium diseases of bermudagrass. Golf course Reptr. 32, 5, 24.

9. FREEMAN, T.E. (1964) Influence of nitrogen on severity of Piricularia grisea infection of St. Augustinegrass. Phytopathology 54, 1187.

10. FREEMAN, T.E. (1965) Rust of Zoysia spp. in Florida. Pl. Dis. Reptr. 49, 382.

11. FREEMAN, T.E. (1967) Diseases of Southern turfgrasses. Fla. agric. Exp. Stn. Bull. (Tech.) 713.

12. FREEMAN, T.E. (1968) Developments in disease control. Proc. Univ. Fla. Turf Mgmt. Conf. 16, 85.

13. FREEMAN, T.E., and MULLIN, R.S. (1968) Turfgrass diseases and their control. Fla. agric. Ext. Cir. 221-C.

14. FREEMAN, T.E. (1969) Influence of nitrogen sources on growth of Sclerotinia homoeocarpa. Phytopathology 59, 114. (abstr.)

15. McCARTER, S.M., and LITTRELL, R.H. (1968) Pathogenicity of Pythium myriotylum to several grass and vegetable crops. Pl. Dis. Reptr. 52, 179.

16. TOLER, R.W., McCOY, N.L., and AMADOR, J. (1969) A new mosaic disease of St. Augustinegrass. Phytopathology 59, 118. (abstr.)

FUNGAL DISEASES OF TURF IN BRITAIN

J.R. Escritt, M.Sc., and A.R. Woolhouse, B.Sc.,

The Sports Turf Research Institute, Bingley, Yorkshire, U.K.

SUMMARY

A short survey of the turf disease position in Britain is presented.

INTRODUCTION

Turf diseases caused by fungi are a major problem in the production of good turf. The use of turf (resulting in damage to the grass plants and to soil physical properties) and necessary management practices (including frequent mowing, rolling and fertilizer application) make for an artificial system requiring much skill to maintain in healthy condition.

Injury to the grass plant and constant depletion of reserves increase susceptibility to fungal attack. As most turf consists of only a few different species of grass, rapid spread of the disease can easily occur, though perhaps not as quickly as in swards of only one species. In the United Kingdom, current practice is to pay close attention to management techniques and thus to avoid encouraging fungal attack as far as possible. Preventive spraying of fungicide is not normally undertaken, not only because of cost of treatment and the relative infrequency of attacks of disease but also because of the possible long term risk of the development of resistant strains of fungi and the lack of knowledge of the total effect of such materials on the turf system, both on the disease-causing fungi and on the beneficial soil microflora. In addition many greenkeepers feel that to apply fungicide shows failure of the management programme! This type of approach and difficulties in ensuring disease where and when wanted certainly make for serious difficulties in arranging field trials with fungicides: turf intended for trials with fungicides to control Fusarium has a habit of remaining stubbornly healthy despite almost every encouragement. For this reason the Institute has a backlog of materials which have not yet been in trials. In the long run a good solution to fungal disease problems is the production of disease resistant varieties of grass and it is expected that the plant breeders will produce more of these in the future. Unfortunately even this solution is unlikely to be permanent.

COMMON TURF DISEASES AND THEIR CONTROL

Fusarium patch disease

One of the most serious fungal diseases of turf in Britain is Fusarium patch disease, caused by Fusarium nivale (Fr.) Ces. and mainly encountered on intensively cultivated fine turf. The causal organism is a facultative parasite which is very widespread in distribution and found as a saprophyte on decaying vegetation ready to attack the living plants when the opportunity arises. The most favourable conditions for the disease include high atmospheric humidity, a moist turf surface and a high surface pH, particularly if the grass is at all forced in its growth. Management practices are therefore designed to minimise these conditions as much as possible. Drainage, spiking and scarifying help keep the surface moisture low and it is customary to remove dew by switching as early in the day as possible. In order to prevent still air over the turf, fences, hedges and similar restrictions to air flow are avoided whenever possible. Care is also required in the application of fertilizer. In long-term trials organic fertilizer and fertilizers leaving an alkaline residue have produced turf particularly susceptible to F. nivale. Heavy applications of active nitrogen in the autumn increase susceptibility and care must be taken with slow-release nitrogen fertilizers applied during the year since, if followed by a dry summer, breakdown occurring when moist conditions return in autumn can release considerable amounts of available nitrogen. Such high nitrogen levels encourage the grass to produce lush growth which is readily bruised by use or mowing and is particularly susceptible to F. nivale. The aim throughout is to keep the balance of conditions such that the grass is encouraged to be healthy and vigorous but tough and resistant to disease attack even if conditions are suitable for the fungus.

Many turfgrasses are susceptible to F. nivale, some varieties of Lolium perenne L. being perhaps the most resistant and Poa annua L. being one of the most susceptible species. Turf with Poa annua is very difficult to keep free of disease and obviously its invasion of the turf should be prevented but unfortunately a great deal of British fine turf contains some Poa annua.

A number of fungicides are available but mercury compounds, either inorganic, (mercurous/mercuric chloride mixtures) or organic (e.g. phenylmercuric acetate) remain popular. Malachite green/Bordeaux mixture is still used occasionally in view of its low cost, and other compounds in use include PCNB (quintozene) and members of the dithiocarbamate group.

Ophiobolus patch disease

Over the past ten years, Ophiobolus patch disease, caused by Ophiobolus graminis Sacc. var. avenae E.M. Turner, has increased in importance and now rivals Fusarium patch as the most serious fungal disease of turf, especially so as it has proved difficult to obtain an entirely satisfactory, reliable and economical method of control. Most frequently incidence of the disease follows application of lime to correct over-acidity in turf dominated by Agrostis spp., particularly in wet areas. Other lime-containing materials, e.g. nitro-chalk, can also cause trouble, a surface pH above 6.0 being sufficient to allow the disease to attack, Agrostis being the main grass affected. The disease seems to be encouraged by wetness as it is more frequent in wet years, in areas with high rainfall and on land with poor drainage. Most frequent occurrence of the disease is when lime is applied to acid golf fairways which have had little or no fertilizer treatment for very many years, particularly if these are wet. Cultural approaches to prevention and cure include circumspection in the use of lime and, where it has to be used, following up with fertilizers which have an acidifying effect on the soil surface. Attention to drainage is often also necessary. Usually on extensive areas of turf like golf fairways, clubs are reluctant to incur the cost of repeated treatments with the high rates of organic mercury fungicides which give useful control. On intensively managed areas such as golf greens these treatments are in fact used.

Corticium

Corticium or "red thread" disease, caused by Corticium fuciforme (Berk.) Wakef., attacks many of the turfgrasses in use in Britáin, especially Festuca spp. Although the disease is quite common, especially in the south, it is not as important as the two preceding diseases since it is rarely as destructive to turf. Smith (1954) has shown that the disease is usually associated with low fertility, particularly low levels of nitrogen. Indeed, application of nitrogen fertilizer is often sufficient for complete recovery of the turf. When fungicide treatment is necessary a mercuric/mercurous chloride preparation is normally used but malachite green/Bordeaux mixture is still used occasionally.

Dollar spot

Dollar spot disease, caused by Sclerotinia homoeocarpa F. T. Bennett, is not common in Britain except on bowling greens laid with sea-marsh turf. It is usually found only on the sea-marsh strains of creeping red fescue (Festuca rubra L. ssp. rubra) although rarely it will attack Agrostis spp. and Poa annua. However, in the warmer parts of Europe it is found affecting Agrostis spp. more seriously.

It is a persistent disease often reappearing in spring after being inconspicuous during the winter months. A heavy dew can supply sufficient water to enable the disease to spread in hot weather. Switching to remove the dew and the provision of free draining conditions help to check this spread.

The disease appears more conspicuous if the nitrogen level in the soil is low and the symptoms can be at least disguised by frequent low rate applications of a nitrogen fertilizer in spring and early summer. If large doses are given, especially in late summer or autumn, this seems to cause a more severe attack the following season and can also precipitate an attack of Fusarium patch disease. Massie et al. (1968) have shown that different isolates of the fungus differ both in virulence and in susceptibility to different fungicides. For this reason results obtained from fungicide trials experiments must be interpreted with care. However, in Britain, treatment with organic or inorganic mercury fungicide, thiram, mancozeb or PCNB is recommended, and usually gives at least some control. Sale of cadmium-based fungicides is frowned upon by the Ministry of Agriculture Toxicology Sub-committee.

Typhula blight

Typhula blight, caused by Typhula incarnata Lasch ex Fr., rarely causes problems in Britain, although it was common after the snowy winter of 1962/63 (Jackson 1962). In Finland, where the disease is more common, good control of Typhula and other low temperature parasitic fungi has been given by PCNB (quintozene) (Jamalainen 1964).

Melting out

Melting out disease, caused mainly by Helminthosporium vagans Drechsler, attacks Poa pratensis L., some varieties being more resistant than others (Jackson 1968). Captan, zineb, maneb and Dyrene have been found to give some control; increased nitrogen and phosphate fertilizer coupled with an increase in height of cut is often beneficial. It is to be noted that Poa pratensis is not as popular in Britain as it is in some parts of the U.S.A. and elsewhere.

Fairy rings

Fairy rings are quite often found in turf, especially if low in fertility. A general list of causal fungi is given by Ainsworth and Bisby (1950) and for sports turf by Smith and Jackson (1965). The most troublesome in sports turf is

<u>Marasmius</u> <u>oreades</u> (Bolt. ex Fr.) Fr. Rings are more conspicuous in dry weather than wet, and watering may at least obscure the ring. The fungus in culture is very susceptible to fungicides. Treatment in the field is rarely effective as it proves extremely difficult to get contact between the fungus and the fungicide because the soil becomes very difficult to wet. Lebeau and Hawn (1963) report control through continuous drenching with water but, in practice in this country, <u>Marasmius</u> fairy rings are either tolerated or treated by the more laborious procedure described by Smith (1955) i.e. digging out and treating the excavation with formalin.

SEEDLING DISEASES

Pre-emergence blight and seed rot sometimes lead to poor stands of new grass. A variety of fungi are implicated, including especially <u>Pythium</u> spp., <u>Fusarium</u> spp. and <u>Helminthosporium</u> spp. which are all soil-borne although the last two can be carried on the seed also. Grasses affected are often small-seeded e.g. <u>Agrostis</u> spp. and <u>Poa</u> spp. Sowing too early in the spring (when soil temperatures are low) or too deeply increase the time taken for germination and thus the time at risk. High soil moisture also aids the fungi. Summer or autumn are better times than spring for sowing grass seed and seed dressings, e.g. with captan, can be beneficial (Jackson 1958), though they are not yet commonly used.

Post-emergence damping-off occurs in damp, slow-growing conditions and is particularly common with <u>Festuca</u> spp. and <u>Agrostis</u> spp. The causal fungus is often <u>Fusarium</u> <u>culmorum</u> W.G. Smith, but other fungi can be troublesome e.g. <u>Pythium</u> spp. and <u>Cladochytrium</u> spp. A list of fungi causing seedling diseases of grasses is given by Sampson and Western (1954). Careful preparation of the seed bed, paying attention to drainage and correct fertilization, is obviously important. Too little nitrogen or phosphorus encourages disease but excess is to be avoided. When sowing it is wise to avoid too high sowing rates and to sow evenly to avoid over-crowding. Fungicide treatments normally used are inorganic mercury preparations or possibly Cheshunt compound.

REFERENCES

1. AINSWORTH, G.C., and BISBY, G.R. (1950) A dictionary of the fungi. Commonw. Mycol. Inst. Kew.

2. JACKSON, N. (1958) Seed-dressing trial, 1958. J. Sports Turf Res. Inst., <u>8</u>, 34, 455.

3. JACKSON, N. (1962) Turf disease notes,1962. J. Sports Turf Res. Inst. <u>10</u>, 38, 410

4. JAMALAINEN, E.A. (1964) Control of low temperature parasitic fungi in winter cereals by fungicidal treatment of stands. Annls. Agric. fenn. <u>3</u>, 1.

5. LEBEAU, J.B., and HAWN, E.J. (1963) A simple method of control of fairy ring caused by <u>Marasmius</u> <u>oreades</u>. J. Sports Turf Res. Inst., <u>11</u>, 39, 23.

6. MASSIE, L.B., COLE, H., and DUICH, J. (1968) Pathogen variation in relation to disease severity and control of <u>Sclerotinia</u> dollar spot of turfgrass by fungicides. Phytopath., <u>58</u>, 12, 1616.

7. SAMPSON, K., and WESTERN, J.H. (1954) Diseases of British grasses and herbage legumes. Camb. Univ. Press. (Brit. Mycol. Soc.)

8. SMITH, J.D. (1954) Fungi and turf diseases. 4. Corticium disease.
    J. Sports Turf Res. Inst., 8, 29, 365.

9. SMITH, J.D. (1955) Turf disease notes,1955. J. Sports Turf Res. Inst.,
    8, 31, 60.

10. SMITH, J.D., and JACKSON, N. (1965) Fungal diseases of turfgrasses.
    2nd Edn. Sports Turf Research Institute. 86 pp.

SOME INTER-RELATIONSHIPS BETWEEN NUTRITION AND TURFGRASS DISEASES

Roy L. Goss,

Associate Agronomist and Extension Turfgrass Specialist, Washington State
University, Western Washington Research and Extension Centre, Puyallup,
Washington, U.S.A.

SUMMARY

There is little doubt that the ratio and the intensity of application
of fertilizer elements cause significant interactions between turfgrasses
and turfgrass pathogens. While certain nutritional elements such as nitrogen and calcium become structural elements of cell walls or cell contents,
others such as potassium are important in many metabolic functions, but do
not become part of the plant structure. The importance of potassium is
underlined by the view, which is quoted, that more plant diseases have been
retarded by the use of potassium fertilizers than any other substance.
Nitrogen produces the most significantly observable effect on turfgrass
diseases. While high levels of nitrogen decrease the severity of leaf rust
in bluegrass and red thread disease in bentgrass and fescues, they cause
greater infection from Fusarium nivale, Helminthosporium spp., and certain
other pathogens. Data presented in this paper deal with tissue nutrient
content and nutrient recovery, and show the effects of different levels of
nitrogen, phosphorus and potassium on various turfgrass diseases.

INTRODUCTION

Many factors, including factors of environment and heredity, combine and
interact to affect both quality and tissue renewal in turfgrasses. Although
quality and growth are definitely not synonymous, they are frequently inseparable
when giving a value to past performance. Some turfgrasses, due to inherited
characteristics, are susceptible to certain diseases, but the severity of infection can be strongly influenced by various environmental factors. Some of these
are temperature, light, wind, water, and soil fertility, which frequently
interact to increase or decrease disease severity.

Fungicides and fertilizers can be used very effectively in controlling
many turfgrass diseases. Certain diseases, such as Ophiobolus patch, caused by
Ophiobolus graminis Sacc. var. avenae E.M. Turner, have no known fungicidal
controls, but can be checked by manipulation of environmental factors, as will
be shown later. It is necessary, therefore, to take the best advantage of both
environment and fungicides for the control of turfgrass diseases.

THE INFLUENCE OF NUTRITION ON PLANT DISEASES

The exact action of nutrition on plant diseases is not well understood.
There are, no doubt, a number of nutritional factors affecting the severity of
turfgrass diseases. Grasses in a low state of vigour due to low levels of nutrition may be more susceptible to certain pathogens than those with a high level of
metabolic activity and in a better state of vigour. Often the plant will renew
tissue more quickly than the disease-causing organism can destroy it. Therefore,
higher levels of nutrition would be an advantage in this instance.

351

Certain diseases, such as Fusarium nivale (Fr.) Ces., spread more rapidly and cause more injury to turfgrasses under high levels of nitrogen than at lower levels. This may possibly be due to succulence of the tissue, making easier entrance of the organism and its spread throughout the tissue. Furthermore, it is possible that higher levels of nitrogen or other mineral elements may be responsible for the formation of metabolites which would provide a suitable substrate for the development of the pathogen.

McNew (16) has stated that potassium plays an extremely important role in the control, or reduction of severity, of plant diseases. The nature of the action of potassium and the mechanisms involved are not well understood. He further states that "unlike other essential nutrients, potassium does not become a structural part of the plant cell. It is the immobile regulator of cell activity and promotes the reduction of nitrates and the synthesis of amino-acids from carbohydrates and inorganic nitrogen. Potassium promotes the development of thicker outer walls in the epidermal cells and forms tissues, which are less subject to collapse." He also states that "a deficiency in potassium enforces the accumulation of carbohydrates and inorganic nitrogen in the plant. Eventually, it retards photosynthesis and production of new tissues. More plant diseases have been retarded by the use of potassium fertilizers than any other substance, perhaps because potassium is so essential for catalizing cell activity."

Soil fertility, according to Kaufman and Williams (10), can affect the populations of soil-born fungi. They found, in both field and laboratory investigations, that total numbers of fungi were greatly increased by nitrogen (N) and to a lesser extent by phosphorus (P) and potassium (K). MacLean (15) found in his investigations that certain fungi can be influenced in their growth rate by adding various amino-acids in different concentrations to a basal growth medium. In the case of Fusarium nivale (Fr.) Ces., the inoculated fungus grew to 6.0 cm in diameter on a basal medium containing DL-lysine HCl and to 10 cm, in five days, on one containing L-proline. The amino-acids were all added at the concentration of 2 g/l. In the case of Corticium fuciforme (Berk.) Wakef., the pathogen causing red thread in turf, MacLean also found the inoculated area grew from 0.8 cm in a control with sodium nitrate to 3.23 cm with L-histidine HCl. The smallest growth was again produced with DL-lysine with 1.36 cm increase in 25 days. All amino-acids in this test were added at a concentration of 1.07 g/l.

Klein(11) reported that increased application of ammonia fertilizer in nutrient solution caused large increases in the glutamin and glutamic acid content of tobacco leaves, explaining in part the high susceptibility to Alternaria, Cercospora and Sclerotinia of plants receiving ammonia. He further stated that high potassium decreased the monosaccharide and free amino-acid content and susceptibility to disease.

Thus the work of both MacLean and Klein indicates that amino-acids play an important role in disease development and potassium is important in amino-acid metabolism.

Cheeseman et al (1) reported in their work with solution cultures that, with Helminthosporium sativum Pammel, King, and Bakke, the number of lesions per leaf blade and the average size of lesions increased with increased levels of nitrogen and decreasing osmotic pressures. According to Davis et al (2), rust on turf of Merion bluegrass (Poa pratensis L.) can be controlled by stimulating vigorous growth with adequate nitrogen and water during dry periods.

THE EFFECT OF ENVIRONMENT ON NUTRIENT UPTAKE

If the level of plant nutrients in turfgrass tissue has an influence upon disease development, then it is necessary to consider briefly some of the environmental factors affecting nutrient uptake. Oxygen levels in the soil greatly influence both nutrient uptake and the growth of most plants. Letey et al (13) found that low oxygen concentrations caused a decrease in P and K concentration in barley shoots, whereas Sodium (Na), Calcium (Ca) and Magnesium (Mg) were not greatly modified by the oxygen treatment. Oxygen levels were controlled from 0 to 21% in specially prepared culture tubes. Later work by Letey et al (14) indicates that soil aeration influences the concentration of many minerals in barley plant shoots. They stated that N, P and K were increased and Na decreased with increased oxygen supply. According to Meyer et al (17), when excised roots of barley were immersed in dilute solutions of certain salts, accumulation of some of the salts within the root cells occurs readily if air is bubbled through the system, but little or no accumulation occurs if nitrogen is bubbled through the solution.

There is ample evidence in the literature that soil temperature affects the uptake of nutrients. Knoll et al (12) have presented evidence that soil temperature affected nutrient uptake, especially of phosphorus, in their studies with corn in greenhouse trials. Uptake of phosphorus and yield increased as temperatures were increased from $15^{o}C$ to $25^{o}C$. Nielsen et al (18) found that phosphorus uptake and yield of both tops and roots of corn increased with increased rootzone temperature. Temperature exerts a marked effect on the nitrate-reducing capacity of plants, according to Meyer et al (17). In the tomato plant, for example, although nitrates are quickly absorbed, their reduction and the synthesis of organic nitrogen compounds occur very slowly at $13^{o}C$. At $21^{o}C$, on the other hand, both absorption and reduction of nitrate ions occur very rapidly. Although these examples are not on turfgrasses, it is reasonable to believe that some of the same reactions do occur. There are many other instances of temperature, oxygen and other environmental factors affecting the uptake of nutrients and the incidence of turf diseases, but these examples should be sufficient to illustrate the point.

TISSUE NUTRIENT CONTENT AND NUTRIENT RECOVERY

Before considering the specific effect of nutrients on certain turfgrass diseases, a brief insight into the nutrient uptake or requirements of turfgrass should be considered.

Investigations by the author (6) on putting green bentgrass turf revealed some interesting relationships between the uptake of N and K and the subsequent recovery of these elements in the clippings. Fertilizer treatments consisted of annual applications of 292, 584, and 974 kg/ha of N as urea; 0 and 86 kg/ha of P as triple superphosphate, and 0, 162, and 325 kg/ha of K as KCl. These treatments were applied in a factorial arrangement every two weeks beginning in March until the season total was applied. After the treatments had been carried out for five years, plots were sampled weekly for dry matter yield and nutrient content. These yields were extrapolated to annual totals for dry matter, N, P, and K. It should be pointed out that 6 from a total of 19 treatments were thus sampled. Only one treatment from the highest levels was selected for analysis since it was felt that these levels were not practical for bentgrass purposes. None were selected from the lower levels since visual observations indicated substandard turf quality (colour, density, and growth).

Table 1 shows the recovery of N and K from the selected treatments. From applications of 974 kg/ha of N, only 26% was recovered in the tissue as compared to 43% recovery from applications of 584 kg/ha. Obviously in both cases high

353

Table 1: yield of N and K per hectare recovered from turfgrass clippings

Application rate (kg/ha)			Recovery of N kg/ha	Recovery of K kg/ha
N	P	K		
974	86	325	251	142
584	86	325	251	153
584	86	162	248	151
584	0	325	199	124
584	0	162	214	120
584	0	0	226	118

Table 2: average number of _Fusarium_ spots per plot as influenced by various treatments of N, P and K

Fertilizer treatment kg/ha/year			Average number of _Fusarium_ spots per plot
N	P	K	
974	0	0	48
974	0	162	46
974	0	325	38
974	86	0	61
974	86	162	38
974	86	325	56
584	0	0	22
584	0	162	26
584	0	325	49
584	86	0	42
584	86	162	15
584	86	325	5
292	0	0	12
292	0	162	18
292	0	325	19
292	86	0	18
292	86	162	11
292	86	325	2
0	0	0	11

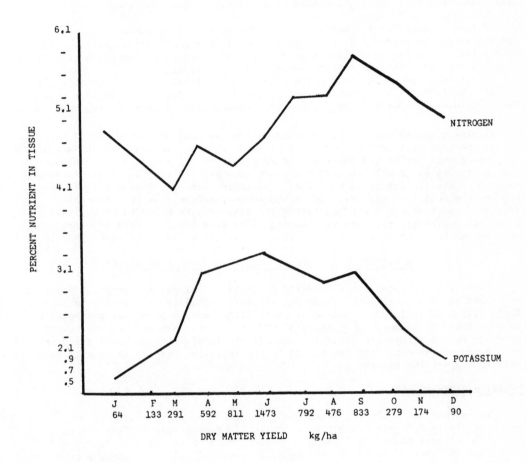

Figure 1: nutrient content and dry matter yield of turf receiving medium
nutritional treatment
(N 584, P 86, K 325 kg/ha/year)

amounts of N were not taken up by the tissue, but the figures for the highest N rate suggest extreme waste.

Potassium recovery presented an entirely different aspect. When K was applied at 325 kg/ha, recovery was 47%, but increased to 93% when 162 kg/ha were applied. The author (in unpublished data) has shown there is a depletion of exchangeable K in the latter case and that part of this recovery must be due to mineralized K. These investigations are being conducted on a Puyallup fine sandy loam soil that usually exhibits high K fixation and supplying power.

Figure 1 shows for the medium nutritional treatment (584-86-325 kg/ha) the percentage of nutrient in the tissue month by month as well as monthly clipping yield, while Figure 2 shows nutrient removal in kg/ha by the month as related to monthly yield. This treatment produced higher clipping yields, percentage tissue nitrogen, and total N than the highest nutritional treatment (984-86-325 kg/ha). Continued high N applications during July and August caused some injury and reduced clipping yields which, in turn, caused reduced nitrogen recovery.

Tissue nitrogen was generally lower during the maximum growth period than during the late fall period. Tissue potassium, conversely, was highest during the peak growth period and lower in the remainder of the year. It is probable that K stimulates growth provided there are no other limiting factors. Although maximum vegetative growth is not highly desirable, plots with high K levels exhibited the best turf quality. In the 584-0-0 treatment, tissue N content increased and tissue K decreased during the maximum growth period of May through July. This probably reflects the importance of K in the reduction of nitrates and the synthesis of amino-acids and their eventual synthesis of plant protein.

NUTRIENT UPTAKE AND ITS EFFECT ON TURFGRASS DISEASES

Quality of turfgrasses is severely affected by turfgrass diseases. Diseased spots and patches cause poor appearance and serviceability on any turfgrass area. Areas killed by turfgrass diseases are most often invaded by undesirable plants, such as broadleaved weeds, Poa annua L. and other weedy grasses. There is ample evidence in the literature regarding the effect of nutrition on turfgrass diseases. A few of these will be considered in the following discussion as well as data to support the hypothesis.

FUSARIUM PATCH DISEASE

The author and Gould (7) found that the number of spots caused by Fusarium nivale decreased as nitrogen applications were reduced from 974 to 292 kg/ha without regard to P and K. There were 48 spots per plot for the 974 kg N rate as compared to 22 for 584 kg N, and only 12 spots for the 292 kg N rate. This is shown in Table 2. Figure 3 shows the effects of P at 86 kg/ha with all combinations of N and K. Less disease was encountered at the two lower N levels but when N was applied at the highest rate, neither P nor K had much effect on the number of disease spots. K exerted its greatest effect in reducing disease at the lower N levels in the presence of P. Gould (9) pointed out that high N levels resulted in more loss from Fusarium patch than lower levels. Smith (20) reported that management which produces succulent growth may stimulate infection by Fusarium nivale. Many other examples relating to this problem are present in the literature.

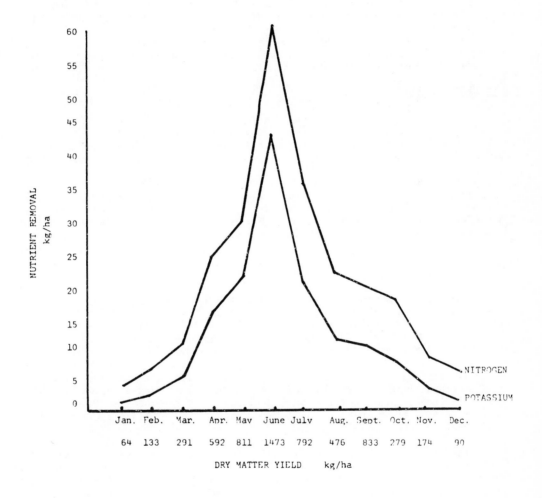

Figure 2: nutrient removal and dry matter yield of turf receiving medium
nutritional treatment
(N 584, P 86, K 325 kg/ha/year)

OPHIOBOLUS PATCH DISEASE

This disease is caused by the fungus O. graminis and is particularly destructive on Agrostis spp. This pathogen also causes the take-all disease in cereal crops. Stumbo et al (21) were able to eliminate O. graminis infection by heavy applications of phosphatic fertilizers when N levels were maintained slightly in excess of those required for good wheat growth. This work correlates closely with that of the author and Gould (8). Nitrogen levels as high as 974 kg/ha helped in reducing the severity of this disease. The beneficial effect of N in increasing new root production on mature plants may have outweighed its adverse effect in increasing susceptibility of individual roots to infection, according to Garrett (5). Both phosphorus and potassium were statistically significant in their effect on the control of this disease.

RED THREAD DISEASE

This disease is caused by Corticium fuciforme and is strongly affected by N levels, and to a lesser degree by P and K. The author and C.J. Gould (unpublished data) have demonstrated that N levels interact with P and K to reduce the severity of infection from this disease on Agrostis spp. and Festuca spp. managed as lawns.

Figure 4 shows the relationship between N, P and K in the control of red thread disease. Ultimately, N is the major factor, but 325 kg/ha of K produced the least red thread disease at both levels of P. Erwin (3) stated that ammonium or sodium nitrate at rates of 1,725 kg/ha would check the pathogen causing red thread.

OTHER DISEASES

A leaf spot disease on coastal bermudagrass was reported by Evans et al (4) at Auburn, Alabama, and was found to be caused by two undisclosed fungi. This disease is much more severe when K levels are kept low and the report is one of the few which definitely link potassium with the problem of turfgrass pathology. Severe attacks were incited under high N treatments with no K being given.

Pritchett and Horn (19) reported significant differences among seven different K compounds in their ability to control dollar spot disease caused by Sclerotinia homoeocarpa on Tifway bermudagrass. They reported that a seasonal application of K at 98 kg/ha, as KCl, K_2CO_3, K_2SO_4, and FN 519 (frit), showed significant effects in yield and in control of dollar spot.

Although many other instances of nutrition and disease interaction may be found in the literature, the foregoing evidence and discussion should be ample to point out this important area of research. No doubt, as more is learnt about the precise ratio and intensity of all nutritional elements required by plants, more will also be learnt about the effects of these nutrients on turfgrass diseases and turfgrass quality as well.

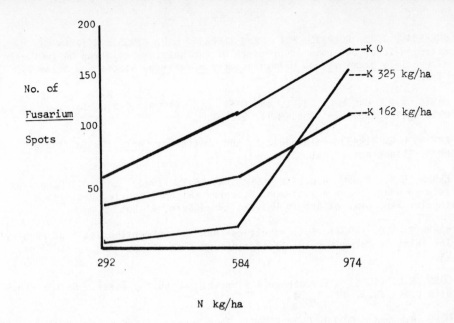

Figure 3: the effects of various rates of N and K on the number of spots of Fusarium nivale on putting green turf when P = 86 kg/ha

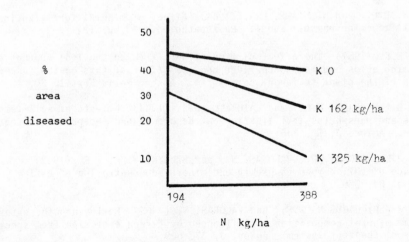

Figure 4: decrease in red thread infection (Corticium fuciforme) with increasing rates of N and K when P = 86 kg/ha at mowing height of 1.8 cm

REFERENCES

1. CHEESMAN, J.H., ROBERTS, E.C., and TIFFANY, L.H. (1965) Effects of nitrogen level and osmotic pressure of the nutrient solution on incidence of Puccinia graminis and Helminthosporium sativum infection. Agron J. 57, 599.

2. DAVIS, R.R., CALDWELL, J.L., and GIST, G.R. (1960) Caring for your lawn. Ohio agric. Exp. Stn. Res. Bull. 271.

3. ERWIN, L.E. (1941) Pathogenicity and control of Corticium fuciforme. Rhode Island agric. Exp. Stn. Bull. 278.

4. EVANS, E.M., ROUSE, R.D., and GUDAUSKAS, R.T. (1964) Low soil potassium sets up coastal for a leaf spot disease. Highlts. agric. Res. 11, 2 (Agric. Exp. Stn. of Auburn University, Auburn, Alabama.)

5. GARRETT, S.D. (1937) Soil conditions and the take-all disease of wheat II. The relation between soil reaction and soil aeration. Ann. appl. Biol. 24, 747.

6. GOSS, R.L. (1965) Nitrogen-potassium team on turf grasses. Better crops with plant food 49, 2, 34.

7. GOSS, R.L., and GOULD, C.J. (1968) Some interrelationships between fertility levels and Fusarium Patch disease of turfgrasses. J. Sports Turf Res. Inst. 44, 19.

8. GOSS, R.L., and GOULD, C.J. (1967) Some interrelationships between fertility levels and Ophiobolus patch disease in turfgrasses. Agron. J. 59, 149.

9. GOULD, C.J. (1965) Research progress on controlling turf diseases. Proc. 19th Northwest Turfgrass Conf.

10. KAUFMAN, D.D., and WILLIAMS, L.E. (1964) Effect of mineral fertilization and soil reaction on soil fungi. Phytopathology 54, 2, 134.

11. KLEIN, E.K. (1957) The effect of mineral nutrition on the leaf content of free amino acids and monosaccharides and the effect of this on the susceptibility of the plant to fungal parasitism. Abstr. Soils Fertil. 20, 1, 303.

12. KNOLL, H.A., BRADY, N.C., and LATHWELL, D.J. (1964) Effects of soil temperature and phosphorus fertilization on the growth and phosphorus content of corn. Agron. J. 56, 145.

13. LETEY, J.L., STOLZY, H., VALORAS, N., and SZUSZKIEWICZ, T.E. (1962) Influence of soil oxygen on growth and mineral concentration of barley. Agron. J. 54, 538.

14. LETEY, J., RICHARDSON, W.F., and VALORAS, N. (1965) Barley growth, water use, and mineral composition as influenced by oxygen exclusion from specific regions of the root system. Agron. J. 57, 629.

15. MACLEAN, N.A. (1964) Amino acid nutrition and turf fungi. Proc. 18th N.W. Turfgrass Conf. 40.

16. MCNEW, G.L. (1953) Plant diseases. The year book of Agriculture 100.

17. MEYER, B.S., ANDERSON, D.B., and BOHNING, R.H. (1960) Introduction to Plant Physiology 296.

18. NIELSEN, K.F., HOLSTEAD, R.L., MACLEAN, A.J., BOURGET, S.J., and HOLMES, R.M. (1961) The influence of soil temperature on the growth and mineral composition of corn, brome grass, and potatoes. Proc. Soil Sci. Soc. Am. 25, 369.

19. PRITCHETT, W.L., and HORN, G.C. (1966) Fertilization fights turf disorders. Better crops with plant food. 50, 3, 22.

20. SMITH, J.D. (1953) Fusarium patch disease. J. Sports Turf Res. Inst. 8, 39, 230.

21. STUMBO, C.R., GAINEY, P.L., and CLARK, F.E. (1942) Microbiological and nutritional factors in the take-all diseases of wheat. J. agron. Res. 64, 653.

TESTING VARIETY RESISTANCE OF POA PRATENSIS AGAINST HELMINTHOSPORIUM SPP.

Bjarne Langvad,

W. Weibull AB., Landskrona, Sweden

SUMMARY

Resistance to _Helminthosporium_ spp. determines to a great extent the turfgrass value of _Poa pratensis_ varieties. It is very important to have an objective method to give data on this resistance, so that varieties can be ranked. The method used at Weibullsholm is presented.

Several species of _Helminthosporium_ occur on _Poa pratensis_ L., but the commonest is _H. vagans_ Drechsler. The disease is manifested as circular or oblong purple or brownish spots on the leaves and on the leaf-sheaths. In severe attacks, which often occur in Sweden in the months of October and November, the spots eventually extend over the entire leaf surface. The damage above the site of the disease is total, and the entire leaf becomes yellow-brown. The sheath is also exposed to attack, and when the disease develops here the whole shoot and the assimilating part of the plant die and this leads to total failure of the turf. It seems that the narrow-leaved varieties on the market lose colour more rapidly when attacked than do the broader-leaved varieties. In severe attacks, especially in the humid moist cold periods in late autumn and early spring, the fungus not only kills most of the leaves but also causes severe damage to the root-crown and rhizomes. Varieties with poor resistance are often completely destroyed and thus easily replaced by _Poa annua_ L.

There are two answers to the question why there is not more _Poa pratensis_ on football grounds in Europe:-

1. Varieties with poor resistance to _Helminthosporium_ spp. have been used.

2. The pitch has been wrongly constructed, using soils which become badly compacted.

In order to investigate resistance to _Helminthosporium_ spp. more closely a number of variety tests have been made at Weibullsholm Plant Breeding Institute since 1964.

To get as objective an assessment as possible of the frequency of attack by _Helminthosporium_ spp. in the different varieties, records of the extent of the disease are made on 1 October, 1 November, and 1 December.

The _Helminthosporium_ spots on leaves and sheaths are classified in four groups according to severity of damage.

Group 1 = spots 1 - 3 mm large
"   2 = spots 4 - 8 "   "
"   3 = spots 9 - 15 "   "
"   4 = spots over 15 mm large, or total attack

The extent of the attack is recorded on the leaf and the sheath. One hundred shoots selected at random in each plot are examined.

Table 1: example of scores of Helminthosporium attack on different bluegrass varieties

Varieties		Number of attacks on sheath at spot size -				Weighted total score for sheath	Number of attacks on leaf at spot size -				Weighted total score for leaf	Weighted total scores in relation to Merion (100)	
		1	2	3	4		1	2	3	4		Sheath	Leaf
Resistant varieties	(Merion	14	19	19	84	445	91	42	44	75	607	100	100
	(W W Birka	24	26	25	85	491	59	39	60	17	385	110	63
	(W W 01	28	28	27	81	489	108	55	66	73	708	110	117
	(Penn State 103	19	15	24	103	533	75	46	72	83	715	120	118
	(W W Sydsport	20	15	26	87	476	126	63	48	77	704	107	116
Moderately resistant varieties	(Penn State 106	17	22	15	121	590	139	41	58	104	811	133	134
	(" " 104	27	22	9	115	558	185	68	65	95	896	125	148
	(" " 107	21	16	19	128	622	151	49	63	106	862	140	142
	(Golf	20	23	30	85	496	243	57	57	188	1330	111	214
	(Prato	19	25	17	167	788	151	72	56	148	1055	177	174
	(Windsor	18	41	15	172	833	271	84	77	136	1214	187	200
	(Primo	36	30	22	192	930	196	89	103	132	1211	209	200
	(Park	33	35	20	197	951	195	77	77	915	1360	214	224
Varieties with poor resistance	(Delft	15	26	35	258	1204	166	103	113	224	1607	271	265
	(Skandia	18	37	30	357	1530	180	87	107	303	1887	344	311

Table 1 gives an example of how this counting can be presented. The weighted total scores in the table were obtained according to the following example:

Merion (1 x 14) + (2 x 19) + (3 x 19) + (4 x 84) = 445

The weighted total scores for sheath and leaf of each variety are expressed relative to the scores for Merion, taken as 100. This way of recording Helminthosporium attacks has shown almost identical results over several years of testing.

The degree of resistance to Helminthosporium spp. is almost identical to the turf value of the variety. In Figure 1 the turf value of 18 varieties is shown, with the accumulated points for value, as given each month, making curves for each variety. It is apparent how Helminthosporium attack bends the curves on varieties which have poor resistance to the disease. Some allowance, however, must be made for, inter alia, resistance to other diseases and the shoot density of the variety.

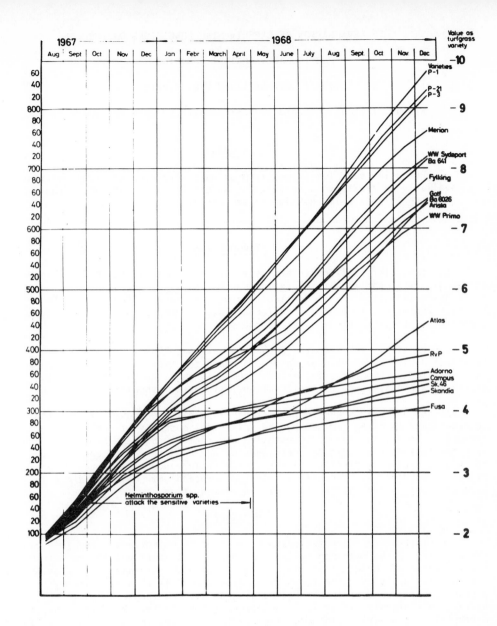

Figure 1: turf value and resistance to Helminthosporium of Poa pratensis varieties

EVALUATION OF EXPERIMENTAL FUNGICIDES ON TURF,

PARTICULARLY AGAINST FUSARIUM NIVALE

J. Mitchell and R.L. Morris,

Fisons Limited, Levington Research Station, Ipswich, Suffolk, U.K.

SUMMARY

Potential turf fungicides from primary screening are frequently not available in sufficient quantity for a full field evaluation. Simple adequate techniques using boxed turf are described.

INTRODUCTION

The demand for turf fungicides is relatively small in the United Kingdom though diseases, particularly Fusarium patch (Fusarium nivale (Fr.) Ces.) occur on intensively managed turf; routine treatment is unusual because of the high cost. For this reason development is confined mainly to compounds offering a broad spectrum of activity for a number of crops.

As part of Fisons' research programme new compounds synthesised at Chesterford Park Research Station are screened for biological activity on a wide range of crops. Promising fungicides from this in vitro and in vivo primary screening are evaluated for their suitability as turf fungicides at Levington.

At such an early stage in product development, the amount of work that can be undertaken is often limited by the very small quantity of chemical available, frequently as little as 1 g. Controlled environment chambers are seldom available for this work but simple techniques using boxed turf have been evolved which give a clear indication of the likely performance of a compound under practical conditions. Thereafter selected compounds are made available in greater quantity for full scale field experimentation.

TECHNIQUES

The small-scale screening tests have two main objectives: (a) to evaluate the activity of the compound against the pathogen in turf and (b) to determine the tolerance of turfgrass species to the compound. At this stage compounds are screened for activity against Fusarium patch only. As this is the most common disease problem on turf in the United Kingdom any new fungicide must show activity against this organism if it is to be commercially viable. Materials appearing worthy of a secondary field screening may then be used in trials on sites naturally infected with any of the major British turf pathogens.

Four operations are involved in this initial screening:-

(i)   production in boxes of suitable turf swards,

(ii) production of suitable disease inoculum,

(iii) disease inoculation and application of treatments,

(iv) assessment.

(i) Production in boxes of suitable turf swards

Tests are carried out on both young and established swards. A pure sward of Agrostis tenuis Sibth. (browntop bent) is used as this species is readily susceptible to Fusarium patch. For young swards, seed is sown direct into John Innes compost in wooden seed trays, 9 x 9 in. (23 x 23 cm) and the boxes used after 10 - 15 weeks. Established swards are obtained by lifting turves from a fine-turf area sown to browntop bent, cutting them to standard size and trimming to uniform depth with a turf box and blade, and boxing up in the same 9 x 9 in. trays. These swards are used 2 - 3 weeks after boxing.

The size of tray used enables the swards to be mown in four directions using a portable belt mower. Regular close mowing is a primary requirement and a machine was developed to enable this to be carried out. A side-wheel mower was mounted over a moving belt, both driven by the same electric motor. Boxes can be passed rapidly beneath the mower at uniform cutting height, which can be quickly adjusted to suit varying requirements, age of sward, etc. Regular use of this machine enables a good, close-knit sward to be maintained.

Ample nitrogenous fertilizer is applied to these swards to increase disease susceptibility.

(ii) Production of suitable disease inoculum

Fusarium nivale is maintained in pure culture on plates of Czapek-Dox agar medium, 0.1% boric acid being added as a bacteriostatic agent. The organism is re-isolated regularly from diseased turf to overcome problems arising from decline in pathogenicity. These cultures are used to seed batches of inoculum as required.

The medium used for preparing inoculum consists of medium-grade sand and maize-meal (ratio 60:40 by volume), moistened with demineralised water until just damp throughout. This is placed in 1 l conical flasks, approximately 500g per flask, and sterilised by autoclaving at 10 lb./sq.in. (700 g/sq cm) for 30 minutes. The cultures are inoculated with small agar cores from the stock culture plates and incubated at 12°C. The inoculum is ready for use in 10 - 14 days.

In earlier experiments, it was found that this type of inoculum comprising actively growing mycelium gave more reliable results than a spore suspension. The environmental requirements are possibly less precise for continued mycelial growth than for spore germination.

(iii) Disease inoculation and application of treatments

Inoculation is carried out by breaking up a fully grown culture and brushing it evenly into the turf. Inoculated and uninoculated control treatments (unsprayed) are included with each batch of tests to ensure that disease potential has indeed been introduced.

It was found that high humidity and lack of direct sunlight are more important factors than temperature in the initiation of Fusarium patch disease. During autumn and winter, prevailing climatic conditions are often conducive to disease and trials sited on benches in the open are usually successful. In summer, tests in high humidity containers (large plastic sandwich boxes) in the laboratory are more likely to succeed.

Treatments of candidate compounds applied, separately as both preventive and curative treatments, are given in water (rate equivalent to 60 gal./ac.=

367

670 l/ha) using a constant pressure sprayer at 40 lb./sq. in. (2.8 kg/sq cm).

(iv) Assessment

Trials are recorded for disease intensity before treatment and then as soon as the inoculated, unsprayed control treatments are showing severe disease symptoms.

On a box-scale the typical patch type of symptom does not usually occur. A general "melting-out" of the grass over the whole area of the box is more common and this type of symptom is difficult to assess quantitatively without resorting to procedures such as weighing mowings. However, a simple score of disease intensity on a 0 - 10 basis has proved adequate in this initial screening.

The tolerance of turfgrass species to the compounds under test was previously determined by treating uninoculated swards in boxes as above with a range of concentrations and assessing phytotoxicity on a similar 0 - 10 scale of intensity. For this purpose, however, strips 1 yd. (0.9 m) wide of five grass species have now been established. Spraying at right angles across these strips gives a convenient quick way of covering the range of species with a minimum quantity of material.

FIELD EXPERIMENTATION

These simple box techniques facilitate the sorting of the few promising compounds from the stream of new materials emerging from primary screening. When the compounds selected are available in greater quantity they are then included in normal large-scale field trials under a wide range of conditions before any final decision is made as to their future use.

ACKNOWLEDGEMENT

It is a pleasure to acknowledge that Dr. C. R. Skogley was associated with this development in its initial stages, in his capacity as a Fisons Research Fellow.

DISCUSSION

Before the discussion began, Dr. I. Yoshikawa showed slides on the following aspects of turf diseases in Japan:-

1. The symptoms and control of "Haruhage", caused by infection by Fusarium nivale (Fr.) Ces. and Pythium spp. during dormancy of zoysiagrasses.

2. The symptoms of the disease connected with "Haruhage" on zoysia greens, called "Shizumi".

3. Fairy rings on zoysiagrass greens.

4. Helminthosporium spp. diseases on zoysiagrasses and their control.

5. Slime mould on zoysiagrasses during periods of high temperature.

6. Symptoms of brown patch (Rhizoctonia solani Kuhn) on Seaside bentgrass and some chemicals effective against it.

7. Symptoms of dollar spot (Sclerotinia homoeocarpa F.T. Bennett) on Astoria bentgrass, and its control.

SNOW MOULD (FUSARIUM NIVALE AND TYPHULA SPECIES)

C.M. Switzer (Canada)

What are the current methods of controlling snow mould?

J.R. Escritt (U.K.)

In the U.K. snow mould is usually Fusarium nivale (Fr.) Ces. This can be controlled by mercurials.

B. Langvad (Sweden)

In Sweden we use PCNB for Fusarium control. It works, but not as well as we would like. It is not permitted to use mercury products in Sweden.

R. Goss (Washington, U.S.A.)

We use phenyl mercury acetate, mercuric chloride and Daconil to control the snow mould caused by Typhula spp. although we do not rate it as a serious disease. Panogen has also been used.

POA PRATENSIS AND HELMINTHOSPORIUM

G.M. Wood (Vermont, U.S.A.)

I was interested in Mr. Escritt's statement that Poa pratensis L. has not done well in England. Could this be due to the very low height of cut of English lawns? Has Poa pratensis been tried at a much higher cut, which would help considerably in control of Helminthosporium spp. disease?

J.R. Escritt (U.K.)

Although a low height of cut, e.g. ¾ in. (2 cm) encourages Helminthosporium spp., we even have trouble at 1 in. (2.5 cm) height of cut.

H. Vos (Netherlands)

Can Mr. Langvad distinguish the spots of <u>Helminthosporium</u> <u>vagans</u> Drechsler from those of <u>Helminthosporium</u> <u>siccans</u> Drechsler? <u>H. siccans</u> is less damaging.

B. Langvad (Sweden)

The <u>Helminthosporium</u> recorded in Sweden is <u>H. vagans</u>; other species may be involved, but are not recorded.

SEED-BORNE DISEASES

D.T.A. Aldrich (U.K.)

Are any of the turfgrass diseases seed-borne, and if so, is seed dressing an effective control?

J.R. Escritt (U.K.)

Some diseases are seed-borne, but seed dressings are not widely used in practice.

T.E. Freeman (Florida, U.S.A.)

The situation is the same in the U.S.A. Seed rates are so high that it is not economic to apply seed dressings.

PYTHIUM BLIGHT (PYTHIUM SPP.)

S.W. Bingham (Virginia, U.S.A.)

Since <u>Pythium</u> spp. occur at temperatures above 21°C, are chemical treatments used as preventative or curative measures?

T.E. Freeman (Florida, U.S.A.)

Control of <u>Pythium</u> blight is entirely on a preventative basis in the state of Florida. Beginning at the date of seeding, weekly applications are recommended when temperatures are above 21°C.

EFFECTS OF HERBICIDES AND FERTILIZERS ON DISEASES

R.L. Morris (U.K.)

Is the increased use of spray chemicals causing more <u>Ophiobolus</u> patch in the U.S.A.?

R.L. Goss (Washington, U.S.A.)

In the U.S.A. we were possibly not identifying the disease properly in the past. Certainly the diminished levels of phosphorus, potassium and sulphur are causing more <u>O. graminis</u>. Methyl bromide fumigation allows the disease to express itself with greater devastation. Much still needs to be found out about the causes of the disease, and work is in progress on the possible effects of sulphur and phosphorus.

J.R. Escritt (U.K.)

In relation to effects of spray chemicals on disease, we have found that maleic hydrazide encourages <u>Corticium</u> <u>fuciforme</u> (Berk.) Wakef.

T.E. Freeman (Florida, U.S.A.)

Dr. Goss commented on the reduction of disease by sulphur. In Dr. Horn's fertility plots did sulphur retard dollar spot development?

G.C. Horn (Florida, U.S.A.)

Yes.

ARTIFICIAL TURF

J.P. van der Horst (Netherlands)

In view of disease damage on natural turf what do the Americans think of the future of artificial turf on greens?

W.H. Daniel (Indiana, U.S.A.)

Use of artificial turf is increasing in the U.S.A.: the cost of maintaining natural turf and the resistance to heavy wear favour increased use of artificial turf. But it solves one set of problems only to create another.

W.H. Bengeyfield (California, U.S.A.)

I do not consider there is a trend towards the use of artificial turf on greens. I know of many situations where artificial turf was installed and has now been removed.

PREVENTATIVE SPRAYING AND THE DEVELOPMENT OF THATCH

A.R. Woolhouse (Steward, S.T.R.I., U.K.)

Do the Americans find that in plots receiving preventative spraying more thatch builds up?

J.H. Madison (California, U.S.A.)

Yes, there is an increase of about 20% in thatch build-up with preventative spraying, but the thatch is clean, bright and straw-coloured. Without preventative spraying, thatch is dark, spotted and decaying. When we have scalped experimental turf we have seen clean uniform thatch under sprayed turf. Under unsprayed turf we have found rings, spots and patches of activity of saprophytic fungi working in the thatch.

R.R. Davis (Ohio, U.S.A.)

Surely anything which encourages the growth of grass will also encourage thatch production? High nutrition and fungicidal treatments will both increase thatch.

SESSION 4C: WEEDS

(Chairman: Mr. J. R. Escritt)

HERBICIDES AND PUTTING GREEN TURFGRASSES

S. W. Bingham,

Associate Professor of Plant Physiology, Department of Plant Pathology
and Physiology, Virginia Polytechnic Institute, Blacksburg, Virginia, U.S.A.

SUMMARY

The weeds that occur in putting green turf are readily divided into
two large groups, broadleaf weeds and grasses. Dicamba and mecoprop are
used widely on broadleaf weeds in putting greens. Dicamba has caused some
root stunting particularly of seedling grasses; however, this was not as
severe as weed competition in some instances. Annual grasses are prevented
from becoming established with pre-emergence herbicides such as DCPA and
bensulide for control of crabgrass and annual bluegrass. Goosegrass control
is only fair to poor with pre-emergence herbicides, and post-emergence
treatments are needed to supplement them for complete control. In cases
where reseeding becomes necessary after pre-emergence treatments, activated
charcoal has been demonstrated to be quite useful to inactivate the herbicide,
especially after bensulide. Treatments of bermudagrass greens with low
levels of herbicide in the fall, in conjunction with overseeding with cool-
season grasses, were very effective for control of annual bluegrass and
provided a desirable putting surface.

INTRODUCTION

Prior to 1945, weeds in lawn and garden areas were controlled by mechanical
means or with various acids and salts (8). For example, shoots of buckhorn
plantain (Plantago lanceolata L.) were cut off and a hole pierced in the crown
for a few drops of carbolic acid. Since that time a number of organic chemicals
have been evaluated for herbicides in putting green turfgrasses.

Herbicides are classified in many ways including their chemical nature and
toxic action. There is also the tendency to group the weeds according to
responses to herbicides. In turfgrass weed research, the effort has been in
two major categories, i.e. broadleaf weeds and annual grasses.

HERBICIDES FOR BROADLEAF WEEDS

For several years 2, 4-D has been a common standard for evaluating new
herbicides for many broadleaf weeds in turf, but in putting green situations
this standard chemical has caused injury to the turfgrasses. In addition,
white clover (Trifolium repens L.) and common chickweed (Stellaria media L.)
are major broadleaf weeds occurring in putting green turfgrasses throughout the
United States. Generally, hard seed of white clover is not killed with fumigation treatments used in establishing such turf. These weeds are not controlled
adequately with 2, 4-D.

During the last few years, dicamba and mecoprop have received considerable
attention in turfgrass research (4, 5). In 1962, dicamba appeared promising for
complete control of white clover and chickweed in bentgrass (Agrostis tenuis
Sibth.) under putting green conditions. In later studies application techniques

were found critical since there was only a four-fold safety margin between complete control of white clover and significant injury to bentgrasses.

Dicamba is a water-soluble herbicide and leaches into the soil quite readily. These chemical characteristics may be utilized for turfgrass advantage. The material is applied and left long enough to give control of the weeds and then leached out of the turfgrass rootzone to reduce the effect on the turf species. In this manner, new seedings are quite successful at the time of, or soon after, dicamba treatments, as shown by the results of the trial given in Table 1. Germination was initially reduced; however, in a relatively short period of time, a good stand of grass was obtained. At low treatment levels, growth of the turf species was better than in untreated control plots. This was possibly due to weed competition without chemical treatment. It would appear practical to seed any bare spots in a few weeks after dicamba application. It has further been demonstrated that competition from weeds can have a more adverse effect than the herbicide on root growth of turfgrass seedlings.

Table 1: effect of dicamba on germination and growth of bluegrass on a sandy loam soil

Dicamba applied 29 March 1968	Dry weight on August 12 (g/160 sq cm)			
	Bluegrass seeded 28 March (1 day before spraying)		Bluegrass seeded 1 May (33 days after spraying)	
kg/ha	root	shoot	root	shoot
0	9	3	12	3
0.28	15	5	11	3
0.56	11	5	12	3
1.12	9	4	9	4
2.24	5	3	11	4
4.48	1	1	4	2

HERBICIDES FOR ANNUAL GRASSES

Crabgrass (Digitaria sanguinalis (L.) Scop.), goosegrass (Eleusine indica (L.) Gaertn.) and annual bluegrass (Poa annua L.) are the important annual grasses occurring as weeds in fine turfgrasses. Although fumigation treatments used in establishing such turfgrasses readily control these weeds, seed from nearby areas reinfests the greens. Herbicides used for pre-emergence control of these species of weeds have gained popularity because they do not cause the discoloration of turfgrasses commonly observed with chemicals used for post-emergence control of crabgrass and goosegrass. These pre-emergence herbicides have given superior control of annual bluegrass and crabgrass (3, 7, 10) but in many instances less than desirable performance in goosegrass control. The post-emergence herbicides have given better control in this case.

i. Crabgrass control in bentgrass

     The herbicides used for crabgrass control are normally applied each year
just prior to germination of this weed. The long-term vigour of the turfgrass
as well as consistent control of crabgrass following treatment with these chemicals has received further study. A location in established bentgrass near the
VPI golf course was selected for this study. The plots were replicated 3 times.
The dates of herbicide application during the last 7 years were: 4 May 1962;
6 April 1963; 16 April 1964; 20 April 1965; 15 April 1966; 18 April 1967; and
18 April 1968.

     A rating in Table 2 indicates that the listed herbicide was used during
that year: a dash indicates that some other chemical or possibly no treatment
at all was used during the year. Annual preparation involved vertical mowing
and overseeding with crabgrass seed at 1 to 2 kg/100 sq m. The area was clipped
to prevent growth beyond 1.5 cm tall, fertilized and irrigated as needed for
growth of bentgrass.

     Crabgrass control was consistently good with DCPA, bensulide, bandane
(polychlorodicyclopentadiene isomers), and granules of DMPA. Slightly poorer
control was obtained with benefin, terbutol (2,6-di-tert-butyl-p-tolyl-
methylcarbamate), siduron and DMPA (EC) (Table 2).

Table 2: crabgrass control in bentgrass turf following annual treatments
          with herbicides

Herbicide	Treatments Formulation (Note 1)	Rate (kg/ha)	Crabgrass control ratings (Note 2) 1963	1964	1965	1967	1968	Average
DCPA	WP	11.20	10	10	10	10	9	10
	G	11.20	10	10	10	10	10	10
Bensulide	EC	16.80	10	10	10	10	9	10
	G	16.80	9	10	. 10	10	9	10
Benefin	G (Note 3)	2.24	–	–	8	4	7	6
	G	3.36	–	–	10	7	6	8
	G	6.72	–	–	–	–	8	8
Terbutol	WP	11.20	–	–	10	9	8	9
	G	11.20	9	9	–	7	5	8
Siduron	WP	13.44	–	–	10	7	7	8
Bandane	G	39.20	10	10	10	9	9	10
DMPA	EC	16.80	8	9	10	8	7	8
	G	16.80	10	10	10	10	9	10
Check			0(24)	0(31)	2(21)	0(27)	0(19)	0(24)

(1) WP = wettable powder: EC = emulsifiable concentrate: G = granules

(2) A 0 to 10 scale was used to estimate crabgrass control where 0 - no control;
     1, 2, 3 = crabgrass stunting; 4, 5, 6 = crabgrass stand reduction and/or
     severe stunting; 7, 8, 9 = major crabgrass stand reduction; and 10 = complete
     control. Crabgrass plants per 930 sq cm are recorded in parenthesis for the
     check only.

(3) The EC formulation was applied during 1965, 1966 and 1967 at 3.36 kg/ha benefin.

Bentgrass injury was noted for DCPA and DMPA in early May, 1963 (Table 3).

The observed injury was thought to be associated with the treatments in May 1962, in the form of delayed growth. As the season progressed, the plots recovered. The symptoms have been minor, if any, since that time. Terbutol has consistently caused some thinning and discoloration. Bensulide, benefin, siduron, bandane and DCPA (WP) have not caused significant injury to bentgrass during the seven-year period.

ii. Control of annual bluegrass in bermudagrass

Bensulide and DCPA applied in the fall have provided control of germinating annual bluegrass in bermudagrass, and the rates required can partly be reduced in the presence of overseeded cool-season grasses, which give some control of annual bluegrass by competition, as well as providing a more desirable putting surface than the annual bluegrass alone. Ryegrass (Lolium multiflorum Lam.) was more effective in this respect than creeping red fescue (Festuca rubra L. ssp. rubra). The competition of the ryegrass reduced the percent cover of annual bluegrass to approximately one-third that in dormant bermudagrass. This amount of annual blue-grass was enough to make the putting surface bumpy during the transition from cool-season grasses back to bermudagrass in May or June. This also allowed the annual bluegrass to flower quite well. It was particularly evident that 5.6 kg/ha of either bensulide or DCPA gave practical control for the season without injury to the cool-season turfgrasses. The higher rates of these herbicides were somewhat injurious to the overseeded grasses, particularly the creeping red fescue. The transition from cool-season grasses to active bermudagrass occurred slowly. Where annual bluegrass died in late May and June, the bermudagrass began to grow more rapidly, giving a higher percentage ground cover, than where desirable cool-season grasses were used. But initially for a short period the green had poor cover at the time annual bluegrass died out in early summer. The ground cover was good during the transition period where there was ryegrass and creeping red fescue.

Table 3: bentgrass injury ratings after applications of annual treatments for crabgrass control

Treatments			Bentgrass injury ratings 1/			
Herbicide	Formulation	Rate (kg/ha)	May 1963	May 1964	May 1967	July 1968
DCPA	WP	11.20	3	0	0	0
	G	11.20	6	3	0	1
Bensulide	EC	16.80	2	0	0	0
	G	16.80	3	0	0	2
Benefin	G	2.24	-	-	3	1
	G	3.36	-	-	1	1
	G	6.72	-	-	-	1
Terbutol	G	11.20	4	4	4	6
Siduron	WP	13.44	-	-	0	1
Bandane	G	39.20	4	2	2	2
DMPA	EC	16.80	9	4	2	0
	G	16.80	8	4	3	0
Check			2	0	1	1

1/ A 0 to 10 scale was used with 10 = complete kill of the bentgrass; 9, 8, 7 = severe loss in bentgrass ground cover; 6, 5, 4 = reduction in ground cover; 3, 2, 1 = colour response only; and 0 = no response

iii. Re-seeding after the use of residual herbicides

The pre-emergence crabgrass herbicides are residual in nature and this is a requirement for continuous control. Where these chemicals were applied annually, residues were found eleven months after the fourth annual application in the case of bensulide (6). Detectable quantities were obtained to depths of 12 cm. In these studies, it was also demonstrated that heavier doses of bensulide were required to give an amount detectable by bioassay in soils with high organic matter content than in soils of low organic content.

A frequent problem encountered with residual chemicals is related to re-seeding desirable turfgrasses after treatments. Loss of existing turf may occur for any number of reasons, usually not related to the herbicide treatment. Normally, turfgrasses cannot be seeded safely for a period ranging from a few weeks to several months after treatment, depending on the herbicide used (6, 9). In recent studies, activated charcoal has been used to inactivate bensulide in the soil (Table 4). The herbicide was applied, de-activated one week later, and the plots seeded to crabgrass and creeping red fescue. At one month after seeding, dry weights were obtained to demonstrate the inactivation of the chemical. Bensulide is normally used at 11.2 kg/ha for crabgrass control; activated charcoal at 168 kg/ha was sufficient for effective immediate establishment of creeping red fescue, after such a treatment. Crabgrass control was also lost as a result of the charcoal treatments. These data demonstrate that, if re-seeding becomes necessary after bensulide had been applied, activated charcoal may be used effectively to inactivate the herbicide.

Table 4: inactivation of bensulide by activated charcoal, as measured by the growth and development of various grasses seeded a few days after herbicide treatment

Rate of bensulide	Dry weight of grass plants (g/160 sq cm) (see footnote)			
		Charcoal (kg/ha)		
(kg/ha)	0	84	168	336
Crabgrass				
0.0	4	6	6	6
5.6	0	3	6	6
11.2	0	3	7	4
22.4	0	0	1	2
44.8	0	0	0	2
Creeping red fescue				
0.0	9	11	10	11
5.6	3	9	15	15
11.2	3	9	14	17
22.4	0	9	9	13
44.8	0	2	6	16

Plugs were taken from each sub-plot, soil washed out, plants dried at 105^{0}C for 24 hours and weighed.

iv.   Effects of crabgrass herbicides on turfgrasses

Some crabgrass herbicides have reduced or temporarily inhibited the growth of roots of turfgrasses (1).   In field studies, stoloniferous turfgrasses showed no signs of foliar injury during the immediate growing season after application of these herbicides.   However, in the second year, turfgrasses so treated sometimes initiated growth later than normal.   Obviously, the effect of the herbicide was not observed and the delayed growth in the second season was a result of the unrecognized injury in the first season.   Specific experiments to determine root responses demonstrated that under field conditions certain crabgrass herbicides delayed normal rooting of bermudagrass from nodes for 12 weeks.   In greenhouse studies, placement of the herbicide at various soil depths reduced the number of roots developing below the treatment; however, normal root growth occurred above the treated layer.

Histological studies of various root tips showed that cell division had ceased following DCPA treatment (2).   In certain instances, cell enlargement continued and excessively large, irregularly-shaped cells were formed.   Several cells were dinucleate and more numerous occurrences of the metaphase stage of mitosis were observed in the treated tissue.

REFERENCES

1.   BINGHAM, S.W. (1967) Influence of herbicides on root development of bermudagrass. Weeds 15, 363.

2.   BINGHAM, S.W. (1968) Effect of DCPA on anatomy and cytology of roots. Weed Sci. 16, 449.

3.   BINGHAM, S.W., and SCHMIDT, R.E. (1964) Crabgrass control in turf. Proc. Southern Weed Conf. 17, 113.

4.   BINGHAM, S.W., and SCHMIDT, R.E. (1965) Broadleaved weed control in turf. Agron. J. 57, 258.

5.   BINGHAM, S.W., and SCHMIDT, R.E. (1965) Broadleaf weed control in turf. Proc. Southern Weed Conf. 18, 130.

6.   BINGHAM, S.W., and SCHMIDT, R.E. (1967) Residue of bensulide in turfgrass soil following annual treatments for crabgrass control. Agron. J. 59, 327.

7.   BINGHAM, S.W., SCHMIDT, R.E., and CURRY, C.K. (1969) Annual bluegrass control in overseeded bermudagrass putting green turf. Agron. J. 61, (in press).

8.   FOGG, J.M., Jnr. (1945) Weeds of lawn and garden. University of Pennsylvania Press, Philadelphia.

9.   JAGSCHITZ, J.A., and SKOGLEY, C.R. (1966) Turfgrass response to seedbed and seedling applications of pre-emergence and broadleaf herbicides. Proc. Northeastern Weed Contr. Conf. 20, 554.

10. JUSKA, F.V., and HANSON, A.A. (1967) Factors affecting Poa annua L. control. Weeds 15, 98.

BROADLEAF WEED CONTROL IN TURF: MIXTURES OF DICAMBA WITH 2,4-D AND MCPA

P. Bowen and R.L. Morris,

Fisons Limited, Levington Research Station, Ipswich, Suffolk, U.K.

SUMMARY

Details are given of experimental methods and results of work carried out from 1966 onwards at various turf sites throughout England on herbicide mixtures based on dicamba combined with either 2,4-D or MCPA. The mixtures were applied to a wide range of weeds commonly found in turf in Great Britain. Results showed that dicamba/2,4-D or dicamba/MCPA gave good control of most of these common weeds, the results being comparable with mecoprop/2,4-D or dichlorprop/2,4-D mixtures.

INTRODUCTION

In Great Britain some 35 - 40 troublesome weed species occur in closely mown turf. There are others but these are mainly annuals associated with newly-sown turf and are not normally a problem once regular close mowing is practised.

Some weeds may present problems in specific locations where soil or climatic conditions are suitable. However, due to their adaptability, certain weeds, notably Bellis perennis L., Trifolium repens L., Cerastium holosteoides Fr., Plantago spp. and Ranunculus repens L., occur commonly in outfield turf and also in home lawns. It is desirable to obtain as effective a control as possible of all these weeds in one application, particularly with outfield turf which is rarely sprayed annually.

Collectively the whole range of these weeds cannot be killed by spraying with derivatives of either phenoxy-acetic or phenoxy-propionic acids since weed susceptibility to either group is incomplete. For example, where 2,4-D or MCPA only have been used a considerable build-up of Trifolium spp. can result, and it becomes necessary to use a phenoxy-propionic material to effect control. To obtain satisfactory broad-spectrum control it is necessary to apply a mixture of one herbicide from each group, and 2,4-D combined with a phenoxy-propionic derivative, notably mecoprop, has been widely used.

Levington Research Station has conducted work for a number of years with selective herbicide mixtures for use on turf both in the home garden and professional sectors. The aim of this work has been the production of herbicide mixtures with the following characteristics:

(i)   good control of a wide range of broadleaf weeds,

(ii)   safety in use without risk of damage to the turf,

(iii) economically acceptable product, which may be sprayed or applied as a combined fertilizer/herbicide.

From 1966 onwards, extensive final stage development trials were carried out with herbicide mixtures for use principally on outfield turf where low-cost and broad-spectrum control were the prime objectives.

Dicamba showed promise in preliminary experiments at Levington and also in the U.S.A., where it gave good control of many broadleaf turf weeds including _Trifolium repens_. The American work (1, 2, 3) showed that control could be obtained at 0.5 lb./ac. a.i. (0.56 kg/ha) and experience in agriculture indicated that dicamba was effective at rates as low as 0.2 to 0.25 lb./ac. a.i. (0.22 - 0.28 kg/ha).

As well as the advantages of considerable activity at a low rate of application, another important attribute of dicamba was its ability to control knotgrass, _Polygonum aviculare_ L. (4), a weed resistant, except at an early stage, to most commonly-used herbicides. This weed can be a severe problem in newly sown areas of turf where it smothers the young grass. It is most troublesome in late spring sowings particularly on football fields where re-seeding of worn patches takes place in late May, at the time when its seed is germinating freely. Dicamba, therefore, showed promise as an alternative to mecoprop or dichlorprop, particularly in formulated mixtures, and a series of experiments was initiated using dicamba in place of these materials.

MATERIALS

Dicamba was used as the sodium salt in combination with sodium and potassium salts of MCPA, while in dicamba/2,4-D mixtures both were present as dimethyl-amine salts. All mixtures were aqueous concentrates. The rates of dicamba used in these experiments ranged from 0.2 to 0.5 lb./ac. a.i. (0.22 - 0.56 kg/ha).

In experiment IV the herbicide carrier used was a peat-based small-granule fertilizer containing 14% N, 4% P_2O_5, 4% K_2O.

EXPERIMENTAL METHOD

The technique used enables weed control experiments to be established quickly and effectively in a large area of England, so that a wide range of weeds is obtained under a variety of climatic, soil and management conditions. An area including Dorking in Southern England, Cheltenham in the West, and Coventry in the Midlands is covered. A two-man team can visit the widespread sites in a week and a round trip of some 4 - 500 miles. Starting in April, sites are established and revisited at 4 - 6 week intervals, throughout the season. On succeeding visits existing experiments are evaluated and further sites laid down; and so the effect of spray timing is additionally examined.

A plot size of 1 sq. yd. (0.84 sq m) is used and treatments are replicated four times. In this way up to seven positive treatments and a control can be examined in a space of 32 sq. yd. (26.8 sq m) which experience has shown to be the maximum area of the desired uniformly high weed density that can readily be found.

The experiment is set out with a terylene net, and permanently marked by inserting steel plugs below ground level. These can be found again by using a mine detector.

Weed density is recorded before treatment application using a 27 x 27 in. (69 x 69 cm) gridded quadrat of 3 in. (7.5 cm) wire mesh, a count being made separately of the number of specific weed species directly underlying grid intersections. Post-treatment recording is carried out similarly, two or three times at four to six week intervals. Results for the pre-treatment count are expressed

Table 1: results of Experiment 1

Weed, site and dates		Assess-ment *	None	Herbicide applied (lb./ac. a.i.) Dicamba 0.2, MCPA 1.5	MCPA 2.3	2,4-D 2.0
Trifolium repens L. (Oxfordshire)						
Sprayed	13 May 1966	0	40	42	52	40
Assessed	7 Jul. 1966	E	-90	100	77	46
"	27 Jul. 1966	E	-124	100	40	-10
"	14 Sep. 1966	E	-121	99	35	-5
Bellis perennis L. (Berkshire)						
Sprayed	13 May 1966	0	47	16	47	35
Assessed	6 Jul. 1966	E	-17	96	47	75
"	14 Sep. 1966	E	-41	56	2	43
Ranunculus repens L. (Berkshire)						
Sprayed	13 May 1966	0	21	22	15	17
Assessed	6 Jul. 1966	E	51	100	100	100
"	14 Sep. 1966	E	19	100	100	100
Bellis perennis (Suffolk)						
Sprayed	1 Jun. 1966	0	23	11	26	17
Assessed	27 Jul. 1966	E	22	86	86	95
"	18 Oct. 1966	E	20	80	80	84
Trifolium repens (Suffolk)						
Sprayed	1 Jun. 1966	0	10	19	14	18
Assessed	27 Jul. 1966	E	-115	100	86	37
"	18 Oct. 1966	E	-188	100	66	-33
Cerastium holosteoides Fr. (Suffolk)						
Sprayed	1 Jun. 1966	0	10	16	15	15
Assessed	27 Jul. 1966	E	-13	100	100	26
"	18 Oct. 1966	E	10	98	100	45

Weed, site and dates	Assess-ment *	Herbicide applied (lb./ac. a.i.)			
		None	Dicamba 0.2, MCPA 1.5	MCPA 2.3	2,4-D 2.0

Plantago major L.
(Warwickshire)

Sprayed	2 Jun. 1966	O	15	21	17	14
Assessed	16 Sep. 1966	E	-35	94	98	100

Ranunculus repens
(Warwickshire)

Sprayed	3 Jun. 1966	O	33	44	45	35
Assessed	16 Sep. 1966	E	-24	100	99	75

Trifolium dubium Sibth.
(Surrey)

Sprayed	8 Jun. 1966	O	37	37	34	30
Assessed	6 Jul. 1966	E	28	57	-14	92
"	21 Sep. 1966	E	12	97	89	98

Plantago lanceolata L.
(Surrey)

Sprayed	8 Jun. 1966	O	15	16	9	10
Assessed	6 Jul. 1966	E	-63	79	83	100
"	21 Sep. 1966	E	-14	100	97	100

Plantago major
(Berkshire)

Sprayed	8 Jun. 1966	O	31	33	21	25
Assessed	27 Jul. 1966	E	-43	62	31	96
"	14 Sep. 1966	E	-54	72	24	93

Trifolium repens
(Gloucestershire)

Sprayed	8 Jul. 1966	O	72	63	73	72
Assessed	15 Sep. 1966	E	-18	97	20	21

Plantago major
(Gloucestershire)

Sprayed	8 Jul. 1966	O	52	31	43	33
Assessed	15 Sep. 1966	E	38	100	99	99

* Note: O = original % cover by weed.
E = % effectiveness of control: a negative figure indicates increased weed population.

Table 2: results of Experiment II

Weed, site and dates		Assess-ment *	None	Dicamba				Mecoprop 2.0, 2,4-D 1.5
				0.2	0.3	0.4	0.5	
Achillea millefolium L. (Suffolk)								
Sprayed	9 May 1967	0	25	25	22	20	12	9
Assessed	22 Jun. 1967	E	5	60	76	92	100	78
Trifolium repens (Suffolk)								
Sprayed	9 May 1967	0	65	67	48	63	50	66
Assessed	22 Jun. 1967	E	-11	100	100	100	100	99
Achillea millefolium (Suffolk)								
Sprayed	13 Jun. 1967	0	23	42	43	32	40	29
Assessed	3 Aug. 1967	E	-9	55	79	86	88	91
"	6 Nov. 1967	E	-19	44	60	71	76	83
Trifolium repens (Suffolk)								
Sprayed	13 Jun. 1967	0	49	36	39	46	54	50
Assessed	3 Aug. 1967	E	-3	98	100	97	99	100
"	6 Nov. 1967	E	-14	97	98	99	100	99
Achillea millefolium (Oxford)								
Sprayed	13 Jun. 1967	0	28	43	32	32	26	34
Assessed	21 Oct. 1967	E	-48	43	59	81	82	95

* Note: O = original % cover by weed.
E = % effectiveness of control: a negative figure indicates increased weed population.

Table 3: results of Experiment III

Weed, site and dates		Assessment *	Herbicide applied (lb./ac. a.i.)					
			None	Dicamba + 2,4-D				Mecoprop 2.0 2,4-D 1.5
				0.2 + 1.5	0.3 + 1.5	0.4 + 1.5	0.5 + 1.5	
Achillea millefolium (Suffolk)								
Sprayed	11 May 1967	0	29	16	21	13	9	27
Assessed	27 Jun. 1967	E	−10	82	84	73	100	86
"	4 Aug. 1967	E	−14	59	69	80	72	77
"	6 Nov. 1967	E	−1	55	51	61	66	74
Trifolium repens (Suffolk)								
Sprayed	11 May 1967	0	48	25	39	30	24	35
Assessed	27 Jun. 1967	E	−8	100	100	100	100	100
"	4 Aug. 1967	E	−6	100	100	100	100	99
"	6 Nov. 1967	E	−14	100	98	100	96	100
Achillea millefolium (Suffolk)								
Sprayed	12 Jun. 1967	0	36	44	22	42	34	40
Assessed	4 Aug. 1967	E	−14	77	89	88	93	92
"	3 Nov. 1967	E	−31	70	70	74	92	88
Trifolium repens (Suffolk)								
Sprayed	12 Jun. 1967	0	37	32	41	27	37	40
Assessed	4 Aug. 1967	E	−14	99	100	100	100	100
"	3 Nov. 1967	E	−28	94	95	100	99	99

* Note: 0 = original % cover by weed.
         E = % effectiveness of control: a negative figure indicates increased
         weed population.

Table 4: results of Experiment IV

| Weed, site and dates | Assess-ment * | Herbicide applied (lb./ac. a.i.) | | |
		None	Dicamba 0.3 + 2,4-D 1.8 in fertilizer	Dichlorprop 2.0 + 2,4-D 1.5 as liquid
Trifolium repens (Suffolk)				
Sprayed 27 Apr. 1967	O	42	59	40
Assessed 30 May 1967	E	-2	97	100
" 21 Jul. 1967	E	33	98	98
Ranunculus repens (Suffolk)				
Sprayed 27 Apr. 1967	O	11	11	23
Assessed 30 May 1967	E	-29	92	100
" 21 Jul. 1967	E	-37	64	95
Cerastium holosteoides (Suffolk)				
Sprayed 27 Apr. 1967	O	15	20	13
Assessed 30 May 1967	E	-4	77	84
" 21 Jul. 1967	E	-14	94	100
Trifolium repens (Surrey)				
Sprayed 10 May 1967	O	52	56	55
Assessed 23 Jun. 1967	E	-21	92	98
" 26 Jul. 1967	E	-8	91	98
Bellis perennis (Surrey)				
Sprayed 10 May 1967	O	74	60	52
Assessed 23 Jun. 1967	E	13	54	50
" 26 Jul. 1967	E	1	38	35

Weed, site and dates	Assess- ment *	Herbicide applied (lb./ac. a.i.)		
		None	Dicamba 0.3 + 2,4-D 1.8 in fertilizer	Dichlorprop 2.0 + 2,4-D 1.5 as liquid
Trifolium repens (Berkshire)				
Sprayed 9 May 1967	O	53	53	73
Assessed 26 Jun. 1967	E	-20	95	98
" 27 Jul. 1967	E	-17	98	100
Bellis perennis (Berkshire)				
Sprayed 9 May 1967	O	42	38	53
Assessed 26 Jun. 1967	E	26	72	56
" 27 Jul. 1967	E	18	57	40
Achillea millefolium (Berkshire)				
Sprayed 9 May 1967	O	26	18	33
Assessed 26 Jun. 1967	E	0	65	83
" 27 Jul. 1967	E	1	68	75
Plantago lanceolata (Warwickshire)				
Sprayed 8 Jun. 1967	O	11	9	9
Assessed 25 Jul. 1967	E	-17	100	100
Hypochaeris radicata L. (Warwickshire)				
Sprayed 8 Jun. 1967	O	26	23	17
Assessed 25 Jul. 1967	E	18	99	100

* Note: O = original % cover by weed.
E = % effectiveness of control: a negative figure indicates increased weed population.

Table 5:   results of Experiment V

A.   APPLIED USING SPRAYER

Weed, site and dates	Assess- ment *	Herbicide applied (lb./ac. a.i.)		
		None	Dicamba 0.3 + 2,4-D 1.8	Dichlorprop 2.0 + 2,4-D 1.5
Hieracium pilosella L. (Surrey)				
Sprayed 7 Aug. 1968	O	37	39	38
Assessed 17 Oct. 1968	E	34	94	92
Lotus corniculatus L. (Surrey)				
Sprayed 7 Aug. 1968	O	19	21	24
Assessed 17 Oct. 1968	E	5	36	55
Leontodon autumnalis L. (Surrey)				
Sprayed 7 Aug. 1968	O	15	19	12
Assessed 17 Oct. 1968	E	2	69	40
Trifolium repens (Oxfordshire)				
Sprayed 6 Aug. 1968	O	69	67	75
Assessed 17 Oct. 1968	E	24	100	90
Prunella vulgaris L. (Oxfordshire)				
Sprayed 6 Aug. 1968	O	15	12	10
Assessed 17 Oct. 1968	E	-43	53	97
Achillea millefolium (Kent)				
Sprayed 5 Aug. 1968	O	66	45	46
Assessed 16 Oct. 1968	E	14	92	92
Trifolium repens (Kent)				
Sprayed 5 Aug. 1968	O	33	39	31
Assessed 16 Oct. 1968	E	19	100	99

B. APPLIED USING WATERING CAN

Weed, site and dates	Assess-ment *	Herbicide applied (lb./ac. a.i.)		
		None	Dicamba 0.3 + 2,4-D 1.8	Dichlorprop 2.0 + 2,4-D 1.5
Plantago lanceolata (Surrey)				
Sprayed 5 Sep. 1968	0	61	50	57
Assessed 24 Oct. 1968	E	-9	88	80
Bellis perennis (Gloucestershire)				
Sprayed 19 Aug. 1968	0	70	69	70
Assessed 2 Oct. 1968	E	-11	83	36
Plantago lanceolata (Gloucestershire)				
Sprayed 19 Aug. 1968	0	13	22	17
Assessed 2 Oct. 1968	E	-2	87	93
Trifolium repens (Gloucestershire)				
Sprayed 19 Aug. 1968	0	13	17	17
Assessed 2 Oct. 1968	E	-159	100	80
Achillea millefolium (Suffolk)				
Sprayed 27 Aug. 1968	0	31	40	35
Assessed 30 Oct. 1968	E	-28	85	78
Trifolium repens (Suffolk)				
Sprayed 27 Aug. 1968	0	84	57	57
Assessed 30 Oct. 1968	E	-115	100	51
Ranunculus repens (Oxfordshire)				
Sprayed 30 Aug. 1968	0	51	55	54
Assessed 19 Oct. 1968	E	-17	66	54
Trifolium repens (Oxfordshire)				
Sprayed 30 Aug. 1968	0	57	46	48
Assessed 19 Oct. 1968	E	9	100	99
Taraxacum officinale Weber (Warwickshire)				
Sprayed 29 Aug. 1968	0	53	70	54
Assessed 19 Oct. 1968	E	26	89	93

* Note: O = original % cover by weed.
          E = % effectiveness of control: a negative figure indicates increased
              weed population.

as % ground cover, and for post-treatment counts as % effectiveness. A site
giving an initial count of 30% or more is considered a good one for most weeds.

Liquid treatments are applied as follows, spray drift being prevented by a
portable folding screen:

(a)   using a specially developed small-plot sprayer usually at a water
       rate of 60 gal./ac. (674 l/ha).

or   (b)   by watering can at a water rate of 605 gal./ac. (6,794 l/ha), this
       method being used when it will be that adopted by the ultimate user,
       for example on the home lawn.

Combined fertilizer/herbicide treatments are applied by hand.

RESULTS

Experiment I (1966)

This experiment (8 sites) examined various herbicide treatments intended to
give an effective low-cost control of outfield weeds. One treatment was MCPA/
dicamba applied at 1.7 lb./ac. total a.i. which was compared with MCPA at
2.3 lb./ac. a.i. and 2,4-D at 2.0 lb./ac. a.i., both of which are used on outfield turf (1.91, 2.58 and 2.24 kg/ha respectively).

The results (Table 1) showed that MCPA/dicamba gives as acceptable weed control as MCPA or 2,4-D, and superior control of Trifolium repens.

Experiments II and III (1967)

These two experiments (5 sites) examined the efficiency of dicamba in controlling Achillea millefolium L. and Trifolium repens, the former being one of
the more difficult weeds to eradicate from turf. The reason is probably the
small leaf area and the extensive underground rootstock, sufficient of which remains alive after herbicide treatment for the plant to re-establish itself.

Dicamba was applied at rates of 0.2 - 0.5 lb./ac. a.i. (0.22 - 0.56 kg/ha)
alone and in combination with 2,4-D at 1.5 lb./ac. a.i. (1.68 kg/ha) and compared
with mecoprop/2,4-D at 3.5 lb./ac. total a.i. (3.92 kg/ha).

In experiment II (Table 2) the degree of control of A. millefolium by
dicamba alone increased with rate, and at 0.5 lb./ac. a.i. the control was as
effective as the mecoprop/2,4-D mixture at 3.5 lb./ac. total a.i.

At one site of experiment III (Table 3) the two higher rates of dicamba/
2,4-D and the mecoprop/2,4-D mixture gave 90% control of A. millefolium six
months after treatment, but at the other site long-term control was less satisfactory from all materials.

In both experiments, all treatments gave almost 100% control of Trifolium
repens at all sites.

Experiment IV (1967)

This experiment (4 sites) examined various herbicides applied in a fertilizer carrier, a method used on home lawns in Great Britain because of the convenience of application.

The herbicide mixtures examined in fertilizer included 2,4-D/dicamba applied at 2.1 lb./ac. total a.i. and were compared with 2,4-D/dichlorprop applied as a liquid at 3.5 lb./ac. total a.i.: fertilizer was applied separately to this treatment, and to the no-herbicide plots.(2.35 and 3.92 kg/ha respectively).

The results (Table 4) show that 2,4-D/dicamba applied in a fertilizer gives a comparable control to that obtained with 2,4-D/dichlorprop applied as a liquid.

Experiment V (1968 - continuing 1969)

This experiment (8 sites) examined the same rate of 2,4-D/dicamba used in experiment IV but applied as a liquid by sprayer and watering can. Comparison was made with a 2,4-D/dichlorprop mixture applied at 3.5 lb./ac. total a.i.

The results (Table 5) show that almost 100% control of Trifolium repens was obtained with all treatments at all sites. With most other weeds 2,4-D/ dicamba at 2.1 lb./ac. a.i. gave results similar to or better than 2,4-D/dichlor- prop.

CONCLUSIONS

The results of these experiments show that dicamba applied at 0.2 - 0.3 lb./ ac. a.i. (0.22 - 0.34 kg/ha) in mixtures with MCPA or 2,4-D gives a control of a wide range of weeds similar to that obtained from 2,4-D/dichlorprop or 2,4-D/mecoprop.

Of the common weeds, Trifolium repens can be completely killed by one application of MCPA/dicamba or 2,4-D/dicamba. With most other weeds the control that can be expected from one application is between 80 and 90%, though 100% is obtained if conditions are favourable. Apart from experiment IV, fertilizer was not applied to the experiments before treatments were applied but experience shows this usually increases the effectiveness of any herbicide.

In many ways the most persistent as well as the most common weed is Bellis perennis, the best long-term control likely to be achieved from one application of any herbicide being about 50%. Generally sufficient rootstock and stem survive a single treatment, particularly in old established plants, for recovery in two months unless a second application is made. However, control from dicamba and mixtures with MCPA or 2,4-D gave equivalent control to that achieved from other herbicides.

Other work not reported here confirms that dicamba used alone or combined with MCPA or 2,4-D gives an excellent control of Polygonum aviculare even when it is well established.

REFERENCES

1. DANA, M.N., and NEWMAN, R. (1964) New products for post-emergence weed control. Proc. 20th N. Cent. Weed Control Conf. 51.

2. BINGHAM, S.W., and SCHMIDT, R.E. (1965) Broadleaved weed control in turf. Agron. J. 57, 3, 258.

3. BINGHAM, S.W., and SCHMIDT, R.E. (1965) Broadleaf weed control in turf. Proc. 18th Weed Control Conf. 1965, 130.

4. DAVIES, R.R., STROUBE, E.W., and MILLER, R.W. (1964) Ohio Fm, Home Res., 49, 28.

ANNUAL GRASS WEED CONTROL

Dr. W.H. Daniel,

Turf Specialist, Dept. of Agronomy, Purdue University, Lafayette, Indiana,

SUMMARY

The advantages of controlling grass weeds are outlined. Various pre-emergence and post-emergence treatments are described, in particular the pre-emergence use of arsenic.

INTRODUCTION

Competitive fast growth by an aggressive weedy grass can often repress and weaken the desired turf so that it fails to perform adequately. Thus the control of the competition of unwanted weeds is the target of fine turf management. This fits the old definition of a weed as "any plant not wanted". For example, Festuca arundinacea Schreb. in F. rubra L., or Poa spp. in Agrostis spp. or vice versa, are weeds of importance under certain turf uses.

Every climate and country has its characteristic problems, such as knotweed (Polygonum spp.), Poa annua L., crabgrass (Digitaria spp.), goosegrass (Eleusine indica (L.) Gaertn.) or other common weeds. Researchers and turf managers often see their greatest advances in the selective control of another competitor, which then encourages additional technology.

Advances in pre-emergence control of crabgrass has permitted better grass production in a wide portion of the United States, and selective control of Poa annua has allowed a recent increase in growing a single turf variety or species.

PRE-EMERGENCE WEED CONTROL

The ability to remove weeds selectively is of the utmost importance. The opportunity for professionalism in understanding and using techniques of application has been challenging to educators and practitioners alike.

Pre-emergence control is old in many respects, but the selective chemicals now available permit a new approach, and offer much scope, in combination with new tools and varieties. The period 1955-65 saw extensive research by many experiment stations and companies. For example for six years at Purdue University there were over 1,000 individual plots on crabgrass control each year.

(i) Warm-season annuals

In the U.S.A. springtime use of pre-emergence herbicides (as given in Table 1), before soil warmth under turf conditions passes $12^{\circ}C$, can prevent the appearance of smooth crabgrass (Digitaria ischaemum (Schreb.) Muhl.), hairy crabgrass (D. sanguinalis (L.) Scop.), goosegrass (Eleusine indica), wiregrass (Eragrostis capillaris (L.) Nees.), nimblewill seedlings (Muhlenbergia spp.),witchgrass (Panicum capillare L.), barnyardgrass (Echinochloa crusgalli (L.) Beauv.), sandburs (Cenchrus spp.), foxtails (Setaria spp.) and others.

Table 1:   herbicides used in the U.S.A. in 1969 as preventative treatments
           (single spring application)

Herbicide	lb./ac. ai. (kg/ha in brackets)	Comments
Bensulide (Betasan)	10 (11.2)	Bentgrass is quite tolerant
DCPA (Dacthal, Chlorthal)	10 (11.2)	Widely used
Siduron (Tupersan)	12 (13.4)	Does not affect perennials or P. annua
Terbutol (Azak)	10 (11.2)	Least used
Benefin (Balan)	2 (2.2)	Replaces diphenatrile and trifluralin
Bandane	40 (44.8)	Replaces chlordane used earlier
Arsenicals	120 (134.4)	Used as equivalent to arsenic trioxide: slow and long lasting: affects old P. annua also

With each chemical skill is required in understanding the rates and methods for proper use, particularly repeat treatments. For example, DCPA, bensulide, benefin and siduron have residual activities measured only in weeks or months. Bandane, DMPA (Zytron) and chlordane which were used earlier, have a carry-over of about 50% into the next year; so repeat rates should be lighter. Arsenic remains as a very dilute amount in the soil and, when phosphorus is not added, arsenic may persist for several years (12 years in one experiment still in pregress, and 10 years in another).

Concurrent reseeding is practical only with siduron and arsenicals, since benefin, DCPA, bensulide and terbutol are non-selective on seedlings. Therefore on established turf areas the renovation, reseeding and fertilizing are closely related to which chemical is used for pre-emergence weed control.

(ii) Cool-season annuals

The use of pre-emergence treatments in the fall has only been slight, but it offers some possibilities. The idea is to kill weed seedlings as they emerge under favourable weather conditions. For example, Poa annua seedlings may emerge in profusion whenever there are cool humid periods in the Midwest U.S.A. after 1 August, and it may not germinate until October unless irrigated. (In contrast, in Sweden and Canada much of the P. annua infestation is in the spring and it may be killed or weakened during the winter). If a thin but uniform stand of the desired grass is present, then timely herbicide use can prevent the establishment of P. annua.

(iii) Arsenic toxicity

The accumulation in the upper root zone of available arsenic ions has given long-term, all-season selective Poa annua removal and control, with adequate survival of perennial grasses. The Poa annua roots will absorb arsenic ions in lieu of phosphorus, and then inside the plant the energy transfer is blocked when arsenic is in compounds, so plants are weak and fail to grow. (Seedlings reach the 3 leaf stage using phosphorus in the seed, before they are affected.) If phosphorus is not added to the soil, less arsenic is needed. Thus a programme of gradual arsenic accumulation and phosphorus decline allows selective Poa annua removal from turf areas.

Research in progress since 1951, but based on much older work of the 1920's and 1930's, has led to procedures now applied on about 500 golf courses. Of these, some 50 are now fairly free of Poa annua, and on a low-rate annual pro-gramme. For example, in 1969 one company produced a special turf fertilizer containing N, K and minor elements, but no P, just for use on arsenic-treated fairways, greens and other turf areas.

Bensulide, benefin, DCPA or Bandane to prevent establishment of Poa annua seedlings can best be used where overseeding is not needed. On some selections of bermudagrass (Cynodon spp.) use of these herbicides in fall is reducing wintertime encroachment of Poa annua. In Poa spp. and Agrostis spp., early fall use can protect from infestation. The toxicity to overseeded grasses is a limitation on the use of herbicides in this way.

POST-EMERGENCE WEED CONTROL

In the 1954-60 period much work was done by many researchers on post-emergence herbicide treatments, which work so well on broadleaf weeds. The herb-icides appropriate for such treatments included disodium methane arsonate (DSMA), amine methyl arsonate and calcium propyl arsonate and related compounds. Excellent control of most summer annuals can be achieved by 2-3 applications at 5-7 day intervals, to a total of about 3-4 lb./ac. (3.4-4.5 kg/ha) of arsenic. If this were mixed with 2,4-D plus mecoprop or dicamba than a host of broadleaf and grassy weeds, including creeping weeds, could be removed from turf in June, July, August or September. Then, after 3 weeks, reseeding could be done if needed.

The general preference, however, is obviously for pre-emergence rather than post-emergence treatments. Whereas post-emergence treatments had 100% of the market in, say, 1957, by 1967 the pre-emergence treatments had over 90% of the market and post-emergence treatments were relegated to corrective and "catch-up" conditions.

Although annual grass kill by foliage burning can be accomplished with sodium arsenite, endothal, cacodylic acid, diquat and paraquat, etc., such treat-ments are risky. Usually humidity, temperature and rain variations affect the results as much as the rate used. Also the discoloration and weakening of desired grasses are serious disadvantages. Repeat treatments at cautious rates can be quite economical and sometimes successful.

CONCLUSION

An extra impetus is given to the use of new dwarf varieties, special turf fertilizers, automatic irrigation, special grooming machines and special root zone materials by having selective herbicide treatments against annual grasses available to turf managers. There is, however, one question always to be asked about the turf on which such treatments may be used - "Can a ground cover be maintained without the weedy grasses? Does the management really wish to be free of Poa annua?"

SELECTIVITY OF TURFGRASS HERBICIDES

R.E. Engel,

Research Professor in Turfgrass Management, Department of Soils and Crops,
College of Agriculture and Environmental Science, Rutgers University,
New Brunswick, New Jersey, 08903, U.S.A.

SUMMARY

The possible methods of herbicide action on weeds are reviewed, and various herbicides are discussed in detail to indicate the bases of their selectivity. Attention is drawn to the wide scope for further research.

The turfgrass field has had a penchant for herbicides throughout its brief history as a formal commodity. In its earlier years, chemical fertilizers were used to destroy weeds. In the 1930's and early 1940's the arsenicals, sodium chlorate, and dinitrophenols were used both experimentally and in applied turfgrass culture. These chemicals were not widely used because they gave little selective kill of the weeds. The common use of herbicides at present is possible because the available chemicals now give greater selective control of the weeds without inflicting serious injury to the turfgrasses. Each additional improvement in the use of a herbicide and each new herbicide that gives more control and less turf injury increases the importance of herbicides on turf.

The basis for a herbicide giving selective kill of a weed varies greatly from chemical to chemical. A precise chemical effect that might be turned on or turned off would simplify the explanation, but it does not exist with most herbicides nor is it likely to in the future. A range of biochemical, physical, physiological, and morphological factors are involved in selective weed control. Often several factors are at work with a successful herbicide.

How plants can be killed by herbicides might aid explanation of the types of selectivity resulting from the use of turfgrass herbicides. The first type, dehydration, is one of the most sensational and efficient ways of killing a plant. It can occur because of inadequate rooting, malformation of roots, blockage of conducting tissues, and failure of the plant to prevent excessive moisture loss from its vegetative parts. Destruction of the protoplasm in vital or major portions of the plant is a second method. The heavy metals such as mercury, copper or iron can produce a precipitation or denaturing effect on the protoplasm, and it is likely that other types of chemicals might function in this manner. Acids or other chemicals that give rise to an abundance of hydrogen ions have herbicidal action. An increase of hydrogen ions that is strong enough to overcome the buffering capacity of the protoplasm and markedly affect the pH destroys the protoplasm quickly. A third category of herbicide kill occurs with blocking of a single and vital function such as photosynthesis, respiration or cell division. Another method might be that of weakening the plant and causing it to succumb to such indirect agents as disease and high or low temperatures. Lastly, some herbicides such as 2,4-D may destroy the plant by causing a general disruption of vital activities. Plant kill from specific herbicides is likely to involve several phenomena. Unfortunately, few proven explanations of herbicide kill are known.

Many arsenical compounds are poisonous, but this very general term may prevent proper appreciation of their variety of herbicidal actions. For example, several modes of action occur with sodium arsenite. First, injury to the plant occurs when the solution of sodium arsenite, which is highly buffered and mildly alkaline, softens the cuticle. As it penetrates the symplast, it may exert the heavy metal effect of protein precipitation (Crafts and Robbins, 1962). Like certain other arsenicals, it is highly phytotoxic. Bonner (1950) attributes the extreme toxicity of arsenic to an uncoupling of oxidative phosphorylation by poisoning of the triosephosphate dehydrogenase system. The pre-emergence herbicide action of the arsenate ion results from destruction of the embryo but the biochemical action is not known. While little is known about the action of the arsonic acid derivatives (DSMA, MAMA, and MSMA) and arsinic acid, it is expected that they behave similarly to the inorganic arsenicals.

Like arsenicals, the dinitrophenols are classified by Bonner (1950) as uncouplers of oxidative phosphorylation. In addition, the dinitrophenols are protein coagulants. While arsenicals and dinitrophenols give some selective control, explanations for this have not been developed. Selectivity may result from relative penetration of these herbicides into different plant tissues and comparative recovery ability of the weed and turf plants.

Herbicide action on enzyme systems offers an efficient method of kill. This action may be utilized more commonly among newer herbicides. Activity of dalapon is believed to arise in part from a disturbance that interferes with pantothenic acid (Hilton et al, 1959).

The s-triazines are hetero-cyclic compounds with 3 N atoms in the ring. Simazine, a commonly used type, enters through the roots, moves acropetally, and accumulates in the apical meristems. Treatment of young seedlings causes them to yellow and die. Apparently this compound and the related herbicides exert action by interfering with the Hill reaction, which is the photodecomposition of water. It is interesting to note that both tolerant and intolerant species degrade simazine. The rate of degradation and the metabolic pathway are important in ascertaining tolerance of plants.

The phthalic acids are dicarboxylic acids in which two carboxyl groups are attached directly to the 6-carbon benzene ring. The two herbicides, DCPA and OCS-21944, are actually esters which have the acid hydrogens replaced by an alkyl group. These chemicals are closely related to the benzoic acids. They kill germinating seeds, but they are not absorbed by the foliage nor translocated. The action of these chemicals on resistant and susceptible weeds and grasses is not known.

Another group of turf herbicides are the amides, which include the carbamates and n-phenyl ureas. These have a peptide linkage or derivations thereof. Bensulide, a sulphonyl derivative of a primary amine, has a long pre-emergence residual effect and is known to inhibit roots. Terbutol, a carbamate, has a good and long-lasting pre-emergence action, but little is known of its action except that it restricts roots at terminal meristems. Siduron, a substituted urea, has good selective action on germinating grasses. Splittstoesser (1968) suggests this chemical may disrupt the normal nucleic acid metabolism that is necessary for protein synthesis and cell wall formation. While these amides may have various modes of herbicidal activity, their action as root inhibitors may account for their kill of the seedlings as contrasted to the survival of perennial grasses that have an established root system.

The anilines, or p-toluidine herbicides, include benefin, trifluralin, and nitralin. This group is characterized by two nitro groups ortho to the modified amino group on the 6-carbon atom ring. These chemicals have low solubility and give a pre-emergence action on grasses. They interfere with cell division and are known also to have effects on root development. Root inhibition may be an oversimplification of their biochemical action. But as with other herbicides that inhibit root development, this may be adequate to account for pre-emergence control of germinating or seedling grasses, as contrasted to survival of the perennial turfgrasses that have an established root system.

Control of crabgrass (Digitaria ischaemum (Schreb.) Muhl. and D. sanguinalis (L.) Scop.) with phenyl mercury acetate is dependent on repeat treatments. A single application of this chemical at the rate used will not kill these weeds. Three to five such applications are necessary to kill these species. The action is manifested by increasing yellowness and the plant dies very abruptly. Turfgrasses such as Kentucky bluegrass (Poa pratensis L.) or bentgrasses (Agrostis spp.) also yellow, but do not die if the application rates are not excessive. This type of selectivity might by interpreted as crabgrass (1) succumbing at a lower toxicity level or (2) absorbing greater quantities of the herbicide.

A great amount of study on mode of action and reasons for selectivity of the phenoxy compounds has occurred. A mechanism of action for these herbicides has not been established definitely. One theory suggests the growth regulator molecules fit into slots or holes of the cytoskeleton of the cell (Van Overbeek, 1959). The active side-chain provides a missing link in the hydrogen bond network of the cytoskeleton interface. This allows the network to oscillate in place. The auxin molecule is not used up and rather than act as a single enzyme, it would affect all enzyme systems of the living cell. Such a theory may be greatly oversimplified, but it could account for a great assortment of changes that occur with 2,4-D treatment in the plant. RNA and protein content of the plants are affected, food reserves may be depleted, and roots of the turfgrasses may develop abnormal anatomy (Callahan and Engel, 1965). Abnormal growth may occur in old tissue and normal meristematic tissue development can be inhibited. Some workers would explain that a plant's death from 2,4-D must occur because of a general disorganization of its essential activities. Decarboxylation of 2,4-D is considered responsible for resistance in some plants (Luckwill and Lloyd-Jones, 1960). Leaf (1962) attributed 2,4-D resistance of cleavers (Galium aparine L.) to the loss of both carbon atoms of the side chain. It is not known whether side chain degradation is responsible for the comparative resistance of the several turfgrasses. The basis for selective action of 2,4-D between weeds and turfgrasses is not established.

Dicamba, a growth regulator of the benzoic acid family, produces many formative responses similar to those of the phenoxy herbicides. Buchholtz (1958) showed that isomers of benzoic acid with no substituent in the 4 position of the ring were able to suppress quackgrass (Agropyron repens (L.) Beauv.) and those with a substituent at this point were inactive. Poa pratensis and other plants are known to metabolize dicamba, but the importance this plays in mode of action or selectivity is not known.

The research information available shows the very complex biochemical nature of selective herbicides. With the development of new chemicals, the emphasis on selectivity will grow in importance as well as complication. This may cause great emphasis on biochemical aspects of selectivity and a loss of attention to such items as selective absorption and agronomic differences of the weed and turfgrass. The nature of weed and turfgrass surfaces has received some attention but precise study of spray retention and foliar penetration is lacking. Surfactants are used for some weeds and a phenoxy that penetrates wild onion (<u>Allium</u> <u>canadense</u> L.) is chosen to control it. Possibly some procedures take advantage of stage of growth of the weed and turfgrass species, yet research projects that deal primarily with plant differences that enhance selectivity scarcely exist. Such items as stage of plant growth, temperature, immediate and long-term precipitation, nature of the carrier, condition of the leaves (in terms of waxiness, cuticle thickness, or hairiness), pH, colloidal conditions of the soil, and many others, often need investigation for their role in selective weed control.

Turf weed control will have an increasingly better future as the developing herbicides show more potential for better selectivity in controlling the weeds. The herbicide chemists will supply an abundance of new chemicals, while the turfgrass agronomists must devise ways to obtain maximum selectivity of the weeds from the various chemicals that might be used.

ACKNOWLEDGEMENT

Appreciation is given to Dr. Richard D. Ilnicki, Research Professor in Weed Science, Soils and Crops Department, for counsel in preparation of this paper.

REFERENCES

1. BONNER, J. (1950) Plant Biochemistry. Academic Press, Inc. New York, 212.

2. BUCKHOLTZ, K.P. (1958) The sensitivity of quackgrass to various chlorinated benzoic acids. WSSA Abstr. 33.

3. CALLAHAN, L.M., and ENGEL, R.E. (1965) Tissue abnormalities induced in roots of colonial bentgrass by phenoxyalkylcarboxylic acid herbicides. Weeds 13, 336.

4. CRAFTS, A.S., and ROBBINS, W.W. (1962) Weed Control, 3rd Ed. McGraw-Hill Book Co. Inc., New York, 210.

5. HILTON, J.L., ARD, J.S., JANSEN, L.L., and GENTNER, W.A. (1959) The pantothenate synthesizing enzyme, a metabolic site in the herbicidal action of chlorinated aliphatic acids. Weeds 7, 381.

6. LEAF, E.L. (1962) Metabolism and selectivity of plant-growth regulator herbicides. Nature, Lond. 193, 485.

7. LUCKWILL, L.C., and LLOYD-JONES, C.P. (1960) Metabolism of plant growth regulators. I. 2,4-dichlorophenoxyacetic acid in leaves of red and black currant. Ann. appl. Biol. 48, 613.

8. SPLITTSTOESSER, W.E. (1968) The effect of siduron upon barley root metabolism. Weed Sci. 16, 344.

9. VAN OVERBEEK, J. (1959) Auxins. Bot. Rev. 25, 269.

10. WELTON, F.A., and CARROLL, J.C. (1947) Lead arsenate for the control of crabgrass. J. Am. Soc. Agron. 39, 513.

THE ROLE OF THE HYDROXYBENZONITRILES AS SELECTIVE WEEDKILLERS IN SPORTS TURF

D. Soper,

May & Baker Ltd., Research Station, Ongar, Essex, U.K.

SUMMARY

This paper reviews experiments carried out in England, Canada, Australia and New Zealand with ioxynil and bromoxynil in seedling turf-forming grasses and with ioxynil/mecoprop mixtures in established turf. Grass tolerance work has shown that both ioxynil (as salt) and bromoxynil (as salt or ester) are safe to apply from the 2-leaf stage onwards, but that ioxynil controls a wider range of weeds likely to be encountered in seedling lawns than bromoxynil. Excellent control of speedwells (Veronica spp.) and some problem weeds of lesser importance in established turf was achieved with an ioxynil/mecoprop herbicide mixed in the proportions 1 : 1½ in terms of active isomer.

INTRODUCTION

The hydroxybenzonitrile herbicides have been developed throughout the world primarily for the control of annual broadleaved weeds in cereals, combining crop safety with activity against weed species not readily controlled by the phenoxyalkanoics.

During the course of field work in U.K. cereal crops, it was noted that several weeds which occur in turf or which are related to species that do, and which are poorly controlled by current practices, were susceptible to either ioxynil or bromoxynil. Treatment of undersown wheat and barley suggested that grasses in the young seedling stages might tolerate these materials, and it was also noted that their performance could be enhanced by use in mixtures with some other herbicides, notably mecoprop. Tests were therefore carried out from 1965 to 1967 in England and during 1967 and 1968 in Australia, Canada, and New Zealand to investigate the use of the hydroxybenzonitriles in turf, concentrating on two approaches:

1.   Application on seedling grasses, i.e. newly-sown lawns, to take advantage of the expected tolerance of turf-forming grasses from the very earliest growth stages and the susceptibility of seedling weeds.

2.   Application on established turf, to examine activity against persistent perennial broadleaved weeds not controlled hitherto by chemical means.

REVIEW OF EXPERIMENTS

1.   Tolerance by seedling grasses: U.K.

Preliminary tests carried out in 1965 at S.T.R.I., Bingley, by Legg (1) showed that, except for a slight setback to growth and some tip burn when sprayed within a week of emergence, ioxynil salt, bromoxynil salt, and bromoxynil ester could be applied safely to turf-forming grasses at low volume (30 gal./ac.; 337 1/ha) at doses up to 16 oz./ac. a.i. (1.12 kg/ha). Results were similar in

Table 1: tolerance of turfgrasses to ioxynil and bromoxynil at three volumes of application (Ongar): mean score of 3 replicate plots, on scale 0 (no effect) to 9 (very severe scorch)

Date of sowing: 28 April, 1965   Date of spraying (grasses at 2-leaf stage): 26 May, 1966

Grass species	Scoring 2 or 4 weeks after spraying	Watering can application c.800 gal./ac. (9,000 l/ha) Ioxynil oz./ac.(kg/ha) 12 (0.84)	18 (1.26)	24 (1.68)	Bromoxynil oz./ac.(kg/ha) 12 (0.84)	18 (1.26)	24 (1.68)	Knapsack application 80 gal./ac. (900 l/ha) Ioxynil oz./ac.(kg/ha) 12 (0.84)	18 (1.26)	24 (1.68)	Bromoxynil oz./ac.(kg/ha) 18 (1.26)	24 (1.68)
Agrostis tenuis Sibth.	2	1.0	1.0	1.0	1.0	1.0	1.3	1.0	1.0	1.0	1.0	1.3
	4	ALL TREATMENTS ZERO						ALL TREATMENTS ZERO				
Lolium perenne L. S 23	2	2.0	3.3	6.7	0.7	0.7	1.3	4.0	5.3	4.0	1.3	1.3
	4	0.3	1.0	3.0	0.0	0.0	0.0	1.7	3.7	3.0	0.0	0.0
Cynosurus cristatus L.	2	8.7	8.7	9.0	3.3	3.3	9.0	9.0	9.0	8.7	8.0	9.0
	4	3.3	4.0	6.7	4.0	4.0	4.0	4.3	5.3	6.3	4.0	4.0
Festuca ovina L.	2	0.7	0.3	0.3	0.3	0.3	0.3	1.0	1.3	1.3	0.3	1.0
	4	ALL TREATMENTS ZERO						ALL TREATMENTS ZERO				
Festuca rubra L. ssp. commutata Gaud.	2	0.3	0.7	0.7	0.3	0.3	0.3	1.0	1.0	1.3	0.3	1.0
	4	ALL TREATMENTS ZERO						ALL TREATMENTS ZERO				
Festuca rubra L. ssp. rubra S 59	2	1.3	1.3	2.3	1.0	1.0	1.0	2.0	2.7	2.3	2.3	2.3
	4	ALL TREATMENTS ZERO						ALL TREATMENTS ZERO				
Phleum bertolonii DC S 50	2	1.3	1.7	1.3	1.7	1.7	1.3	1.7	2.7	2.3	1.7	1.7
	4	ALL TREATMENTS ZERO						ALL TREATMENTS ZERO				
Poa trivialis L.	2	2.7	2.7	3.0	3.0	3.0	3.0	3.7	2.3	3.0	3.0	3.0
	4	ALL TREATMENTS ZERO						ALL TREATMENTS ZERO				
Poa nemoralis L.	2	2.3	2.7	3.0	2.3	2.3	4.0	3.0	3.0	3.7	2.7	4.3
	4	ALL TREATMENTS ZERO						ALL TREATMENTS ZERO				

Table continued on next page

Continuation of Table 1: tolerance of turfgrasses to ioxynil and bromoxynil at three volumes of application (Ongar): mean score of 3 replicate plots, on scale 0 (no effect) to 9 (very severe scorch) Date of sowing: 28 April 1966 Date of spraying (grasses at 2-leaf stage): 26 May 1966

Low volume sprayer application 30 gal./ac. (337 l/ha)

Grass species	Scoring 2 or 4 weeks after spraying	Ioxynil oz./ac. (kg/ha)			Bromoxynil oz./ac. (kg/ha)	
		12 (0.84)	18 (1.26)	24 (1.68)	18 (1.26)	24 (1.68)
Agrostis tenuis Sibth.	2	1.3	1.0	1.0	1.3	1.0
	4	ALL TREATMENTS ZERO				
Lolium perenne L. S 23	2	3.0	4.3	6.0	1.0	2.3
	4	2.0	2.3	4.3	0	0
Cynosurus cristatus L.	2	9.0	9.0	9.0	9.0	9.0
	4	4.7	5.3	6.0	4.0	4.3
Festuca ovina L.	2	1.0	1.0	1.0	0.7	1.3
	4	ALL TREATMENTS ZERO				
Festuca rubra L. ssp. commutata Gaud.	2	1.0	0.7	1.0	0.3	1.0
	4	ALL TREATMENTS ZERO				
Festuca rubra L. ssp. rubra S 59	2	1.3	1.7	3.0	2.0	3.0
	4	ALL TREATMENTS ZERO				
Phleum bertolonii DC S 50	2	1.7	1.7	2.7	2.0	2.0
	4	ALL TREATMENTS ZERO				
Poa trivialis L.	2	3.3	3.0	3.7	3.0	3.3
	4	ALL TREATMENTS ZERO				
Poa nemoralis L.	2	3.7	2.7	3.3	3.3	4.0
	4	ALL TREATMENTS ZERO				

the spring and autumn. Even under the cold and wet germinating conditions of late September and October, the experimental treatments made no noticeable difference to the stand of grasses (Agrostis tenuis Sibth., Cynosurus cristatus L., Festuca rubra L. ssp. commutata Gaud., Lolium perenne L., Poa pratensis L. and P. trivialis L.) on the treated plots compared with the controls.

Because of this promising report a field experiment was set up at Ongar, Essex, in 1966, to obtain confirmatory evidence of the safety of ioxynil and bromoxynil salts to individual grass species (see Table 1) at volumes of application likely to be used in practice. As at Bingley, the grasses were sown separately in strips, replicated three times, and cross-treated with the hydroxybenzonitriles. Ioxynil, as sodium salt, was applied at 12, 18 and 24 oz./ac. (0.84, 1.26 and 1.68 kg/ha) and bromoxynil, as potassium salt, was applied at 18 and 24 oz./ac., when the majority of grass seedlings were at the 2-leaf stage. Each treatment was applied by:

(i)   Watering can, fitted with a fine rose, delivering c.800 gal./ac. water (9,000 l/ha).

(ii) 'Kestrel' Knapsack sprayer, delivering 80 gal./ac. (900 l/ha).

(iii) 'Colwood' small-plot pressurised sprayer, delivering 30 gal./ac. (337 l/ha).

Also during spring 1966 the ioxynil salt formulation was supplied to a leading seed merchant for application to a range of turf grasses and two seeds mixtures. Treatments of 24 and 32 oz./ac. a.i. (1.68 and 2.24 kg/ha), replicated twice, were made by means of a low-volume sprayer.

The results of visual assessments of the effect on the grasses between one and four weeks after spraying are given in Tables 1 and 2. All treatments initially caused slight tip scorch. This was unimportant on most species, the one exception being Cynosurus cristatus. Whereas the tip burn caused by ioxynil at 24 oz./ac. or less (1.68 kg/ha) on Lolium perenne - the species worst affected in this respect - would be removed by the first mowing, the damage to C. cristatus was much more severe and was judged to be unacceptable in practice. (Inadvertently this has since been verified). Both experiments were in agreement on this point, but it was unexpected, since neither grass had been damaged like this in the 1965 S.T.R.I. trials. The only difference observed between ioxynil and bromoxynil was that the latter was slightly less phytotoxic to L. perenne. There was little difference in scorch between the water volumes used but at similar herbicide doses the watering-can treatment caused slightly less damage than the knapsack or low-volume applications.

Further trials were carried out at Bingley in 1967 by Legg (1), using the 10% w/v ioxynil product marketed that year. Apart from a reduction in grass establishment by treatments at 2 and 3 weeks after sowing, doses up to 16 oz./ac. a.i. (1.12 kg/ha) were safe to the range of species tested in 1965 and also to Poa annua L. and Festuca rubra L. ssp. rubra. The volume of water applied was 80 gal./ac. (c.900 l/ha).

2.   Tolerance by seedling grasses: Australia and Canada

In 1967 a replicated trial was laid down in Victoria, Australia, by Combellack and Gilbertson (6) to examine the tolerance by a seeds mixture containing Cynosurus cristatus (40%), Festuca pratensis Huds. (15%), Poa pratensis (25%), Lolium perenne (18%) and Trifolium repens L. (2%) of the alkali salts of ioxynil and bromoxynil at 12 and 18 oz./ac. a.i. (0.84 and 1.26 kg/ha). Applications were made by watering-can at 600 gal./ac. (6,750 l/ha); knapsack sprayer at 80 gal./ac.

(c.900 l/ha); and low volume sprayer at 10.7 gal./ac. (120 l/ha). It was observed that all treatments caused scorch which was soon outgrown and no permanent damage to grass seedlings resulted. As in the U.K. the bromoxynil formulations were less phytotoxic than ioxynil to Lolium perenne.

Tolerance work in Canada has demonstrated the safety of ioxynil at 1 lb./ac. (1.12 kg/ha) to Festuca rubra ssp. commutata, Poa pratensis (Park) and Agrostis tenuis (Highland), sown separately (pot experiment) or in a mixture (2, 3). In a further pot experiment (5) ioxynil salt even at 2 lb./ac. (2.24 kg/ha) had little adverse effect on seedling bluegrass (Poa pratensis) when 3.5 cm high. The bluegrass varieties treated were Adorno, Altra, Arista, Belturf, Delta, Fylking, Kentucky, Merion, Newport, Park, Prato and Windsor.

Table 2: tolerance of turfgrass species and mixtures to ioxynil (Chester):

mean score of two replicates, 1 week after spraying (0 = no effect, 9 = very severe scorch)

Grass species	Ioxynil oz./ac. (kg/ha)	
	24 (1.68)	32 (2.24)
Agrostis tenuis	0	2
Lolium perenne	2	4
Cynosurus cristatus	4	6
Festuca ovina	0	0
Festuca rubra ssp. commutata	0	2
Festuca rubra ssp. rubra S.59	0	0
Phleum bertolonii S.50	0	2
Poa annua	2 ·	2
Poa nemoralis	0	2
Poa pratensis	0	0
Poa trivialis	0	2
Mixture A1)	(2	2
) See footnote	(	
Mixture B2)	(0	2

Mixture A1   30% Agrostis tenuis
              70% F. rubra ssp. commutata

Mixture B2   10% A. tenuis
              45% F. rubra ssp. commutata
              35% F. rubra ssp. rubra
              10% Poa trivialis

3. Control of weeds in newly-sown grass

A considerable amount of data is available from many sources on the activity of the hydroxybenzonitriles on a wide range of broadleaf annuals at the seedling stage, but the list in Table 3 has been compiled solely from the results of experiments in newly-sown grasses. An asterisk indicates susceptibility to ioxynil at 8 oz./ac. (0.56 kg/ha), though this information is not necessarily derived from work in young turf.

Table 3: weeds susceptible (up to 4-leaf stage) to ioxynil (Na salt) at 16 oz./ac. (1.12 kg/ha). * = susceptible to ioxynil at 8 oz./ac. (0.56 kg/ha)

Species	Source of information
Amaranthus retroflexus L.	Canada
Ambrosia artemisiifolia L.	Canada
Anagallis arvensis L.	Australia
Anthemis cotula L.	Canada
*Brassica kaber (DC.) Wheeler (= Sinapis arvensis L.)	Canada
*Capsella bursa-pastoris (L.) Medic.	Canada, U.K.
*Cerastium vulgatum L.	Canada, U.K.
*Chenopodium album L.	Australia, Canada, U.K.
Cryptostemma calendula (L.) Druce	Australia
Equisetum spp. (top growth only)	U.K.
Fumaria spp.	Australia
Matricaria recutita L.	U.K.
*Medicago lupulina L.	Canada
Plantago lanceolata L.	Australia, Canada
Polygonum aviculare L.	Australia, Canada, U.K.
*Polygonum convolvulus L.	Canada, U.K.
*Polygonum persicaria L.	Canada
Ranunculus spp.	U.K.
*Raphanus raphanistrum L.	Australia
Senecio vulgaris L.	U.K.

(continued on next page)

(Table 3 continued)

Silene gallica L.	Canada
*Sonchus oleraceus L.	U.K.
Spergula arvensis L.	Canada
Stellaria media (L.) Vill.	Australia, Canada, U.K.
Taraxacum officinale Weber	Canada, U.K.
Trifolium pratense L.	Canada, U.K.
Trifolium repens L.	Canada, U.K.
Veronica agrestis L.	U.K.
*Veronica persica Poir.	Australia

A similar range of weeds was controlled with bromoxynil salt at 16 oz./ac. (1.12 kg/ha) with the important exception of Stellaria media (Canada, U.K. and Australia). In the U.K., bromoxynil salt, applied at 18 oz./ac. a.i. (1.26 kg/ha) gave slightly better control than ioxynil salt of P. aviculare seedlings, particularly with the watering-can treatment, and in Australia both ester and salt formations of bromoxynil at 18 oz. and 9 oz./ac. a.i. (1.26 and 0.63 kg/ha) gave better results against Rumex acetosella L. and R. obtusifolius L.

4. Control of weeds in established turf: U.K.

Good activity of ioxynil-based herbicides against annual Veronica spp. (V. hederifolia L., V. persica and V. polita Fries.) in cereals led to the testing of ioxynil/mecoprop mixtures against Veronica filiformis Sm. infesting turf in the U.K. During 1965/66 two mixtures were compared, giving application rates of ioxynil + mecoprop at 9 + 13.5 oz./ac. (0.63 + 0.95 kg/ha) and 6 + 15 oz./ac. (0.42 + 1.05 kg/ha), mecoprop being expressed as d-isomer. The treatments were applied by means of pressurised sprayers, mainly knapsack-type, using water volumes of 80-100 gal./ac. Strips were treated at the various heavily-infested sites from early spring (May) through to early autumn (Sep.). The turf on sites 1, 6, 8, 9 and 10 was close-mown, less than 1 in. high (2.5 cm) at the time of treatment; at the other three sites the turf was regularly cut, but was more than 1 in. high when treated. Weed control was assessed 6 weeks after application, according to the following scale:

0 = no effect

1 = less than 50% control (recovering 6 weeks after treatment)

2 = 50-70% control (limited regrowth)

3 = 70-90% control (persistent check to survivors)

4 = 90-100% control

the mixture containing the higher proportion of ioxynil gave marginally better weed control of <u>V</u>. <u>filiformis</u> (see Table 4). In fine turf this mixture also gave the better control of parsley piert (<u>Alchemilla</u> <u>arvensis</u> L.) so it was decided to release this formulation to trade users during 1966/67.

A summary of users' reports, given in Table 5, shows that a severe check of <u>V</u>. <u>filiformis</u> was normally achieved (mean control at 28 sites - 73%). Out of 26 sites sprayed correctly, 9 treatments gave weed control of at least 90% and 14 others were rated 70-90%. The requirement for good control was application when the weed was growing vigorously in spring (usually before many blue flowers appeared) on well-maintained close-mown turf.

Table 4: activity of ioxynil/mecoprop mixtures on <u>Veronica</u> <u>filiformis</u> and <u>Alchemilla</u> <u>arvensis</u> - U.K. 1965/66

Weed species	Site number & type of turf	Date of application	Weed control score*6 weeks after applying ioxynil + mecoprop (oz./ac.)	
			9 + 13.5	6 + 15
<u>Veronica</u> <u>filiformis</u>	1. golf green	10 May 1965	2	2
	7. golf fairway	30 May 1965	4	3
	5. school sports-field	18 Jun. 1965	1	1
	2.) football pitch 2.)	(9 Jun. 1965 (13 Sep. 1965	1 4	1 3
<u>Alchemilla</u> <u>arvensis</u>	6. bowling green	12 May 1965	4	4
	9. golf green	28 May 1966	4	2
	8. golf green	15 Jun. 1965	3	3

* see text.

Table 5: activity of ioxynil/mecoprop at 9 + 27 oz./ac. on _V. filiformis_: U.K. Survey 1966/7

County	Class of user	Spray date	Initial infestation	% control (estimate) and comments
Buckinghamshire	Parks dep't	Apr. 1967	Severe	70
Buckinghamshire	School	May 1967	Severe	50 Rain shortly after spraying
Devonshire	Parks dep't	May 1967	Severe	95
Glamorganshire	Bowls Club	end Jun. 1967	Moderate	80
Glamorganshire	Bowls Club	Apr. 1967	Moderate	70
Gloucestershire	School	Apr. 1967	Severe	33 Underdosed
Hampshire	School	29 Apr. 1967	Severe	95
Hampshire	School	late May 1967	Moderate	10 Application at late flowering
Herefordshire	Parks dep't	Autumn 1967	Severe	50 _Veronica_ growth poor at spraying
Kent	Parks dep't	Spring 1966	Severe	90
Monmouthshire	School	May 1967	Severe	50 Rain after spraying
Monmouthshire	School	20 Oct. 1966	Severe	90)
Monmouthshire	School	15 May 1967	Severe	90) Slight overdosing
Shropshire	Parks dep't	29 Jun. 1967	Severe	80
Shropshire	Parks dep't	Apr. 1967	Severe	70
Somerset	School	26 Apr. 1967	Moderate	90
Somerset	School	15 Apr. 1967	Moderate	75
Somerset	Golf Club	late May 1967	Severe	90
Surrey	Golf Club	May 1966	Moderate	75
Sussex	Parks dep't	Spring 1966	Moderate	85
Sussex	Golf Club	Spring 1966	-	75
Sussex	Parks dep't	Spring 1966	Severe	75
Sussex	School	Autumn 1966	Severe	70
Sussex	Golf Club	17 May 1967	Moderate	60
Warwickshire	School	18 Apr. 1967	Severe	65
Warwickshire	Golf Club	Sep. 1966	Moderate	100
Warwickshire	Parks dep't	Spring 1966	Moderate	75
Yorkshire	Golf Club	Apr. 1966	Severe	90

5. Activity of ioxynil/mecoprop mixtures on Veronica filiformis and
    Alchemilla arvensis: Canada, Australia and New Zealand

    Tests with the 1:1½ ioxynil/mecoprop formulation were arranged in
British Columbia during 1967/68 where a creeping speedwell presented a problem in
many ways comparable to Veronica filiformis in England. In three experiments
(7, 8 and 9) comparing a range of doses, repeated treatments at 16 and 32 oz./
ac. total a.i. (1.12 and 2.24 kg/ha) gave excellent control. An ioxynil/dicamba
mixture at 8 + 8 oz./ac. (0.56 + 0.56 kg/ha), applied twice, was also effective.

    Trials in Eastern Canada have shown that 1:1½ ioxynil/mecoprop will also con-
trol Taraxacum officinale, Polygonum aviculare and Stellaria media, but not
Bellis perennis L.

    In a single observation trial in New Zealand good control of Alchemilla
arvensis, Sagina procumbens L. and Soliva sessilis, Ruiz and Pav. (Onehunga weed)
has been reported, but Hydrocotyle spp. were little affected. In Australia,
bromoxynil plus MCPA, as esters, show promise for the control of Soliva sessilis
(jo-jo) and Cryptostemma calendula (capeweed) (6).

DISCUSSION

    The fine seedbed that is essential for good establishment of turf-forming
grass is also favourable to annual weeds, many of which can be quicker to germinate and grow than the young grass seedlings. Although most annual weeds are
removed by the first mowing, it may be 6-8 weeks after sowing before the sward is
firm enough to allow the mower to be used. In these circumstances a quick-acting
herbicide such as ioxynil, which can be applied at an early stage of sward establishment, is a useful addition to the range of weedkillers that can be used on
turf. It is obviously laborious to hand-weed a young lawn, and this procedure
is harmful to young grass roots. Moreover, although 'hormone' weedkillers such
as MCPA or mecoprop (either alone or combined) can be applied to newly-sown turf
at low doses, there is always the risk of some grass damage, particularly at the
2-leaf stage.

    The use of ioxynil combined with mecoprop in controlling persistent weeds of
established turf in many areas has shown that activity against Veronica spp. and
Alchemilla arvensis is especially interesting. The nature and incidence of these
weed problems have been discussed elsewhere (4), but it is quite clear that this
mixture is the first herbicide to give a severe check to them without harm to
the sward.

CONCLUSIONS

1. All species of commonly-used turfgrasses, with the exception of Cynosurus
cristatus, can be treated safely with ioxynil (sodium salt) at a dose of up to
16 oz./ac. a.i.

2. Bromoxynil herbicides are also safe to grasses, but inactivity against
Stellaria media is a disadvantage in seedling turf.

3. An ioxynil/mecoprop mixture applied at 9 + 13½ (d-isomer) oz./ac. a.i.
gives satisfactory control of Veronica spp. and Alchemilla arvensis in established
turf.

REFERENCES

1. LEGG, D.C. (1967) Selective weedkiller for use on young turf.
   J. Sports Turf Res. Inst. 43, 40.

2. TURLEY, R.H., and ADAMSON, R.M. (1967) Effects of 2,4-D and ioxynil
   upon three species of seedling lawn grasses - a growth room study.
   Res. Report Nat. Weed Committee, Western Section (Canada) 209.

3. TURLEY, R.H., and ADAMSON, R.M. (1967) Rate and time of ioxynil and
   2,4-D applications for controlling weeds in seedling lawns. Ibid. 210.

4. SOPER, D. (1967) Special Weed Problems. Proc. B.W.C.C. Symposium on
   Control of Weeds, Pests and Diseases of Cultivated Turf.

5. ADAMSON, R.M. (1968) Sensitivity of seedlings of twelve bluegrass varieties
   to ioxynil. Res. Report Nat. Weed Committee, Western Section (Canada) 208.

6. COMBELLACK, J.H., and GILBERTSON, N.J. (1968) Weed Control in turf with
   hydroxybenzonitriles. Proc. Victorian Weeds Conf.

7. ADAMSON, R.M. (1968) Chemical control of Veronica filiformis in a lawn.
   Res. Report Nat. Weed Committee, Western Section (Canada), 206.

8. REIMER, E., and RENNEY, A.J. (1968) Tests with ioxynil mixtures to control
   4 persistent lawn weeds. Ibid. 212.

9. HUGHES, E.C., and STRONG, M. (1968) Herbicide trials on speedwell
   (Veronica persica) in turfgrass. Ibid. 211.

CONTROL OF BROADLEAF WEEDS IN TURF

C.M. Switzer,

Department of Botany, Ontario Agricultural College, University of Guelph, Guelph, Ontario, Canada.

SUMMARY

The herbicide 2,4-D is the best single chemical for general broadleaf weed control in turf. However, since certain species that infest turf are resistant to 2,4-D, herbicides such as MCPA, mecoprop, fenoprop, dicamba, and 2,4,5-T also have been used. In more recent times, mixtures of 2,4-D with one or more of these other herbicides have become popular, and give a very broad spectrum of control. To facilitate application, mixtures of herbicide with fertilizer have been made available and are popular with many home-owners. Slightly higher rates of the active material are required in these mixtures than when used as liquid sprays. Regardless of the formulation, best results are obtained by applying the herbicides when the weeds are in a state of active growth.

The common dandelion (_Taraxacum officinale_ Weber) is the most wide-spread and best known broadleaf weed that infests lawns in Canada. From the time that home-owners first became conscious of the beauty of a well-kept lawn, they have been concerned with ways and means of controlling dandelions. Chemicals such as iron sulphate and copper sulphate were tried with some slight success in the early 1900's, but until the introduction of 2,4-D following the second world war there was really little that could be done except to dig out the offending plants.

The discovery of the herbicide 2,4-D meant that for the first time the home-owner could have a dandelion-free lawn. However, it was not long before he realised that other weeds were coming into the areas formerly occupied by the dandelions. The phenoxyacetic herbicides 2,4-D and MCPA did not seem to control some of these other plants. Therefore, new herbicides were tried and with the discovery of each succeeding chemical, considerable testing was carried out as to the best way to use it, its safety on the various turf species, and the susceptibility of various weedy species to it. Thus, over the years, a considerable amount of literature has been built up on the experimental work carried out on the control of broadleaf weeds in turf.

The phenoxyacetic herbicides gave excellent control of dandelions, plantains (_Plantago_ spp.), docks (_Rumex_ spp.) and several other species of weeds found in turf. However, some common species were not controlled, such as black medick (_Medicago lupulina_ L.), mouse-ear chickweed (_Cerastium vulgatum_ L.), heal-all (_Prunella vulgaris_ L.), speedwell (_Veronica_ spp.) and knotweed (_Polygonum aviculare_ L.). In the mid 1950's the phenoxypropionic herbicides, fenoprop and mecoprop, were discovered and these were found to be most useful in the control of species resistant to 2,4-D. Fenoprop was, however, found to be rather harmful to certain types of grass, notably _Agrostis_ spp. and some _Festuca_ spp., and mecoprop did not give satisfactory control of dandelions. Therefore, the next obvious step was to try various mixtures of these materials and this was done with a considerable degree of success. This is illustrated in Table 1 taken from data presented by Brown in 1962 (1).

Table 1: effects of phenoxyacetic and phenoxypropionic acid herbicides on broadleaf weeds in turf (Brown, 1962)

Treatment		Number of weeds per plot			
Herbicide	oz./ac. (kg/ha)	Plantain	Dandelion	Clover	Chickweed
Control	-	60	5	15	15
2,4-D (amine)	12 (0.84)	0	1	8	10
	24 (1.68)	0	1	6	10
fenoprop (K salt)	12 (0.84)	23	5	0	1
	24 (1.68)	4	1	0	0
mecoprop (K salt)	12 (0.84)	6	5	1	3
	24 (1.68)	1	1	0	0
2,4-D + mecoprop	12 + 12 (0.84 + 0.84)	0	0	0	0

In the early 1960's a new type of chemical, dicamba, became available and was immediately tried for the control of weeds in turf. It was found to give good control of most species of weeds found growing in grass, with the notable exception of the plantains. In particular, it gave excellent control of members of the Polygonum family which are resistant, once they are past the seedling stage, to the phenoxy compounds. Again, it became obvious that mixtures should be tried and mixtures of 2,4-D and dicamba, and of 2,4-D, mecoprop and dicamba were investigated (Switzer, 2,3).

In one of these experiments various rates of dicamba and 2,4-D were tested in an attempt to establish the minimum rates of dicamba and 2,4-D necessary to give satisfactory weed control. Dicamba at 0, 2, 4, 6 and 8 oz./ac. (0.14, 0.28, 0.42 and 0.56 kg/ha) was applied with 2,4-D amine at 0, 8, 16 and 24 oz./ac. (0.56, 1.12 and 1.68 kg/ha) on 11 June 1965. One litre of spray solution was applied to each 92.9 sq m plot at approximately 2.1 kg/sq cm, using a knapsack sprayer. Weed species present included dandelion, ribgrass (Plantago lanceolata L.), common plantain (Plantago major L.), black medick, wild strawberry (Fragaria spp.), heal-all, ox-eye daisy (Chrysanthemum leucanthemum L.), hawkweed (Hieracium spp.), Veronica serpyllifolia L. and fall dandelion (Leontodon autumnalis L.).

Excellent control of all weeds except wild strawberry was obtained in plots treated with 2 oz. dicamba plus 16 or 24 oz. 2,4-D, or with 4, 6 or 8 oz. dicamba plus 8 oz. or more of 2,4-D.

In another series of experiments (Table 2) herbicides were tested on a very heavy infestation of weeds in a park near Guelph, Ontario. Relatively poor results were obtained in plots sprayed with single chemicals (except picloram) because of the wide spectrum of weed species present. But the plots treated with mixtures of 2,4-D and mecoprop, or with 2,4-D and dicamba, had satisfactory control.

Table 2: a comparison of various herbicides on turf heavily infested with dandelion, black medick, yarrow (<u>Achillea</u> <u>millefolium</u> L.), ribgrass, wild carrot (<u>Daucus</u> <u>carota</u> L.), vetch (<u>Vicia</u> spp.), ox-eye daisy, common plantain, wild strawberry and hawkweed (Switzer and Wein, 3)

Herbicide	oz./ac. (kg/ha)	Weed control rating 0 = no control 10 = 100% control
2,4-D (amine)	15 (1.05)	5.0
2,4-D + mecoprop	12 + 12 (0.84 + 0.84)	8.0
2,4-D + fenoprop	16 + 8 (1.12 + 0.56)	8.0
dicamba	18 (1.26)	5.0
2,4-D + dicamba	18 + 18 (1.26 + 1.26)	9.0
2,4-D + dicamba	9 + 9 (0.63 + 0.63)	4.0
Picloram	16 (1.12)	9.5
2,4-D + picloram	16 + 6 (1.12 + 0.42)	9.5

Methods of application

In the 1950's almost all broadleaf weed control in turf was carried out by applying herbicides in the liquid form. Normally they were diluted in water and sprayed over the grass and weeds as a post-emergence application. This was effective and still is a widely-used technique, but when the home-owner began to use herbicides more and more widely to control the weeds in his lawn, he seemed to want a method of application that fitted in better with his general lawn maintenance procedures. Since most home gardeners give fertilizer to their lawns as a routine and possess some sort of a fertilizer applicator, it was natural that granular formulations of herbicides should be tried. This led to the development of herbicide-fertilizer mixtures. These were tested widely throughout the late 1950's and early 1960's and as each new herbicide and herbicidal mixture was developed, it was immediately tried as a granular formulation with or without fertilizer. In these experiments, the type of fertilizer and the size of the fertilizer granules did not seem to affect the herbicide activity.

The relative effectiveness of herbicide-fertilizer mixtures applied to wet or dry grass was studied. It had been suggested that better results would be obtained if the grass were wet, because more granules would stick to the leaves. Experiments by the author showed that this was partially true (4). More rapid results were obtained when application was made to wet leaves, but there was no difference in the final weed control. These results would indicate that absorption of herbicide through the crown or roots of weeds is of major importance when granules are used.

The major problem that developed with the granular formulations was that there were so many fine particles in some formulations that uniform distribution was not possible. This problem has been solved by better quality control procedures so that most products available today are very uniform in particle size.

Time of treatment

Many experiments have been carried out in an attempt to find the best time to spray broadleaf weeds in turf. The author's work indicates that almost any time is satisfactory if the weeds are in a state of active growth. Even if they are not, as in a severe dry spell, good control will usually be obtained once the weeds start to grow again.

Regarding the time of day, there is little difference whether spraying is done during the daylight hours or at night. In fact, on golf courses, spraying at night seems to be completely satisfactory. There is little or no wind and the heavy dew that sometimes occurs does not seem to be a harmful factor. In fact, the dew may lead to even greater effects as the herbicide is kept in solution longer than it is during the day and more of it penetrates into the plant. Also, of course, spraying at night avoids interference with the golfers.

New herbicides

Some of the newer herbicides that might have a place in broadleaf weed control in turf should be mentioned. Picloram has been tried in several turf areas (see Table 2) with considerable success as far as weed control is concerned (5).

In one of these experiments, picloram at 2, 4, 8 and 12 oz./ac. (0.14, 0.28, 0.56 and 0.84 kg/ha) was tested on turf with a high population of ribgrass, dandelions, common plantain, black medick, ox-eye daisy, and heal-all. Treatments were carried out on 12 Jul. and plots rated 10 Sep. 1964. All rates tested gave excellent control (9.5 or 10). Common plantain was the only species left in any of the plots. No injury to the grass (mainly Poa pratensis L. and Festuca rubra L.) was noted.

In 1965, these plots were checked again for re-growth of weeds and for evidence of movement of the herbicide out of the plot area. By the end of the growing season, in 1965, no weed growth had been noted in any of the plots with two exceptions. At the 2 oz./ac. rate, some broadleaf plantain was observed and, at all rates, Veronica serpyllifolia L. was found.

Injury (browning) of a well-established cedar hedge adjacent to a plot treated with 16 oz./ac. picloram was noted late in 1964, as was injury to a spruce tree in another 16 oz./ac. plot. These woody plants partially recovered in 1965, but still showed fairly strong injury symptoms. Injury appeared to be related to uptake by roots of the trees beneath the treated area rather than lateral movement of the picloram, because there was a sharp line of weed control at the edge of the treated area. Since it is most probable that there would be desirable woody plants in the vicinity of most turf areas, it does not seem likely that picloram will find a place in the control of broadleaf weeds in turf.

Bromoxynil and ioxynil have been tested alone and in mixtures with other herbicides for the control of seedling annual weeds in newly seeded turf. These treatments seem satisfactory, but generally do not seem to have a very important place as most of the weeds that would be killed by bromoxynil would also be killed during the first mowing of the grass.

REFERENCES

1. BROWN, R.H. (1962) Control of broadleaf weeds in turf. Res. Rept., National Weed Committee (Canada) Eastern Section, p. 97.

2. SWITZER, C.M. (1965) Effects of various mixtures of 2,4-D and dicamba on turf weeds. Res. Rept., National Weed Committee (Canada) Eastern Section, p. 154.

3. SWITZER, C.M., and WEIN, R. (1964) Control of weeds in turf. Res. Rept., National Weed Committee (Canada) Eastern Section, p. 124.

4. SWITZER, C.M. (1964) Granular herbicide - fertilizer mixture application to wet and dry turf. Res. Rept., National Weed Committee (Canada) Eastern Section, p. 125.

5. SWITZER, C.M. (1964) Effect of tordon on turf weeds. Res. Rept., National Weed Committee (Canada) Eastern Section, p.125.

DISCUSSION

CONTROL OF VERONICA FILIFORMIS

E.W. Schweizer (Switzerland)

Veronica filiformis Sm. is becoming a serious problem in Switzerland, not only on lawns but also in agricultural pastures, where it is crowding out grasses. Control is possible with combinations of 2,4-D, mecoprop and dicamba, but the problem is that V. filiformis soon comes back from clippings. Good results have been obtained with residual herbicides such as bensulide, but the trials are of recent date and nothing definite can be said as yet.

R.L. Goss (Washington, U.S.A.)

At Washington State University (Puyallup, Washington), post-emergence application of DCPA at 12 lb./ac. a.i. (13.4 kg/ha) has given good control of Veronica filiformis. The weed is associated with wet soil conditions, and if these are corrected control will be improved.

J.R. Escritt (U.K.)

The worst area for this weed in the U.K. is Northern Ireland, where the climate is very wet.

CONTROL OF POA ANNUA

H.H. Williams (California, U.S.A.)

In studies on selective control of dallisgrass (Paspalum dilatatum Poir.) and kikuyugrass (Pennisetum clandestinum Hochst. ex Chiov.) in bermudagrass (Cynodon spp.), monosodium methanearsonate (MSMA) at 4-8 lb./ac. a.i. (4.5 - 9.0 kg/ha) suppressed seed head formation in dallisgrass. MSMA applied to stands of Poa annua L. in February and March, 1969, resulted in seed head suppression. Dr. W.H. Daniel mentioned the hazards of starting at zero in control. Is it possible that MSMA might be a means of slowly eliminating Poa annua and permitting desirable grasses to dominate? Has anyone had similar experience?

W.H. Daniel (Indiana, U.S.A.)

I have not much experience of this, but you can undoubtedly affect plants if you put enough arsenicals on to them.

R.E. Engel (New Jersey, U.S.A.)

We have prevented seed head development of Poa annua with maleic hydrazide, but we considered the necessary rates harmful to the turf.

J.R. Escritt (U.K.)

We had similar results at Bingley. The turf damage was less, but we decided not to proceed with the work.

H. Vos (Netherlands)

Is there any breeding work on Poa annua in the U.S.A.?

W.H. Daniel (Indiana, U.S.A.)

In conditions where Poa annua is likely to be killed out completely in three years, there is no case for selection work on it, and it is better to use Poa pratensis L. In any case, several states now prohibit sales of seed of Poa annua.

B. Langvad (Sweden)

Are there any chemicals to bring us nearer the control of Poa annua other than those mentioned by the speakers? We regard Poa annua as without question a serious weed: I have been hoping to hear how to eliminate it from red fescue and bent. Arsenicals are prohibited in Sweden, so can anyone suggest an alternative?

W.H. Daniel (Indiana, U.S.A.)

I suggest using paraquat to achieve a "zero point", and then reseeding with the desired grass. Then use a pre-emergence herbicide, such as bensulide, before germination of the Poa annua. It may be necessary to return to the "zero point" two or three times.

C.E. Wright (U.K.)

A long term means for the complete eradication of Poa annua in turf is the breeding of new turfgrass varieties resistant to herbicides such as dalapon, paraquat and simazine. Genotypes resistant to such herbicides have already been isolated. Sowing with a variety resistant to paraquat, for example, would permit treatment with paraquat which would eliminate not only Poa annua but also other grass weeds such as Dactylis glomerata L. and Holcus lanatus L.

R.L. Morris (U.K.)

You would also have to apply wormkiller, as seeds of Poa annua germinate in worm casts.

W.H. Daniel (Indiana, U.S.A.)

I agree that there are possibilities for the selective use of paraquat. The additional use of bensulide before the paraquat treatment might give even better results.

S.W. Bingham (Virginia, U.S.A.)

Where Poa annua occurs in the transition zone it behaves as an annual grass, although in cooler climates it sometimes behaves as a perennial plant. Some success in controlling Poa annua may be obtained with pre-emergence herbicides such as bensulide over a period of several years. The perennial types of Poa annua eventually go out through good management, for example as a result of the water regime during the warmer periods of the year. Treatments may have to be made at least twice a year since Poa annua germinates over long periods of time.

R. Goss (Washington, U.S.A.)

To eliminate any species, it is necessary to control seeding. I feel that Poa annua control may be achieved through the use of growth regulators for the

control of seed formation. Overseeding with desirable species in conjunction
with Poa annua seed inhibition treatment will help.

J.R. Watson (Minnesota, U.S.A.)

In Minnesota we find when using arsenates that calcium arsenate precipitates
over winter and causes trouble. I therefore advocate cultural methods as well
as chemicals. We make use of varieties that become green early in the year, for
example the Northland variety of bentgrass. On one golf course, Penncross
Agrostis palustris Huds. is overseeded each year and this has reduced Poa annua
considerably.

G.C. Horn (Florida, U.S.A.)

We have had good results with RH-315 at rates from ½ to 2 lb./ac. a.i.
(0.56 - 2.2 kg/ha) in both pre- and post-emergence treatments. Bermudagrass
tolerated these treatments, although I do not know if cool-season grasses would
do the same.

W.A. Adams (U.K.)

The various games played on turf make very different demands on the nature
and properties of the playing surface. The dislike of Poa annua is by no means
universal. More than one groundsman in Britain in charge of high quality
bowling greens is very satisfied with turf which is virtually 100% Poa annua.

THE COMPETITIVE ABILITY, AND GENERAL VALUE, OF LOLIUM SPP.

R.W. Schery (Ohio, U.S.A.)

Can anyone comment on the suggestion that secretions from Lolium spp.
can suppress competition from other species?

R.E. Schmidt (Virginia, U.S.A.)

We have found that there is something associated with seedlings of Lolium
perenne L. which actually stimulates germination of Poa pratensis L. Our conclusion is that the normal suppression of Poa pratensis in mixtures with Lolium
is due to competition for light.

J.R. Escritt (U.K.)

Why has L. perenne not received as much attention in the U.S.A. as in Europe?

R.C. O'Knefski (New York, U.S.A.)

In recent years, we have used in Long Island some of the new varieties of
L. perenne, such as NK100, Pelo and Manhattan, and good results have been obtained.
One of the reasons against using L. perenne is that our climate is hotter than in
the European countries that use it.

J.R. Watson (Minnesota, U.S.A.)

Lolium spp. are used extensively for temporary or emergency cover. Their
use for permanent turf has been limited because of lack of good varieties of
L. perenne, but some are now becoming available.

R.A. Keen (Kansas, U.S.A.)

Lolium spp. rarely survive more than one year because of crown rust (Puccinia coronata Cda.) during the first hot weather in May.

G.S. Robinson (New Zealand)

In regard to the suppressing effect of Lolium spp., we in New Zealand have generally considered that this is due to rapid seedling establishment which makes them exceedingly strong competitors at this stage.

R.W. Schery (Ohio, U.S.A.)

In Tennessee, it has been found that Lolium spp., even when dead, inhibited the recovery of bermudagrass, so I still believe that we should look for some factor apart from competition. We do not like L. perenne because it is more difficult than Poa pratensis to mow; it does not have the ability to spread by rhizomes or stolons: and its fast growth requires extra maintenance.

G.M. Wood (Vermont, U.S.A.)

Two points that have not been mentioned regarding use of Lolium spp. in the U.S.A. are lack of winter hardiness, causing inadequate persistance, and poor summer colour, perhaps associated with a lack of drought resistance.

SESSION 5: EDUCATION

(Chairman: Dr. R. E. Engel)

UNIVERSITY EDUCATION

Dr. James B. Beard,

Department of Crop and Soil Science, Michigan State University, East Lansing, Michigan, U.S.A.

TWO-YEAR TECHNICAL TRAINING PROGRAMMES

Two-year technical programmes in turfgrass management have proved quite popular. Upon completion of a minimum number of credits with a minimum grade average and completion of two terms of placement training at an approved location, the student receives a certificate. Programmes of this type are now offered at Michigan State University, Pennsylvania State University, the University of Maryland and the University of Massachusetts. For illustrative purposes a detailed outline will be given of the programme offered at Michigan State University.

The Turfgrass Management programme is offered by the Department of Crop and Soil Sciences in cooperation with the other departments at Michigan State University, the Michigan turfgrass industry and the Michigan Department of Vocational Education. It starts in late September and lasts eighteen months. There are four academic quarters of on-campus study and six months of placement training within the turfgrass industry. Students live in university housing and participate in all campus activities. The programme of study is as follows:-

Fall Quarter, September-December: required courses	Credits
Accounting	3
Agricultural biochemistry	4
Basic plant science	3
Turfgrasses and their use	3
Writing and Speaking (I)	3
One elective subject required	
Effective study and reading	2
Maintenance of gardens and grounds	3

Winter Quarter, January-March: required courses	
Basic soil science	3
Insect pests and insecticides	3
Plant diseases	3
Practical mathematics	3
Turf culture	3
One elective subject required	
Landscape drafting	2
Plant propagation	3
Shade and lawn trees	3

Spring and Summer Quarters, March-September	
Placement training	30

Fall Quarter, September-December: Credits
required courses

Arboriculture	3
Landscape equipment	3
Personnel practices	3
Turf irrigation and drainage	3
Turf seminar	1
Turf soils and fertilizers	2
One elective subject required	
Business law	3
Fundamentals of golf	1
Landscape construction	3

Winter Quarter, January-March:
required courses

Business management	3
Small engine operation	3
Turf practices	3
Writing and speaking (II)	3
Two elective subjects required	
Financial and credit practices	3
Landscape planning	2
Ornamental plant ecology	3
Psychology	3
Salesmanship	3

After two quarters of course work, extending from late September to early March, the student is placed for 6 months at a job training site approved by the programme coordinator, to obtain practical working experience, eg. in golf course maintenance, sod production, etc. In addition, this employment can finance part of his education. The placement training is a required portion of the educational programme, counting 30 credits towards the required minimum of 95 for graduation. Both the student and his employer are required to submit periodic reports during the placement training period, and the programme co-ordinator makes two visits to observe, consult and advise both the student and his employer.

Graduation is in early March, sufficiently early for students to be placed without difficulty in appropriate permanent positions within the turfgrass industry. The coordinator assists the student and advises him in locating and interviewing for prospective jobs. So far there are far more job opportunities than there are trained graduates. The 1968 graduates of the programme received an average starting salary of $7,500 per year with excellent opportunities for advancement for those individuals showing promise for the more challenging positions within the industry.

TURFGRASS UNDERGRADUATE PROGRAMMES

Undergraduate ciriculums leading to a Bachelor of Science degree specializing in turfgrass management are now being offered by a majority of the land grant universities in the United States. The ciriculum is usually associated with the Agronomy, Crop Science, Horticulture or Soil Science Departments within the College of Agriculture. Generally, students enrolled in the four-year turfgrass ciriculum do not receive as detailed a technical training in turfgrass culture as the two-year technical programmes give, but receive a much broader training with emphasis on principles. A certain minimum number of credits are required in the sciences, humanities and communication arts, with an additional number of credits in the specific major culture of turfgrasses.

Undergraduate students in turfgrass culture can select from a wide variety of allied elective courses in such areas as ornamental horticulture, park management, resource development, soil science, plant pathology, entomology, landscape architecture, urban planning, forestry, accounting, business practices and business law. An outline of a typical ciriculum which might be selected by an undergraduate student in Turfgrass Management is as follows:

Freshman year

Fall	Winter	Spring
American thought & language (I)	American thought & language (II)	American thought & language (III)
Chemistry (I)	Chemistry (II)	Chemistry (III)
Geography	Mathematics (I)	Mathematics (II)
Speech	Plant ecology	Soil Science
Physical education	Physical education	Physical education

Sophomore year

Social science (I)	Social science (II)	Social science (III)
Biochemistry	Botany (I)	Botany (II)
Plant genetics	Economics	Entomology
Genetics laboratory work	Physics (I)	Physics (II)
Soil management	Communications	Psychology

Junior year

Humanities (I)	Humanities (II)	Humanities (III)
Geology	Ornamental plants (I)	Ornamental plants (II)
Soil fertility	Plant physiology	Plant pathology
Meteorology	Climatology	Microbiology
Engines	Labour management	Microbiology laboratory work

Senior year

Seed science	Weed control	Drainage and irrigation
Turfgrass culture (I)	Turfgrass culture (II)	Resource development
Landscape architecture (I)	Landscape architecture (II)	Business management
Ornamental plant management	Park management	Special problem in turf
Accounting	Political science	Journalism

424

Undergraduate turfgrass students are encouraged to seek summer employment in the turfgrass industry although this is not mandatory as in the two-year technical programme. Like graduates of the two-year technical programme, those who obtain degrees at the end of the four-year Turfgrass Management ciriculum have many opportunities for employment. The demand exceeds the supply. The future outlook is for a continued shortage of professionally trained turfmen in the United States.

GRADUATE LEVEL PROGRAMMES IN TURFGRASS MANAGEMENT

Some state universities offer graduate level programmes leading either to a Master of Science or a Ph.D degree with the thesis research training oriented towards some phase of turfgrass culture. Both degrees normally require original research, culminating in a thesis describing it. Some formal course work is also required for both degree programmes. The student may select major and minor fields of study from the following: breeding and genetics, ecology, entomology, management, pathology, physiology, and soils and nutrition. Individuals receiving M. S. or Ph.D degrees in the turfgrass management field are employed by the private turfgrass industry in research and development work or by public institutions for turfgrass research, education or adult extension work.

THE USGA GREEN SECTION ADVISORY SERVICE

W.H. Bengeyfield,

USGA Green Section, Garden Grove, California, U.S.A.

The Green Section of the United States Golf Association is a scientific agency whose mission is to assist USGA member clubs in the upkeep of their golf courses. It was created to meet the need for a turf research and advisory agency, impartial and authoritative. It was founded in 1920 and, like all USGA agencies, operates for service, not for profit.

During the 1920's and 1930's, emphasis was placed on research, and close co-operation with the U.S. Department of Agriculture was established. It was during this time that Dr. John Monteith developed the first effective chemical control of turfgrass diseases. He also worked on weed control and improved turfgrass selections. Many of his findings are still applied today.

Support of research continues to be a major part of the Green Section effort. More than $1,000,000 has been spent by the USGA on turfgrass research since 1920. Today, however, most of the research work is done by Universities on grants received from the Green Section. Included among recent projects are the Specifications for Putting Green Construction; development of improved bermudagrass strains; a study of golf shoe damage to turfgrasses; broadleaf weed control with 2,4-D; and many other research activities.

In 1960, it became apparent that available research information was not being fully utilized by golf courses throughout the country. The Visiting Service of the USGA Green Section was established. By paying a fixed fee ($200 for an 18-hole course), subscribing clubs receive a half-day visit by a Green Section agronomist trained in applying technical information to golf course problems. Four district offices have been established and are staffed with a total of nine agronomists. Over 900 clubs subscribe to the Service.

Today golf course conditions bear little resemblance to those of 1920. Plainly, the Green Section has worked for better turf for better golf. That is its continuing mission in the future.

WEST GERMAN ADVISORY SERVICES

Prof. P. Boeker,

Institut für Pflanzenbau, University of Bonn, West Germany.

The oldest advisory service for sports turf is that of the German Sports Association, which was founded in 1954. At first it was loosely connected with that Association, while it later became a part of the Institute for the Construction of Sports Fields in Cologne. The main work of this Institute deals with the technical aspects of the construction of stadia, indoor swimming pools, etc., but there is a special Sports Turf Research Station in Steinach which gives advice to those who intend to establish new sports fields or who have difficulty with their existing turf. Each year there are training courses for greenkeepers.

There are also a few private experts who give advice to our golf clubs; some of these come from foreign countries.

Some firms offer advice to their customers. For instance seed firms offer assistance to town and road authorities in proposing special mixtures and in solving problems concerned with sowing. Machinery firms advise their customers on the most economic use of special machines, which often leads to advice on the maintenance of good turf.

Advice is also given by Schools of Horticulture and Agricultural Institutes, insofar as they are working with turf. This applies especially to the Turf Research Station at the Institute for Grassland and Fodder Crops at Giessen and to the Agronomy Institute at Bonn.

Finally, mention must be made of the German Turf Association in Bonn which advises its members by publications and seminars and by direct advice on turf areas where there are problems. This work will be intensified in future.

TURFGRASS FIELD DAYS AS A TECHNIQUE FOR EDUCATION

R.R. Davis,

Professor of Agronomy,

Ohio Agricultural Research and Development Center, Wooster, Ohio, U.S.A.

INTRODUCTION

The establishment of turfgrass research plots at a university or experiment station in the United States is usually followed with a field day in 2-5 years. With the continuation of the turfgrass research programme, field days continue on an annual or biennial schedule. Several state universities which have held field days for many years were contacted to survey their feelings and intentions concerning this education technique. Of the nine universities answering the questionnaire, all intend to continue their field days. Attendance is either stable or increasing in each state.

ADVANTAGES AND DISADVANTAGES

The principal advantages of field days are:-

1.   There is no more convincing teaching method than showing results under actual field growing conditions. "Seeing is believing."

2.   Turfgrass field days encourage public and private support for the turfgrass research programme. Competition for funds is keen at any tax-supported university or research centre and a "pressure group" for turfgrass research can be of assistance.

3.   Turfgrass interest groups are primarily urban groups. Colleges of agriculture have much contact with rural groups but little with urban groups. Properly handled, turfgrass field days can encourage urban support for the whole university or research centre.

4.   Field days attract a clientele which may not be contacted any other way. The informality of field days as compared to conferences appeals to some. There is normally no registration fee, banquet, etc., for field days. Most states report that 80-95% of attendance is from the home state.

Although very effective, field days are not without fault. Some of the principal disadvantages are:-

1.   It is very time-consuming and expensive to prepare experimental plots and demonstrations for a field day. One respondent likened it to preparing for a tournament. There are also many details in arranging the programme and providing for those who attend.

2.   The research effort is diluted. A successful field day requires that the plots show differences, so effort that might otherwise go for true research will be put into demonstrations.

3.   Relatively small audiences (90 to 550 reported on questionnaire with average of about 300) attend field days. Many more people can be contacted through mass media.

4.   There is always a weather hazard with field days. A rainy day dampens
enthusiasm as well as visitors. Experienced planners provide an alternative
programme in case of rain.

BLUEPRINT FOR A SUCCESSFUL FIELD DAY

There is no one best way to plan and conduct a field day. There are, however,
some principles which can help those inexperienced in the art.

1.   Organize a planning committee with representatives from all subject matter
departments and agricultural agencies concerned (Research, Extension, Resident
Teaching). This committee should meet many months ahead of a field day to plan
the programme and arrange for handling the visitors to provide effective teaching
and reasonable comfort. The chairman should appoint sub-committees to help with
the many details.

The techniques for handling 500 people are greatly different from those
required for 100 visitors. Groups at a location must be kept small enough to see
and hear the demonstration and discussion. Ohio uses a "cafeteria" system offering a wide choice of subjects, when handling more than 550 people. Maps, signs
and a public address system are used to help visitors locate the areas of interest.

2.   Publicize the event. The institutional editor can be a great help if his
services are used. Have the programme printed well in advance and sent to those
likely to be interested. Ohio has a constantly changing mailing list of about
3,500 on computer cards and addresses are printed on tape by the computer. The
list is made up of organization memberships and registrations at field days for
the past three years. The computer is programmed to eliminate duplication in the
list.

Non-professionals are sensitive to publicity in the mass media and brief
stories illustrated with good photographs in major city newspapers are very
effective. Garden editors are generally very cooperative in printing stories
about field days.

3.   Aim the programme content and publicity at the invited group or groups.
Some states have field days for golf course superintendents and the related commercial group only. Others appeal to a broader group or have different days for
the different interest groups. Above all, have several things of interest to
show any group invited.

4.   Have well maintained, attractive plots to show. While it requires much
effort to reach and keep the desirable quality of maintenance, the alternative
is a serious "credibility gap" with visitors. Poorly maintained plots will not
do much of the intended teaching. Have the plots clearly labelled and select
something to show that makes a point.

5.   Prepare literature which the visitors can take with them. Some states prepare booklets with information about the areas to be shown and the principal results. Individual leaflets about a single experiment can also be used.

6.   Select a date with a high probability for fair weather. Rainfall probability
records can be of assistance. Plan an alternative inside programme in case of
rain.

TURFGRASS EDUCATION IN THE BRITISH ISLES

J.R. Escritt,

Director, Sports Turf Research Institute, Bingley, Yorkshire, U.K.

Having regard to the long history of sport on turf in Britain it is surprising that more has not been done for the education or training of ground staff. Until very recently the only system has been that of unofficial apprenticeship, young people taking junior jobs and working their way up by learning from their more experienced workmates.

At the present time there is considerable awareness of the need for turfgrass education stimulated by various interested parties such as the National Association of Groundsmen which has introduced its own examination scheme, the British Golf Greenkeepers Association (which in co-operation with the National Golf Unions has initiated a formal apprenticeship scheme), the Institute of Park and Recreation Administration and the National Association of Playing Field Officers (a small body consisting of officers who run school playing field maintenance schemes for Education Authorities). The universities and various Government Organisations are becoming increasingly aware of the importance of the turfgrass field. The Department of Education and Science, the Local Government Training Board, the National Joint Council (dealing with manual workers) and the City and Guilds Examination Board are at this very moment investigating the general position.

There are no university courses in turfgrass management, and the main facilities available are as follows:

1. Local Education Authorities run day-release courses in amenity horticulture.

2. Some local authorities have training schemes for their own staff.

3. The Institute of Park and Recreation Administration has a one-year residential course in Parks Management.

4. The National Association of Groundsmen and the British Golf Greenkeepers Association have regular group meetings addressed by selected speakers on turfgrass matters, many of these being from the Trade. The N.A.G. has also started short courses in various areas.

5. The Sports Turf Research Institute runs each year several one-week residential courses covering a comprehensive range of turfgrass information.

The Sports Turf Research Institute helps turfgrass education in other ways. Its staff give lectures to evening meetings of groundsmen or greenkeepers, and also speak at various conferences, for example, of Playing Field Officers or Educational Associations. The sporting journals call upon the Institute frequently for technical articles, and associate members of the Institute receive the annual Journal and quarterly Bulletin. (The Bulletin is of a topical advisory nature and does not normally go to those overseas subscribers who are subscribers for the Journal only.) The Institute is also consulted by Government Departments.

The Institute's advisory service is available only to associate members who pay fees related to the size of their turf areas and the number of pitches involved, charges for advice on construction being generally higher than those for advice on maintenance. Associate members range from home lawn owners to large local authorities. Areas on which advice is given include such famous centres as Ascot Racecourse; Lords Cricket Ground; Wembley Soccer Ground; Twickenham, Cardiff Arms Park and Murrayfield Rugby Union Grounds; the well known golf courses at St. Andrews played upon by the Royal and Ancient Golf Club; and several clubs on the Continent of Europe.

ADVISORY WORK IN THE NETHERLANDS

J.P. van der Horst,

Nederlandse Sport Federatie, 's-Gravenhage, The Netherlands

Work on sports facilities can be divided into four main sections:-

1.   Long term planning.

2.   Design of an individual project.

3.   Construction.

4.   Maintenance.

1.   Long term planning

All municipalities in the Netherlands are members of a working bureau which plans the future needs of all types of sport.

2.   Design

The municipalities are in most cases the principals on behalf of which plans are made. In most cases, the drawings are made by the two big contractors specializing in this work or by the town architect. There is an agreement between the two contractors, the municipalities and the Netherlands Sports Federation that all plans are vetted by the Federation, so that ideas and suggestions from the sports organisations can be incorporated. This stage is called prior consultation.

3.   Construction

The contractors normally advise on how the plans are put into effect in construction. Payment is generally by the municipalities, but when the Government gives a subsidy, as occurs with 25% of all projects, there must be checking by the Federation. In this respect, there is close liaison between the Federation and the contractors, who have well-equipped research sections, to improve construction methods. Because of the Federation's experience in land reclamation, the co-operation is always at a high technical level.

4.   Maintenance

The Federation and the football association itself (both non-commercial bodies) and some other commercial organisations give advice on maintenance to the municipalities who are normally responsible for looking after the sports facilities. If they are subscribers, they receive an advisory visit from the Federation twice a year. Every two years a soil sample has to be examined in a special laboratory to give such important information as humus %, pH, etc.

TURFGRASS ADVISORY SERVICES IN SWEDEN

B. Langvad,

W. Weibull A.B., Landskrona, Sweden.

The turf advisory service in Sweden depends mainly on the seed firms. A large amount is spent to build and equip a stadium, but then only a pensioned player is given the responsibility of maintaining it. The author himself lectures ten hours a week, but this is only a small contribution in view of the great need for a fuller advisory service. There is only one adviser for the hundred golf courses in Sweden, and the Danish Golf Union started to employ an adviser last year. The Swedish Football Association has no professional adviser. Training courses on the maintenance of stadia are held, but one week, in which ice-rinks and indoor arenas have to be dealt with in addition to turf, is not long enough.

It is hoped that a start will soon be made to build up an adequate turf advisory service in Sweden, but there is a long way to go.

TURFGRASS CONFERENCE ORGANIZATION

Robert W. Miller,

Associate Professor of Agronomy, The Ohio State University, Columbus, Ohio,
and the Ohio Agricultural Research and Development Center, Wooster, Ohio, U.S.A.

The first consideration in Turfgrass conference organization is the type of audience, which may be in one of three categories:-

1. Special interest groups, such as golf course superintendents.

2. General professional turfgrass managers, for example a mixed audience of golf course superintendents, sod producers, sports field managers, park superintendents and others.

3. Home owners and other amateurs who do not earn a living producing turf.

Selection of topics to be discussed

The selection of subject matter is simplified if the conference is held for a specific interest group. Unique problems of the group may be discussed in detail. Often a special interest group will have a good knowledge of basic principles and will understand technical presentations better than many other audiences.

Conference organization for a general professional audience presents some problems. There are two ways to select subject matter for this group:

1. To break up the general audience into specific interest groups and conduct two or more educational sessions concurrently. Each session is designed to meet the needs of a special interest group such as golf course superintendents, sod producers, ground maintenance personnel and others. This system requires a large number of speakers and several meeting rooms.

2. To present basic subjects which are of interest to all of those in attendance. This does not meet the specific needs of any one individual as well as programmes designed for special interest groups, but requires fewer speakers and meeting rooms than split sessions.

Subject matter for conferences of home owners and other amateurs must be simple and easy to understand. Most people attending this type of conference do not have the basic background to understand highly technical information. Conferences for amateurs are more successful if they only last one day or less.

The selection of subject matter interesting to the audience is probably the most important factor affecting the success of any conference. Usually presentations of subject matter fall into one of three categories:

1. Discussions of topics such as weed control, fertilization, irrigation, diseases and insects. If the audience is composed of a special interest group the topics may be more specific, such as Poa annua control on golf courses.

2. Reports on research projects. These may or may not be interesting to people attending a conference. The practical turfgrass manager usually is not interested in hearing in detail how a study was conducted. He is interested in the results of the study provided he can apply it to solve his problems in turfgrass production.

3.   Panels consisting of three or more members, to discuss particular topics. To be successful, panels must be well organized and have an effective moderator to lead the discussion.

Ample time for questions from the floor is a vital part of any conference. Time for questions and answers should be reserved either after each presentation or after a series of presentations on one subject matter area. An individual will feel cheated if he does not have the opportunity to find the answers to a problem that has troubled him in his operation.

Selection of speakers

Any conference will be a failure unless good speakers are selected. The most interesting topic will not hold the attention of the audience if the speaker makes a poor presentation. Visual aids such as slides are a part of good presentation.

Speakers may be selected from professionals involved in research and education, industrial representatives and laymen in turfgrass production. It is advisable to have some speakers representing each of these three groups. At least half of the speakers should be research and educational personnel from colleges, universities, research stations and similar organizations.

Most industrial representatives will present information in an unbiassed way even on subject matter related to their commercial interests. Many representatives are knowledgeable in turfgrass production and should not be overlooked as prospective speakers.

An individual enjoys hearing how his peers solved their problems. Presentations by qualified turfgrass managers are well attended and add to a conference. Discretion in selecting laymen as speakers is necessary to avoid presentation of misinformation.

Each speaker should adapt his presentation to the level of understanding of the audience. Most audiences are composed of individuals of diverse backgrounds; therefore the speaker should attempt to direct his comments to the average person attending the conference.

Speakers vary in their ability to hold the attention of the audience. A few can speak effectively for one hour or more. For most speakers 30 to 45 minutes is ample time to present a topic without boring those attending.

Selecting physical facilities

A conference should be held in pleasant surroundings conducive to learning. There should be comfortable and adequate meeting rooms and dining areas. Entertainment is desirable but may detract from the conference. The ability of the participant to pay must be a consideration in selecting a location for a conference. The site should be centrally located and be easily reached by air and ground transport.

Participation by local organizations

Local leaders in the turfgrass industry are willing workers and can contribute in organizing and conducting a conference. Members of local organizations should be included in planning and should serve on committees such as programme, registration, finance, and banquet committees. Attendance will increase if these people feel they play an active role. Basic planning for the conference should start at least one year in advance. In many cases it is necessary to reserve hotel space two or three years in advance.

Promoting the conference

The best promotion for a conference is by word of mouth at meetings held by organizations such as golf course superintendents' associations. Advance mailing of programmes and other promotional material is necessary. Advertisement in trade magazines, journals, newspapers, radio and other news media is desirable. As a conference becomes established, people plan to attend each year.

Registration and fees

Registration may be accomplished either at the conference site or as pre-registration by mail. In either case enough people should be available to register people without delays. A registration fee ample to cover expenses is necessary. A volume of proceedings, consisting of the talks given at the conference, is desirable, and the registration fee should cover the cost of printing and mailing the proceedings.

Commercial exhibits

In Ohio a successful trade show has been combined with the educational sessions. Last year, 60 turfgrass dealers and distributors filled 125 exhibit spaces with equipment, chemicals, seed, and other turfgrass products. Exhibitors were charged for spaces about 10 sq m in size. The 2½ day conference was attended by 951 people from 22 states and Canada. The commercial exhibits have not detracted from the educational sessions.

COMMERCIAL ADVISORY SERVICES

Wayne C. Morgan,

Kellogg Supply Inc., Wilmington, California, U.S.A.

There is more to business than making money. If it is possible to make contributions to the profession one is engaged in, one's life will be enriched beyond the remuneration received.

In its efforts to be of service, the author's company has tried to determine needs existing in the turfgrass field that it might be able to fill. It seems that there are four major needs:-

1.   To supply basic technical information on the culture of landscape plants and turfgrasses. A class in landscape and turfgrass management is taught through the newsletters which are sent free to landscape architects; landscape contractors; those responsible for maintenance of school grounds, parks and memorial parks; golf course superintendents; school teachers; etc. Many articles from the newsletter are also picked up and reprinted in trade journals.

2.   A tremendous amount of new information is constantly being received from universities and commercial research centres. The wider dissemination of this technical information, in an easily understood form, is a service of great importance. Reviews of research articles are published in the newsletter as well as being published regularly in a trade journal.

3.   There is a need for expert advice on specifications and their preparation, problem solving and management programming. This service is provided free by field representatives who are well educated and taught to strive honestly to help people.

4.   Management programmes have been developed based on how plants grow and are affected by, or affect, different cultural operations. Programmes for turfgrass management have been published based on growth curves for tops and roots. Consideration is also given to disease potential, strength of the turf, mowing frequency, thatch build-up, drought tolerance and irrigation requirements. New programmes for landscape, trees, shrubs, ground covers and bedding plants are to be developed. A series of "problem-solving charts" is being developed for turfgrass and landscape diseases, insects, nematodes, rodents and weeds. Information on soil deficiencies, fumigation, sterilization, etc., will also be included. A booklet on "Soils and soil preparation" is also being prepared.

THE COOPERATIVE EXTENSION ADVISORY SERVICE

Robert C. O'Knefski,

Cooperative Extension Agent, Nassau County, Mineola, New York, U.S.A.

Many people in the United States and other countries are familiar with County Agricultural Agents and the work they do with agriculture. When farms are taken over by homes, the new homeowner turns to the local County Agricultural Agent for answers to his problems with lawns, trees, shrubs, house plants, flowers, fruits, vegetables and household insects.

In New York State the funds to continue furnishing information to homeowners rather than to farmers depends largely on the support of the local County government. Similar programmes in several states are entirely financed by the State government through a land grant college or university.

Programmes to provide information to homeowners vary considerably from presenting a single piece of printed literature to an individual to presenting a regularly scheduled television programme to many thousands.

The approach in Extension is to help people help themselves. One of the really great contributions of Extension education is its development of people as individuals, leaders, and cooperative members of their local community and the world society.

Situation in Nassau County, New York

Nassau County was once a farming community producing potatoes and a variety of vegetables for the New York City market. Today, there are nearly 1,500,000 residents in the County. There is a population of 4,858 per square mile. These people live in about 400,000 dwelling units. The number of multiple dwelling units has been very small, but they are now beginning to increase. Individual homes became very popular after World War II. Many thousands of people from New York City moved out to the "country" to have a home of their own.

The average property size is about 6,000 sq. ft. (558 sq m). The house usually covers between 1,500 and 2,000 sq. ft. (139 - 186 sq m). About 4,000 - 5,000 sq. ft. (372 - 465 sq m) is covered by lawn and 500 - 1,000 sq. ft (47 - 93 sq m) by trees, shrubs, ground covers, annuals, perennials, etc. The lawn area is sometimes reduced by a small vegetable garden, a swimming pool, a patio, etc.

The higher population, more leisure time, and the tendency towards "country life" means more interest in lawns, trees, shrubs, flowers and surroundings. More than one-half of the work done by the Extension Service is with lawns.

Homeowners have a great diversity of experience relative to home ground plantings. Many are just out of metropolitan apartment buildings, while others have had the experience of having maintained one or more previous homes. The need for information by homeowners is unlimited.

Programmes for professionals

The Agricultural Division of the Cooperative Extension Association of Nassau County has specific educational programmes for professional groups such as garden supply dealers, pest control operators, landscape maintenance men, school groundskeepers, golf course superintendents, park maintenance personnel, nurserymen and estate superintendents. These programmes are usually planned by an Advisory Committee of 6 to 17 people from a particular profession. The Advisory Committee meets the Agents to decide the industry problems and suggests topics, programmes and speakers. Several types of school or meeting are set up depending on the needs indicated. They arrange two- or three-hour evening sessions, a one-day school, or a series of evening meetings.

Usually someone from the Advisory Committee conducts the meeting with County Agricultural Agents (now called Cooperative Extension Agents), Cornell University specialists and industry people making up the speakers' panels.

There are also Turfgrass Field Days for professionals arranged by Extension Agents with the help of University specialists. Several groups have also had late afternoon sessions of several hours looking over a series of home grounds which one or more participants maintains in his business. Other late afternoon sessions are held at parks or arboretums. Extension Agents also make personal visits upon request to help solve problems on the spot.

Programmes for the homeowner

The Agricultural Division has a limited number of formal educational programmes for homeowners. At present the 54 local school districts are offered programmes for their evening adult education classes in Lawn Maintenance and Landscape Maintenance. These are two-hour courses taught by an Extension Agent. He uses a slide presentation supplemented with free bulletins and leaflets. There is always a question and answer period.

The Extension Agents also, upon request, speak about lawns, trees, shrubs, flowers, etc., to professional horticultural groups, garden clubs, civic associations, religious groups, fraternal organizations and others.

Most of the advisory work is unorganised. Last year, the office answered 20,650 telephone calls on horticultural problems. There were over 3,000 office visitors with problems, and an equal number of sick plant specimens sent by mail. In addition, over 29,000 people called the daily recorded one-minute telephone message of timely gardening advice. Agents made 733 personal visits to diagnose homeowner or commercial production problems, usually after inspecting specimens in the office.

Over 500,000 circulars, bulletins, and leaflets were sent out of the office last year.

Staff

There is a staff of 6 Cooperative Extension Agents and 6 secretaries. There are also two or three college students in the summer as summer agents, and two summer assistant secretaries. Two of the present staff were former summer assistants.

Recently a seventh agent was hired to work with the local horticultural industries as a business management specialist.

Budget

The budget for 1969 is $165,000. The County pays 85%, the State 4% and the Federal Government 1% of this amount. The rest comes from membership and miscellaneous sources.

G. S. Robinson,

Agronomy Dept., Massey University, Palmerston North, New Zealand

The New Zealand Institute for Turf Culture is responsible for most of the advisory work in turf improvement in New Zealand. Sports clubs occasionally receive some assistance from Farm Advisory Officers of the Department of Agriculture, while one or two private consultants have operated at different times. But their influence is relatively small compared with that of the Institute.

The Institute had its beginnings in the Greens Research Committee of the N.Z. Golf Association. This latter body was set up in 1932 and immediately arranged for an experimental area to be established at the Manawatu Golf Club in Palmerston North. A comprehensive research programme was initiated by Sir Bruce Levy and the late Mr. E.A. Madden, who were stationed at the Plant Research Bureau in the same city. This included:-

(a) Seeds mixtures, rates of seeding, species and strains;

(b) Manuring;

(c) Mechanical and chemical treatments;

(d) Pre-treatments of seed-beds for destruction of seeds, diseases and pests;

(e) The establishment of a turf garden and nursery of new species and strains.

Within a few years a mass of significant results had accumulated and in order that more complete use of these results should be made, the Golf Council appointed a Greens Advisory Officer. Within two or three years over 150 sports clubs were being visited annually.

At the same time as research and advisory work were developing, the golf greenkeepers formed an Association which provided an avenue of contact between practice and experimental findings. This resulted in a rapid improvement in the standard of green-keeping in New Zealand.

In 1949 it was decided to widen the interests of the Greens Research Committee by inviting other sporting bodies and educational institutions to assist in the organisation. This move resulted in the Institute for Turf Culture being formed. Finance was almost entirely dependent on grants from the affiliated sporting bodies, with golf and bowls making the major contribution. But in the early years this was not sufficient to permit the appointment of an advisory officer.

Increasing interest in turf research brought about demands for membership of the Institute by private individuals and clubs, and the constitution was changed to allow associate members to be elected. These have now reached a total of about 1200 and their annual subscriptions have helped to improve the financial position of the Institute to such an extent that it has been possible to reinstitute the advisory service which had lapsed through lack of funds. One part-time officer was employed for about 10 years, 'and in the last year or so two further advisors have been appointed to cope with the increasing demands for advice.

The objectives of the Institute have not changed over the years and are related to the following aspects of turf culture:-

1. Research

The plot area at the Manawatu Golf Club was used for 25 years and provided the basis for recommendations which are still made by advisors. When the Golf Club required the land for course extension the Department of Agriculture established a research area at Milson not far from Palmerston North and this has been in operation for about 12 years. Many suggestions for research topics have been provided by Institute members, and many problems have been elucidated. Owing to the shortage of suitable technical staff, some of this research is now being transferred to Grasslands Division, D.S.I.R., whose Director, Dr. L. Corkill, is also Chairman of the Institute.

2. Advisory work

Each advisory officer has his own district. He is paid a retaining fee, travelling expenses depending on the extent of his area and a fee from each club, sports body or institution for whom he provides services. A written report follows each visit. The fee to be paid by the club is set down by the Institute.

In one or two urban areas, local advisory committees were appointed at a time when the Institute did not have any advisory staff. These have continued to function up to the present time and perform a very useful service in collaboration with the more recently appointed officers of the Institute.

3. Publication of the Newsletter

One of the duties of the Senior Advisory Officer is to produce a Newsletter every two months. This is sent out to all members and is the main service available to associate members. The Newsletter, which runs to 24 pages or more, contains seasonal advice on all classes of turf, feature articles on special subjects and reprints of papers presented at Conferences.

The Newsletter has resulted in much more widespread dissemination of knowledge on turf culture and through it the work of the Institute has become much better known.

4. Conferences

An annual conference of golf greenkeepers is held over a period of 3 days in a different district each year. This is organised by the Institute with the help of the Greenkeepers' Association. Attendance is generally between 50 and 80. Technical papers are presented by scientists on such topics as soils, fertilisers, grass species, pests, diseases and drainage. Practical topics are often presented by greenkeepers and an opportunity is given for firms to display and demonstrate machinery.

For bowling greenkeepers, there is greater reliance on regional conferences, which may extend to 2 days, or perhaps a single day in the form of a field day is held on a particular green where problems are discussed.

Recently special courses lasting up to a week have been held for junior greenkeepers. Their object is to attract young men into greenkeeping work by showing them that the work is more than a daylight-to-dark chore.

Another special form of conference is one arranged for committeemen of sports clubs who are responsible for allocation of funds for various greenkeeping operations in their clubs. It is very necessary that they should understand the basic principles of greenkeeping. This leads to much better co-operation between committees and greenkeeping staff.

Visits of greenkeepers to the Research Area are encouraged and the Senior Advisory Officer has normally taken an active part in showing them the work in progress. Many useful suggestions for future research come from visitors to the area.

5. Diploma in Turf Culture

Thirty years ago the Greens Research Committee of the N.Z. Golf Association instituted a Diploma in Turf Culture. This was a very far-sighted policy and the value of it is seen in the calibre of the greenkeepers in New Zealand today.

When the Institute for Turf Culture became established, it continued the examinations and these have been gradually modified over the years; at present it is necessary to:-

(a)   achieve a minimum of 4 years satisfactory service in greenkeeping or allied work;

(b)   pass two stages of written and oral examinations generally taken at yearly intervals;

(c)   pass a practical examination after at least three years of satisfactory service in greenkeeping.

When their applications to sit the Diploma are received, candidates are given a curriculum with references to suitable books and articles. The Newsletter is becoming invaluable as a source of up-to-date material for the examination and it is recommended that candidates familiarise themselves with recent copies.

Diploma holders are eligible for increased rates of pay, and a Diploma is a necessity in applying for any of the better positions in greenkeeping.

6. Publishing of books

The Institute's main venture in this respect has been the publication of "Turf culture" which has been regarded as the best general text in the subject in New Zealand. Earlier, two other valuable publications were issued under the auspices of the Institute for Turf Culture. These were "Construction, renovation and care of the golf course" by E. Bruce Levy and "Garden lawns & playing greens" by E.A. Madden.

To ensure that subject matter in turf culture be kept up-to-date the Institute is now arranging for "Turf culture" to be re-written. The great advances that have taken place in this field since it appeared originally in 1961 make re-writing rather than revision absolutely essential.

7.   New developments

Advisory Officers in the course of their duties meet many difficult problems, for some of which they have no answer. From time to time they can suggest ways and means of overcoming these problems, but are unable to recommend them without further knowledge. A recent example was the occurrence of drainage problems on golf greens that had been spiked and cored, but often developed poor sub-surface drainage. The suggestion was made that a mole plough might be the appropriate implement to use. But the idea of using an ordinary mole plough was discounted because of the surface damage it would cause. To be successful a miniature was required.

The Institute decided to get such a mole plough designed and made. The results to date have been very promising.

Conclusions

Members of the N.Z. Institute for Turf Culture feel that the surface has only been scratched in the big job of improving playing turf in N.Z. Finance has been a problem, but increased grants from sports bodies seem probable in the near future. This should result in the better provision of technical knowledge to those who can benefit from it. The principles of modern management and improvement are not sufficiently recognised and it is the Institute's aim to rectify this.

THE USE OF TEST DEMONSTRATIONS FOR
PRACTICAL RESEARCH AND EXTENSION TEACHING

J.F. Shoulders,
Extension Specialist in Turf,

Agronomy Department, Virginia Polytechnic Institute, Blacksburg, Virginia, U.S.A.

The Cooperative Extension Service is the division of the College of Agriculture which provides non-credit instruction for farmers and others on a statewide basis. Supported by federal, state and local governments, Extension maintains a field staff of Extension Agents located in counties or cities and a specialist staff headquartered at the University in close proximity to their counterparts in Research. The Extension specialist is closely associated with research workers on the one hand, and with Extension Agents in the field and the problems they encounter on the other. He supports the Agents by making available and interpreting research data and conferring with research workers with respect to problems encountered in the field.

Virginia Agronomy Extension specialists are improving the statewide agronomy programme by making use of a long accepted research method, the incorporation of replicated treatments using statistical design in field test demonstrations. Formerly, Extension demonstrations involved the establishment of a practice or combination of practices, without replication, for observation and use in county Extension teaching, but no actual data were collected.

Now in the Virginia Extension Programme, replicated tests similar in design to experiments conducted by the Research Division are located on property furnished by a cooperating turf superintendent or farmer at carefully selected sites for which available research data may not be applicable. These revised types of test demonstrations are proving to be more effective teaching tools than were the traditional Extension demonstrations and are supplementing the overall research programme by obtaining needed and reliable data from locations and under conditions not feasible for the Research Division.

Several factors led to the development of the Extension Agronomy test demonstration programme. First, Virginia has three general ecological areas with wide climatic differences associated with altitude changes from mountains, with elevations in excess of 5,000 ft. (1,500 m), to sea level on the Atlantic Coast. Soils, temperature extremes, rainfall patterns and exposure vary widely within and between areas. It is not practical for research workers to locate experiments in more than the most representative conditions in a given area. Extension, with Agents located in each county and a specialist staff, is equipped to cover critical areas more completely and to contribute a great deal of applied research. Secondly, Extension's clientele has become more educated and includes new groups such as golf course superintendents. More exact information is demanded for a given situation than is available from an unreplicated, single practice demonstration or than can be obtained from experiments conducted elsewhere. Thirdly, Extension personnel are now better trained in research methods at both specialist and unit level, are capable of accepting responsibility in the area of applied research, and are more cognizant of the value of research. These factors, and encouragement from agricultural commodity groups, resulted in Extension administrators making available funds for a limited number of adequately trained technicians and equipment for starting a test demonstration programme. This was done with the approval of the Research Division.

Due to the acute need for turfgrasses which can better tolerate the stresses caused by climatic conditions prevalent in much of Virginia, the first priority in the turfgrass phase has been to evaluate in stress areas certain varieties that have exhibited very good characteristics in Research Division experiments. For example, twenty varieties and strains of Kentucky bluegrass (Poa pratensis L.) are currently being tested under two nitrogen levels at Richmond, Virginia, two hundred miles from the main research station. Richmond has high summer temperatures, frequent periods of inadequate moisture, and un-favourable soil conditions which result in a high degree of summer stress for this species. Near the east coast at Newport News, conditions are even more critical for cool-season species. Here 30 varieties of Kentucky bluegrass and 8 of tall fescue (Festuca arundinacea Schreb.) are being evaluated. It is expected that these test demonstrations will be valuable aids in selection of the varieties of Kentucky bluegrass and tall fescue best adapted for turf in these areas.

Another test demonstration has provided useful information needed by the City of Virginia Beach in improving turf near the ocean front of this resort city. By locating a test demonstration in this critical situation, varieties of bermudagrass (Cynodon spp.) that can successfully withstand the combination of unusual circumstances involving location, exposure, salt spray, and traffic at Virginia Beach have been identified. Other test demonstrations include the evaluation of mixtures of cool-season species overseeded on bermudagrass greens with different levels of thatch build-up for winter turf quality, and the evaluation of certain recently released varieties of perennial ryegrass in an area of high summer temperatures.

In all test demonstrations the county or city Extension Agent in agriculture is a cooperator along with the specialist and the turfgrass superintendent and is a key individual in the success or failure of a test demonstration. The specialist relies heavily on him in the location of the actual site and selection of the superintendent. It is the Agent's responsibility to observe the demonstration frequently and to contact the specialist when unexpected changes or problems occur.

The test demonstration programme is a valuable aid to the Extension Agent. Although he is not primarily research oriented, test demonstrations provide him with the opportunity to work with replicated tests, and often improve his ability to make more effective use of data from the Research Division. They increase the Agent's awareness of the importance of problems in the area, and improve his confidence in meeting and his effectiveness in solving problems. A successful demonstration provides a cooperating Agent with an effective teaching tool located in his own county or city.

Although far outweighed by advantages, certain limitations of test demonstrations should be recognised. These include the time required to conduct this type of demonstration successfully and the lack of control as compared to an experiment conducted in its entirety by the Research Division. It requires the same time and care for an Extension specialist to conduct a replicated test as it does for a research worker. Due to other responsibilities in the Extension programme, it is important to limit the number of test demonstrations to those that can be included within the framework of the specific Extension programme. It should again be emphasized that selection of the cooperating superintendent is of utmost importance. Since the time limitation prevents close professional supervision of much routine maintenance, test demonstrations are often subject to somewhat less careful management than a Research Division experiment.

The experience in Extension Agronomy to date with the test demonstration programme is most favourable. The Extension teaching programme in Agronomy has been strengthened and data from demonstrations have tended to strengthen the findings of the Research Division. Demonstrations are proving valuable in determining whether or not a specific practice applies, or a variety is adapted, to a given location, and on occasion they indicate areas in which the Research Division might increase its effort. The adoption of this method has improved the effectiveness of the research and Extension teams.

OPERATION GREEN CARPET

H. Hamilton Williams, Ph.D.,

Los Angeles State and County Arboretum, Arcadia, California, U.S.A.

The problems of growing a satisfactory lawn are the greatest and the most varied in gardening, but there is very little effective organization for teaching and guidance. Most South California residents have very little knowledge of the cultural requirements of grasses, the complexities of soils, the inter-relation of climate and location, or the control of insects, diseases and weeds. This is especially true of new-comers who are totally unfamiliar with the unique and arid climate. Home gardeners spend considerable amounts of money for equipment and materials, without success, through failing to follow instructions or through receiving misleading information from sales personnel. Home gardeners often fail to take advantage of the abundance of horticultural information and know-ledge available through publications, radio and television, as well as through schools and garden clubs. They become discouraged and settle for an inferior lawn, or move to an apartment to escape the responsibility of lawn care alto-gether. Many others, however, relegate lawn care to professional gardeners, thus creating and supporting a thriving business in Southern California.

"Operation Green Carpet" was conceived by the author as a cooperative effort in public service and education for home lawn keepers; it was launched jointly by the Los Angeles State and County Arboretum at Arcadia, the University of California Agricultural Extension Service, related horticultural and civic org-anizations, and the South California turfgrass industry.

Facilities currently devoted to turfgrass education in Southern California include the University of California at Riverside, California Polytechnic College at Pomona, Pierce Junior College at Woodland Hills, Mt. San Antonio College at Walnut, Los Angeles Trade-Technical College in Los Angeles, Fullerton Junior College at Fullerton and Pasadena City College. Courses are also given at city and vocational schools throughout the county, as well as at several county and state corrective institutions. The County Agricultural Extension Service offers continuing seminars in cooperation with the Southern California Turfgrass Council and the Golf Course Superintendents Association. This instruction is almost exclusively directed towards the full-time student or professional in service training. In recognition of the tremendous importance of the non-professional home gardener in relation to the turfgrass industry, as well as the aesthetics and economy of the community, "Operation Green Carpet" was initiated.

The Los Angeles State and County Department of Arboreta and Botanic Gardens, a public facility with gardens located conveniently throughout the County, can most effectively disseminate lawn care information to the home gardener. Its staff includes specialists in taxonomy, genetics, pathology, entomology, plant physiology and education. It has meeting halls for lawn institutes and exhibits, and at Arcadia has maintained since 1953 demonstration plots of grasses and ground covers for homes.

Following a conference in January 1964 committees were set up to plan "Operation Green Carpet". The main one was the Nucleus Committee, each member representing a separate interest, e.g. irrigation, seed, equipment, chemicals, fertilizers, etc.

At the initial meeting of this Nucleus Committee, it was decided that the first effort of the cooperating agencies should be a Home Lawn Exposition. This consisted of demonstrations and displays to illustrate approved steps in the establishment and care of a home lawn. Also, there were displays of equipment and materials available commercially. The general aim was to teach the basic principles of horticulture and botany, and how to use the approved lawn care methods, materials and equipment developed through research and made available commercially by the industry. The ultimate goal was, of course, better and more beautiful lawns throughout South California. These Expositions, staged every spring and fall, have become increasingly popular as indicated by an attendance of over 10,000 at the 3rd Annual Spring Home Lawn Exposition. An important factor in this increase of public interest has been the support of the press, radio and television. Participation in the Home Lawn Expositions by professional gardeners representing the Southern California Gardeners Council has been mutually beneficial from the standpoint of education and public relations. As an association, this group has staged a series of community home lawn shows throughout South California with the cooperation of the Arboretum.

A further development of "Operation Green Carpet" was a "Better Lawns Week" in spring and fall. In this, retail nurseries and garden centres are urged to encourage wider use by home gardeners of the approved materials and equipment required to build and maintain better lawns.

Emphasis on better lawns assisted the current drive of the community organization, Los Angeles Beautiful, for more colour in the California landscape, especially as a feature of the State's bicentennial celebration in 1969. The organisers of "Operation Green Carpet" offered their assistance to President and Mrs. Lyndon B. Johnson in their effort to preserve and develop the natural beauty of the U.S.A., and were commended by Mrs. Johnson for their programme to promote beautiful home lawns in Southern California. "Operation Green Carpet" was also honoured in resolutions by both the Los Angeles City Council and the Los Angeles County Board of Supervisors.

The annual spring Home Lawn Expositions of the past two years have been held in conjunction with the "Festival of Flowers" before an estimated 300,000 visitors. The 1969 display contained 200 varieties of turfgrasses and basic information on varietal identification.

Through the cooperative effort of the California Fertilizer Association, the California Association of Nurserymen, the Southern California Gardeners Council, the California Landscape Contractors Association, the Southern California Turfgrass Council and the Arboretum, a permanent display booth was built that has been shown at numerous events in Los Angeles and neighbouring counties. A hundred thousand copies of a Home Lawn Management Chart, containing graphic and factual information, were printed and are being distributed widely. This effort represented the recognition by the Fertilizer Association - previously concerned mainly with the rural market - of the problems and potential of urban landscape horticulture.

After the successful staging of the Home Lawn Expositions, the next step has been the establishment of a turfgrass centre at the Arboretum, by cooperation between the suppliers of turfgrass equipment, materials, chemicals, and services through their professional trade associations; local universities and colleges; the Extension Service; and the Arboretum itself. A Cooperative Horticultural Educational and Diagnostic Centre is being established to prepare recommendations for the home gardener, with particular emphasis on lawn and landscape development and maintenance. This Centre will provide cooperative resources for studying optimum growing practices, analysing home garden and lawn problems, and disseminating preventive, remedial and cultural information. It will make basic soil and plant analyses, salinity determinations, pH measurements and studies of the growing media.

The Centre will also evaluate the effectiveness of the programme in upgrading standards of home horticulture, and will be an educational adjunct for industry and college departments. It may thus help to initiate and conduct research and educational projects independently or in cooperation with universities and colleges, the California Agricultural Extension Service, and industry, especially where the combination of laboratory and field practice facilities are required.

To initiate this programme the Soil Improvement Committee of the California Fertilizer Association has allotted an initial grant of $3,000, subject to matching and supplementation by other industry organizations and resources. It is hoped that, once established fully, the Centre may be partially self-sustaining through nominal service fees and the sale of educational material.

The planning of the Centre will logically begin with the formation of a steering Committee composed of selected members of the SIC-CFA, the Arboretum Turfgrass Advisory Committee, and representatives from other funding and industry organizations. The County of Los Angeles has provided the basic physical structure for the Centre headquarters, with space and laboratory facilities within a new Research Building. Eventually it is hoped to establish at the Arboretum a full time qualified Agronomist to take over direction of the Centre and its future development.

If all the lawns in Los Angeles County were put together in a strip 500 ft. (150 m) wide, a green carpet could be laid from Los Angeles to New York City. It is estimated that well over 100,000 acres of turf (40,000 ha) beautify the County's homes, public buildings, factories and industrial centres, as well as providing playing surfaces in parks, golf courses and other recreational areas (Kimball 1955; Morgan 1961).

In terms of money invested, residential lawns account for over $300,000,000 in irrigation and maintenance equipment alone. In addition, it costs over $100,000,000 each year to keep these lawns vigorous and healthy. Apartment dwellers usually are relieved of the responsibility for lawn care, but they are assessed for the cost of this operation in rental charges to the extent of over $16,000,000 yearly.

City and county parks, playgrounds and athletic fields include over 5,000 acres in turf (2,000 ha) valued in excess of $20,000,000. Annual maintenance for these areas costs almost $5,000,000. Golf courses, public and private, cover more than 3,000 acres (1,200 ha) and are valued at over $20,000,000. An additional $7,000,000 is spent each year for upkeep.

The total investment throughout Los Angeles County is estimated to amount to over $400,000,000, which represents only the cost of turf installation, irrigation systems and other maintenance equipment, and does not include the value of the land. In addition, there is an annual expenditure of $150,000,000 for gardening services, equipment operation and repairs, and for horticultural chemicals and supplies.

Considering the increasing amount of money involved in providing Southern California (and elsewhere) with this carpet of green, the question arises as to whether the public gets its money's worth. Concurrent with an expanded urbanization requiring thousands of new home lawns each year, there is a growing demand for higher quality turf that is pest-free, evergreen, versatile and durable. Towards these ends, extensive studies and experiments are being conducted continuously to discover better management methods, more effective equipment and materials, and new varieties of grasses with improved performance and greater adaptability.

If this new information about the home lawn is given to the home gardener, there will be:-

1. More beauty in the community.

2. More 'grass roots' support for university research at public expense because of a broadened understanding of the problems involved.

3. More support from the informed home lawn gardener for landscape maintenance programmes at civic buildings, schools, parks, playgrounds, etc.

4. More market potential for improved horticultural products, equipment and plants, as well as for professional services.

"Operation Green Carpet" focusses attention on an area of vital concern that has been long neglected by science, education and industry.

REFERENCES

1. ANON. (1963) Continuing home audit: lawn maintenance. Marketing Research Dept., Los Angeles Times.

2. BOSTER, DEWEY O. (1966) Turfgrass survey. Pennsylvania Crop Reporting Service, State Department of Agriculture, Harrisburg, Pennsylvania.

3. DAVIS, WILLIAM B. (1966) California's 50,000 acre golf course. California Turfgrass Culture 16, 1, 2.

4. DAVIS, WILLIAM B. (1968) California's golf course boom. California Turfgrass Culture 18, 4, 25.

5. KIMBALL, MARSTON H. (1955) Turfgrass by the thousands of acres. California Turfgrass Culture 5, 1, 1.

6. MORGAN, WAYNE C., et al. (1961) Turfgrass survey of Los Angeles County. Turfgrass Advisor, July, 1961. Agric. Extension Service, Univ. of California.

7. WILLIAMS, H. HAMILTON (1944) A study of landscaping in negro communities of the Southeastern states. Thesis, Cornell University, Ithaca, N.Y.

8. WILLIAMS, H. HAMILTON (1946) A study of landscaping in negro communities of the Southeastern states. J. negro Education 15, 4, 628.

DISCUSSION

J.E. Howland (Nevada, U.S.A.)

As the Editor in Chief of Lawn Care magazine in the U.S.A. for the past 12 years, I should like to share some of our research data on what happens on American lawns. There are approximately 42 million homes with lawns. Of these, approximately 18 million receive fertilizer at least once a year; 7 million receive herbicides; 3 million receive insecticides; and 1 million receive fungicides.

SESSION 6A: MOWING AND GROWTH CONTROL

(Chairman: Prof. P. Boeker)

MOWING PRACTICES

J.R. Watson,

Director of Marketing, Turf Products, Toro Manufacturing Corporation,
Minneapolis, Minnesota 55420, U.S.A.

SUMMARY

Mowing is a basic cultural technique necessary for turf production.
Good mowing practices enhance the aesthetic values of a turfgrass facility
and contribute, as much as any single factor, to the well-groomed appearance
of turfgrass. Mowing is necessary to develop and to maintain a satisfactory
playing surface on those turf sites used for recreational activity. Mowing
restricts root development, but proper clipping of adapted grasses stimulates
development of tillers and shoots either from the crown or from basal buds
of rhizomes and stolons. Thus, proper mowing encourages more rapid coverage
of newly established turfgrass and promotes density of established turf.
Also, since grasses exhibit basal as opposed to terminal growth, mowing
serves to check the growth of weeds. In addition, grass cutting is probably
the most time-consuming phase of the turfgrass maintenance programme. Hence,
selection and care of mowing equipment is particularly significant in development of sound mowing practices.

EFFECTS OF MOWING ON TURFGRASSES

Turfgrass is judged by the standards established for its beauty, use or
playability; and by its density, its freedom from pests and its uniformity of
growth and colour. Because of the necessity of mowing and because of the influence
clipping has on the grass plant and on other cultural techniques, mowing practices
play a key role in determining the adaptability or suitability of grasses for
turf purposes. For to be suitable for the production of turf, a grass plant must
be able to grow and to persist in the environment to which it is subjected.
Musser (18) indicates that less than 40, and Hanson (9) substantially fewer,
species are normally used for turf in North America. Thus it seems likely, since
a high percentage of these are introduced, that less than 50 grass species are
suitable for turf throughout the world.

The suitability of grasses for turf and their ability to withstand frequent
and close clipping is related to certain of their growth characteristics and to
their leaf structure (19). Grasses exhibit basal growth as opposed to terminal
growth of most other plants. For this reason, normal mowing does not destroy the
growing areas of the grass leaf. These are located in the crown and at the base
of the leaf, and thus are unaffected when normal amounts of leaf surface are
removed. The long flattened grass leaf is peculiarly adapted for intercepting a
maximum of the sun's rays and from the standpoint of photosynthesis is an efficient
structure. A reduction in the plant leaf areas exposed to sunlight reduces the
capacity of the plant to carry on photosynthesis. This is a vital and basic consideration when determining height and frequency of cut for turfgrasses (25, 26).

The height to which a given perennial grass can be mowed and still survive
for extended periods is directly related to its ability to produce sufficient
leaf mass for the photosynthetic activity required to support its growth and development. This ability is related to the anatomical and morphological characteristics of the species. Among those that influence suitability for turf are: the length

of internodes; the number of stolons, rhizomes or tillers; the number of basal buds; and the habit of growth. In general, short internodes, profuse development of stolons, rhizomes and tillers and abundant basal buds are characteristics of permanent turf species. They occur in greater or lesser degree, and the extent to which they occur determines the heights of cut between which a given species will grow most satisfactorily. Thus, Poa pratensis L. will produce satisfactory turf only when cut from 3 to 7 cm; whereas, Agrostis palustris Huds. and related species will, if properly maintained, produce turf when cut 0.2 to 1.0 cm and Cynodon dactylon (L.) Pers. from 0.2 to 3.0 cm.

Differences within species permit the selection and development of cultivars more tolerant of a lower height of cut. For example, within Poa pratensis, Merion, Fylking, Windsor, Cougar and Prato are tolerant of a lower height of cut than Park, Delta, Newport or Common (3, 13, 20, 29). So likewise with the improved cultivars of Cynodon dactylon. Nevertheless, when any of these, or any other turfgrass, is cut lower than the minimum of its normal range, the deficiencies in root system, food reserves and general susceptibility to pests that result must be compensated by adjustment and modification of other cultural techniques (27).

Mowing practices must be keyed to the use for which the turfgrass area is being produced. If for recreational activity, the height of cut must meet the demands of play. More often than not mowing at the heights necessary for playing purposes restricts or limits root development. Beard and Daniel (1), Davis (4), Juska and associates (11 & 12), Madison (15), Stroh and Law (22) and Roberts (21), among others, have shown there is a reduction in root growth of a given species as a result of decreasing height of cut. Such a reduction may have a very direct and interacting effect upon other cultural practices and therefore, upon the microclimate of the sward. This, in turn, may produce significant ecological changes in an established turf. A number of investigators (5, 7, 8, 10, 17, 23) have shown the differential response on a fairway of a mixed turf of Poa pratensis, Festuca rubra L. and Agrostis palustris when the height of cut is lowered. In general, all showed a decrease in Poa pratensis and Festuca rubra and an increase in Agrostis palustris. Under many conditions there is a good possibility that Poa annua L., Digitaria spp. and other weeds may also invade such a turf. Thus, when clipping height is lowered, it is necessary to adjust watering, fertilizing, cultivation and pest control programmes (weeds, diseases and insects) in an effort to compensate for the reduction in root system and for the resulting general weakness of the turf.

BENEFITS TO TURF FROM MOWING

Mowing is an effective means of controlling or eliminating many weeds. Mowing is especially effective against those weeds that invade newly established turf and those that grow in areas such as highway rights-of-way, airports and similar areas. Control is based on the habit of growth - basal as opposed to terminal in the case of dicotyledons - and on the inability of grassy weeds to develop sufficient leaf mass to produce adequate carbohydrates to support growth activity.

Mowing within the established height of cut range for a given species of grass encourages lateral shoot growth and therefore increases density of a turf (6, 14, 16). Proper mowing of newly established turf or of thin turfs may be used to speed the rate of coverage and to increase density, provided that adequate fertility and moisture are available to support the increased leaf area. Likewise, increased density or additional leaf mass resulting from a height of cut in the upper range of adaptability will provide additional insulation, which may play a role in counteracting winter adversity in marginal regions of adaptation of turf species.

FREQUENCY AND HEIGHT OF MOWING

Frequency of mowing is an important consideration in the maintenance programme and plays a significant role in the grooming of turf. Turf areas should be mowed often enough so that no more than ¼ - ⅓ of the leaf area is removed at any one clipping. This will greatly enhance the beauty, appearance, and playability of a turf area. Juska and Hanson (12) indicate that frequent mowing will not permit a decrease in height of cut without a reduction in the quantity of roots per tiller. Madison (14) has shown that a longer interval between mowings will result in improved colour during summer months. On the other hand, removal of excessive amounts of leaf surface will produce a stubbly, unsightly turf, cause excessive greying and browning of leaf tips and curtail photosynthesis. The resultant reduction in carbohydrate production will cause a serious depletion of root reserves, with attendant problems (7).

The frequency of mowing must be related to the rate of growth rather than to a time schedule. The rate of growth is a function of the environment (temperature, moisture and soil fertility), the natural growth rate of the grass, and - most important - the use for which the turf is being grown.

The use factor plays a major role in respect to frequency of mowing because of its relation to height of cut. For example, golf greens must be maintained at 5 - 7 mm to assure uniformity of the playing surface. They must be cut each time growth of only 1 - 2 mm occurs. This is once per day under most conditions. Fairway or park turfs are maintained at a higher height of cut and thus do not require such frequent clipping.

When circumstances are such that clipping of excess amounts of leaf surface cannot be avoided and if the clippings cannot be collected and removed, then the area should be recut as quickly as possible to stir the deposits. Otherwise, the excessive clippings may smother the grass or produce an environment highly favourable for pathogens and insects.

If excess growth occurs and the use factor does not prevent a gradual lowering of the height of cut, this procedure should be followed. In this case, frequency will need to be increased and, although it is doubtful whether it will affect the grass plant, there will be a substantial improvement in appearance.

SPECTATOR APPEAL AND THE PROBLEMS OF MAINTAINING GOOD TURF APPEARANCE

In addition to the basic considerations relating to height and frequency of clipping and their impact on choice of grass and cultural practices, there are several other factors of importance in the proper application of mowing practices.

Colour telecasting of major sporting events has emphasized the importance of turf colour and grooming. Spectators have come to expect uniformity and compatability of colour. Certainly colour is important from an aesthetic standpoint and is one criterion by which the general public judges the quality of turf. Removal of clippings from sports fields improves their appearance, as it does on golf greens.

Mowing to develop ribbons is an accepted practice on golf greens. It is becoming so on sports fields. The use of the mower to create a diamond pattern on baseball fields and to delineate five yard increments on football fields is a technique used to enhance their aesthetic values (28). Appearance is enhanced by choosing a reel (cylinder) mower with a clip compatible with the height of cut (See Figure 1).

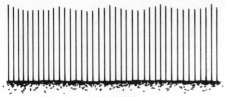

1-1/2" CLIP-1-1/2" HEIGHT OF CUT
ACCEPTABLE

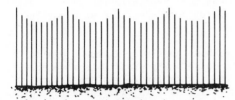

1-1/2" CLIP-3/4" HEIGHT OF CUT
UNACCEPTABLE-VISIBLE CORRUGATIONS

3/4" CLIP-3/4" HEIGHT OF CUT
ACCEPTABLE

OBSERVATIONS

A. WHEN THE CLIP EQUALS OR IS LESS THAN THE HEIGHT OF CUT, THE OVERALL APPEARANCE IS ACCEPTABLE.

B. AN EXCELLENT STAND OF GRASS CAN BE ACCEPTABLY CUT AT A SHORTER CLIP IF NO MORE THAN ONE-THIRD OF THE LEAF STRUCTURE IS REMOVED.

C. A POOR SCRAGGLY STAND OF GRASS IS BEST CUT WHEN THE CLIP EQUALS OR EVEN EXCEEDS HEIGHT OF CUT BECAUSE FEWER BLADES OF GRASS SUPPORT EACH OTHER AND THE TIME BETWEEN REEL BLADE PASSAGE IS GREATER.

Figure 1: mowing with a reel

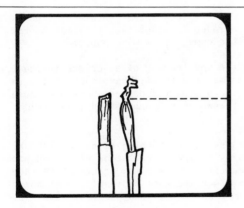

3 HOURS AFTER CUT

24 HOURS AFTER CUT

Figure 2: effect of sharp and dull cut on growth rate of two nearly identical blades of bluegrass (sketched from time-lapse photographs)

457

The maintenance of sharp, properly adjusted cutting edges on reel and on rotary mowers is essential to a well groomed appearance of turf. Figure 2 shows the effect of cutting with a sharp and a dull blade. Growth of the mutilated grass blade is slower and in addition it provides a ready entrance for pathogens and insects.

The stage of growth of turfgrass plays a major role in mowing practices. Young tender growth in the spring is generally soft and succulent. The moisture content of young immature turf is higher and the fibre content substantially lower than that of mature grass. Tender young grass should always be cut with a sharp, properly adjusted mower to avoid mechanical damage to the plant. Early growth should be cut frequently to avoid the problems associated with cutting wet grass.

Mowing wet grass should be avoided as much as possible, although available labour and time often make it impractical to do so. Dry grass cuts more easily, does not ball up and clog the mower, and gives a much finer lawn appearance. Timing tests show that mowing dry grass requires less time than mowing wet grass.

Turfgrass areas regularly cut with reel (cylinder) type power mowers or gang mowers sometimes develop a series of wave-like ridges running at right angles to the direction of mowing. The development of this washboard effect may be prevented or partially remedied by regularly changing the direction of mowing (going diagonally across or at right angles to the previous cut). Alternate directions of cut will partially control runners of creeping grasses and aid in the prevention of grain and thatch.

A very similar washboard appearance is often observed on turf areas, but is not the fault of the mowing equipment or the operator. Often land is ploughed for seedbed preparation and not properly disced and levelled prior to seeding. Settling then takes place in the plough furrows and unevenness develops. Such a situation may be reduced in severity over a period of years by heavy cultivation followed by dragging. The dragging operation generally will remove most of the soil cores from the high areas and deposit them in the low areas.

Mowers are not built for grading purposes. Turf areas containing high areas which are continually scalped should be regraded in order that they may be cut properly and to reduce the wear and possible damage to mowing equipment.

Inadequate insect control may cause the development of a serious mowing problem. Areas heavily infested with earthworms or ants will have many soil mounds caused by their activity. This will result in a poor appearance and may cause damage to mowing units. Mounds of earth thrown up by gophers and other soil-burrowing animals will have the same result.

Irregular or uneven cutting often occurs due to bobbing of the mowing units. This may be caused by the bouncing of mowers at excessive speeds or by equipment not built correctly for the grass it is cutting. This often occurs where the grass is extremely heavy or dense and the mower, because of insufficient weight or inadequate cutting ability, bobs or jumps as reel blades pass the bedknife.

On specialized areas such as putting greens, bowling greens, and lawn tennis courts, improper handling of the mower on turns will result in turf damage through bruising and wearing of the grass.

Terraces and banks offer a difficult mowing problem. Scalping generally will occur if the bank or terrace is mowed across the slope. Up and down mowing generally is the most satisfactory method of cutting these areas.

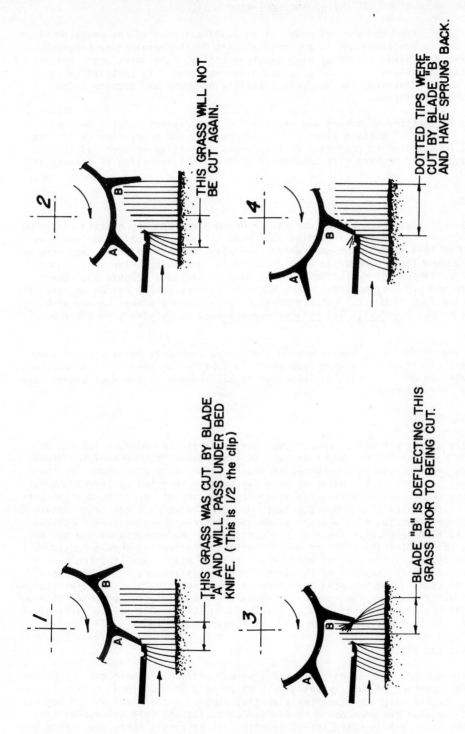

Figure 3: cutting diagram for a reel-type mower cutting several blades of grass (bed knife moves forward at half the speed that cutting edge of reel moves backwards)

THIS GRASS WILL NOT BE CUT AGAIN.

DOTTED TIPS WERE CUT BY BLADE "B" AND HAVE SPRUNG BACK.

THIS GRASS WAS CUT BY BLADE "A" AND WILL PASS UNDER BED KNIFE. (This is 1/2 the clip)

BLADE "B" IS DEFLECTING THIS GRASS PRIOR TO BEING CUT.

MOWING EQUIPMENT

The proper type and size of mower is an important part of the development of sound mowing practices and is an integral part of the maintenance programme. Good mowers are characterized by high manoeuvrability, easy adjustment, durability and adequate horse-power for the size and usage expected. In addition to these inherent design features, the ready availability of parts and service is an important consideration.

Four basic types of mowers are available - reel, rotary, sickle bar and vertical. Choice of a given type will be governed by the particular duties the unit will be expected to perform. Each type has certain advantages and limitations which should be carefully considered before final selection of a mower is made.

1. Reels

Reel (cylinder) type mowers are always recommended for the cutting of formal and semi-formal turf areas, including golf greens, tees, fairways and lawns cut at 2.5 cm or less. Reel type gang mowers are also the most efficient and economical for mowing large open areas such as airfields and parks. The reel cuts by shearing action similar to the action of a pair of scissors (Figure 3). Reels, when sharp and properly adjusted, give a clean, even cut which cannot be equalled by any other type of mower. Certain kinds of grass should always be cut with reel type mowers. _Agrostis_ and _Cynodon_ species used on putting greens are an example.

The use of reel type mowers may be limited in some turf areas because they require relatively smooth ground upon which to operate and they will not cut tall, rank-growing weeds. In addition, the cost of maintenance is somewhat higher than for other types of mowers.

2. Rotary mowers

Rotary mowers are widely used. They are versatile and adapted for use on most home lawns as well as larger areas. They are always recommended for rough conditions and on areas where control of grass, rather than appearance, is the predominant consideration. Rotaries also may be used to grind up leaves, to cut tall stemmy weeds, and to trim. The rotary cuts by impact, like the cutting action of a scythe. For this reason, a sharp properly balanced blade is necessary to avoid ragged tearing of the grass blade and to prolong engine life. Cutting with a dull blade generally results in a greying and subsequent browning of the leaf tip. When selecting a rotary mower, particular attention should be given to the safety features, the type of blade and method of blade mounting, the ease of adjustment and the horsepower of the unit. Power requirements - the highest of any type of mower - and scalping on uneven or rough terrain, are the major limitations of rotary mowers. The cost of maintenance is low on a rotary unit, although the cost of engine maintenance may be much higher than on reel units, particularly if the unit is under-powered or used under dusty conditions.

3. Sickle bar mowers

Sickle bar mowers have no place under normal turfgrass conditions. They may be used to advantage in rank, weedy growth where only an occasional mowing is required. Sickle bars are extensively used by highway departments to cut highway rights-of-way used for game preservation and where foreign objects such as cans, bottles and other debris often interfere with reel or rotary operation. They have a very high cost of maintenance and relatively slow ground speed and consequently are an expensive method of mowing.

4. Vertical mowers

Vertical mowers are made with fixed blades or with free swinging blades (hammerknife). They cut by impact similar to the rotary mower, except that the blades travel in a vertical rather than a horizontal plane. Hammerknife mowers can be used on rough terrain more satisfactorily than rotary mowers because the wheel base is shorter and scalping is therefore lessened. They are also excellent for clearing light brush and undergrowth. They have a very high cost of maintenance.

Vertical mowers having fixed blades are used primarily for controlling thatch and grain on golf greens and other highly specialized turf areas. Also, they are effective in promoting establishment of annual grasses in a permanent turf (30).

It is essential that all types of mowing equipment, whether reel, rotary, vertical or sickle bar, be kept sharp and in good operating condition. Dull, improperly adjusted equipment not only destroys the aesthetic value of the area, but also bruises the leaf tips, thus providing ready access to pathogens and insects.

CONCLUSION

The design and layout of many turf facilities plays an important role in choosing mowing equipment (24). Many large turfgrass areas were designed and constructed during an era when labour costs were negligible and mechanization of little importance. This created many time-consuming operations, which today require the use of low capacity and often costly equipment. This does not contribute to efficient mowing practices. A long range programme of redesign in keeping with modern trends may prove worthwhile for managers and supervisors of turfgrass facilities, and, further, may contribute to an improvement in mowing practices.

REFERENCES

1. BEARD, J.B., and DANIEL, W.H. (1965) Effect of temperature and cutting on the growth of creeping bentgrass roots. Agron. J. 57, 249.

2. BENSON, D.O. (1963) Mowing grass with a reel type machine. California Turfgrass Culture 13, 2, 11.

3. DANIEL, W.H., and ROBERTS, E.C. (1966) Turfgrass management in the United States. Adv. Agron. 18.

4. DAVIS, R.R. (1958) The effect of other species and mowing heights on persistence of lawn grasses. Agron. J. 50, 671.

5. FITTS, D.B. (1925) Root growth of five grasses. United States Golf Ass. Green Section Bull. 5, 58.

6. GOSS, R.L., and LAW, A.G. (1967) Performance of bluegrass varieties at two cutting heights and two nitrogen levels. Agron. J. 59, 6, 516.

7. GRABER, L.F. (1931) Food reserves in relation to other factors limiting the growth of grasses. Pl. Physiol. 6, 43.

8. GRAW, F.V., and NOER, O.J. (1948) Golf is played on grass. U.S.D.A. Yearbook of Agriculture - Grass.

9. HANSON, A.A. (1965) U.S.D.A. ARS. Agriculture Handbook 170.

10. HARRISON, C.M. (1931) Effect of cutting and fertilizer application on grass development. Pl. Physiol. 6, 669.

11. JUSKA, F.V., TYSON, J., and HARRISON, C.M. (1955) The competitive relation-ship of Merion bluegrass as influenced by various mixtures, cutting heights, and levels of nitrogen. Agron. J. 47, 513.

12. JUSKA, F.V., and HANSON, A.A. (1961) Effects of interval and height of mowing on growth of Merion and common Kentucky bluegrass. (Poa pratensis L.) Agron. J. 53, 385.

13. LAW, A.G. (1966) Performance of bluegrass varieties clipped at two heights. Weeds, Trees and Turf 5, 5, 26.

14. MADISON, J.H., JNR. (1960) The mowing of turfgrass. I. The effect of season, interval, and height of mowing on the growth of Seaside bentgrass turf. Agron. J. 52, 449.

15. MADISON, J.H., JNR. (1962) Mowing of turfgrass. II. Responses of three species of grass. Agron. J. 54, 250.

16. McBEE, G.G. (1966) Effects of mowing heights on texture of bermudagrass turf. Texas A & M University, Soil and Crop Science Department, Technical Report 10.

17. MUSSER, H.B. (1948) Control of weeds in special purpose turf with 2,4-D. Pa. agric. Exp. Stn. Progress Report No. 1.

18. MUSSER, H.B. (1962) Turf Management. McGraw Hill, New York, New York. Second Edition: Chapter 5.

19. NORTHERN, H.T. (1958) Introductory Plant Science, Second Edition. The Ronald Press Company, New York.

20. ROBERTS, E.C. (1958) The grass plant — feeding and cutting. Golf Course Reptr. 26, 3, 5.

21. ROBERTS, E.C. (1965) Getting to the root of turfgrass maintenance problems. Minnesota Turfgrass Conf.

22. STROH, J.R., and LAW, A.G. (1967) Effects of defoliation on the longevity of stand, dry matter yields and forage quality of tall wheatgrass (Agropyron elongatum (Host) Beauv.) Agron. J. 59, 10, 432.

23. WATSON, J.R. (1950) Irrigation and compaction of established fairway turf. PhD. Dissertation. Pennsylvania State University, State College, Pa.

24. WATSON, J.R. (1961) Patterns of mowing. Northern California Turfgrass Institute, March.

25. WATSON, J.R. (1965) Mowing practices - agronomic principles. Oklahoma Turfgrass Conf.

26. WATSON, J.R. (1967a) Mowing theory and practices. 18th Annual Central Plains Turfgrass Conf.

27. WATSON, J.R. (1967b) Watering practices as a function of clipping height and frequency. Weeds, Trees, and Turf, June issue.

28. WATSON, J.R. (1968) Turfgrass culture on athletic fields. Rutgers University Turfgrass short course.

29. WOOD, G.M., and BURKE, J.A. (1961) Effect of cutting height on turf density of Merion, Park, Delta, Newport and common Kentucky bluegrass. Crop Sci., 1, 317.

30. YOUNGNER, V.J.(1968) Vertical mowing, aerification and Poa annua invasion. California Turfgrass Culture 18, 1, 6.

GROWTH CONTROL

P. Boeker,
Professor of Crop Husbandry,

Friedrich-Wilhelms Universität, Bonn, West Germany

SUMMARY

The growth-retarding effects of maleic hydrazide and chlorflurenol are discussed, with the benefits of using them together or combined with a herbicide against broad-leaved weeds. The best times and rates of application are described: early spring is preferable, although exact timing is important. The risk of discoloration is a disadvantage: and this, together with problems of cutting and management, limit the use of these growth regulators at present to roadsides, embankments and similar types of turf.

INTRODUCTION

In the last two decades the use of growth regulators has aroused world wide interest. These are substances which promote growth as well as substances which retard growth by prohibiting cell-proliferation or by retarding only some stages during the development of plants. In this paper will be discussed only those substances which in recent years have been of interest for retarding the growth of turf along roadsides and the embankments of watercourses.

GROWTH REGULATORS FOR RETARDING GROWTH

The first to be used was maleic hydrazide (MH) which as a substance was discovered about 60 years ago, although its specific growth retarding qualities were only discovered in 1947 by the Naugatuck Chemical Division of the US Rubber Company. After promising results in the U.S.A. and Great Britain it was introduced into Germany shortly after 1960 where its use is now widespread along roadsides. It mainly retards the growth of grasses, while on dicotyledonous plants there is very little effect to be seen.

In addition, a second product came on the market in 1964, developed by E. Merck, Darmstadt. It belongs to a novel group of plant-growth regulators named morphactins and is called chlorflurenol (Chlorflurecol: 2-chloro-9-hydroxyfluorene-9-carboxylic acid). Like maleic hydrazide it is taken up by the leaves. Though it retards the growth of grasses, it is more effective in retarding dicotyledonous plants.

In spraying these substances on a mixture of monocotyledonous and dicotyledonous plants there are various problems. Maleic hydrazide applied at the proper time will control the growth of grasses satisfactorily, by preventing stem development completely or for a very long time, while the leaves remain relatively short and low on the ground. But as the growth of dicotyledonous plants is not affected, the grass area becomes rather rough in appearance, with flowering heads which can, for example, block the line of sight at bends in the road. In order to prevent this maleic hydrazide is often mixed with herbicides, and there is then the additional and important advantage that there is a synergistic effect in increased retardation of the grasses. Something similar occurs in using chlorflurenol. While the effect on dicotyledonous plants is satisfactory, good results

464

with grasses can only be obtained by applying uneconomic amounts of the substance. But here too there is a synergistic action between chlorflurenol and maleic hydrazide if they are applied as a mixture. In this case there is good control of grasses as well as of the other plants.

According to the composition of the turf, use can be made in various ways of the two combinations of substances just described. If it is the aim to eradicate tall-growing plants then a mixture of maleic hydrazide with herbicides will be used with advantage. If the turf consists of a satisfactory combination of grasses and rather low herbs then the mixture of maleic hydrazide with chlorflurenol is to be preferred.

The main interest in growth control on turf is up to now among road authorities. The first cut of the grass has to be taken in June and July, coinciding with the peak of holiday traffic. On the main roads and Autobahnen there occur serious delays because of the maintenance work, and for the men who work on the road and roadsides, there is a great danger of being hurt or even killed by cars.

TIME OF APPLICATION

There are three possibilities:-

1) application in spring when growth starts, in order to shift the first cut to a later time or to prevent it altogether.

2) application after the first cut, to retard the growth in late summer and autumn.

3) application in autumn before growth stops in order to get the retarding effect in the early spring.

By contrast to results in the U.S.A., the application of maleic hydrazide in autumn in Germany did not prove to be effective as it is very difficult to spray at the best time, which is just before the start of winter dormancy of the grasses. This time varies with weather and often after a period of cold there can occur a spell of warm weather again favourable for the growth of grasses. Slightly better was the effect of spraying one half of the dose in autumn and the other in the spring, but this caused higher labour costs.

The application after the second cut does not save much labour as the regrowth after this cut is normally not very great. Many grasses do not develop stems in the aftermath, or develop only very few.

The most important time for spraying is in early spring. Phenologically it coincides with the full flowering of the dandelion (Taraxacum officinale Weber), but to strike the correct time for spraying is still rather difficult. It seems to be best to adapt it to the height of the grasses. It is now recommended to spray when the higher grasses such as tall oat (Arrhenatherum elatius (L.) J. & C. Presl), cocksfoot or orchardgrass (Dactylis glomerata L.), meadow fescue (Festuca pratensis L.) and Yorkshire fog (Holcus lanatus L.) have reached 10-15 cm: and the lower grasses such as red fescue (Festuca rubra L.), smooth-stalked meadow-grass (Poa pratensis L.), bentgrasses (Agrostis spp.) and sheep's fescue (Festuca ovina L.) are 5-10 cm high. If the grasses are higher than that the rate of application may be increased but this does not always give adequate results. Normally spraying from the beginning of April onwards gives the best results, but the time has to be varied according to floral development in each part of Germany and the height above sea level.

Very good results are obtained when at the time of spraying the soil is moist and the relative humidity is high. The the leaves absorb the substances very quickly and they will be transported to the meristems without delay.

RATE AND METHOD OF APPLICATION

Maleic hydrazide is sprayed in the formulation of MH-30 at 16 l/ha or in some cases on very rapid growing turf at 18 l/ha. The species of weeds which occur on the grass area determines the herbicides to be used. Those mainly in use are combinations of mecoprop with 2,4-D, and of mecoprop with 2,4,5-T. As the herbicides are applied rather early some weeds which develop late in the season are not affected sufficiently, e.g. thistles (Cirsium spp.). Where such species occur frequently it is necessary to spray with herbicides again some weeks later, which may perhaps give a further check to the growth of grasses. According to experience gained up to now chlorflurenol should be sprayed at 10-15 l/ha in mixture with 10 l/ha of MH-30. It is not necessary to add herbicides.

In all cases it is advisable when spraying to prevent drift on to neighbouring fields, gardens and orchards. A special problem is even distribution of the solution as the width of the road verges may vary and the turf may be interrupted by bushes, etc.

EFFECTS OF TREATMENT, AND MANAGEMENT OF TREATED TURF

The effect of spraying growth-control regulators may sometimes be seen in a few days, depending on the weather. It becomes apparent that growth has ceased. Sometimes there is a very undesirable side-effect, which consists of a brown colouring of the grasses: this happens most often with late sprayings, especially if the rate of application is increased. For 6 to 8 weeks the turf at the roadsides may be very ugly in its appearance. Unfortunately, it cannot be predicted when discoloration is to be expected. Under some circumstances there can be such heavy damage that the plants die. In any case plants and species which show a brown colour are weakened in their competition with others which remain green. The grasses most likely to show a brown colour are tall oat grass, cocksfoot and couch (Agropyron repens (L.) Beauv.).

The degree of growth retardation varies with the grass species and the stages of development in which they were sprayed. If the flowering heads were already fully developed in the buds, heading and the height of the stems will be slightly retarded but not fully suppressed. When this is not the case, under favourable conditions the heading of flowering stems will be fully suppressed or there will be only a very few stems in the turf, developed from a few early maturing plants. But not only do species react in different ways. The same is the case with different cultivars sprayed at the same time, but this again is probably due to variation in the stages of development. How big this influence can be, can sometimes be seen very easily in adjacent areas of turf, when one part is situated in shadow while the other is exposed always to the full sunlight, or when one field is exposed to the south and the other to the north.

It would be ideal if by spraying growth regulators, the mowing of the turf could be avoided completely. At the moment this is not possible, at least not on areas where there are many higher grasses in the turf and where tall growing plants rather resistant to herbicides are occurring in abundance, and particularly not on stands where it is desirable to keep up a good green appearance of the turf. In all these cases in late summer or autumn a cut has to be taken to remove the surplus of green and dead material. This avoids the danger of fire and reduces the danger of mice establishing themselves. More important, however, is the reason that in the following spring a repeated spraying with growth regulators will be more successful as the solution will have better access to the green parts of the plants.

EFFECTS OF REPEATED APPLICATIONS

According to observations over several years it is apparent that the composition of the turf will improve when appropriate treatments are made. The discoloration of grasses mentioned above occurs mainly on undesirable tall-growing species which are weakened in their competitive ability so that in a few years they are reduced to insignificance or are suppressed completely. Thus turf develops which consists mainly of red fescue, smooth-stalked meadow-grass and browntop bent (Agrostis tenuis Sibth.). These grasses form a low dense turf which by its nature develops only a few stems. It then becomes a question whether it is worthwhile to spray this turf regularly with growth-retarding substances.

A further benefit of the change in the botanical composition is the better winter colour of the turf. The grass remains green in appearance for longer at the beginning of the winter compared with turf which was not sprayed with maleic hydrazide, in which the colour is rather brown or grey because of the many dead stems and leaves. In spring, turf which has been sprayed becomes green earlier as the tips of the leaves do not have to penetrate a thick layer of dead material.

FUTURE DEVELOPMENTS

There seems to be much future for using plant-growth regulators on turf. But this is only the case on areas which are used and managed extensively, such as roadsides, embankments of water courses, air fields, etc. Up to now it is impossible to apply them to turf which is intensively used. Especially it is the danger of discoloration which prohibits their use, and the fact that there are some grass species which cannot be retarded sufficiently. This is particularly so with annual meadow-grass (Poa annua L.) which is to be found nearly everywhere: many experiments in U.S.A., Great Britain and Germany have proved this. On the other hand calculations have shown that in the case of extensive areas of lawns, and by the use of big mowers, it is more economic to mow them continuously and mulch the grass than to mow them only once in autumn, after one application of growth retarders, as this is a very hard task because of the matted turf, and the great amount of mown material to be carried off.

REFERENCES

1. ANON. (1956) Malazide, Plant Growth Regulator. Fisons Chemicals Ltd., London.

2. BOEKER, P. (1968) Wirkung und Einsatzmöglichkeiten wuchshemmender Mittel. Z. Pfl. Krankh.(Pfl. Path.) Pfl Schutz. Sonderheft IV, 91.

3. BOEKER, P., RICHTER, W., and SAUER, G. (1965) Beobachtungen auf Versuchen mit wuchshemmenden Mitteln entlang der Autobahnen und Bundesstrassen. Z. Pfl. Krankh. (Pfl. Path.) Pfl. Schutz. Sonderheft III, 341.

4. ESCRITT, J.R. (1953) Grass growth stunting with maleic hydrazide. J. Sports Turf Res. Inst. 29, 269.

5. FRANCE, J.A. de, and HART, S.W. (1954) The effect of maleic hydrazide on the growth of lawn turf grasses. Northwestern Sect. Am. Soc. for Hort. Sci. (cited in "Chemical mowing with MH-30." Booklet No. 11, U.S. Rubber, Naugatuck, 1961).

6. GRIEGER, Fr. J. (1965) MH-30 - ein Wachstumsregulator für Gräser. BASF. Mittl.f.d. Landbau, April 1965.

7. RICHTER, W. (1965) Über die Wirkung von wuchshemmenden Mitteln, insbesondere MH-30 auf Gräser. Z. Pfl. Krankh. (Pfl. Path.) Pfl. Schutz. Sonderheft III, 347.

8. SAUER, G. (1965) Über den Einsatz chemischer Mittel zur Pflege von Grünflächen an Strassen. Die neue Landschaft 11, 556.

9. SKIRDE, W. (1964) Reaktionen von Gräserarten und Gräsersorten und von Klee auf hemmendwirkende Wachstumsregulatoren. Z.Acker-u. Pfl. bau 119, 263.

10. SKIRDE, W. (1965) MH-30 - ein Rasenhemmstoff? Die neue Landschaft 10, 368.

11. VEGIS, A. (1965) Die Bedeutung von physikalischen und chemischen Aussenfaktoren bei der Induktion und Beendigung von Ruhezuständen bei Organen und Geweben höherer Pflanzen. Handbuch der Pflanzenphysiologie, Band XV/2, S. 534-668, Springer-Verlag, Berlin-Heidelberg-New-York.

12. YEMM, E.W., and WILLIS, A.J. (1964) The effect of maleic hydrazide and 2,4-dichlorophenoxyacetic acid on roadside vegetation. Weed Res. 2, 24.

RELATIONSHIPS BETWEEN PLANTS AND MOWING

John H. Madison,

Associate Professor of Environmental Horticulture, Department of Environmental Horticulture, University of California, Davis, California, U.S.A.

SUMMARY

Turfgrasses tolerate much mowing stress in N. Europe's favourable climate. In the U.S. transition climates two growth cycles per year occur with summer growth depressed. Under summer's climatic stress, added stress from mowing may limit extent of survival. To minimize management stress, interactions need to be considered between mowing and other practices. An example is given of mowing, irrigation and nitrogen fertilizer interactions.

For a given set of conditions, there appears to be a minimum plant population below which tillering occurs to increase population, and a minimum plant size below which survival fails. More intensive mowing lowers the size limit and increases minimum population. Sophisticated data about defoliation benefit other research workers, not the practical man.

The Panicoid and Chloroid grasses have evolved largely in the tropics, Festucoid grasses in temperate zones. Many tropical grasses grow vigorously with both roots and tops favoured by warm temperatures. Such grasses soon shade out lower leaves and may require mowing at four to six week intervals to make maximum growth (3, 24). As turf, such grasses may need close and frequent mowing to reduce vigour and keep growth manageable. Festucoid grasses exhibit seasonal growth, and top and root growth are out of phase much of the year. Optimum growth is during the summer in northern Europe, during spring and fall in the United States. Winter temperatures are too cold for growth and summer temperatures exceed optima for top growth, and suppress root growth except at cool soil depths. Mowing results in interactions affecting other management practices and is a matter requiring judgement. Judgements may be made as to the frequency, height, time, pattern and manner of mowing. Scientific data elucidating effects of mowing was provided by investigations early in the century by workers such as Graber, Lovvorn and Harrison (7, 8, 9, 10, 11, 17). Information they provided has been sufficient for making management judgements. Later research has refined their data, confirmed it using other parameters, and has better defined some interactions. Mowing height and frequency are considered here as applied to temperate season grasses, ignoring sub-tropical grasses, mowing patterns, and equipments. Literature information is tabulated in Table 1.

Plant geographers have noted that plants tolerant of environmental conditions at the centre of their range, may be demanding at the limits of their range. A plant tolerant of soil pH or moisture at its centre, may be a calcophile, or grow only on light well-drained soils, at the limits of its range. In the essentially ideal climate of England, turf withstands appreciable stress from mowing without suffering visible effects. In the transition zone in California, climatic stress is often so severe in the summer that mowing stress must be minimized if grass is to survive as a uniform turf. This has on occasion been interpreted in terms of a "stress budget" for plants. In the centre of adaptation, stresses

Table 1: summary of literature information on mowing interactions and effects on _Poa pratensis_ turf (figures denote items in list of References)

Factor	Yield	Verdure	Competition	Rooting	Rhizome growth	Carbohydrate storage
Mowing height lowered	Decreased (may increase at scalping heights)	Decreased (increased if lowered from hay heights)	Increased; more, smaller plants	Temporary decrease in growth, stopped growth, or loss of roots: higher oxygen requirement	Decreased	Decreased
	7,8,9,10,11,12, 13,14,18,19,25	8,12,13,19,21,25	12,13,14,18, 19,21,23	1,4,6,10,11,12,15, 16,21,22,23,25	2,10,11,12,25	2,22,23
Mowing frequency increased	Decreased	Increased slightly for that height	Some increase	Shallower and decreased rooting	Decreased	Decreased
	5,9,11,12,13,18, 19	6,10,12,13,19,21	12,13,18,19, 21	2,4,6,12,20,23	9,12	2,9
Mowing stress increased as temperature exceeds optimum	Growth retarded: recovery set back if heat continues	Decreased	Decreased: weaker plants lost	Root quality decreased, then loss of roots	Growth stopped: may be some loss	Storage decreased: reserves used
	17			1,17	17	1
Mowing x N (fixed mowing stress as N increases)	Increased	Increased, then decreased at very high stress	Increased, then lessened at high stress	Large decrease	Growth and number decreased	New equilibrium between growth and storage: less storage
	19,21	10,19,21	19,21	10,14	10,14	17,18

(continued ....)

Treatment						
Mowing x N x temperature (mowing and N stress fixed as temperature exceeds optimum)	Drops: recovery slow — 10,11,17	Decreased: loss of smaller plants	Decreased: loss — 10,11,17	Growth stopped: severe loss — 10,11,17	Death of rhizomes — 10,11,17	Loss of reserves — 10,11,17
Mowing x Irrigation (slight water stress between irrigations)	Decreased — 20,21	Decreased — 19,20,21	Rooting may increase — 19,20,21	Rhizome survival enhanced — 10,11	Increased — 2	

With ineffective use of nitrogen fertilizer, irrigation stress dominates

Mowing x Season

Spring – Temperatures favour growth, and storage takes place if stresses are not too severe.

Fall – Cool temperatures and short days favour storage and procumbent growth. Less growth is removed by mowing. Same mowing programme is less severe in effect in fall.

Summer – During heat stress, rhizomes and crowns are protected by dormancy if N is low and irrigation is only at high tension. With high N and water there is loss of rhizomes and innovations.

are few and easily withstood. As one gets further from the centre of adaptation the more stress is imposed by the environment and the less freedom remains for the turfgrass manager to impose management stresses. Interactions become important. Thus with high nitrogen and frequent irrigation, leading to increased competition from high population densities, and with temperatures exceeding 38°C, chances for loss of grass increase rapidly as mowing height is decreased or frequency increased. The practical turfgrass manager will probably become increasingly aware of the importance of the interactions between his management practices and will come to appreciate that the lowest height at which he can mow may depend on his irrigation practices as well as on the kind of grass. Presumably, one day, when there is sufficient information, a computer could be used to follow seasonal trends, and to show needed changes in management. Figure 1 gives an example of the kind of data needed for computer predicting. Figures 1a and 1b give regression curves for yield and chlorophyll index in turf, after mowing. Plots of Kentucky bluegrass (KB) (Poa pratensis L.) and Seaside creeping bentgrass (S) (Agrostis stolonifera L.) were mowed weekly at two heights. After a regular mowing the subsequent experimental mowings were of a new sample taken each day for 22 days. With bluegrass, the slope of the "recovery" growth curve is steeper for the shorter cut but it takes 16 days before the shorter cut bluegrass is yielding at the same rate as the longer cut. Figure 1c shows fresh weight of grass at different heights of cut. This is to show that the flatter slope of the yield curve of higher mowed bluegrass does not necessarily indicate slower growth, as much growth is below the cutter bar.

In another experiment, sample strips were mowed daily following a regular weekly mowing of a bluegrass area. A grab sample of about 1000 clippings was taken each day and sorted into new uncut leaves, and old leaves with previously cut ends. Each of these groups was sorted into size groups, 0-1 cm, 1-2 cm, 2-4 cm and so on. For the first five days growth was by extension of old cut blades. On the sixth day clippings contained about equal areas and numbers of new and old leaves. By the 18th day, number of new blades cut was double the old blades but they were longer and (assuming comparable width of blades) the area of new blades had quadrupled.

A second interesting refinement of data is presented in Figure 2. At the time rate of seeding was being studied, and there was a series of plots with uniform management but with different populations resulting from different rates and depths of seeding. Average weight per innovation plotted against number of innovations gives the points in Figure 2. The points suggest a hyperbolic type of curve approaching asymptotes. An asymptote parallel to the abscissa suggests there is a minimum plant size, i.e. below a certain plant size an innovation fails to survive competition. An asymptote parallel to the ordinate implies a minimum population density for the conditions of growth. With fewer plants present, tillering will introduce new innovations until the minimum density is exceeded. Note that the minimum plant size occurs at high populations, where there is much competition. With competition removed and conditions favourable, smaller plants might survive.

For Kentucky bluegrass, the minimum plant size, under competition at 35 mm, seems to be about 25-30 mg: the minimum population with regular maintenance about 175-200 plants. With Seaside bentgrass at 22 mm this is reduced to a plant of 8-9 mg fresh weight and over 400 plants per sq dm (40,000/sq m). At putting green height a minimum plant may weigh only 3 mg fresh weight.

If the use of qualifying adjectives seems imprecise, it is because the limits may be shifted by changes in mowing height, mowing frequency, irrigation frequency, air temperature, soil temperature, light intensity, daylength, grass variety, herbicide use, and other common variables. Plots of data produce sim-

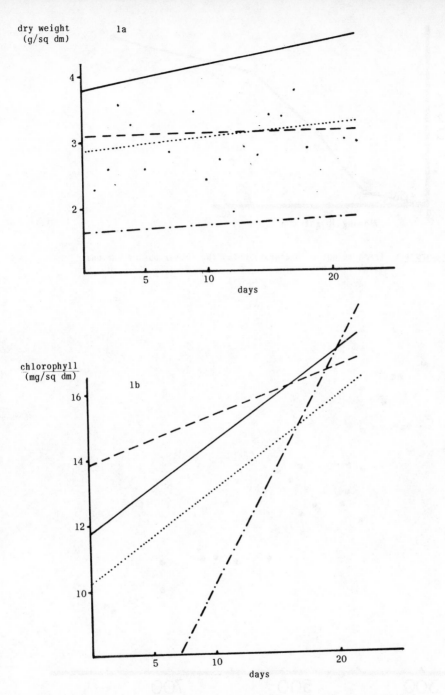

dry weight
(g/sq dm)   1a

chlorophyll
(mg/sq dm)

1b

Figures 1a and 1b: regression lines for yield (1a) and chlorophyll index
                    (1b) with time, for 22 days after mowing

        Kentucky bluegrass mown at 22 mm ...... 44 mm ─ ─ ─
        Seaside bentgrass   "   "   11 mm ─ ∙ ─ 22 mm ─────

        (Points in Figure 1a are for bluegrass at 22 mm,
         and show scatter of data)

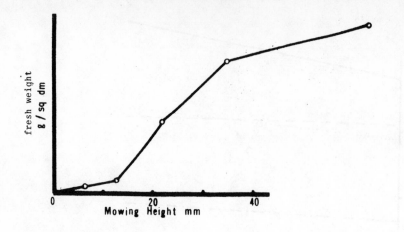

Figure 1c: fresh weight of bluegrass below the cutter bar at various
heights of cut

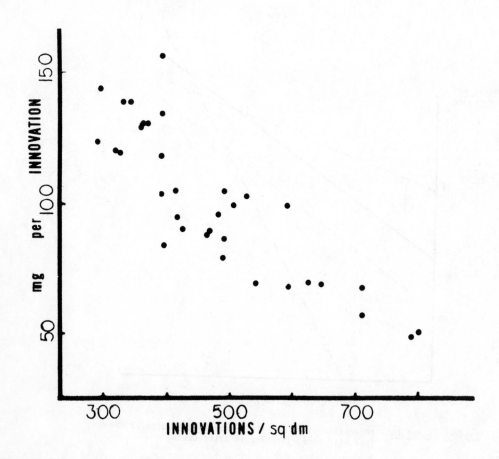

Figure 2:   size of innovations plotted against population density

ilar curves but the curves shift position with respect to the axes as the above factors are varied.

Other experiments illustrate effects of interactions. The results shown in Figure 3 are selected for lack of space rather than didactic reasons.

Figures 3a and 3b show size in relation to density for Highland bentgrass (A. castellana Boiss. and Reut.) for two irrigation frequencies (once and five times per week), three mowing heights (35, 22 and 12.5 mm) and with two levels of nitrogen (ca. 25 and 100 kg/ha as UF with low recovery of N). In the figures, secondary lines break each change into its size and density components. Each increase in irrigation frequency results in a decrease in average size of innovations with some variation due to mowing height, and in greater decreases with higher nitrogen. Increased irrigation frequency substantially affects population density. With high nitrogen, density is decreased when frequent irrigation is combined with low mowing. Lowered mowing height has generally caused a decrease in size and an increase in density except, as noted, the combination of high nitrogen, frequent irrigation, and low mowing causes a decrease in density. This last combination illustrates an over-loaded "stress budget".

In Figures 3c to 3f there are similar diagrams for population density plotted against dry weight yield and fresh weight size in Seaside bentgrass. Mowing was all at 6 mm with a difference in frequency (1 cut and 5 cuts per week). Nitrogen was at 25 and 50 kg/ha. Size decreases and density increases with increasing frequency of either mowing or irrigation. The density component of the change is much higher at higher nitrogen levels. When yield is considered rather than plant size (Figures 3e and 3f), yield is decreased by increasing mowing unless irrigation is decreased; yield is decreased by increased irrigation unless mowing frequency is decreased, and nitrogen level lowered.

There appears no limit to the minuteness of the interactions that can be studied, given the patience to make careful measurements and gather copious data. It is, however, necessary to ask the value. As increasingly critical data is programmed into the computer, a point is quickly reached where recommendations change with the changes in environmental parameters between morning and noon. With too much data the decision-making process can be inhibited. The turfgrass manager can know too much to know what to do.

At the same time the plant integrates all of the variables and the result is expressed as rate of growth; and, so, as the amount of clippings in the box. This provides an empirical guide to mowing. A second empirical guide to frequency of mowing is whether the clippings will fall out of sight or lie on top of the turf. This is more apt to determine mowing frequency than is data from laboratories.

Laboratory data has been available for some 40 years. In spite of that a mythology persists among turf managers which substitutes rationalization for data. The myth may be stated thus: "short intervals between mowing cause less damage to grass than longer intervals, because less is removed at each mowing". An alternate statement: "grass mowed regularly (daily) adapts to the programme and grows better under a fixed programme than under a programme where intervals vary". In the U.S. this myth has contributed to the demise of bluegrass fairways from mowing stress during the past 15-20 years. That some turf managers will persist in their ignorance does not negate the value of research.

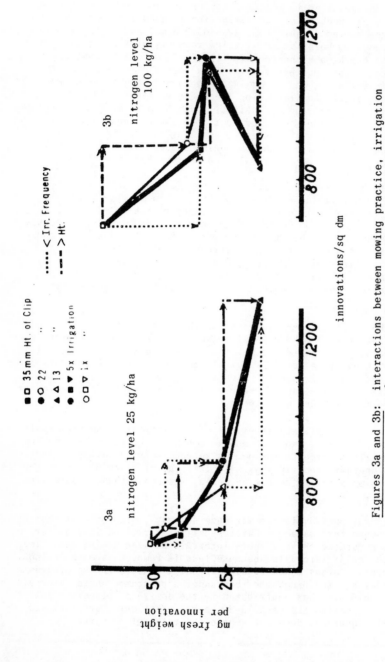

Figures 3a and 3b: interactions between mowing practice, irrigation frequency and nitrogen levels in Highland bentgrass (A. castellana)

(low mowing, frequent irrigation and increased nitrogen lead to denser turf until all are combined, when density is reduced)

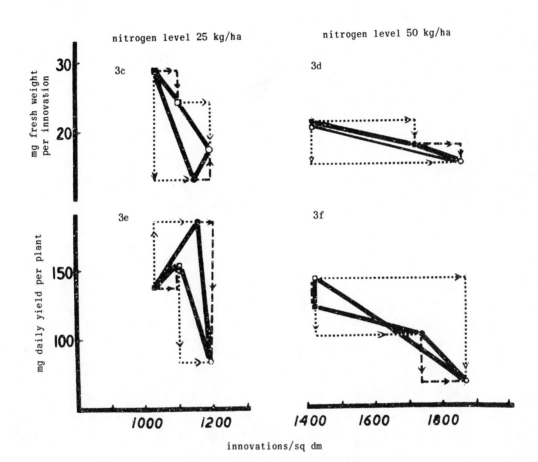

Figures 3c - 3f: interactions between mowing practice, irrigation frequency
and nitrogen levels in Seaside creeping bentgrass
(irrigation and mowing responses interact strongly with
nitrogen: with high nitrogen, turf density is highly
responsive, especially to irrigation)

One of the better lines of research today with respect to defoliation, is breeding bluegrasses that make effective growth below the cutter bar, even when the bar is set low. The kind of minute data presented in this paper may have some use in evaluating characters that make grasses effective at low cuts. In the transition climate zone, studies of interactions become important, because it is necessary to understand the interactions of other variables with mowing, if turf is to be kept viable under climatic stress.

In conclusion, research done today to elucidate effects of mowing (defoliation), is not for the benefit of the practical manager. For the practical grower, the grass plant is itself the most effective computer of environmental effects. If the data the plant provides is interpreted with a knowledge of general principles, sufficient information results for decision making. Research on defoliation is directed to research colleagues. If the research orientation is suitable, it will contribute to the understanding of production (energy conversion) and of interactions important in producing ecological responses.

REFERENCES

1. BEARD, J.B., and DANIEL, W.H. (1965) Effect of temperature and cutting on the growth of creeping bentgrass (Agrostis palustris Huds.) roots. Agron. J. 57, 249.

2. BROWN, E.M. (1943) Seasonal variation in the growth and chemical composition of Kentucky bluegrass. Univ. Missouri Coll. agric. Exp. Stn. Res. Bull. 360.

3. BURTON, G., JACKSON, J.E., and HART, R.H. (1963) Effects of cutting frequency on nitrogen yield, in vivo digestibility, and protein, fibre, and carotene content of 'Coastal' bermudagrass. Agron. Abstr. p. 34.

4. CRIDER, F.H. (1955) Root growth stoppage resulting from defoliation of grass. USDA Tech. Bull. 1102.

5. DAWSON, R.B. (1939) Practical lawncraft. Crosby Lockwood and Son Ltd., London. pp. 96-99.

6. DEAL, E.E. (1963) Regulating growth of 'Merion' Kentucky bluegrass (Poa pratensis L.) turf with cultural and management techniques. Ph.D. thesis. Rutgers. Diss. Abstr. 24, 3, 2643.

7. GRABER, L.F. (1933) Competitive efficiency and productivity of bluegrass (Poa pratensis L.) with partial defoliation at two levels of cutting. J. Am. Soc. Agron. 25, 328.

8. GRABER, L.F., NELSON, N.T., LEUKEL, W.A., and ALBERT, W.B. (1927) Organic food reserves in relation to the growth of alfalfa and other perennial herbaceous plants. Wisc. agric. Exp. Stn. Res. Bull. 80, 100.

9. GRABER, L.F., and REAM, H.W. (1931) Growth of bluegrass with various defoliations and abundant nitrogen supply. J. Am. Soc. Agron. 25, 328.

10. HARRISON, C.M. (1931) Effect of cutting and fertilizer applications on grass development. Pl. Physiol. 6, 669. (Also USGA Greens Sect. Bull. 11,11, 210. An informal treatment with added data.)

11. HARRISON, C.M., and HODGSON, C.W. (1939) Responses of certain perennial grasses to cutting treatments. J. Am. Soc. Agron. 31, 418.

12. JUSKA, F.V., and HANSON, A.A. (1961) Effects of interval and height of mowing on growth of Merion and common Kentucky bluegrass on extensive turfgrass areas. Agron. J. 53, 385.

13. JUSKA, F.V., and HANSON, A.A. (1963) The management of Kentucky bluegrass on extensive turfgrass areas. Park Maintenance 16, 9, 22.

14. JUSKA, F.V., TYSON, J., and HARRISON, C.M. (1955) The competitive relationship of Merion bluegrass as influenced by various mixtures, cutting heights, and levels of nitrogen. Agron. J. 47, 513.

15. LAW, A.G. (1965) Performance of bluegrass varieties under two heights of clipping. Annual Northwest Turf. Conf. Proc. 19, 27. (Also in Weeds, Trees, and Turf, 5, 5, 26.)

16. LETEY, J., STOLZY, L.H., LUNT, O.R., and VALORIS, N. (1964) Soil oxygen and clipping height. Golf Course Reptr. 32, 2, 16.

17. LOVVORN, R.L. (1945) The effect of defoliation, soil fertility, and temperature, and length of day on the growth of some perennial grasses. J. Am. Soc. Agron. 37, 570.

18. MADISON, J.H. (1960-2) The mowing of turfgrass. I, II, and III. Agron. J. 52, 449; 54, 250; 54, 252.

19. MADISON, J.H. (1962) Turfgrass ecology. Effects of mowing, irrigation, and nitrogen treatments on Agrostis palustris Huds. Seaside and Agrostis tenuis Sibth. Highland on population, yield, rooting, and cover. Agron J. 54, 407.

20. MADISON, J.H., and HAGAN, R.M. (1962) Extraction of soil moisture by Merion bluegrass (Poa pratensis L. Merion) turf as affected by irrigation frequency, mowing height, and other cultural operations. Agron. J. 54, 157.

21. MADISON, J.H., and ANDERSEN, A.H. (1963) A chlorophyll index to measure turfgrass response. Agron. J. 55, 461.

22. PARKER, K.W., and SAMPSON, A.W. (1931) Growth and yield of certain Gramineae as influenced by reduction of photosynthetic tissue. Hilgardia 5, 10, 361.

23. ROBERTS, E.C., and BREDAKIS, E.J. (1960) Turfgrass root development. Golf Course Reptr. 28, 8, 12.

24. STANLEY, R.L., BEATY, E.R., and POWELL, J.D. (1967) Effect of clipping height on forage distribution and regrowth of Pensacola bahiagrass. Agron. J. 59, 185.

25. WOOD, G.M., and BURKE, J.A. (1961) Effect of cutting height on turf density of Merion, Park, Delta, Newport, and common Kentucky bluegrass. Crop Sci. 1, 317.

CHEMICAL REGULATION OF GROWTH IN TURFGRASS

D.B. White, Associate Professor, Dept. of Horticultural Science, University of Minnesota, St. Paul, Minnesota;

D. Heng and T.B. Bailey, Graduate Assistants, and
L. Foote, Director, Environmental Services, Minnesota Department of Highways, U.S.A.

SUMMARY

After a review of published information on the effects of growth regulators in general and some main ones in detail, the authors describe their own experimental procedures and results. Creeping bentgrass was treated with CCC, B-995 and Phosphon: CCC reduced growth, but also caused damage, more than the others. There was a significant interaction of these chemicals with DMSO. In experiments with MH, it was evident that timing of application was critical and complete coverage was necessary for effective treatment. Use of a broadleaf herbicide was necessary for satisfactory results. Ethrel treatments on Kentucky bluegrass resulted in growth retardation of both roots and tops for limited periods. Increased tillering and leaf number were noted after growth was renewed.

INTRODUCTION

Success in chemical regulation of growth in turfgrasses has been limited. Most of the efforts have been associated with modifying growth patterns on turf areas under limited maintenance regimes. Chemical regulation of grass growth is dated by the use of maleic hydrazide (MH) on highway rights-of-way during the 1950's. Application of MH usually resulted in inhibition of cell division in all parts of a plant (32). The physiological activity of MH places it more in the category of growth inhibitor than growth regulator.

In the early 1960's, B-995, Phosphon and CCC came into commercial use as growth regulators in the florist industry. These chemicals tend to influence cell activity in selected tissue systems resulting in shorter internodes and more profuse flowering (15, 41). Research has shown that the activity of these chemicals in grasses is limited and often associated with chemical burn (4, 18).

More recently, several new chemicals have shown promise in regulating growth in grasses. Of these, Ethrel is receiving the most research attention at the present time.

The philosphy of approach to this subject by the authors does not include complete elimination of mowing. Rather it is to eliminate the need for very frequent mowing or to lengthen the time between mowings. There are many other potential benefits if the chemicals act on grasses in somewhat the same manner as known growth regulators act on other plants. Some potential benefits are: (1) control of growth during wet seasons where conventional mowers could not be used; (2) control of growth during the most rapid growth period which is often the most demanding work period of the year; (3) control of growth on large areas which need not display a "manicured" surface at all times; (4) control of growth in areas not suited for mowers; (5) decrease in labour costs; (6) prolongation of fungicide effectiveness by reducing new growth; (7) increase in

abrasion resistance by developing thicker cell walls and denser plant structures; (8) reduction of damage to fine turf under stress by increasing resistance to water, salt and other stress situations; (9) darker green colour; and
(10) improved chances of a "better lie" be providing sturdier growth and better
support of the golf ball.

The following actions of growth regulators have been reported (5, 9, 10,
12, 14, 15, 20, 30, 36) :-

influence on -
  flower bud initiation,
  time of flowering,
  number and length of internodes,
  tuber initiation,
  leaf size, colour and dry matter,
  maturity,
  tillering,
  resistance to water stress:
stimulation of shoot growth:
depression of respiration:

inhibition of -
  growth in grasses and woody plants,
  bud break,
  runner production,
  apical dominance:
prevention of -
  sucker development,
  bolting in celery and spinach,
  flowering in sugar cane:
promotion of -
  male sterility in sorghum,
    cucurbits, wild oats and corn,
  abscission of cotton leaves.

Growth regulators have been rather specific in activity for most plant
species. There seems to be no correlation between taxonomic relationships and
plant response to a particular compound (7). It has also been suggested that
Phosphon, CCC, and B-995 inhibit gibberellic acid biosynthesis (24, 29), resulting in the dwarfing response associated with these chemicals.

REVIEW OF INFORMATION ON GROWTH REGULATORS

Maleic hydrazide (MH)

Maleic hydrazide was originally presented as a plant growth inhibitor and
herbicide. Later the term herbicide was excluded from the label. MH-30 is the
diethanolamine salt containing 30% acid equivalent of maleic hydrazide (27, 37).
The mode of action of MH is reported to be nondiscretionary inhibition of cell
division by competing with uracil in synthesis of RNA (32). Inhibition of cell
division seems to be by interference with mitosis (32). MH is readily translocated in xylem and phloem (12, 13). A comprehensive review of the literature on
MH is given by Zukel (43, 44).

Phosphon (2,4-dichlorobenzyltributyl phosphonium chloride)

Phosphon was first reported in 1955 (1). It is completely soluble in water
and is persistent in the soil for more than one year. It is reported to be
effective on a wide spectrum of dicotyledonous plants and on certain grasses (6,
7, 8). House plants treated with Phosphon have shown greater than normal tolerance to water stress (10), salt and pH changes (30). Growth in Ormond and Tifgreen bermudagrass (Cynodon spp.) was retarded for 14 weeks by Phosphon at
25.2 and 50.4 g/sq m. Darker green colour was also observed on treated areas.
There was no response to Phosphon in St. Augustinegrass (Stenotaphrum secundatum
(Walt.) Kuntze), centipedegrass (Eremochloa ophiuroides (Munro) Hack.), Pensacola bahiagrass (Paspalum notatum Flugge), and common bermudagrass (Cynodon
dactylon (L.) Pers.) (6).

B-995 (B-9 or Alar) (N-dimethyl aminosuccinamic acid)

B-995 was first reported in 1962 for activity in legumes, vine crops, potatoes and a broad spectrum of ornamentals (32). Riddell et al (33) also reported B-995 as having a long residual effect; being readily translocated and relatively non-toxic; and having no adverse effect on root, vegetative or reproductive development. Compactness in treated plants was associated with a reduction in internode elongation or internode number (7, 14, 15, 20).

CCC (Chlormequat) (2-chloroethyl-trimethyl-ammonium chloride)

CCC was first described in 1960 (40) and was effective in a large number of plants (6, 11, 38). Use resulted in increased tillering; shorter, thicker stems and darker green leaves in wheat (41) and a large number of ornamentals (11). Shorter leaves, prostrate habit, increased tillering and dwarfing were observed on treated plants of Phleum pratense L. (38). Effects varied with time of application, maximum effect being associated with the three-leaf stage. Treatment with CCC at 47.7 g/sq m reduced growth and clipping weight of Tifgreen and Ormond bermudagrass for 14 weeks. St. Augustinegrass, centipedegrass, Pensacola bahiagrass and common bermudagrass did not respond as markedly (6). Effects of CCC were counteracted by IAA (25), with the conclusion that CCC retarded growth by lowering auxin levels in plants.

DMSO (Dimethyl sulphoxide)

DMSO was reported in 1965 (23) as an excellent solvent for organic chemicals and inorganic salts. It enhanced transport in plants (22) and also enhanced translocation of certain herbicides (26). Schiuchetti reported potentiation with DMSO of the inhibiting effects of B-995, CCC and phosphon (35).

Ethrel (2-chloroethylphosphonic acid)

Ethrel was first reported in 1946 by Kabachnik and Rossiiskaya (21). It is very soluble in water and stable in aqueous solutions below pH 3.5. The activity of Ethrel seems to be related to release of ethylene in plant tissues. Ethrel has affected a large number of dicotyledonous and monocotyledonous plant species. It has been reported to stimulate rhizome development in Johnsongrass (Sorghum halepense (L.) Pers.), quackgrass (Agropyron repens L.) and sedges (Cyperus spp.). Tillering stimulation has been recorded in Kentucky 31 tall fescue (Festuca arundinacea Schreb.), Pennlawn fescue (Festuca rubra L.), annual ryegrass (Lolium multiflorum Lam.), Kentucky bluegrass (Poa pratensis L.), Penncross bentgrass (Agrostis palustris Huds.), Merion Kentucky bluegrass and zoysiagrass (Zoysia matrella (L.) Merr.) (2). It should be noted that almost all of the information on effects of Ethrel is from preliminary or unpublished works.

EXPERIMENTAL PROCEDURES AND RESULTS

1. CCC, Phosphon, B-995 and DMSO

Field and greenhouse experiments with CCC, Phosphon, B-995 and DMSO were conducted on the Penncross variety of Agrostis palustris. Penncross is a synthetic polycross of three strains selected for high quality (28).

DMSO was applied to Penncross at concentrations of 0.1, 1.0, 10.0 and 20.0%, and in combination with the three growth regulating chemicals. Thirty chemical treatments were made at the following concentrations (ppm):-

```
Phosphon  -  nil;  250;  500;  1,125;  2,000     )
                                                 )
B-995     -  nil;  2,000;  4,500;  6,000; 10,000 ) with and without
                                                 )     DMSO 1,000
CCC       -  nil;  2,000;  5,500;  9,000; 10,000 )
```

Data on injury, growth (height), number of vegetative buds, and fresh and dry weight of roots and clippings were collected. Data analysis was completed under standard analysis of variance procedures and because each chemical was acting differently the data were subsequently divided into three groups (by chemical) and analysed independently. Because plants with the greatest injury were also the shortest, the use of analysis of covariance was also employed with injury as the concomitant variable.

Application of 0.1% DMSO spray resulted in no visible injury. A 1.0% treatment resulted in a slight discoloration of the leaves on the day after treatment but no further indications were evident after the first day. Tip burn of 2-6 cm was observed one day after treatment with 10% or 20% DMSO solution. The 10% treatment resulted in 40-70% and the 20% treatment 80-90% leaf kill within seven days of application. DMSO seemed to enhance the activity of the growth regulators, presumably by increased absorption or translocation.

Growth regulator treatments which included a water spray wash after treatment resulted in reduced regulator activity. Grass treated with CCC produced less fresh and dry weight of clippings than grass treated with Phosphon or B-995. Plants treated with the two highest levels of all chemicals had fewer clippings than the checks. Low concentrations of the regulators were not different from the checks. The amount of injury was reflected in the amount of clippings.

Phosphon and B-995 resulted in less injury than CCC which produced severe injury in increasing amounts with concentrations. Injury typically showed as yellowing and browning of stems, leaf tips and edges. A significant (P=0.01) chemical by level interaction indicated that injury depended upon the concentration of the chemical treatment. The amount of injury ranged from 46% injured leaves with CCC at high levels to no injury with B-995 at low levels.

A significant (P=0.01) interaction between chemicals and treatment levels indicated that height reduction depended on concentration. B-995 was not effective in reducing height at the low concentrations but higher concentrations resulted in grass that was shorter than the checks. CCC and Phosphon resulted in reduction of plant height according to treatment concentrations (Figure 1).

A significant interaction between concentration of chemicals and DMSO was evident upon analysis of bud numbers (Figure 2). The greatest effect of DMSO in increasing bud numbers per unit area occurred at the high chemical concentrations (up to 93% with Phosphon). This effect might be useful in developing a turf with an increased recovery capacity after stress situations. This effect might also be exploited in increasing density during establishment.

Reduction in growth with all chemicals was attributed, to a great extent, to injury of the plants. Although height and other differences were detected statistically the practical differences were not of a magnitude to be useful in the field. The injury alone, associated with growth reductions, places rather severe restrictions on use of these chemicals. Certain aspects of the results such as increases in bud number, however, do deserve further research and consideration.

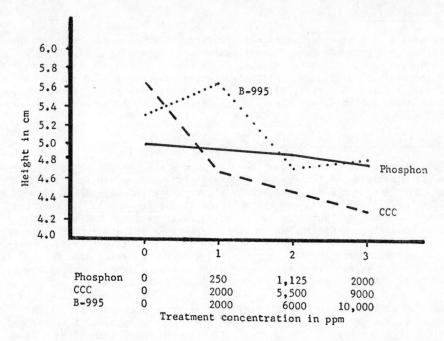

<u>Figure 1</u>: interaction between growth regulators and increasing concentrations, on Penncross bentgrass

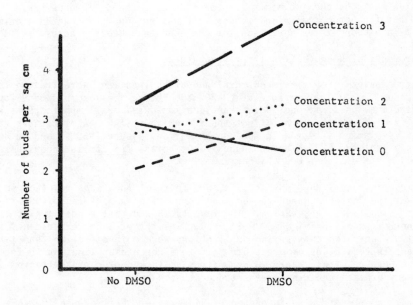

<u>Figure 2</u>: interaction of Phosphon, CCC and B-995 concentration and DMSO on bud number in Penncross bentgrass

2. Maleic hydrazide

Several series of experiments were conducted from 1961 to 1964 with both conventional and variable dosage logarithmic spray apparatus. Experiments were conducted under highway conditions in 23 separate areas in nine locations around the state of Minnesota. Plot size varied from 1.2 x 33.0 m with the logarithmic sprayer to several miles of right-of-way with conventional equipment. Treatment dates varied from 7 May to 25 September according to individual experiments.

(a) Experiments with logarithmic spray apparatus

Turf selected on one site for the experiments was several years old, consisting of bluegrass and bromegrass (<u>Bromus inermis</u> Leyss.) in full sun with uniform cover and weed distribution on a highway right-of-way. Dandelion (<u>Taraxacum officinale</u> Weber) and white clover (<u>Trifolium repens</u> L.) were the predominant weeds. Another site had a turf of bluegrass and redtop (<u>Agrostis alba</u> L.) containing dandelion, white clover, plantain (<u>Plantago major</u> L.) quackgrass, bromegrass and chickweed (<u>Cerastium</u> spp.). Applications of MH-30 were made with a logarithmic sprayer to plots 1.2 x 33.0 m at rates from 0 to 12 lb./ ac. a.i. (0-13.4 kg/ha) along the length of the treated area. Chemicals were applied on 12 June 1963 and 7 May, 27 May, and 19 June in 1964.

In 1963 no retardation was observed in the brome-bluegrass site. The higher rates, however, resulted in thinner grass populations. Dandelions and plantain were discoloured at high rates. There were no visible effects on white clover. Seed head production of redtop was almost completely controlled. By early October most of the redtop was dead in the treated plots. Kentucky bluegrass height was not affected by the treatments. The 1964 treatments resulted in growth retardation in the wheel tracks of the applicator; otherwise there were no visible differences on 30 June. Analysis of data indicated differences between treatments on the two early treatment dates. The differences were judged to be of no practical significance. It was evident that the MH treatments did result in a competitive advantage for the weeds and weedy grasses.

(b) Experiments with conventional spray apparatus

Twenty separate areas in seven rural and urban locations were treated in 1961, 1962 and 1963. Applications of MH-30 at 6 lb./ac. (6.7 kg/ha) on 9 June were ineffective, possibly due to late application date. Fall applications at 4 lb./ac. (4.5 kg/ha) showed no effect the following spring. Applications of MH-30 and 2,4-D amine at 4 + 6 lb./ac. on 29 May and 4 June 1963 showed no difference in height on 25 June and 20 August. Crabgrass (<u>Digitaria sanguinalis</u> (L.) Scop.) was a dominant weed by September.

Applications on 18 May 1961 at 6 lb./ac. to rural roadsides resulted in a reduction of one mowing. However, the weed population was not inhibited, resulting in an unsightly vegetation. The results showed that a positive programme of weed control is essential when MH is used. Results of other experiments in 1961 and 1962 indicated that spring applications were more effective than fall applications in regulation of grass growth. In Minnesota applications before 1 June gave best results. Where MH was effective in stopping or shortening growth, weedy grasses and other weeds tended to predominate.

Several experiments were conducted by highway personnel during 1963-65. Treatments were at the rate of 4 or 6 lb./ac. MH-30 with or without 6 lb./ac. 2,4-D amine and included several miles of right-of-way.

Results from the 1963-64 experiments indicate that grass height was inhibited to the extent of 57% and that bromegrass and bluegrass respond differently to MH-30 (Figure 3). The herbicide treatments were effective in reducing weed populations. MH-30 did not add to the effect of the herbicide. Timing of application greatly affected success. Generally, applications made during the last two weeks in May resulted in the greatest success.

Complete coverage was necessary for satisfactory inhibition and was difficult to obtain under the best of conditions. Results of skips may be particularly evident where MH-30 and herbicides are used in combination. Practical estimates of costs, including chemicals, reveal that one spray application compares with two mowings.

(c) Control of vegetation along fence lines

Control of vegetation along fence lines was studied using MH-30 at 0, 8, 10 and 12 lb./ac. applied on 15 and 16 May 1963 and 20 May 1964.

Grasses most affected by MH were redtop, reed canarygrass (Phalaris arundinacea L.), rye (Secale cereale L.), smooth bromegrass, and timothy (Phleum pratense L.). It tended to increase the infestation and size of rust pustules on reed canarygrass and smooth bromegrass. Application of MH often results in death to redtop. Response to MH-30 treatments was variable under field conditions and between different plant species. MH-30 at 10 lb./ac. was effective in reducing or eliminating mowing without removing all vegetation along fence lines.

3. Ethrel

Field, greenhouse and growth chamber experiments were conducted on Kentucky bluegrass plants and seed. Ethrel was selected for investigation from field experiments with a large number of chemicals. Standard germination and growing techniques were followed except where solution culture was used. Solution culture was under a technique modified from Roberts (34).

Treatments included applications of 3,000 ppm to 25,000 ppm buffered to pH 6.7, and unbuffered (pH 2.2).

In solution culture experiments with Park Kentucky bluegrass, linear retardation of both roots and topgrowth was observed according to level of chemical during the second and fourth weeks after foliar application. During the sixth week a reversal of the trends was associated with renewed growth of the material as evidenced by yield (Figure 4). Internode elongation, increased leaf number and tillering were also observed.

Foliar applications of Ethrel were made in October to Windsor Kentucky bluegrass newly established from seed in the greenhouse, at the following concentrations (ppm) :-

Ethrel	0	(pH 6.6)
"	3,000	(pH 2.5)
"	6,000	(pH 2.4)
"	9,000	(pH 2.3)
"	12,000	(pH 2.2)
HCl		(pH 2.2)

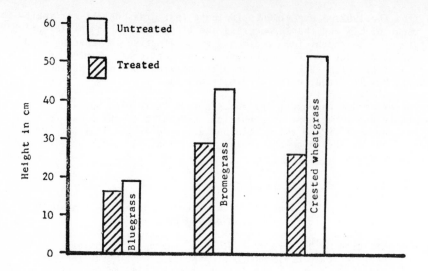

Figure 3:   random effect of MH-30 (6 lb./ac.) on average height of
some grass species

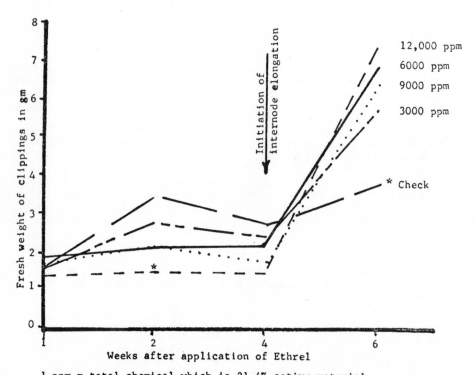

1 ppm = total chemical which is 21.4% active material
* (.01 sig. within weeks)

Figure 4:   effect of foliar application of Ethrel on yields of
Park Kentucky bluegrass

A reduction in leaf number was observed on treated material during the first two weeks after treatment. This was completely reversed by the seventh week after treatment. General growth retardation also lasted only two weeks. The HCl treatment was not difficult from the check. Tillering was not affected by any of the treatments and no injury was observed from the treatments.

Experiments with foliar and soil applications of Ethrel to six week seedlings of Windsor Kentucky bluegrass were conducted during October 1968 in the greenhouse. Treatments of 0 to 25,000 ppm Ethrel were applied in 5,000 ppm increments.

Leaf tip necrosis was observed on all soil treatments excluding the check. Leaf number was increased by most treatments while leaf blade length was reduced in all Ethrel treatments. The 25,000 ppm treatment resulted in growth retardation. Internode elongation was evident; but there were no observable effects on plant numbers or tillering.

Several experiments with seed or "pre-germinated" seed were conducted in the greenhouse and growth chamber. ("Pre-germinated" seed is brought to germination before treating and sowing.) Treatments of 0, 3,000, 6,000, 9,000, 12,000 ppm and HCl at 2.2 pH in a 1½ hour soak were included.

With standard seed treatment, no effects were observed from the HCl treatments. At 12,000 ppm, Ethrel resulted in a reduction in fresh weight, increased numbers of plants and increased tillering.

Results of Ethrel treatments on pre-germinated seed included a reduction in number of culms per unit area during the first three weeks after treatment. Subsequently, no differences were observed between the Ethrel and check treatments. The HCl treatments, however, resulted in higher numbers of culms per unit area than other treatments. Plant heights were not affected by the acid treatments.

REFERENCES

1. ANON. (1955) National Academy of Science, National Research Council. Publ. 3811. CBCC Positive Data Series No. 2.

2. ANON. (1969) Technical Service Data Sheet H-96. Ethrel. Amchem Products Inc., Ambler, Penna. April.

3. APPLEBY, A.P., KRONSTAND, W.E., and ROHDE, C.R. (1966) Influence of CCC on wheat (Triticum aestivum L.) when applied as a seed treatment. Agron. J. 58, 4, 435.

4. BAILEY, T.B., JNR. (1969) Effect of three selected growth regulators on Penncross bentgrass (Agrostis palustris Huds.). Unpublished Thesis, University of Minnesota.

5. BATJER, L.P., WILLIAMS, N.W., and MARTIN, G.C. (1964) Effects of N-dimethyl amino succinamic acid (B-nine) on vegetable and fruit characteristics of apples, pears and sweet cherries. Proc. Am. Soc. Hort. Sci. 85, 11.

6. CABLER, J.F., and HORN, G.C. (1963) Chemical growth retardants for turfgrasses. Golf Course Reptr. 31, 1,35.

7. CATHEY, H.M. (1961) The relation of phosfon structure to its growth-retarding activity. Pl. Physiol. Supple. 36, xxxviii.

8. CATHEY, H.M. (1963) Horticulturists study effects of growth retardants on plants. Florist Review 132, 3426, 35.

9. CATHEY, H.M., HALPERIN, F., and PIRINGER, A.A. (1964) Relation of N-dimethyl amino succinamic acid to photoperiod, kind of supplementary light, and night temperature, in its effect on the growth and flowering of garden annuals. Hort. Res. 5, 1, 1.

10. CATHEY, H.M., and PIRINGER, A.A. (1961) Relation of phosphon to photoperiod, kind of supplementary light, and night temperature on growth and flowering of garden annuals. Proc. Am. Soc. hort. Sci. 77, 608.

11. CATHEY, H.M., and STUART, N.W. (1961) Effects of certain growth substances on elongation and geotropic curvature of wheat roots. Bot. Gaz. 123, 51.

12. CRAFTS, A.S. (1961) The chemistry and mode of action of herbicides. Interscience Publishers. New York, New York. p. 186.

13. CRAFTS, A.S. (1961) Improvement of growth regulator formation. Plant Growth Regulation Fourth Int. Conf. The Iowa State University Press, Ames, Iowa.

14. DYSON, P.W., and HUMPHRIES, E.C. (1966) Modification of growth habit of Majestic potato by growth regulators applied at different times. Ann. appl. Biol. 58, 2, 171.

15. FIELDHOUSE, D.T., and READ, P.E. (1966) Summary of researches and observations with Alar. University of Delaware. Mimeographed Report.

16. FOOTE, L.E., and HIMMELMAN, B.F. (1965) Maleic hydrazide as a growth retardant. Final Report, Investigation No. 616. Minnesota Highway Department, United States Department of Commerce and Minnesota Local Road Research Board.

17. FOOTE, L.E., and HIMMELMAN, B.F. (1967) Vegetation control along fence lines with maleic hydrazide. Weeds 15, 1, 38.

18. HART, S.W., and DEFRANCE, J.A. (1955) Effect of maleic hydrazide on the growth of turfgrasses. Golf Course Reptr. Sept.-Oct.

19. HENG, D.H. (1969) Unpublished data, University of Minn., St. Paul, Minn.

20. JAFFE, M.J., and ISENBERG, F.M. (1965) Some effect of B-995 on the development of various plants with special reference to the cucumber (Cucumis sativus L.). Proc. Soc. hort. Sci. 87, 420.

21. KABACHNIK, M.I., and ROSSIISKAYA, P.A. (1946) Izv. Akad. Nauk S.S.S.R. o. ph. n. 406. Tech. Serv. Data Sheet H-96. Ethrel. Amchem. April.

22. KEIL, H.L. (1965) DMSO shows great promise as a carrier of agricultural toxicants. Agric. Chem. April.

23. KEIL, H.L., SMALE, B.C., and WILSON, R.A. (1965) Control of peach bacteria leaf spot with sprays of oxytetracholine plus DMSO. Phytopathology 55, 505.

24. KHAN, A.A., and FAUST, A.M. (1967) Effect of growth retardants on X-amylase production in germinating barley seed. Physiologia Pl. 20, 673.

25. KURAISHI, S., and MUIR, R.M. (1964) Mode of action of growth retarding chemicals. Pl. Physiol. 38, 19.

26. LAPHAM, V.T. (1966) The effectiveness of some DMSO-herbicide combinations. Proc. Southern Weed Conf. 19, 438.

27. MILLER, D.M., and WHITE, R.W. (1956) The structure of maleic hydrazide as inferred from the ultraviolet spectra of its methyl derivatives. Can. J. Chem. 34, 1510.

28. MUSSER, H.B. (1952) Merion bluegrass, new strains of fescues and polycross bent. Proc. 21st Annual Turf Conf. pp. 7-16.

29. PALEG, L., KENDE, H., NINNEMANN, H., and LANG, A. (1965) Physiological effects of gibberellic acid. VIII. Growth retardants on barley endosperm. Pl. Physiol. 40, 1, 165.

30. PILLAY, D.T.N. (1965) Responses of soyabean seedlings to B-995, a growth retardant. Can. J. Bot. 43, 2, 1477.

31. POVOLOTKAYA, K.L. (1961) Mechanism of the action of maleic hydrazide in Plants. Izv. Akad. Nauk S.S.S.R. 26 ser. Biol. No. 2, 250. Chem. Abstr. 55, 27549.

32. RIDDELL, J.A. (1962) Memorandum, Naugatuck Chemical Company, March 22.

33. RIDDELL, J.A., HAGEMAN, H.A., ANTHONY, C.M.J., and HUBBARD, C.M. (1962) Retardation of plant growth by a new group of chemicals. Science 136, 391.

34. ROBERTS, E.C. (1959) Relationships between turfgrass foliar and root development. II. A solution culture approach to the study of clipping and nutritional interactions in turf. Unpublished Mimeograph. Iowa State University.

491

35. SCIUCHETTI, L.A., and MINGIS, N.C. (1965) The effect of DMSO and Phosphon on growth and alkaloid synthesis in _Datura ferox_. Lloydia **28**, 3, 230.

36. SHAW, M.S., AMBORSKI, D.J., and OAKS, A. (1958) Some effects of indoleacetic acid and maleic hydrazide on respiration and flowering of wheat. Can. J. Bot. **36**, 233.

37. SMITH, A.E., and STONE, G.M. (1954) Tautomeric structures of maleic hydrazide. Unpublished Data, August. (Naugatuck Chemical Division of United States Rubber Company, Naugatuck, Connecticut.)

38. STODDART, J.L. (1964) An assessment of CCC as a potential aid to grass seed production. J. Br. Grassld. Soc. **19**, 373.

39. STUART, N.W. (1961) Initiation of flower buds in rhododendron after application of growth retardants. Science **134**, 1, 50.

40. TOLBERT, N.E. (1960) (2-Chloroethyl) trimethylammonium chloride and related compounds as plant growth substances. I. Chemical structure and bioassay. J. biol. Chem. **235**, 475.

41. TOLBERT, N.E. (1960) CCC and related compounds as plant growth substances. II. Effect on growth of wheat. Pl. Physiol. **35**, 380.

42. WITTWER, S.H., and HALEVY, A.H. (1965) Growth promotion in the snapdragon by CCC, a growth retardant. Naturwissenschaften **52**, 11, 310.

43. ZUKEL, J.W. (1957) A literature summary on maleic hydrazide, 1949-1957. United States Rubber, Naugatuck Chemical Division, Naugatuck, Connecticut, p. 170.

44. ZUKEL, J.W. (1963) A literature summary on maleic hydrazide, 1957-1963. United States Rubber, Naugatuck Chemical Division, Naugatuck, Connecticut, p. 111.

DISCUSSION

SYNERGISM BETWEEN MALEIC HYDRAZIDE AND HERBICIDES

C.M. Switzer (Canada)

There has been some indication of interaction (synergism) between maleic hydrazide and other growth regulators. Would anyone care to comment on this?

G.G. Fisher (U.K.)

In the U.K., mixtures of maleic hydrazide with TBA have given enhanced growth regulation, apparently synergistic, compared with maleic hydrazide alone.

D.B. White (Minnesota, U.S.A.)

Maleic hydrazide results in ragged-looking vegetation because of selective inhibition of permanent grasses. Under these conditions it must be used in conjunction with a herbicide. The cost of an application of MH-30 and broad-leaf herbicide is similar to the cost of 2 mowings.

MORPHACTINS

L.E. Moser (Ohio, U.S.A.)

Has anyone obtained good growth-regulating effects by the use of the morphactins alone on the Gramineae?

J.H. Madison (California, U.S.A.)

We have used morphactins alone on Tifgreen bermudagrass (Cynodon hybrid), Poa pratensis L. and Agrostis stolonifera L. On all three grasses our responses were toxicity responses, not growth regulator responses. We only got growth retardation at high rates and accompanied by discoloration and phytotoxicity. Our data is presented in "California Agriculture" for September, 1969.

H.H. Williams (California, U.S.A.)

We have observed an increase in smog resistance by Tifgreen bermudagrass treated with morphactin.

P. Boeker (West Germany)

The effect of a morphactin was completely insufficient when it was applied as a pure substance, but it was good when mixed with MH-30. The effect was better than that of MH-30 with herbicides.

W.W. Huffine (Oklahoma, U.S.A.)

We have noticed that morphactins definitely suppress seed head formation on Cynodon dactylon (L.) Pers.

ETHREL

J.A. Simmons (Ohio, U.S.A.)

What are the rates of Ethrel found effective in field tests and what is the future of this chemical in growth regulation?

D.B. White (Minnesota, U.S.A.)

Ethrel is currently one of the most promising chemicals for growth retardation of grasses, but several new chemicals, on initial evaluation, seem to
be active at lower rates than Ethrel. If the new chemicals do prove satisfactory
they will offer strong competition to Ethrel. All the chemicals, including
Ethrel, need much more research before any can be recommended for use.

SESSION 6B: THATCH, CULTIVATION AND TOP-DRESSING

(Chairman: Prof. P. Boeker)

THATCH, CULTIVATION AND TOP-DRESSING
OF CLOSELY-CUT TURF

Ralph E. Engel,

Research Professor in Turfgrass Management, Department of Soils and Crops, College of Agriculture and Environmental Science, Rutgers University, New Brunswick, New Jersey 08903, U.S.A.

SUMMARY

The nature and causes of thatch are discussed, particularly in relation to fertilizer, mowing and watering practices. Cultivation methods and effects are reviewed, and it is questioned whether the benefits are as great as supposed and whether present techniques are best. Top-dressing is considered; some generally-held opinions are quoted, and needs for research defined.

THE PROBLEM OF THATCH AND ITS IMPORTANCE

Turf is distinguished by several of its special practices. The current topics of thatch, cultivation and top-dressing are scarcely paralleled in production of other plant commodities. These subjects are somewhat related. Separate discussion of these three topics is not intended to minimize this relationship.

By definition, thatch is a tightly intermingled layer of living and dead stems, leaves, and roots of grasses. It develops between the layer of green vegetation and the soil surface and interferes with growth and maintenance.

Condition of the thatch layer, rather than quantity of thatch, appears critical. Often a hardened low fertility turf exhibits "thatch phenomena." Correction of the problem seems to occur with repetitious fertilization to restore vigorous growth. This suggests that part of the thatch problem is resistance to wetting. A wax-like condition of the grass materials is implied. While a low fertilization level may give very slow growth and appears to enhance thatch-like behaviour, Engel and Alderfer (1967) reported greater depth of thatch and organic matter on creeping bentgrass (Agrostis palustris Huds.) at high nitrogen than at low nitrogen after 10 years. However, Schery (1966) reported that five years of heavy nitrogen fertilization gave no increase in thatch on Kentucky bluegrass (Poa pratensis L.) as compared with low nitrogen. Roots are considered a part of and a contribution to thatch. On areas with an abundance of surface rooting, the mass of roots may add to the resistance to decomposition because of their chemical and physical nature.

Species appear to have different thatch problems because of variation in growth rate and ease of decomposition. Bermudagrass (Cynodon spp.) and bentgrass (Agrostis spp.) make rapid and abundant growth. In contrast, zoysiagrass (Zoysia spp.) is an example of a grass that grows slowly but whose tissue is one of the most resistant to decay. The most severe thatch problems occur with close mowing rather than with high mowing, according to the writer's observation. Measurements on Kentucky bluegrasses (Beard and Rieke 1964; Schery 1966) report more thatch development with high cut. A greater amount of residue is a logical development with the higher cut, but often this appears trash-like rather than thatch-like in behaviour.

POTENTIAL ANTIDOTES FOR THATCH

Direct removal of thatch was practiced commonly in the past and is still used. Power machines have made this more feasible, but it still poses logistical problems of removal and disposal. Huffine (1967) reported that removal of thatch prior to regrowth of bermudagrass in the spring aided quality and early greenness. Schery (1966) measured no reduction in thatch one year after removal of thatch over a 5-year period. Recovery of the turf after direct removal of the thatch is a major deterrent to the practice. A study in progress at the New Jersey Agricultural Experiment Station contains treatments that have received severe annual defoliation for five years on a mixed turf of Kentucky bluegrass, bentgrass, and red fescue (Festuca rubra L.). The turf has recovered good quality regularly, but 60-90 days growing time is required.

Turfgrass cultivation gives some removal of thatch, modest thinning, and dresses some soil back into the turf. Data reported by Engel et al (1967) on creeping bentgrass demonstrated some benefit from cultivation for thatch control. Thompson and Ward (1965) concluded that frequent mechanical dethatching and cultivation that leaves the soil cores on the turf will reduce thatch accumulation on bermudagrass. However, the low efficiency of the treatments in these studies is disappointing. These same studies indicated that regular top-dressing was a good antidote for thatch. Some of its benefits might derive from inoculation effects, nutrient additions that benefit microbes, and the improved moisture retention in the thatch layer.

Unfortunately, the top-dressing treatment is impractical for many turf areas where thatch is a problem. Ledeboer (1966) conducted a thesis study that included sugars, fertilizers, dolomitic limestone, gypsum, cellulose, and top-dressing; and he concluded they were unsatisfactory for decreasing thatch on lawn turf.

A number of thatch studies are in progress in the United States which will increase our information on this subject. Further study might consider specific influences of fertilization, mowing, and watering on thatch and its development. Also, the nature of thatch should be studied. The writer has observed that thatch may exist in moderate and troublesome amounts, and later that it seems to be non-existent on the same site. Is it possible that reactions in the thatch render it more resistant temporarily? Bartholomew (1965) relates a theory of microbial protein or other nitrogen carrying materials combining with non-protein decomposition materials to give aromatic products (probably polyphenols). Yet it has been observed that thatch decomposes rather quickly when incorporated with a productive plant soil. Is it possible the residue of grass materials develop into thatch rather than decompose because they lack intimate association with the soil? Thatch involves complex relationships that will defy solution without intensive research.

TURFGRASS CULTIVATION

The definition of turfgrass cultivation by the American Society of Agronomy is "... a mechanical procedure that produces spiking, cutting, or core-removing action on the soil under established turf without destroying the sod characteristics." Turfgrass cultivation has many projected benefits which have given rise to a host of machines and mechanical devices. These are soil aeration, reduction of soil hardness, deeper rooting, better penetration of water and water-borne materials, destruction of thatch, a levelling action (with some machines), thinning that encourages new shoots, and creation of crevices for germination and development of the seed and seedling in established turf.

Possible disadvantages may accrue from turfgrass cultivation. In most instances, it detracts from appearance and on occasions it interferes with turf use. The voids created by cultivation can be an opening for weed encroachment. However, it is the opinion of this writer that weeds are not commonly increased by this practice. Development of major infestations appear likely only where viable weed seed is submerged in the sod, the turf is nearly weed-free, and cultivation is practiced at a season when the weed seed can develop into established plants. The breaking, cutting, and tearing by cultivation is damaging to the grass plant and would appear to enhance parasitism of several diseases, but there are no reports of such difficulty. Cultivation will cut numerous rhizomes of grasses, and this might be damaging on occasions. Some closely-cut turf surfaces are reported to lose trueness quickly as a result of the soil collapsing into the cultivation holes. This suggests too many large holes. Possibly the most serious question about turfgrass cultivation is the structure-destroying nature of soil cultivation.

Correction of soil compaction is an often desired result of turfgrass cultivation. Studies by Engel (1951) and Harper (1952) did not demonstrate relief from compaction with spoon-type cultivation. Cultivation creates voids in turf, but it also is actively destructive of soil structure; and some machines can produce localized soil compaction by their weight and forcing action. Some golf course superintendents believe that cultivation of greens relieves hardness. Since these types of areas may have severe surface compaction, it is conceivable that cultivation should correct this condition temporarily. With severe compaction throughout the soil depth, it is difficult to envision current cultivation machines as a cure.

Better penetration of water and water-borne turfgrass materials has been a goal of cultivation. Again, data from the previously quoted studies were not too encouraging. Harper's work at Pennsylvania State University did show increased phosphorus penetration readings on soil samples taken near the holes, but the New Jersey work did not show any significant increases in penetration with random sampling of the soil. Better water penetration seems a logical result of turfgrass cultivation. The limited research data show that it does not happen with all treatments. Nelson and Baver (1940) state that continuous pore spaces are important for good percolation of soil water, and that soils that are uncultivated for years are likely to have a more continuous pore system. On the basis of this theory, plugging of such channels by cultivation, and the destruction of soil structure with cultivation, may cause a negative influence on water penetration. The roughening of the surface and the creation of small, dry wells in very compact turf soils should have a positive influence on water penetration. The most beneficial aspect of turfgrass cultivation reported in research is thatch control. The work reported by Thompson and Ward showed a measurable benefit on bermudagrass. Engel (1951) showed an increase in available phosphorus and a slight decrease in pH at the soil surface. Both of these results suggest that cultivation was producing decomposition of surface residue. The value of cultivation for introducing seed into established turf is generally accepted.

Soil aeration is a benefit that is often attributed to turfgrass cultivation, but this is difficult to determine. Some inferences on aeration can be made from soil density measurements, water percolation rates and root development.

The limited measurements on soil density and water penetration rates do not suggest aeration benefits from cultivation. It is commonly known that roots develop readily in most cultivation openings with regrowth of the turf, but root measurements in the Pennsylvania and New Jersey studies did not show appreciable increases with cultivation. Accurate root measurements are difficult to obtain because of inability to separate new roots from those of previous growth periods. The actual evaluation of benefits of cultivation to soil aeration and rooting remains a challenge to research.

Turfgrass cultivation was practiced before its theory was tested in research. It seems clear that (1) some of the theoretical benefits of turfgrass cultivation do occur in some environments; (2) some of the proposed benefits are not occurring commonly; and (3) many turfgrass growers will continue to use cultivation. The practice is more popular in North America than in Europe, which suggests the influence of climate, management, or both. The need for cultivation will increase with greater use and ageing of turf areas. More discrimination is needed on when and when not to cultivate turfgrass sod. Some soils may be too mellow to benefit. Possibly each soil has an optimum water content for cultivation that minimizes damage to soil structure. Some grass species may tolerate or need cultivation more than others. Methods of anticipating dangerously low oxygen levels of turfgrass soils are needed. The effect of cultivation on root development and survival should be known. Most important of all, we might test the hypothesis that cultivation is not giving us the best opening in the turf. Smaller, more frequent holes and deeper openings are theoretically better. Possibly, we need a machine that can simulate earthworm channels or grass root action.

TOP-DRESSING

Top-dressing, as defined in turf, is the spreading of a prepared mixture of soil-like material over established turf for the purpose of trueing the surface and improving the growth of the grass. The material may contain useful amounts of plant nutrients or pesticides. Top-dressing is a practice that developed on fine turf through the need for levelling, and as a method of adding nutrients when commercial fertilizers were rare. In addition to these benefits, top-dressing is beneficial because it encourages rooting of stoloniferous growth, aids decomposition of grass residues, stimulates growth of new shoots, and increases the base of desirable soil. Very little formal research on top-dressing of turf exists. The previously reported studies from Mississippi and New Jersey support the value of top-dressing as a deterrent to thatch. Several opinions have developed over the years as follows: (1) do not bury a layer of thatch with top-dressing; (2) if the base soil of the turf site is quite acceptable, the top-dressing should be of similar nature; (3) development of layers through use of unlike top-dressing materials should be avoided; (4) a top-dressing should be a natural blend of the desired materials rather than a mechanical mixture of the salt and pepper type; (5) water-stable aggregates are desirable in top-dressing; and (6) the top-dressing should have a desirable microbial activity potential.

Top-dressing of turf in the United States was often a secretive and home-styled process 25 to 50 years ago. During World War II most top-dressing of putting greens was omitted. Some growers were reluctant to renew the laborious and expensive practice after the ware because they had survived without it for several years. However, turf cultivation and observation of results with and without top-dressing encouraged revival of the practice. The New Jersey area has had a unique association with top-dressing. A Scots emigrant took great interest in golf turf maintenance, recognized the value of good top-dressing, spent hours of study in libraries and laboratories with Dr. H.B. Sprague on the agronomic aspects of the problem, and he developed a commercial product as a major endeavour. This business firm is still operated by the son and grandsons of the family, and the product is sold not only to most of the golf courses in New Jersey, but to many courses in a radius of 150-200 miles that includes Albany, New York, eastern Long Island, eastern Pennsylvania, and Delaware. One of the great tributes to this firm is the repeated simulation of their product by competitors. Also, it shows that mechanization and a carefully prepared top-dressing product are very important with the ever-increasing costs of labour.

Top-dressing of fine turf, recently considered an old-fashioned practice, will continue. Beleaguered research should study such concerns as: (1) the varied reaction of turfgrass species to top-dressing; (2) the microbial relationships of top-dressing to turf production; (3) the value of combining top-dressing with other turfgrass treatments; (4) the possibility of top-dressing through cultivation; (5) increasing the efficiency of top-dressing for thatch control; (6) natural and artificial materials for use in top-dressing; and (7) the soil texture and aggregation requirements of top-dressing.

REFERENCES

1. BARTHOLOMEW, W.V. (1965) Agron. Monogr. 10, 293.

2. BEARD, J., and RIEKE, P. (1964) Management factors in thatch formation in Merion. Michigan State University Turf Field Day Report, 8.

3. ENGEL, R.E. (1951) Studies of turfgrass cultivation. Ph.D. Thesis, Rutgers University.

4. ENGEL, R.E., and ALDERFER, R.B. (1967) The effect of cultivation, top-dressing, lime, nitrogen and wetting agent on thatch development in ¼-inch bentgrass over a ten-year period. New Jersey agric. Exp. Stn. Bull. 818, 32.

5. HARPER, J.C. (1952) Relationship of aerification, irrigation, and compaction to phosphorus penetration, root development, and population changes of mixed turf. Ph.D. Thesis, Pennsylvania State University.

6. HUFFINE, W.W. (1968) Turfgrass production and management research report. Oklahoma agric. Exp. Stn. Series P-580, 19.

7. LEDEBOER, F.B. (1966) Investigations into the nature of lawn thatch and methods for its decomposition. M.S. Thesis, University of Rhode Island.

8. NELSON, W.R., and BAVER, L.D. (1940) Movement of water through soils in relation to the nature of the pores. Proc. Soil Sci. Soc. Am. 5, 69.

9. SCHERY, R.W. (1966) Remarkable Kentucky bluegrass. Weeds, Trees and Turf 5, 16.

10. THOMPSON, W.R., and WARD, C.Y. (1965) Prevention of thatch. Mississippi agric. Exp. Stn. Sheet 912.

THATCH, CULTIVATION AND TOP-DRESSING OF HIGH-CUT TURF

John F. Cornman,

Professor of Ornamental Horticulture, Cornell University, Ithaca, New York, U.S.A.

SUMMARY

Thatch is the mass of living and dead plant material between the layer of green vegetation and the soil. The most obvious way to get rid of it is to encourage bacterial activity; methods are described for improving the critical factors. Mechanical methods of dealing with thatch are also discussed, such as removal of clippings and raking or slicing the turf.

Thatch is defined as "a tightly intermingled layer of living and dead stems, leaves, and roots of grasses, which develops between the layer of green vegetation and the soil surface." Thatch problems are severe on closely cut putting greens and lawns, especially when vigorous grasses are amply fertilized. Thatch can also become a serious problem in some situations with grasses normally grown at a higher cut. Merion Kentucky bluegrass (Poa pratensis L.) may form a heavy thatch, as will red fescue (Festuca rubra L.) under some circumstances. A moderate amount of thatch does no harm but when the accumulation is too great the blanket of material interferes with the penetration of water and of fertilizers, insecticides and fungicides. Heavily thatched turf recovers very slowly or not at all from injuries, and where areas of such turf die, for whatever reasons, the repair is most awkward.

Logic suggests that the simplest way to reduce thatch or prevent the accumulation of thatch is to encourage normal bacterial activities so that the carbonaceous material is decomposed by vigorous operation of the nitrogen cycle. The aerobic bacteria are the most useful organisms in decomposition and for their greatest activity certain environmental conditions must be present. In addition to a suitable temperature there must be an adequate supply of oxygen, adequate moisture to dampen the organic matter, a suitable level of soil acidity, and a supply of nitrogen adequate for both bacterial multiplication and turf nutrition. Fortunately, levels of the factors most suitable for bacterial multiplication and activity are about the same as those for maximum turf growth.

For all practical purposes, temperature is not controllable but steps can be taken to adjust the other critical factors. A pH of about 6.0 to 8.0 is optimum for most bacteria. The supply of nitrogen is easily augmented. Logically, of course, over-stimulation would increase rather than decrease thatch. It seems reasonable that nitrogen adequate to provide green colour appropriate to the particular grass should be adequate for both vigorous bacterial activity and for normal turf growth.

Oxygen supply is sometimes critical, as is evidenced by the fact that organic matter decomposes very slowly where there is a surplus of soil moisture. Hence artificial drainage may be the first step if soil moisture levels are so high as to exclude oxygen. In addition, the time honoured spikers and hollow tine forks serve a useful purpose in admitting air to the soil but require much hand labour. In America various power driven machines that function like hollow tine forks have reduced this labour problem.

A moisture supply adequate to moisten the dead organic material presents a problem in some circumstances. Rainfall and irrigation are sometimes insufficient because the waxy coating on the thatch prevents proper moistening. It is here that top-dressing with compost serves such a useful purpose on putting greens. Unfortunately, on the erect-growing grasses used for American lawns top-dressing has little appeal because of the large areas and extensive efforts involved. The use of wetting agents to lower the surface tension of the moisture and thus let the water through the resistant coatings on the dead carbonaceous material seem promising theoretically, though experimental evidence of their potential in this regard is very scanty.

Despite the ease with which each of these nitrogen cycle factors can be demonstrated under one circumstance or another, their action and interaction on high cut turf has not been adequately demonstrated under experimental conditions.

Quite aside from efforts to influence the bacteria, various mechanical means for preventing the deposition and the accumulation of organic matter should be helpful. The catching and removal of grass clippings will avoid one potential source of organic matter supply. Various raking and slicing devices operated by hand or by machine can be used effectively to remove large quantities of dead organic matter without destroying the live turf. The amount of clippings removed each season from an area of turf can easily be measured, as can the large quantities of thatch that can be removed by mechanical means. Nevertheless, a reduction in the weight of the residual organic matter in turf so treated has not been adequately demonstrated. Perhaps the methods of measurement of organic matter are not delicate enough to detect the benefits of clipping removal. As for the results of removal of vegetation by various raking and slicing devices, it may be that the "border effect" and stimulation from the thinning of the turf may so encourage more vigorous growth as to cancel out some or much of the benefit of removing organic matter.

DISCUSSION

CONTROL OF MOSS AND ALGAE

M.A. Wood (U.K.)

In Northern Ireland our wet climate leads to severe moss infestation on much of our fine turf. This aggravates the thatch problem. Control is normally carried out by means of ferrous sulphate or mercurial preparations. Has anyone experience of other effective control methods?

T.E. Freeman (Florida, U.S.A.)

If you are referring to algae, we have found in Florida that certain fungicides will control algae under wet conditions. They are thiram, Dithane M-45 (zinc ion and maneb product) and mercury fungicides.

THE IMPORTANCE OF THATCH

R.W. Schery (Ohio, U.S.A.)

I support the idea that the need for thatch removal has been overstressed. It is not the cure-all for disease and other troubles that is often claimed. In the north-east U.S.A. there are many enquiries from home owners, who complain that after following advice to "de-thatch", often at great expense, problems are not corrected and sometimes new ones are created. There are some good reasons for mechanical thatch removal (e.g. better penetration of fertilizer and water) but perhaps half the time thatch removal is recommended to cure something it is unable to correct. Among our plots, those from which thatch has been removed have developed disease and been invaded by Poa annua L. before the untreated plots. Poa pratensis L. in its natural condition is never thinned at all, and grows well.

R.E. Engel (New Jersey, U.S.A.)

On many occasions de-thatching has been done unwisely, but its application will increase because it has potential value and we should learn the appropriate ways of using this technique.

SESSION 6C: CULTURAL SYSTEMS

(Chairman: Prof. P. Boeker)

CULTURAL SYSTEMS ON GOLF COURSES

W.H. Bengeyfield,

USGA Green Section, Garden Grove, California, U.S.A.

SUMMARY

Turfgrass management and research in the United States has been largely spurred by the game of golf. In some areas, golf clubs spend over $200,000 annually for the maintenance of an 18-hole golf course. Labour costs are the largest single item accounting for 70% of expenditure.

Automatic irrigation is an important step forward in efficient turf-grass production. However, an automatic system must be properly designed, engineered and installed if it is to be effective. There are innumerable opportunities to make major mistakes in automatic irrigation installations.

Soil compaction and _Poa annua_ are major problems on heavily used turf-grass areas. Studies in soil mixtures and the use of new chemicals for pre-emergence control offer real hope for the future. Many improved grasses have been introduced by Experiment Stations and quality turfgrasses are on the increase. The technique and proper timing of cultural practices such as cultivation, vertical mowing, top-dressing and over-seeding are receiving renewed attention. Chemicals are widely used for preventing rather than curing turfgrass diseases and weed invasion.

One problem will apparently not yield to improved cultural practices, i.e. excessive traffic on turf. Very heavy traffic and the use of electric golf cars and hand golf carts offer research opportunities for the future.

In the United States, there are over 10 million golfers. The game is played on well over 8,000 courses. Golfers come from all segments of the economy, from truck drivers to corporation presidents. There are public fee courses where over 350 rounds of golf per day are played 365 days of the year. With this heavy play and the demands by golfers for excellence, the cultural practices or systems must be adjusted to fit the purpose of the crop; i.e. golf is played on grass.

Economics play an important role in cultural practices. Expenditures will vary from $40,000 annual maintenance costs to over $200,000 for an 18-hole course. A recent survey in Southern California showed an average figure of $123,000 per year for maintaining 18-hole golf courses in that area.

Seventy per cent of the expenditure is for labour. On an "average course" there will be a maintenance crew of 11 or 12 men, but on the "better courses" as many as 18 to 20 men will be employed. The starting salary is about $2.50 an hour while experienced workers will receive $3.80 an hour or more. In some cases, trade unions now represent the workers. The men are usually capable of doing a wide variety of jobs and are frequently assigned to sections of a golf course. They are responsible for the mowing and the other maintenance requirements in their particular section. Supervisors or golf course superintendents receive approximately $13,000 a year or more in salary. Some may receive as much as $25,000 a year.

Because of high labour costs and the fact that water is so critical to high quality turfgrass production, automatic irrigation is of vital concern to the manager of golfing turf in the United States. Many golf courses are now completely irrigated by automatic systems that are under the control of the golf course superintendent. In order to do a good job of irrigation, i.e. to provide the correct rate of precipitation and adequate coverage, it is imperative that the systems be properly designed, engineered and installed.

Some common errors include spacing sprinkler heads too far apart (70 ft. or 20 m is the maximum spacing in the author's judgement); placing too many sprinkler heads under the control of one automatic station; using incorrect pipe sizes; and incorrect programming on the part of the superintendent. In most areas of the U.S., the maximum water use rate for grass is 1½ in. (4 cm) of water per week. Unfortunately and in every area, far more water is applied to turfgrasses than is needed; sometimes over 200,000 gallons (900,000 l) per day on an 18-hole course.

At these high irrigation rates and under conditions of heavy traffic and soil compaction, it is little wonder that Poa annua L. is a major problem. If possible, golf courses should be rid of it, especially on putting greens. It does not provide championship putting qualities, especially when in the seeding stage. Its longevity is doubtful both summer and winter. It is extremely variable in types or varieties and it is very susceptible to disease. Furthermore, it does not withstand heavy traffic.

There is an ever-increasing interest in the use of improved grasses. On greens, selected varieties of Agrostis palustris Huds. (creeping bentgrass) are gaining popularity. Named varieties such as Toronto, Cohansey, Congressional and Old Orchard are being used. Penncross is the best seeded form of creeping bentgrass, although Seaside bent is still being widely used. The colonial bents (Agrostis tenuis Sibth.) are not recommended by the USGA for putting green use.

On fairways, tees and rough areas, selected varieties of Poa pratensis L., Festuca spp. and Agrostis spp. are used.

In southern climates, the improved varieties of Cynodon dactylon (L.) Pers. (Tifgreen, Tifdwarf, Santa Ana, etc.) are receiving wide acceptance for greens, tees and fairways.

Greens are usually cut at ¼ in. (7 mm) and sometimes at 3/16 in. (5 mm). However, a "bench setting" is of dubious value. The final height of cut should be determined visually as well as by actual playing qualities. Greens should be mown daily but, because of labour costs, most clubs find a 5 or 6 day-a-week mowing schedule acceptable. Four mowings weekly is a minimum for greens.

Golfers are demanding closely cut tees, usually ½ in (13 mm) or less, and fairways at ¾ in. (19 mm) or less. These are mown twice-weekly. Roughs are usually 2 in. (50 mm) or more in height of cut and mown every week to ten days.

In recent times, 'contour mowing' of greens and fairways has received attention. Greens are being developed with pleasing outlines rather than the usual oval or circular pattern. Fairways too are being 'contoured' by mowing practices to develop a natural appearance and, at the same time, to demand more strategy and better placement of the golf shot.

The timing of maintenance practices such as cultivation and vertical mowing of greens has gained importance. Cultivation or severe vertical mowing in the autumn or early spring months definitely favours Poa annua invasion. Therefore, these practices are now often delayed until the summer months. Autumn aeration is most favourable to Poa annua.

Annual overseeding of bentgrass greens with Seaside or Penncross bentgrass is returning to popularity. There is evidence to indicate that early summer is the best time for the practice, rather than the spring or autumn. During the summer, greens are irrigated on a regular schedule, there is less competition from Poa annua, disease controls are in effect and soil temperatures are usually favourable. Two pounds of Agrostis palustris (creeping bentgrass) per 1,000 sq. ft. (1 kg/100 sq m) immediately after cultivation or spiking is suggested.

Many golf course superintendents now use the vertical mower on a light but frequent schedule; perhaps once a month during the active growing season. The mower is adjusted for a very light cut so that neither the crown of the plant nor the soil itself are touched, but only the longer grass blades. Top-dressing on a light but frequent basis is also returning to popularity. Three or four top-dressings annually at ¾ cu. yd. (0.6 cu m) each per green provides for greater new shoot growth and smooth playing surfaces.

Regarding the use of chemicals, the turfgrass industry could not long survive without them. Where once it was enough to gain control of a difficult situation with chemical treatments, the aim now is to be ahead of the problem and prevent it from developing into a serious condition. Thus there is a tendency more and more to preventative disease control applications and pre-emergence weed control measures. There may be a lot of unnecessary spraying, but the feeling is that the results more than justify this expenditure and effort.

There is one problem that cannot be controlled with chemicals or cultural practices. That is the electric golf car and hand cart traffic on turf. There are some golf courses where over 300 electric cars are in almost daily use. The average number per 18-hole golf course is around 50 golf cars. The only solution so far for the traffic problem is through development of cart paths from the First Tee to the 18th Green, or partial paths and a "scatter principle" for cars at the path end. Concentrated traffic areas, i.e., around greens and tees, present a most difficult problem. Aeration, additional fertilization and even sodding help, but paved paths are so far the only real answer. The great day will be when an air-cushion-type golf car is developed and placed on the market.

SOD PRODUCTION OF KENTUCKY BLUEGRASS

J.B. Beard, P.E. Rieke and J.W. King,

Department of Crop and Soil Science, Michigan State University, East Lansing, Michigan, U.S.A.

SUMMARY

Commercial sod production is the most rapidly expanding segment of the agricultural industry in the United States. During the rapid period of growth sod has increasingly been produced on organic soils. It is ready for harvest and shipment to the consumer site when sufficient roots and rhizomes have developed to permit handling without tearing. The sod is normally harvested in 0.8 or 1.2 sq m units with a thickness of 1.2-2.0 cm. A relatively thinly cut sod is necessary to ensure most rapid rooting and to remove a minimum amount of soil. Following cutting, the sod pieces are usually rolled mechanically and loaded on pallets or directly onto trucks for shipment to the consumer site. Injury to sod can occur during shipment due to an interaction of effects between a build-up of high temperatures and an alteration of the gaseous microclimate within the stack. A number of considerations are discussed for minimizing sod injury during shipment. Proper sodding techniques are necessary in order to ensure successful establishment of the commodity on the consumer site. Of most importance are proper seedbed preparation; a moist soil at the time of laying; proper laying techniques; and regular watering following laying in order to avoid atmospheric drought during the rooting period.

INTRODUCTION

The term sod describes plugs, blocks, squares or strips of turf (plus the adhering soil) which are used for vegetative planting. Commercial sodding has been practiced in the United States since the 1920's with most sod obtained by pasture stripping. Pasture stripping gradually developed toward commercial sod production which encompasses the establishment, maintenance and harvesting phases involved in producing quality sod. However, it was not until approximately 1950 that a significant expansion of the commercial sod production industry occurred. Factors contributing to this expansion were the development of:-

(a) the mechanical sod cutter

(b) release of improved sod-forming cultivars of Kentucky bluegrass
       (Poa pratensis L.)

(c) availability of improved herbicides for weed control.

During the 1960's commercial sod production was one of the most rapidly expanding agricultural industries. Figure 1 shows the growth rate of the sod production industry in Michigan. Sod production has increased from 400 ha in 1955 to almost 10,000 ha in 1969. This 1969 production in Michigan represents a total sale of $32,000,000. The expansion rate of the commercial sod production in other states has paralleled that in Michigan, although somewhat delayed. At the same time pasture stripping operations are declining and in Michigan are now limited primarily to providing sod for roadside sodding. In addition to Michigan, sizeable commercial sod production acreages are found in Florida, Ontario, Illinois, Wisconsin, New York, Maryland and New Jersey. In 1965 it was estimated that 40,500 ha of sod were being produced on the North American continent (3).

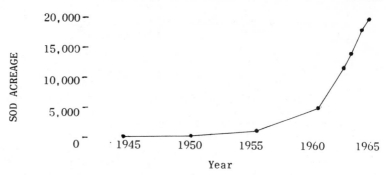

Figure 1: growth rate in acreage of the commercial sod production acreage in Michigan from 1945 to 1965

The recent rapid expansion of the sod production industry is attributed to several key factors (4). First is the acceptance by the consumer of sodding as a quick and relatively easy means of obtaining a quality lawn which is available for immediate use. Second is the favourable economic climate, in terms of high rates of new home and commercial business construction and funds available to purchase sod. Third, sod can be harvested and marketed any time during the growing season if irrigation is available. In contrast, seeding is restricted to certain selected periods.

Two types of sod enterprises predominate. One type encompasses the production, harvesting, shipping and laying phases: the second type combines an organisation which is concerned with the establishment, production and harvesting of sod with another which is responsible for the shipping and laying phases. During the 1960's the trend has been towards an increasing percentage of the sod being produced on organic soils, if available. For example, in 1963 50% of the sod produced in Michigan was grown on organic soil, while 80% of the production was on organic soil in 1968, just five years later. The remainder of this paper will be concerned primarily with the sod harvesting and utilisation phase.

SOD QUALITY

A sod can be harvested when the roots and rhizomes have developed sufficiently to permit handling without tearing. The length of time to produce a marketable Kentucky bluegrass sod varies from six months in more favourable climates up to two years under less favourable conditions. A high quality sod is one possessing:-

(a) uniformity,

(b) good shoot density,

(c) acceptable colour,

(d) freedom from serious weeds, weed seeds, insects, diseases and nematodes,

(e) adequate sod strength for handling,

(f) sufficient maturity in terms of carbohydrate reserves to
     root effectively, and

(g) a minimum thatch layer.

SOD HARVESTING

Harvesting is accomplished with a mechanical sod cutter which cuts the
sod into widths of 30, 40, 45 or 60 cm and a length sufficient to give a total
area of 0.8 to 1.2 sq m per piece. The thickness of sod varies with the turfgrass species, uniformity of the soil surface, type of soil, shoot density of
sod and degree of rhizome and root development. Thin-cut Kentucky bluegrass,
of 1.2 - 2.0 cm, is easier to handle and roots faster than when cut thicker
(1, 5). Sod cut thick is usually more drought resistant but is slower to root,
whereas extremely thinly cut sod is quite prone to injury from atmospheric
drought (6). The sod knife should be kept sharp at all times and is best operated if the soil is somewhat moist at the time of cutting. However, excessive
soil moisture should be avoided in order to reduce shipping costs and facilitate
ease of handling.

The sod pieces are generally rolled for convenience in handling and laying.
Prior to 1965 most sod was rolled and loaded manually. Since then a number of
different types of sod cutters and rollers have been developed to facilitate
the harvesting operation and reduce the labour requirements and cost. Following
harvesting and rolling the sod is then loaded for shipping. Several different
methods have been utilised. In one, the sod is stacked on pallets which are then
placed upon the truck by the means of a fork lift. In another, a mechanical
conveyor attached to the truck conveys the sod onto the truck for direct stack-
ing. After loading, a canvas is frequently placed over the top of the load to
prevent drying during shipment. The amount of soil removed with the sod depends
on the depth of cut and frequency of harvest (7). In fact, the rate of soil removal is not as great as might be thought, especially when compared to normal
cropping practices. Studies on a Houghton muck soil showed that only slightly
more soil is removed by harvesting a sod crop annually than is lost by natural
subsidence under an annual crop of onions.

SHIPPING

Sod is being shipped considerable distances in the United States to market
areas where sod production has not been developed on a local basis. For example,
sod is shipped from Michigan production areas to markets in Cleveland and
Pittsburg, which is a distance of from 325 to 550 km. Sod is usually loaded one
afternoon, shipped overnight and is on the consumer site the following morning
ready for sodding.

Sod is a perishable commodity which can be stored for only a limited length
of time. Under certain conditions what has been termed "sod heating" can result in serious damage to the sod during shipment. The length of time before
lethal effects are evident in a load can vary from 12 to 60 hours depending on
the time of year, physiological condition of the grass and prevailing temperatures. Studies of the post-harvest physiology of stacked sod have been conducted at Michigan State University (Unpublished data of J.W. King and J.B. Beard,
Michigan State University). Lethal effects are evident when temperatures in the
sod stack reach approximately 40°C. Preliminary evidence indicates that actual

kill is due to an interaction between the gaseous composition of the stack microclimate and the temperature, rather than the direct effect of high temperature alone.

Factors which contribute to a rapid kill of stacked sod include:-

(a) high soil temperatures at the time of harvest,

(b) a physiological condition of the sod which results in the initiation of seedheads, and

(c) height of cut.

The higher the soil temperature at the time of harvest the sooner lethal damage occurs. Growers sometimes prefer to cut and roll sod in the early morning when the soil temperatures are at a minimum in order to avoid harvesting sod which has been warmed by the midday high temperatures. The use of a ventilation system through the load also assists in alleviating sod damage during shipment. Vacuum cooling has also been utilised to cool sod loads artificially prior to shipment. This method has proved quite effective but as yet is not widely used.

SODDING

Although the sod producer has developed a quality product, proper techniques in sodding are still necessary to assure satisfactory long term performance of the sod. Sodding can be practiced at any time during the growing season, if there is irrigation to alleviate moisture stresses which may develop. The methods involved in soil preparation for sodding are the same as those required for seeding. Basically the area should be contoured; the soil amended to improve the texture as needed; stones, rocks and debris removed from the area; lime and fertilizer applied as needed and worked into the upper three inches of the seedbed; and the final, level seedbed firmed prior to sodding.

In a study of the response of sod rooting to nutrient levels in the soil, it was found that maximum rooting occurred when 0.5 kg of nitrogen and 1.0 kg of P_2O_5 per 100 sq m were incorporated into the soil. (Unpublished data of R.N. Carrow and P.E. Rieke, Michigan State University.) Application rates above or below these levels resulted in decreased root counts.

Studies have clearly shown that sodding should be done on a soil which is moist rather than dry (6). A moist soil greatly facilitates the knitting of roots into the underlying soil. Rooting can be delayed by as much as ten days if the sod is placed on a dry soil even though the area is completely saturated with water following the sodding operations.

During the laying process it is important that the sod pieces are not stretched and that the ends meet squarely rather than being overlapped or leaving voids. If the sod is stretched during laying, the sod pieces will shrink as drying occurs in spaces or voids between individual sod pieces. After sodding the area should be rolled to provide firm contact between the sod and the underlying soil as well as to avoid any air pockets under the sod which might result in drying and death of the roots.

After the area has been sodded it is important to apply a small amount of water each day at approximately noon. It is during this period that maximum rates of evapotranspiration are occurring. Since the sod does not have an adequate root system for water absorption during the initial two to three week period, it is very prone to damage from atmospheric desiccation. Regular midday watering will avoid injury of this type.

REFERENCES

1. ANON. (1925) How thick to cut sod for putting greens. U.S. Golf Ass. Green Sect. Bull. 5, 8, 172.

2. ANON. (1964) Vacuum cooling of sod aids shipping problems. American Nurseryman 120, 6, 52.

3. ANON. (1965) WTT survey shows sod industry headed for vast expansion, increased sales. Weeds, Trees and Turf 4, 8, 22.

4. BEARD, J.B., and RIEKE, P.E. (1964) Sod production in Michigan. Michigan State University Extension Mimeo. 1.

5. HODGES, T.K. (1958) Cutting sod for rhizome value. Proc. 1958 Midwest Regional Turf Conf. 40.

6. KING, J.W., and BEARD, J.B. (1967) Soil and management factors affecting the rooting capability of organic and mineral grown sod. Agron. Abstr. p.53.

7. RIEKE, P.E., BEARD, J.B., and LUCAS, R.E. (1968) Grass sod production on organic soils in Michigan. Proc. Third Int. Peat Congress. Quebec City, Canada.

FACTORS IN SOD PRODUCTION OF KENTUCKY BLUEGRASS

P.E. Rieke and J.B. Beard,

Department of Crop and Soil Science, Michigan State University, East Lansing, Michigan, U.S.A.

SUMMARY

Sod production has grown into a significant agricultural industry in North America since about 1950. Because it is a young industry, scientific research is limited. In developing efficient sod production there are several key factors which should be considered, including (a) market development, (b) adequate soil resources, (c) desirable climatic conditions, (d) sufficient capital for site development and equipment, (e) labour supply, and (f) water available for irrigation. Michigan and surrounding states have been able to develop large sod production industries because of very favourable climatic and soil conditions.

Merion Kentucky bluegrass presently comprises over 90% of the sod crop in Michigan because of its vigorous rhizome and sod forming characteristics, plus its outstanding resistance to Helminthosporium spp.

The sod piece is held intact by roots and rhizomes. Optimum soil nutrient levels, especially nitrogen, are necessary for encouragement of root and rhizome growth. In 1965, excessive nitrogen levels caused decreases in root and rhizome weights, soluble carbohydrates in the rhizomes, and sod strength of Merion Kentucky bluegrass grown on an organic soil. This response varies with soil and year, depending on the general weather conditions. Timing of nitrogen application is also important in affecting rhizome growth and sod strength.

In intensive sod production, other cultural practices such as rolling, irrigation and control of weeds, insects and diseases are necessary for production of a high quality crop.

INTRODUCTION

Growing grass for the ultimate purpose of removing the resulting sod and re-establishing it on another location has been practised for many years. However, only since about 1950 has commercial sod production become a significant industry. Very little scientific literature exists. The technology of production has been developed primarily through individual grower experience and experimentation.

Several factors contribute to an efficient sod production enterprise. They include climate, soil, capital investment, market development, grass species, technology, water availability, equipment and labour supply (1).

The predominant species of grass used in sod production in northern United States and southern Canada is Poa pratensis L, (Kentucky bluegrass). A relatively long growing season, extensive periods of desirable soil temperatures for growth of this grass (13 - 20°C) and adequate precipitation are important contributing factors in the widespread use of Kentucky bluegrass for sod.

Irrigation is often practised when precipitation is inadequate, especially during establishment and prior to harvest if the grass had become dormant due to soil drought. The water supply must be adequate in terms of both quantity and quality.

The major market outlet for sod is associated with construction of homes, businesses, and institutions. It is imperative for the grower to find out the likely demands for sod and to develop marketing channels. Accessibility to the market, market price and cost of hauling are important factors as well.

TURFGRASSES USED IN SOD PRODUCTION

The turfgrass species and cultivars utilized in sod production are determined by (a) the sod-forming characteristics of the grass, (b) the market demand for it, (c) its adaptability to the environment where it is to be marketed, (d) its speed of establishment from seed, and (e) its tolerance of insects, diseases, heat, cold and moisture stress (1). Merion Kentucky bluegrass comprises over 90% of the sod produced in Michigan because of its vigorous rhizome, tillering and sod-forming characteristics, plus its excellent resistance to leafspot (Helminthosporium spp.). It also requires a high intensity of culture. Merion is quite susceptible to powdery mildew (Erysiphe graminis DC.) under shade conditions. In addition, stripe smut (Ustilago striiformis (West.) Niessl), flag smut (Urocystis agropyri (Preuss) Schröt.) and Fusarium blight (Fusarium spp.) are threats to the widespread use of Merion for commercial sod production in the future.

A number of other bluegrass cultivars are presently being grown for sod, including Delta, Fylking, Kenblue, Newport, Park, Prato, and Windsor. Blending of two or more Kentucky bluegrass cultivars is encouraged for better adaptability to the market site environment and cultural conditions. Mixtures of Kentucky bluegrass and creeping red fescue (Festuca rubra L. ssp. rubra) provide even greater flexibility for use in the shade and on unirrigated sandy sites but the weak sod-forming ability of red fescue and its susceptibility to leafspot (Helminthosporium spp.) has limited the widespread use of this turfgrass mixture by the producer. Only when the public demands turfgrass mixtures and pays an appropriate price differential, will red fescue-Kentucky bluegrass mixtures become important.

Tall fescue (Festuca arundinacea Schreb.) and Kentucky bluegrass are commonly mixed in growing sod on a more limited acreage in the transitional zone between the warm and cool-humid climatic regions. The sod-forming characteristics of tall fescue are weak compared to Kentucky bluegrass, resulting in longer production periods.

Sod production of creeping bentgrass (Agrostis palustris Huds.) is very small and limited primarily to rapid establishment of high quality, closely-mowed sports turf. High production costs prevent more extensive sod production of creeping bentgrass.

A technique was developed to evaluate cultural factors in sod production research (4). This is accomplished by measuring the weight required to tear a piece of sod in two. This technique can be used to evaluate turfgrasses for use in sod production. Data in Table 1 illustrate sod strength measurements for several Kentucky bluegrass cultivars and a red fescue. The five-month old sod strengths point out the stronger sod-forming ability of the Kentucky bluegrass cultivars compared to the red fescue. In seventeen-month old sod the weakening influence of Helminthosporium spp. is reflected in reduced sod strengths for Delta, Common and Pennlawn. The outstanding sod-forming ability of Merion is also evident.

Table 1: sod strengths of five turfgrass cultivars grown on organic soil

Species and cultivar	Sod strength measured in kg required to tear sod	
	5 month old sod	17 month old sod
Poa pratensis		
Delta	50.5	31.4
Common	46.4	32.7
Merion	42.3	45.0
Newport	40.0	39.5
Festuca rubra		
Pennlawn	26.8	17.3

SITE SELECTION AND DEVELOPMENT

Considerable investment is required in site selection and development and in obtaining adequate equipment for an intensive sod enterprise. Land levellers, cultipacker seeders, fertilizer spreaders, land rollers, mowers, sod cutters, sod rollers and other harvesting equipment are necessary. Tractors and other heavy equipment must be equipped with special over-sized balloon tyres or metal extension rims to provide flotation and prevent ruts, especially on organic soils. Depressions are undesirable because they interfere with the efficient harvest of high quality sod.

An adequate labour supply must be available for peak periods of activity such as harvest and seeding. Improvement of mechanization must continue to offset a limited labour force.

Sod can be grown on either organic or mineral soils. Availability of land is a basic consideration in selecting a site in relation to roads and markets. With good transportation facilities, sod has been shipped as far as 650 km for utilization. Other considerations are the type, depth and uniformity of soil; whether the land will require drainage, clearing or levelling; and development of an irrigation system.

The topography of the land should be level, or no more than gently sloping, and the soil should be free from excessive quantities of stones, stumps or other materials which would interfere with drainage, tillage and harvesting. Weedy perennial grasses must also be controlled before establishment of a crop. The most serious perennial weedy grasses in the cool-humid climatic regions are Agropyron repens (L.). Beauv., Agrostis palustris, Phalaris arundinacea L., and Cyperus esculentus L. Fallowing, chemical sprays or fumigation may be necessary to eradicate these species.

Large acreages of sod are produced on organic soils in north central United States, southern Canada and Florida. The soils range from nearly undecomposed sphagnum moss peat, which is not common in present sod-growing areas, to finely-divided, well-decomposed, shallow muck, high in mineral content (5). The depth and quality of soil varies considerably. Most sod is produced on farms which were formerly in vegetable production, so that clearing land of trees and other troublesome vegetation is not necessary. In order to expand operations, however, expensive site clearing and development are necessary.

Organic soils, by the nature of their formation, are poorly drained and require artificial drainage to prevent injury to turf and to allow maintenance and harvesting operations to proceed smoothly. In many cases the drainage water must be lifted by pumping into an outlet. A drainage reservoir will allow control of the water table in the soil, if adequate tiling exists. Maximum flexibility is obtained if the water table can be varied field by field and according to the season of the year. Maintaining a high water table will reduce soil subsidence and increase water use efficiency. Lowering the water table is essential for harvesting and establishment operations.

A typical sod piece grown on organic soil in Michigan is 1.25 sq m in size; weighs 15 kg; and contains 10 kg water, 3 kg oven dry soil, primarily organic matter, 1.7 kg roots and rhizomes (dry weight) and 0.18 kg dry grass.

Sod production on mineral soils is accomplished most readily on textures of sandy loam or loam. Consideration should be given to depth of soil, presence of hardpan layers, stones and drainage. Sod grown on mineral soils is preferred for heavy traffic areas such as athletic fields, tees and playgrounds. Sod produced on mineral soil weighs more than sod from organic soil. The lighter weight of the organic soil allows cheaper transportation costs and greater ease in harvesting and handling. The time required to produce a harvestable crop is 12 to 18 months on organic soil while the production period on mineral soil is often 3 to 6 months longer. However, the cultural practices affect the production time considerably.

ESTABLISHMENT

It is essential to establish a uniform population of turfgrass plants for rapid sod formation. Open areas resulting from poor establishment prevent development of a dense sod and delay harvest.

The soil must be tilled sufficiently to develop a level, uniform seedbed. Lime and fertilizer must be worked into the seedbed prior to seeding. Desired pH levels are 6.0 to 7.0 on mineral soils and 5.5 to 6.5 on organic soils. Satari (6) pointed out that optimum levels of phosphorus and potassium are necessary for maximum root and rhizome growth. Seedbed nitrogen has been found to be important for rapid establishment of seedlings when the soil temperature is low during the spring and fall seasons. Optimum levels are between 17 and 68 kg/ha of nitrogen, depending on soil and season of year.

A seeding in late summer (15 Aug. - 1 Sept.) is generally the most successful in north central United States because of more favourable soil moisture and temperature conditions. This allows time for the seedlings to develop root systems extensive enough to withstand the rigours of winter heaving and desiccation. Spring seedings are subject to greater competition from annual broadleaf and grass weeds.

Seeding rates depend on seed quality, seedbed conditions, species and cultivars of turfgrass, and environmental conditions including irrigation. Current recommendations for Michigan conditions are: 30 to 45 kg/ha for Kentucky bluegrass; 70 to 115 kg/ha for red fescue; and 40 to 75 kg/ha for Kentucky bluegrass-red fescue mixtures. Excessively high rates of seed provide more rapid cover but the rate of sod development is decreased. In the less desirable seeding periods, however, higher rates of seeding may be necessary. Most seeding is done with a cultipacker seeder which allows uniform distribution of seed and good seed-soil contact at the proper depth.

Some sod fields are allowed to re-establish from Kentucky bluegrass rhizomes left in the field after the sod crop is removed. Five succeeding crops or more have been removed without tillage or reseeding. This technique cannot be followed if an uneven surface is left after harvesting is completed. Frequently a light rate of overseeding is helpful in attaining uniform re-establishment.

CULTURE

A high quality sod is held intact by roots, rhizomes and stolons. Cultural practices should encourage root and rhizome development. Mowing frequency, for example, should be determined by the height of cut and rate of growth of turfgrass. As a general guide, it is suggested that no more than one-third of the top growth be removed by mowing. The preferred cutting height for Kentucky bluegrass and red fescue is 3.8 - 5.1 cm, while 1.3 cm or less is preferred for the bentgrass.

Fertilization following establishment is usually restricted to nitrogen, on the assumption that phosphorus and potassium requirements have been met in seedbed fertilization. Only a few cases of deficiencies of other nutrients such as manganese and iron have been reported in Michigan.

Satari (6) studied the influence of nitrogen rates on sod development of Merion Kentucky bluegrass grown on an organic soil. Plots were seeded 5 May 1965. Nitrogen was applied at rates of 0, 17, 34 and 68 kg/ha beginning 1 July. Increasing the rate of nitrogen application resulted in decreased root and rhizome weights in September (Table 2). The higher nitrogen treatment increased shoot growth, causing a decrease in the soluble carbohydrate levels found in the rhizomes in September. A corresponding decrease in sod strength measurements was also observed as determined in October.

The release of nitrogen from the organic soil is an important variable which must be considered. Table 3 illustrates the influence of climatic differences between years. The experimental conditions were similar to those described in the 1965 study by Satari (6). Plots were seeded 12 May 1967. Sod strength increased with the addition of the first increment of nitrogen, but was unchanged by additional nitrogen. One year later only the 68 kg nitrogen treatment showed reduced sod strength compared to the 17 kg treatment. In 1967 weather conditions were cool and wet, causing increased leaching of soil nitrogen and decreased microbial activity which reduced the release of nitrogen from the organic soil. This was in contrast to climatic conditions in 1965 (Table 2) when the situation led to the accumulation of soluble nitrogen in the soil.

The nitrogen response of turfgrass grown for sod on mineral soils is more consistent than that of turfgrass on organic soils. Kurtz (2) reported in 1967 that increasing the annual nitrogen applications on a sandy clay loam soil up to 175 kg/ha resulted in an increase in the number of rhizomes, the average length of the rhizomes and the sod strength.

Timing of nitrogen applications is also an important factor in sod production. By doubling the rate of nitrogen application in September, Kurtz (2) found a significant increase in the rhizome length compared to uniform monthly applications. Sod strength was also increased by the higher nitrogen application in September.

Table 2: influence of monthly nitrogen applications on Merion Kentucky bluegrass grown for sod on Houghton muck (6)

Nitrogen applied	Roots in Sept.	Rhizomes in Sept.	Carbohydrates in rhizomes in Sept.*	Sod strength in Oct.
kg/ha	gm/sq dm	gm/sq dm	%	kg
0	0.90	0.69	19.4	17.2
17	0.69	0.57	18.0	14.0
34	0.34	0.28	16.4	8.5
68	0.30	0.18	17.0	9.2
LSD (.01)	0.16	0.08	0.5	6.0

*Determined by the takadiastase enzyme extraction modified by Lindahl et al (3)

Table 3: influence of monthly nitrogen application on Merion Kentucky bluegrass grown for sod on Houghton muck in 1967 and 1968

Nitrogen applied kg/ha	Sod strength measured in kg required to tear sod	
	Oct. 1967	Sept. 1968
0	14.5	51.9
17	26.3	60.9
34	29.4	52.2
51	27.0	51.4
68	29.9	40.0
LSD (.05)	7.4	15.9

Most nitrogen is applied in the spring and fall. In some cases light rates are applied in the summer to maintain colour and shoot density or to improve colour before harvest. Nitrogen use should be based on (a) soil texture, (b) rate of nitrogen release from the soil, especially on organic soils, (c) requirements for the turfgrass species or cultivars, (d) moisture conditions and (e) growth rate of the grass, giving particular attention to the effect of temperature. Present nitrogen usage for sod ranges from almost none to as high as 280 kg/ha on intensively cultured sod.

Irrigation is being used increasingly to reduce production time and to supplement natural precipitation. Frequent light irrigations are practiced during establishment while heavier less frequent applications are made as the sod crop matures.

Rolling helps to provide a level surface which facilitates a uniform depth of cutting during harvest. The effects of winter heaving can often be corrected and ruts and other small depressions levelled out. Rolling is generally more effective on organic soils because of their more elastic nature.

Most of the broadleaf weeds which are problems in sod production in the cool, humid climatic regions can be controlled with 2,4-D. Certain broadleaf weeds which are more difficult to control may require repeated applications or more specific herbicides.

Insect pests have not been a serious problem in sod production in the cool, humid climatic regions. With continued production on the same soil potentially harmful populations of insects and nematodes could develop.

Susceptibility to Helminthosporium spp. has discouraged the use of certain Kentucky bluegrass cultivars for sod production. Fusarium spp. and Ustilago striiformis have proved serious in some areas. Effective economical controls are not available for these diseases on sod at the present time.

REFERENCES

1. BEARD, J.B., and RIEKE, P.E. (1969) Producing quality sod. Ch.17, Turfgrass Science. Am. Soc. of Agron. Monogr. A.A. Hanson, editor. In press.

2. KURTZ, K.W. (1967) Effect of nitrogen fertilization on the establishment, density and strength of Merion Kentucky bluegrass sod grown on a mineral soil. M.S. Thesis, Western Michigan University.

3. LINDAHL, I., DAVIS, R.E., and SHEPHERD, W.O. (1949) The application of total available carbohydrate method to the study of carbohydrate reserves of switch cane (Arundinara tecta). Pl. Physiol. 24, 285.

4. RIEKE, P.E., BEARD, J.B., and HANSEN, C.M. (1968) A technique to measure sod strength for use in sod production studies. Am. Soc. Agron. Abstr. 60.

5. RIEKE, P.E., BEARD, J.B., and LUCAS, R.E. (1968) Grass sod production on organic soil in Michigan. Proc. Third Int. Peat Congr., Quebec City. In press.

6. SATARI, A.M. (1967) Effects of various rates and combinations of nitrogen, phosphorus, potassium and cutting heights on the development of rhizome, root, total available carbohydrate and foliage composition of Poa pratensis L. Merion grown on Houghton muck. Ph.D. Thesis, Michigan State University.

TURFGRASS MANAGEMENT IN THE NETHERLANDS

Ir. J.P. van der Horst,

Nederlandse Sport Federatie, 's Gravenhage, The Netherlands.

SUMMARY

An outline is given of the main faults found in Dutch sports fields and the remedies for them.

The quality of a sports field in the Netherlands is determined by the three following factors:-

1.   Drainage,

2.   Levelness of surface, and

3.   Turf cover.

The importance of these factors varies according to situation, and there is a certain amount of interaction between them.   The following notes elaborate these three items in more detail: the letters refer to subsequent explanatory paragraphs.   Table 1 summarises these notes in the form of a chart of faults and remedies.

1.   Drainage

The drainage can be unsatisfactory either by letting the soil become too wet or by letting it become too dry.   The consequences are:-

Too wet: (a)   unwanted rising of subsoil water.

(b)   stagnation of water from the upper surface in the vertical drainage.

(c)   too high a field capacity.

Too dry: (d)   insufficient moisture available for optimum growth.

2.   Levelness of surface

A sports field must be level except for the intended drainage gradient. The degree of levelness may be unsatisfactory because of:-

(e)   faults in "macro-relief" (differences in height over distances of half a metre or more).

(f)   faults in "micro-relief" (differences in height over short distances).

3.   Turf cover

The turf cover may be of inferior quality because of:-

(g)   wrong composition of the turf.

(h)   incorrect management.

The lettered points (a) - (h) are considered in more detail below.   All can affect the quality of a sports field unfavourably.

(a)   Unwanted rising of subsoil water

Assuming that it is possible to lead water out of the area by drainage, the rising of subsoil water may be due to an insufficiently intensive drainage system or a badly functioning one.   If the drainage system is insufficiently intensive, it can be improved by digging supplementary ditches or laying supplementary drain pipes.

If the drainage system is functioning badly, the ditches should be cleaned carefully and the drain pipes flushed out.

(b)   Stagnation of surface water in the vertical drainage

With intensive use the structure of the top layer of soil is often destroyed.   It is crushed and pressed tight together, and therefore water stays in pools after rain.

To prevent this the turf must be opened up with a fork, a verticut or rotorake.

Immediately after forking a top-dressing with a good sand (M ± 250 mu) without organic matter or loam greatly improves the drainage of the top soil.

An impervious subsoil layer in the area above the drainage system can also cause vertical stagnation of the water.   To solve this problem it is necessary to drain the soil above the layer or to make vertical "pipes" of sand through the layer.

(c)   Too high a field capacity

This is a problem of frequent occurrence though it is not often diagnosed. It occurs in sports fields with a high percentage of organic matter, or a high percentage of clay particles, or both.

These fields are very soft at maximum field capacity.   There is only one way to solve this problem, namely, to give top-dressing with good sand after forking.

(d)   Insufficient moisture available for optimum growth

Drying out occurs when the evaporation exceeds the precipitation plus moisture available in the soil minus drainage loss.   To prevent this one must water.

(e)   Faults in "macro-relief"

These may be the result of bad construction, unequal settling of the soil, etc.   Often the unevenness is acceptable for the sport, but levelling is needed to avoid pools forming from surface water.

The remedy, underfilling, is often delayed because it needs a lot of manpower.   This is a conspicuous illustration of the universal rule that the worst part of the ground determines the playing quality of the whole.

(f)   Faults in "micro-relief"

These faults may be the result of vermin (moles or worms) or of use (players sliding, etc.). Hockey pitches in particular have much trouble in their micro-relief.

The first measure is to kill moles. Whether it is necessary to kill worms is an open question. The worst result of worm activity is that the top soil becomes "fat". To prevent this one must use sand without loam and humus for dressing.

(g)   Wrong composition of the turf

A good strong turf must consist of varieties resistant to wear. Having sown these, one must combat weeds and use the same good varieties when over-sowing bare patches.

(h)   Incorrect management

Often mowing is too short and too irregular; fertilizer application insufficient and uneven; and aeration of the top soil is hardly ever done. Better use of fertilizer and the use of a rotorake, verticut or spiking machine is necessary.

Table 1: summary of turfgrass faults and remedies

MAIN FACTOR	DRAINAGE			LEVELNESS OF SURFACE		TURF COVER	
	GROUND TOO WET		GROUND TOO DRY	bad "macro-relief"	bad "micro-relief"	wrong com-position of the turf	incorrect management
FAULTS	rising of the subsoil water	stagnation in the vert-ical drainage	too high a field capacity	insufficient moisture available for optimum growth			
REMEDIES	1) intensi-fying drainage	1) spiking, "verticutting", rotoraking	1) top-dressing	1) Watering	1) under-filling	1) control of moles	1) control 1) mowing weed control
	2) cleaning ditches	2) top-dressing				2) top-dressing	2) oversowing, 2) spiking new sowing "verticutting" rotoraking
	3) flushing drains	3) vertical "pipes" of sand					3) controlling fungi, vermin
							4) manuring

525

ATHLETIC FIELD MAINTENANCE

R.W. Miller,

Associate Professor of Agronomy, The Ohio State University, Columbus, Ohio and the Ohio Agricultural Research and Development Center, Wooster, Ohio, U.S.A.

SUMMARY

Few turfgrass areas receive as much concentrated traffic in short periods of time as do athletic fields. This heavy use often results in marked deterioration of the turf largely because of soil compaction, the physical tearing of turf and the intensified wear during games. Recommendations are made on the appropriate soil preparation, grasses and maintenance programme, and the renovation of the Ohio State University football stadium is described in detail as an example of some of these recommendations applied in practice.

SOIL PREPARATION

Sandy loam, fine sandy loam, and very fine sandy loam soils are preferred for athletic fields. No more than 10% of the total soil volume should be clay. If a substantial portion of the soil is composed of fine particles, clay and fine silt, poor drainage is likely to be a serious problem.

When a soil is in optimum condition for plant growth, it contains approximately 50% solids and 50% pore space. If the pore space is less than about 33% grass growth, especially root development, may be impeded. A desirable water infiltration rate for soils on athletic fields is a minimum of 2.5 cm per hour. Also, the soil should have adequate water holding capacity to prevent drought conditions and a high enough exchange capacity with the proper distribution of ions to be favourable to plant growth without very frequent applications of fertilizers. Toxic materials must not be present in sufficient quantities to limit growth.

Sometimes natural soils with the proper requirements are available. Usually, however, soil modification will be necessary. Conditioning materials most commonly used are sand, peat or some other form of organic matter and fired clay aggregates (calcined clay). Heavy clays and silts may require 60% or more sand by volume to correct the physical condition so that good athletic turf can be grown. Sand to be used for this purpose should contain a majority of particles between 0.50 and 0.75 mm in diameter. No more than 10% should exceed 1.25 mm.

Peat is the organic matter source most commonly used to modify athletic field soils. The amount needed must be determined by the organic matter level and other physical characteristics of the soil. It is seldom necessary to apply peat at rates of over 10% by volume.

Fired clay aggregates have been extensively used for soil modification on athletic field and golf greens in the United States during the past 10 to 15 years. It is difficult to determine what advantages, if any, calcined clays have compared to sand and other materials of like particle sizes.

Benefits from any soil-conditioner will be fully realized only if it is uniformly mixed into the soil. Layering of materials because of poor mixing may cause soil modification to be more detrimental than helpful. The final seedbed should be a homogeneous mixture of the original soil, physical amendments and lime and fertilizer when needed to correct the fertility level and pH of the soil.

A good drainage system is essential. A tile system to provide internal drainage must be designed to meet the requirements of each separate facility. Crowning of athletic fields facilitates quick removal of surface moisture especially when tarpaulins are used on rainy days just prior to the athletic events. This is one of the most important phases of maintaining turf under concentrated traffic. No grass will stand up under play if the soil is nearly saturated with moisture at the time the contest begins.

GRASSES AND MIXTURES

Good athletic field turfgrasses should be wear-resistant, not easily torn from the soil, recover rapidly from injury, provide a good footing for players and be attractive to the spectators. The grass or mixtures of grasses and the varieties that best meet these qualifications vary with climatic conditions.

In the northern United States grasses often used for athletic fields are Poa pratensis L., Festuca arundinacea Schreb. and Festuca rubra L. Mixtures of Poa pratensis and Festuca arundinacea are widely used, especially on fields under low maintenance. Festuca arundinacea, fertilized with high levels of nitrogen, has been found to be killed out in winter in Ohio and some other northern states. Agrostis palustris Huds. is not considered wear-resistant enough for use on most athletic fields.

In the warmer regions Cynodon dactylon (L.) Pers. is widely used. Zoysia japonica Steud. and Zoysia matrella (L.) Merr. have not attained popularity on many athletic fields because of their slow rate of establishment. Overseeding of Cynodon dactylon and Zoysia spp. with Lolium perenne L., Agrostis alba L., and sometimes Poa pratensis to give winter growth and colour is a common practice.

MAINTENANCE

Once a satisfactory athletic field turf is established a sound maintenance programme is necessary to insure quality turf. Harper (3) lists the following essentials of such a programme:

1. to produce tough grass with maximum wear resistance.

2. to maintain high density to resist weed invasion and encroachment of undesirable grasses.

3. to encourage deep rooting to provide good anchorage and firm footing.

4. to adjust mowing height to both grass requirements and playing demands.

5. to arrange fertilizing and watering at such times and in such manner as to provide steady growth with maximum quality.

6. to consider the endurance limits of the turf in scheduling the use of the field.

7. to provide for repairs of injury due to wear or other causes.

Moisture control

The moisture control programme should provide for removing excess water from the field as well as for irrigation when needed. Covering the field with a tarpaulin to insure that the soil moisture conditions are optimum for play is an essential step in good management. Weather conditions will dictate when and for how long the field must be covered. During rainy weather the tarpaulin should be left on the field until the game starts.

Water should be applied to established turf when signs of wilting occur. Water the field until it is soaked to a depth of about 15 cm. The amount of time required for watering will be determined by the infiltration rate and water holding capacity of the soil. The tendency of most stadium managers is to water too often and to apply insufficient water to wet the soil in the root zone. Water may have to be applied in split applications to prevent run-off if infiltration rates are low.

Fertilization

The species of grass, length of the growing season and type of soil must be taken into account in planning the fertilization programme. A soil test is vital in determining fertilizer needs. If the phosphorus and potassium levels are low corrective applications should be made in addition to the regular maintenance fertilizations. Large corrective applications of phosphorus, potassium and lime when needed will be more beneficial if applied following aerification. Soils having extremely high levels of phosphorus and potassium require only nitrogen applications.

Proper nitrogen fertilization of turfgrasses is vital for good turf. The species of grass, type of soil and amount of rainfall will determine how often and at what rates applications should be made. For example, Cynodon dactylon grown on sandy soils should receive up to 800 kg/ha of actual nitrogen in several applications during the growing season. In contrast, Poa pratensis will form a good turf in its area of adaptation with about 250 kg/ha of actual nitrogen in 3 to 4 applications.

Either organic or inorganic sources of nitrogen may be successfully used provided the athletic field manager knows how to apply them.

Weed control

No turf on an athletic field will escape damage under a substantial amount of play. Weeds are likely to invade damaged areas and good control programmes are essential.

Weeds such as Taraxacum officinale Weber, Plantago lanceolata L., Cerastium vulgatum L. and Polygonum aviculare L. are easily controlled with mixtures of 2,4-D and dicamba. Two or more applications may be necessary.

Annual grasses, especially <u>Digitaria sanquinalis</u> (L.) Scop., are successfully controlled with pre-emergence herbicides for annual grass control. Most
of these herbicides will prevent the establishment of desirable grasses as well
as undesirable annual ones. Since it is a good practice to overseed athletic
fields in the winter and early spring the use of most pre-emergence herbicides
is limited. Siduron may be used without damaging the establishment of <u>Poa</u>
<u>pratensis</u> and some other grass species.

Disease and insect control

Effective control measures have been developed for insects and most turfgrass diseases. The problem is in diagnosing the problem before serious damage
occurs. If an area has a history of disease problems, preventative control
measures are advisable.

Mowing

A sharp well-adjusted reel type mower is best to use for mowing athletic
field turf. <u>Cynodon</u> <u>dactylon</u> should be maintained at a height of about 1.25 cm
and <u>Poa</u> <u>pratensis</u> at about 4.0 - 5.0 cm. <u>Festuca</u> <u>arundinacea</u> should be cut at
6 cm or higher. Grass should be mowed frequently enough so that excessive
amounts of topgrowth are not removed.

Cultivation

Mechanical cultivation is needed to retain soil aerification, water infiltration and promote deep root growth. Following the last game the field should
be aerified at least twice in one direction and once in the opposite direction.
This should be followed with a vertical slicing, a sweeping operation and top-
dressing. Seed sowed at this time usually will not germinate until spring but
will have a head start on spring-sown grasses.

Aerification equipment should be used during the growing season as needed.
Playing schedules must be taken into consideration when planning an aerification
programme.

Repair and renovation

A planned repair programme is an essential part of athletic field management. Overseeding prior to each game is beneficial but will not solve the total
problem.

A turfgrass nursery with grass of the same variety and species as used on
the athletic field and grown on the same soil type will provide a ready source
of repair material. Smal spots may be plugged and large areas resodded. If
the sod was grown on the same soil type as present in the athletic field thick
sod pieces may be used without disturbing the physical condition of the soil.
Thin slices of sod will be kicked out too easily under play. Repair should be
done after each game if needed.

RENOVATION OF THE OHIO STATE UNIVERSITY FOOTBALL STADIUM

The Ohio State University Athletic Department, in 1961, decided that a
renovation programme was necessary for its football field. Some of the procedures followed will be outlined. It should be emphasized that not all phases of
this programme would be practical for everyone. It is not proposed as a model

to improve all athletic fields but rather as an example of one programme which has been considered successful.

The Ohio Stadium turf, during the 1961 football season, consisted of a poor Poa pratensis sod heavily infested with Agrostis palustris, Cyperus esculentus L., and various other obnoxious weeds. Complete renovation was considered necessary.

Since a poor grade of sod existed all vegetation was removed with a sod cutter after the last football game on 18 November 1961. This was followed by the establishment of a new set of drainage lines over the field. Longitudinal lines of 10 cm tiles were laid 6 m apart and 45 cm deep. Pea gravel was backfilled to a depth of 20 cm over the tile lines before filling with soil. The grade for each tile line was established from the centre of the field to each end where they were connected with 15 cm lines running across the field. Soil samples were collected from various locations on the field and sent to the Ohio State University Soil Testing Laboratory for routine chemical analysis.

After the tile trenches were backfilled, fertilizer was applied in accordance with the soil tests results. Calcined clay at 24 tons/ha was spread evenly over the field. The area was ploughed to an approximate depth of 20 cm, and another 24 tons/ha of fired clay added prior to ploughing in the opposite direction at a depth of 10 cm. Several discings served to smooth the field. The original soil was a fine sandy loam and required less modification than soils containing larger amounts of clay.

The soil was then fumigated to destroy the perennial weed seed and plant remnants remaining after the sod removal. Most fumigants are not active at low soil temperatures. Fumigation in the late summer or early autumn is preferred whenever possible.

Fumigation was completed by the end of the first week in December. The soil was covered with a canvas for a period of six weeks to improve the activity of the fumigant. After this the soil was left exposed over the winter to settle. It was decided to seed rather than sod because sod of the type and quality desired was unavailable. The seed would consist of 90% Festuca arundinacea (by seed count) and 10% Poa pratensis (equal parts of Delta, Newport, and Merion). The seeding rates were to be 395 kg/ha of Festuca arundinacea and 10 kg/ha of Poa pratensis.

With the first break of spring weather the field area was worked with a field cultivator to loosen the soil. Another 24 tons/ha of calcined clay and a starter fertilizer were applied and cultivated into the top 5 cm of the soil. Grading in some areas had to be accomplished with hand tools. The field was graded with a 45 cm crown sloping away to each end and side to provide surface drainage.

The two grass species were seeded separately in early April. The seeding was made in two directions. A light straw mulch was applied after the seed was lightly raked into the seedbed. The straw and seedbed were kept moist until germination and growth of the seed occurred.

This seed mixture, particularly Festuca arundinacea, exhibited considerable seedling vigour. The turf was maintained by mowing at approximately 7 cm. High mowing during the summer was utilized to favour the vegetative development of the Festuca arundinacea. The grass was frequently mowed so that no more than

2.5 cm of clippings were removed at one time. Approximately 5 cm of water was applied at 7 to 10 day intervals, depending on the natural precipitation. Good sod cover was present by 8 June.

The summer programme consisted primarily of mowing and irrigation. The field was fenced so that all traffic was kept off. Nitrogen at 60 kg/ha was applied the first week of July. A mixture of 2,4-D and silvex (fenoprop) at 10 + 30 kg/ha was sprayed over the area on 10 July, to kill Trifolium repens L. Due to the fact that the grass was extremely succulent, a fungicide was applied at two week intervals to maintain disease-free turf.

As the first football scrimmage neared (22 September) the cutting height was gradually reduced to 5 cm. At this point it became necessary to use a tarpaulin to cover the field before and after games to prevent rain from interfering with the optimum soil moisture condition for playing. For five of the six home games during the 1962 season it either rained heavily before the game or it rained during it. The success of this programme was due, in part, to the fact that the field was covered and soil moisture was below field capacity before the start of most games.

Preceeding the last two games, Festuca arundinacea was overseeded in the existing turf. Subsequent football play resulted in "cleating in" of the seed. Some of this seed did germinate and contribute somewhat to the appearance and density of the sod. After the last game on 23 November the turf area was aerified, overseeded with Festuca arundinacea, and top-dressed with a calcined clay-soil mixture. The turf had been maintained through six games and two practice scrimmages under adverse weather conditions. Nearly all the Festuca arundinacea was killed during the following two winters and was replaced by Poa pratensis.

REFERENCES

1. DANIEL, W.H. (1962) Purdue stadium renovation. Proc. Midwest Regional Turf Conf. 87.

2. GRAU, F.V. (1954) Tough grasses for hard wear. Journal of Housing October, 336.

3. HARPER, J.C., II. Athletic fields. Pennsylvania State Univ. College of Agriculture Ext. Service.

4. HIGGINS, N. (1961) The management of high school athletic fields. University of Florida Turfgrass Mgmt. Conf. 9, 182.

5. LAFKIN, W.E. (1957) Athletic fields and their maintenance. New York State Turf Ass. 59, 229.

6. TATE, H.F., and FOLKNER, J.S. (1966) Turf on large recreation and play areas. Univ. of Arizona Cooperative Ext. Service and agric. Exp. Stn. Bull. A-48.

7. WATSON, J.R., JNR. (1962) Managing athletic turfgrass areas. Proc. Midwest Regional Turf Conf. 87.

SOIL FACTORS AFFECTING THE CONTROL OF PACE ON CRICKET PITCHES

V.I. Stewart and W.A. Adams,

Soil Science Unit, University College of Wales, Aberystwyth, U.K.

SUMMARY

In the game of cricket the bowler may take advantage of bounce off the pitch to deceive the batsman into making a false stroke. The pitch surface is essentially a soil surface, and different pitches are recognised to vary in pace. Differences in pace can be related to the single parameter of rebound height achieved by a cricket ball dropped vertically on to the prepared surface from 16 ft. (488 cm). These bounce heights vary from 15-20 in. (38-51 cm) on an "easy" paced pitch to over 30 in. (76 cm) on a "very fast" pitch. This paper reports how pace is controlled by the texture of the soil, primarily through the effect of clay content on soil strength.

INTRODUCTION

The skill of the players in bowling, striking and fielding the ball are all important elements in the game of cricket but so also is the playing character of the pitch. The pitch constitutes that strip of 22 yd. (20 m) between the point at which the bowler is required to deliver the ball and the wicket in front of which the batsman stands. Although it is within the rules to bowl the ball directly at the wicket the chances of such a trajectory deceiving the batsman are slight and bowlers prefer to take advantage of the fact that they may utilize the effect of the bounce of the ball off the ground in front of the batsman either to deceive him into missing the ball altogether or causing him to misjudge the bounce sufficiently to ensure a false stroke.

Although cricket is generally considered to be played on turf, in fact a prepared first class County pitch is so severely shorn that, even at the start of the normal three-day period of play, bare soil constitutes more than 50% of the surface. Cricket, therefore, is a game played on a soil surface.

The Marylebone Cricket Club (M.C.C.), the body responsible for the selection of our national cricket teams, is concerned that first class cricket should be played under conditions conducive to the promotion of the skills necessary for success in international cricket. They would argue that this requires the game be played on fast true wickets. The authors' aim has been to identify those soil characteristics which distinguish pitches described by players and umpires as "slow" or "easy paced" from those considered "fast". At the same time they have carried out a systematic review of groundsmen's methods of preparing pitches in case these differences in behaviour might be more the result of management than of raw materials.

METHODS

1. The objective assessment of pitch pace

It was soon discovered that players' opinions on the pace of pitches tended to vary, so that an objective test had to be devised. The test adopted was the rebound height of a cricket ball dropped vertically on to the main impact area of the pitch from 16 ft. (488 cm). As the bounce heights recorded were those of the top of the ball these rebound values include the diameter of the ball (approximately 3 in. or 73 mm).

Generally twenty-four bounce heights were recorded from each pitch immediately after final close of play. These measurements were made according to a systematic sampling plan covering the main impact area at either end of the pitch. The range of individual values recorded has been used to provide the following evidence:

(i)   Uniformity of bounce.

(ii) Any pattern of variation in bounce between ends.

(iii) The maximum pace developed.

An average of the two highest bounces at either end of the pitch was taken to represent the best evidence available of the maximum pace developed and is the value implied whenever values for bounce are discussed in this paper. The extent to which this value exceeds the general average for all bounces may be taken as a measure of variability in bounce at the end of the match.

2.   Soil character

A wide range of physical and chemical determinations were carried out in the course of general surveys of County pitches. Those considered in the present paper are: soil density, soil moisture state, soil texture and soil strength.

(a) Soil density and soil moisture state

For these determinations the same core samples were used throughout the whole procedure. 2 x 2 in. (5 x 5 cm) square cores were extracted intact from the surface of the pitch into special centrifuge tins ¾ in. (2 cm) deep. Subsequently the samples were weighed fresh, saturated, and progressively dried on a soil centrifuge supplied by Measuring and Scientific Equipment Ltd., London, England, so as to determine the moisture release characteristics of the sample and hence, to discover the moisture tension of the sample in the field. The general principles involved in the centrifuge procedure have been described by Piper (1950A) and developed by Stewart and Adams (1968). From this one procedure the following information was obtained about the soil on the pitch at time of sampling:

(i)   Moisture content per unit volume.

(ii) Soil moisture tension in atmospheres.

(iii) Bulk density.

Also determined was the bulk density of these same samples at 2.5 atmospheres tension and when air dry.

The air dry bulk density of soil balls prepared for the A.S.S.B. test (see (c) below) was determined by direct measurement of weight and volume.

(b) Soil texture

A full mechanical analysis procedure was carried out (Piper, 1950B), but only the percentage clay values will be discussed in detail.

Each sample for mechanical analysis was pretreated with hydrogen peroxide but not with acid. The clay was dispersed with sodium hexametaphosphate and sampled by pipette.

(c) Soil strength

The A.S.S.B. test (the Adams Stewart Soil Binding test) used for the determination of soil strength has been described by Stewart and Adams (1969). In this test a sample of soil is moistened until it becomes just plastic, then, by firm finger pressure, all field aggregation is broken down before the moist clod is remoulded firmly into spheres approximately ¾ in. (2 cm) in diameter. The moulded spheres are then slowly and progressively air dried over a period of four or five days before they are tested to determine the weight in pounds required to shatter the dry soil ball. A very satisfactory feature of this test is the clearly defined end-point. Values so far obtained for natural soils range between 0 and 360 lb. (0 and 163 kg). The A.S.S.B. rating is merely this weight in lb.

A schedule of practical details for the A.S.S.B. test is given as an Appendix to this paper.

RESULTS

Bounce

Tables 1 and 2 indicate the variations in bounce found on County pitches in England and Wales during the 1966 and 1967 cricket seasons. The average bounce is of the order of 23 in. (58 cm) but values for individual pitches may fall as low as 13 in. and rise to as high as 31 in. On solid concrete the average value for five County quality balls, used for this test after sixty overs wear, is of the order of 52 in. though one did reach 56 in. Under equivalent conditions a partially worn (60 overs and 260 runs) Australian Kookaburra Sheffield Shield ball was found to bounce 57 in.

It is for cricketers to decide the precise significance of the bounce values obtained but since pitches with average values above 20 in. were generally considered not to be easy paced by the players and only the two pitches with best bounce average values of 28 in. and 31 in. were rated fast, the authors have used the following scale to relate bounce and pace:

Bounce	Pitch pace
Over 30 in. (76 cm)	Very fast
25 - 30 in. (64 - 76 cm)	Fast
20 - 25 in. (51 - 64 cm)	Moderately fast
15 - 20 in. (38 - 51 cm)	Easy paced
less than 15 in. (38 cm)	Slow

Table 1: bounce of a cricket ball dropped vertically on to a pitch from a height of 16 ft.

Ground	Sampling date	Bounce (in.)	
Worcester	18 Jul. 1967	New Road end 9 12 13 14 18 22 19 31 17 17 16 16	Scoreboard end 25 17 20 20 24 23 24 20 22 22 11 10
Edgbaston	25 Jul. 1967	Pavilion end 17 23 28 26 16 28 13 21 18 28 16 17	Constance Road end 21 22 22 14 22 18 15 26 24 23 13 17
Oval	26 Aug. 1966	Pavilion end 25 25 24 25 25	Vauxhall end 20 21 20 18 19

Notes. The variability in bounce on the pitch at Worcester was due to the surface breaking up. The variability at Edgbaston was caused by turf cracks still present 32 months after the pitch had been relaid. The pitch at the Oval shows a clear pattern of variation between ends; fewer samples were taken, at wider spacing, in the 1966 survey.

Table 2: range of average bounce values from 16 ft. for single pitches assessed after close of play on the final day. (Bare, solid concrete under equivalent conditions gives a value of 52 in.)

1966

Pitch and sampling date	Edgbaston (Old square) 6 Jul.	Leicester 27 Jun.	Swansea 27 May	Lord's 26 Aug.	Northampton 4 Jul.	Derby 23 Aug.	Oval 26 Aug.	Cardiff (Arms Park) 22 Jul.	Trent Bridge 19 Aug.	Worcester 1 Jul.
Average for pitch	14	17	17	19	19	22	23	23	27	30
Average of 4 highest bounces (2 from each end)	15	18	20	20	21	23	23	26	28	31

1967

Pitch and sampling date	Old Trafford 20 Jul.	Gloucester 10 Jul.	Cardiff (Sophia Gdns.) 1 Aug.	Hove 19 Aug.	Swansea 13 Jun.	Worcester 18 Jul.	Chelmsford 28 Aug.	Edgbaston (New square) 25 Jul.	Taunton 30 Jun.	Leicester 14 Aug.
Average for pitch	11	15	15	16	19	19	21	21	22	23
Average of 4 highest bounces (2 from each end)	13	19	17	22	21	26	26	27	24	24

Soil density

Field bulk density, bulk density at 2.5 atmospheres moisture tension, and air dry bulk density for the same sample were all strongly correlated.

Field bulk density & bulk density at 2.5 atmospheres moisture tension:

$$r = 0.91^{***} \ (n = 25)$$

Bulk density at 2.5 atmospheres moisture tension & air dry bulk density:

$$r = 0.94^{***} \ (n = 25)$$

This suggests that the resaturation of field samples within their sample tins and their subsequent centrifugation and air drying did not affect their relative air dry bulk densities through any marked differential response between samples in their reaction to these treatments. It is probable, in fact, that field structure was unaffected so that the air dry bulk densities obtained could be considered equivalent to those which the field samples would themselves have attained after complete air drying in the field.

The range of air dry bulk densities for samples packed in their field condition and for air dry spheres of the same soil material firmly worked by hand and remoulded in the laboratory, as for the A.S.S.B. test, are recorded in Table 3. Also shown is the extent to which the consolidation brought about by groundsmen in the field approaches the state of maximum consolidation achieved in the laboratory.

There would appear to be no simple relationship between bounce height and field density ($r = 0.20$ N.S.: $n = 20$). This perhaps is not surprising for, whilst bulk density may decrease with organic matter content and degree of aggregation, it will increase with sand content and all these factors together will tend to decrease soil strength.

Table 3: values for rolling efficiency based on the bulk densities of field cores uniformly consolidated by re-wetting and centrifuging before air drying compared with the same material air dried after re-moulding moist

Ground	Date sampled	Air dry bulk densities gm/cu cm		Rolling efficiency i.e. field density as % of density after remoulding
		From field	After re-moulding	
Chelmsford	28 Aug. 1967	1.286	1.482	89
Worcester	1 Jul. 1966	1.473	1.655	89
Worcester	18 Jul. 1967	1.464	1.674	88
Taunton	30 Jun. 1967	1.514	1.720	88
Hove	29 Aug. 1967	1.358	1.573	86
Old Trafford	20 Jul. 1967	1.346	1.529	86
Cardiff - Arms Park	22 Jul. 1966	1.269	1.531	83
Cardiff - Sophia Gdns.	1 Aug. 1967	1.195	1.473	83
Oval	26 Aug. 1966	1.296	1.560	83
Edgbaston - new	25 Jul. 1967	1.203	1.498	82
Leicester	14 Aug. 1967	1.233	1.507	82
Lord's	26 Aug. 1966	1.482	1.815	82
Trent Bridge	19 Aug. 1966	1.300	1.580	82
Derby	23 Aug. 1966	1.185	1.458	81
Leicester	27 Jun. 1966	1.306	1.625	79
Swansea	13 Jun. 1967	1.161	1.559	79
Edgbaston - old	6 Jul. 1966	1.269	1.638	78
Gloucester	10 Jul. 1967	1.219	1.656	76
Northampton	4 Jul. 1966	1.249	1.673	75

Soil moisture

The soil moisture states encountered during the 1967 and 1968 County pitch surveys fell within the range pF 3.3 - pF 4.3. Within this range the authors' data indicate no direct relationship between soil moisture content and bounce. There is a general relationship between soil moisture tension and bounce at the 5% level of significance, but when bounce, A.S.S.B. rating and soil moisture tension are examined together in a multiple regression analysis the moisture/bounce relationship is seen to be solely a reflection of the high correlation between moisture tension and A.S.S.B. rating. Once this effect has been removed any effect of variations in soil moisture tension on bounce, within the narrow range of soil moisture states encountered, is insignificant.

Multiple regression coefficients:-

B1: bounce & strength = 2.29* (n = 13)

B2: bounce & moisture tension = 1.83 N.S. (n = 13)

The influence of slight changes in moisture state on pitch character experienced by players is probably more to be related to the effect on forward movement off the moistened surface rather than any marked effect on rebound height for a ball dropped vertically from 16 ft. (488 cm). In the present paper, therefore, no attempt is made to make any allowance for a possible effect of soil moisture state on the bounce heights recorded.

Soil strength and soil texture

Various correlations between selected texture grades and soil strength have been examined:-

Sand (2 mm - 0.05 mm) & A.S.S.B. rating r = -0.44* (n = 29)

Sand (2 mm - 0.02 mm) & A.S.S.B. rating r = -0.60*** (n = 29)

Clay (<0.002 mm) & A.S.S.B. rating r = 0.72*** (n = 29)

As the values for different texture grades are not independent of each other it is important to consider only the best of these relationships, i.e. clay and A.S.S.B.

If the data are split to consider separately the relationship between clay and strength for samples with three different levels of clay content (less than 30%; over 30%; and over 35%) it becomes evident that only clay contents of about 30% or more have any marked direct influence on soil strength and this influence of clay content progressively increases over the range 20-40% clay.

Range of % clay values used	Regression equations for soil clay content and A.S.S.B. rating	Significance level	No. of observations
All	(i) A.S.S.B. rating = 6.44 x % Clay - 60	***	29
<30% Clay	(ii) " " = 4.01 x % Clay + 15	N.S.	11
>30% Clay	(iii) " " = 11.21 x % Clay - 233	***	18
>35% Clay	(iv) " " = 16.24 x % Clay - 424	**	11

540

Soil strength and bounce

Soil strength, whether determined after oven drying at 100^0C, as was done initially, or after air drying, is significantly related to bounce:-

Oven dry A.S.S.B. rating & bounce   r = 0.67** (n = 17)

Air dry A.S.S.B. rating & bounce   r = 0.68* (n = 13)

As the A.S.S.B. ratings based on air dry strength are now the standard used, only these values will be considered further.

If the relationship between soil strength and bounce is split so as to eliminate those pitches which the density measurements suggest were least well prepared, i.e. those where the rolling efficiency was less than 80%, then the relationship between the A.S.S.B. rating and bounce is as follows:-

Bounce height in inches = 0.1 x A.S.S.B. rating + 9.0 (n = 11: Significance level**)

Experimentally determined values for bounce heights determined for dry loose sand and a heavy loam in a plastic condition were of the order of 3 in. (8 cm). (This figure means in fact that the ball failed to bounce and partially buried itself in the soil surface.) However, on the root-bound, consolidated surface of a sandy golf green soil (A.S.S.B. rating 8) bounce heights for a 16 ft. (488 cm) vertical drop were 10 - 13 in. (25 - 33 cm). This agrees with the bounce value of 10 in. (25 cm) predicted for an A.S.S.B. rating of 8 from the general correlation between strength and bounce when rolling efficiency exceeds 80%. Thus any properly prepared pitch, when reasonably dry, should give a bounce value of at least 10 in. (25 cm). It is only increments of bounce above this which are to be related to factors affecting the general relationship between soil strength and bounce.

Soil texture and bounce

If all values for clay content and bounce are considered then there would appear to be no linear relationship between clay content and bounce.

% clay & bounce   r = 0.189 N.S. (n = 20)

When those values for bounce and clay content are eliminated where the efficiency of pitch preparation is suspect, i.e. rolling efficiency is less than 80%, then a significant relationship can be found for clay content. This takes the following general form:-

Equation (v): Bounce (in.) = 0.43 x % Clay + 10.6* (n = 14: significance level*)

The residual value of 10.6 in. (27 cm) for bounce when clay is nought suggested by the above relationship agrees with the residual value of 9.0 in. (23 cm) for bounce when the A.S.S.B. rating is nought.

DISCUSSION

Bounce height for a 16 ft. (488 cm) vertical drop can now be predicted for properly prepared pitches either from the A.S.S.B. rating or from percentage clay. It is of interest, therefore, to compare, for different pace categories classified according to bounce, the percentage clay values calculated via the A.S.S.B. determination with those calculated direct from the relationship between bounce and percentage clay. These values are shown in Table 4.

Table 4: estimated contents of soil clay required to enable the bounce heights appropriate to various pitch pace categories to be achieved

Pace	Bounce (in.)	A.S.S.B. rating	% Clay Calculated via A.S.S.B. using regression equation (i) (iv) (iii) (ii)	Calculated direct using regression equation (v)
Very fast				
	30		210..........41.9 38.9	
Fast			....	45.1
	25		160..........34.1......35.1	
Moderately fast			....	33.5
	20		110..........26.4......30.6 (23.5)	
Easy paced			....	21.9
	15		60...........18.6.......... (11.0)	
Slow			....	10.2
	10		10 (15).......10.9......... (0.0)	
			....	0.0

Table 5: pace predictions for certain Test pitches in Australia and Jamaica (Clay percentages for the Australian pitches from Piper (1932) and Greenland & Quirk (1966)).

Ground	% Clay		Predicted bounce using		Potential pace rating based on English standards
	1932	1964	English ball	Australian ball	
Adelaide	56				
		52	33	36	Very fast
Brisbane	71				
		73	41	45	Exceptionally fast
Melbourne	68				
		48	31	34	Very fast
Sydney	73				
		52	33	36	Very fast
		1968			
Sabina Park	49 (ASSB 215)		32	–	Very fast

For predictions of bounce from percentage clay via A.S.S.B. it would appear that the regression relationship between percentage clay and A.S.S.B. rating that should be used is that most appropriate to the clay content of the sample.

For any degree of pace on properly prepared pitches clay contents in the surface ¾ in. (2 cm) of soil need to exceed 22% (A.S.S.B. rating 110). Anything less will be easy paced or slow. For fast pitches the clay content should exceed 33% (A.S.S.B. rating 160).

Where clay contents or A.S.S.B. ratings are known, predictions about pace can be made for properly prepared pitches outside Britain. Table 5 indicates the form these predictions would take for grounds from which the authors have the appropriate information.

It should be remembered, however, that the predictions on bounce and pace in Table 5 are extrapolations from the relationships established for County pitches in England and Wales. Clay content, for example, need not continue to influence bounce in the same way above 45% clay as it does between 35 and 45%. Other factors also may influence the potential pace developed, for example, degree of clay dispersion, type of clay and general form of texture spectrum. For these reasons, therefore, it would be of considerable interest to know how far the predictions made actually conform to the bounce levels achieved on these pitches. There is no doubt, however, that the pace of these overseas pitches may well be significantly faster than anything experienced in Britain. Whether or not this extra pace potential in the pitch is fully exploited by the groundsman concerned is not known as the authors have no bounce records for comparison, but if it is, then, taking account also of the possible 10% extra bounce in an Australian ball, it would not be surprising if English players visiting Australia took time to settle down to the new playing conditions.

Only on three English grounds have pitches been found with surface soil clay contents in excess of 40%. These were at Gloucester in 1967 (42%), Worcester in 1966 (42%) and Bristol in 1968 (40%). Of these, only at Worcester has there been bounce evidence that the groundsman has been able, on occasion, to develop the full strength potential of this soil and for this, he would maintain, consistent heavy rolling was required from early spring onwards. The authors' experience with moulding soil in the laboratory suggests that not only is intensity of rolling important but so also is moisture control during rolling in the period of actual pitch preparation, and the rate and efficiency of drying.

It would be interesting to know how groundsmen in the West Indies and in Australia set about their task of preparing pitches from soils with 50% clay, and just how successful they are at developing the full pace potential that is available. A major problem for them must be to transfer the structural strength within clay granules to the surface as a whole.

CONCLUSIONS

1. Nature of soil has a dominating influence on the playing character of a cricket pitch.

2. For fast pitches a soil with over 33% clay is required.

3. Within the range of soils investigated the A.S.S.B. rating may confidently be used to predict potential pace. Predictions on the basis of clay content alone may be upset by factors influencing the effectiveness of the clay.

4. The actual pace developed on a pitch will depend upon the efficiency
with which the groundsman develops the potential soil strength available.

ACKNOWLEDGEMENTS

The authors would like to acknowledge their gratitude to the Marylebone
Cricket Club and the County Cricket Clubs of England and Wales for the continuing interest they have shown in their work; to the M.C.C. in particular for a
grant of a sum now totalling £430 to assist with travelling and other expenses;
to Mr. Leslie Ames for sending a sample of the 1968 Test pitch at Sabina Park,
Jamaica; and to Mr. D.C. Pugh for his technical assistance both in the field
and in the laboratory. Dr. A. Durrant gave valuable advice on statistical
procedures.

REFERENCES

1. GREENLAND, D.J., and QUIRK, J.P. (1966) Waite Research Institute,Univers-
    ity of Adelaide. Personal communication, received 3 May 1966.

2. PIPER, C.S. (1932) Included in data from Greenland and Quirk (1966)

3. PIPER, C.S. (1950A) Soil and Plant Analysis. University of Adelaide,
    Adelaide, 89.

4. PIPER, C.S. (1950B) Ibid. 59.

5. STEWART, V.I., and ADAMS, W.A. (1968) The quantitative description of soil
    moisture states with special reference to moist soils. In "The Measure-
    ment of environmental factors in terrestial ecology". (Ed. R.M. Wadsworth)
    Oxford, 161.

6. STEWART, V.I., and ADAMS, W.A. (1968) County Cricket Wickets. J. Sports
    Turf Res. Inst. 44, 49.

APPENDIX:

PRACTICAL PROCEDURE FOR A.S.S.B. TEST

At each stage select order of working by random choice of numbers.

1. Add 15-20 ml water (according to texture) to 50 gm soil.

2. Rub down, by finger pressure and smearing on a glass surface, to break down all aggregation.

3. (a) Ball, and then thump clod on filter paper or a porcelain tile to test for and eliminate excess moisture. Too wet samples will smear and stick to filter paper; too dry samples will shatter and crack.

    (b) If too wet to thump drier, leave to stand for a while on filter paper.

    If too dry add 1 ml water, smear and try 3 (a) again. Add further 1 ml increments of water if necessary.

4. (a) Place clod in 1 ml water on dish and cover. Leave to equilibrate overnight.

5. Check first thing next morning on the moisture state of the clod:

    (a) If too dry the surface will be dull and a further 1 ml of water may require to be added.

    (b) If too wet there may be a pool of water in dish and the clod will be glistening wet. Pour off any free water and leave the wet clod to dry for a while on filter paper.

    (c) If ideal the clod will be glistening wet but there will be no free water in the dish.

6. When the clod is satisfactorily wet, rework in the hand and then roll into a cylinder of 1 in. diameter. Cut off any involuted ends. Cut cylinder into 3 or 4 sections ¾ in. long, discarding any residue. Ensure that all sections used are of equal size.

7. Finger cylinder sections into round balls, again avoiding folds. Add one drop of water and rework if they tend to crack. Round off by rolling firmly between the palms of the hands for at least 45 seconds, aiming to form a perfect sphere with shining surface and no cracks. If slightly too wet the imprint of the grain of the hand will remain to give a matt finish. (Rolling on filter paper will complete any necessary drying off at this stage.)

8. Leave the moulded soil balls uncovered overnight to begin drying. If they were rolled too wet they will be moist at the base next morning; they will have a flattened base and may stick to the dish.

9. Place the drying soil balls to equilibrate in a chamber controlled approximately at 60-70% R.H. and 20°C. Make up sulphuric acid of specific gravity 1.270 at 20°C (approx. 36 gm conc. H_2SO_4 made up to 100 gm with water) to provide 70% R.H. at 20°C.

    Equilibration is normally complete in 5 days. Check humidity, weights of sulphuric acid dishes and temperatures daily.

545

10. Break direct from drying chamber by sandwiching between two flat metal surfaces using a bathroom scales or special instrument (e.g. Proctor Needle) to record the applied pressure required to shatter the dry soil ball.

11. Because of the risk of errors in preparation affecting individual cases it is advisable always to include a standard soil with each batch of determinations and, as a matter of policy, to eliminate the lowest breaking value in every three determinations carried out before averaging the remaining values to give the A.S.S.B. rating for the sample.

DISCUSSION

SOD PRODUCTION

W.A. Eschauzier (Netherlands)

For how many years is it possible to continue sod production on the same piece of land? Every time a crop is taken a layer of the fertile top soil is removed.

P.E. Rieke (Michigan, U.S.A.)

We have measured the soil removed with sod by making soil height measurements after each crop is removed from organic soils. Our data indicate that 0.8 - 1.2 cm of soil is removed with the crop under average conditions. The length of time cropping can continue depends on the depth of the soil. In Michigan the organic soils range from 0.2 to 8.0 m in depth, over extensive acreages. A very small percentage of these soils is at present being cropped for sod production so we do not foresee limitation in future. Continued soil removal may, however, necessitate re-establishment of drainage systems.

R.W. Miller (Ohio, U.S.A.)

How does the soil loss in sod production compare with that in other crops?

P.E. Rieke (Michigan, U.S.A.)

We have a study comparing the soil levels under annual sod removal and under a row crop (onions) where the soil is tilled. The soil levels indicate that only slightly more soil is lost with the sod removal compared to the natural soil loss from decomposition and wind erosion under row crop conditions.

J.B. Beard (Michigan, U.S.A.)

One grower producing sod continuously since 1931, except during World War II, has lost 16 in. of soil. Since the deposits are about 30 ft. deep, there is no problem.

C. Eisele (West Germany)

Is there any method to speed up establishment of Poa pratensis L., for sod production, by soaking or pre-germinating the seed?

J.B. Beard (Michigan, U.S.A.)

There was work on pre-soaking in the 1930's, but the field application of this technique requires a moist soil for establishment. Many sod producers do not have the means to provide such conditions over large areas. It is better to rely on natural conditions for germination. There can be severe wind erosion on organic soils, which may cause total stand loss even when seedlings are 2 cm high. Solid set irrigation is used to prevent this. In this way, sod production can be achieved in 6 months, or even 3 months experimentally, although most growers average approximately 12 - 14 months per crop.

E.W. Schweizer (Switzerland)

Do U.S. sod producers re-sow the cut surfaces of sod production fields immediately after harvest, in order to avoid weed establishment, or is the seeding only done in mid-August, to obtain optimum conditions?

547

P.E. Rieke (Michigan, U.S.A.)

Based on experience with Poa pratensis in Michigan most of the seeding is done as close to 15 August as possible. Fewer weeds germinate at this time and most of the broadleaf weeds are killed during the winter. Spring seedings face competition from broadleaf weeds and annual grasses, and much less success is attained in achieving the necessary uniform dense stand. Chemical control of broadleaf weeds is usually necessary with spring seedings and is even commonly used during the following summer on fall seedings to give a weed-free high-quality sod. Some growers harvest the sod carefully so that the field is left in a level condition. Rhizomes which remain in the field are allowed to grow and these can provide rapid establishment. This does not, however, always provide uniform establishment, and often must be supplemented with a light overseeding.

J.B. Beard (Michigan, U.S.A.)

In Michigan Euphorbia maculata L. and Portulaca oleracea L. are the most persistent weeds after the first 4 or 5 years of production. Grass weeds and sedges are also important. Weeds such as Taraxacum officinale Weber, Plantago spp. and Trifolium repens L. disappear after 3 - 4 years of production.

D.B. White (Minnesota, U.S.A.)

We find in Minnesota that sod produced on organic soil is completely unsatisfactory for use under heavy play or heavy traffic. For such uses we recommend sod grown on mineral soil.

J.B. Beard (Michigan, U.S.A.)

I agree. We do not recommend sod grown on organic soil for greens, tees or sports fields.

SOD REPAIR OF FOOTBALL FIELDS

J.F. Shoulders (Virginia, U.S.A.)

In regard to repair of the Ohio State football field during the playing season, can Dr. Miller say how thick were the sods, how near to the next game they were laid, and whether they held reasonably well?

R.W. Miller (Ohio, U.S.A.)

Pieces of turf to repair football fields are cut 4 in. thick or more: they must be from the same soil type as the field. The repair can be made up to the day before the game, and areas repaired in this way have stood play satisfactorily.

FESTUCA ARUNDINACEA FOR FOOTBALL FIELDS

W.A. Eschauzier (Netherlands)

Would Dr. Miller comment on the extremely high seed rate of Festuca arundinacea Schreb. mentioned in his paper.

R.W. Miller (Ohio, U.S.A.)

The seeding rate of Festuca arundinacea is high, because we consider this gives a finer textured turf than that obtained with lower seeding rates.

W.A. Eschauzier (Netherlands)

But why sow Festuca arundinacea at all when it will disappear after two winters to be replaced by Poa pratensis L.?

R.W. Miller (Ohio, U.S.A.)

I agree that the Festuca arundinacea was killed out in winter under the climatic conditions in Ohio. We did not anticipate this and would alter our procedure in future. But this winter kill does not occur everywhere, and F. arundinacea gives a good cover quickly, whereas Poa pratensis will not give a playing surface so soon.

TURF WEAR ON FOOTBALL FIELDS

R.L. Morris (U.K.)

I should like to comment on the statement that U.S. football, at some 6 or so games each season, imposes the highest wear of any game. In this country it is not uncommon to play up to 100 games a year on winter play areas, especially where Rugby football is played. On school fields play is very intensive and the situation is worsening, because adults use the fields at week-ends and in the evenings.

J.R. Escritt (U.K.)

I agree that professional football grounds have to stand 60-100 games each year.

R.W. Miller (Ohio, U.S.A.)

In commenting on wear, I was comparing American football with other sports, game for game. Although I gave an example of a field with comparatively few games per year, we do have football fields on which 50 games are played each year.

R.L. Goss (Washington, U.S.A.)

In comparing English and U.S. football, the intensity of rainfall during the period of active use of the field is a major consideration. On the north-western coast of the U.S., 15 - 20 in. of rainfall are not uncommon during the 2 month period of intense play. In addition, in American football play is concentrated in small areas. For these two reasons, very sandy soils with excellent internal drainage are most essential. One of our best fields, sown with Poa pratensis, withstood 33 games in 60 days.

R.W. Schery (Ohio, U.S.A.)

I have played both Rugby and American football. The churning action of a scrum movement in Rugby probably gives more intense wear on a small area than line play in American football, but the play in Rugby is spread more over the field and the field is larger, so the net affect on turf should be much the same, game for game.

TOP-DRESSING WITH PURE SAND

W.H. Daniel (Indiana, U.S.A.)

I should like to ask Mr. van der Horst about his recommendation for top-dressing with pure sand in various situations. I wonder if there is a problem of traction, and should like to know how often such top-dressing is done.

J.P. van der Horst (Netherlands)

We use coarse sand during the growing season, giving three top-dressings of not more than 0.75 cm each time. This serves two purposes, to reduce the percentage of humus (as clippings are returned) and to give more grip for players during the playing season.

R.L. Morris (U.K.)

Does Mr. van der Horst not get problems with alternate layers of sand and humus, producing root breaks?

J.P. van der Horst (Netherlands)

We do not get layers formed using the methods I have described. Every pitch is constructed with a large amount of sand (20 cm). The clay and sand particles are mixed well, but in such a way that the top is sandy and the roots can find their way easily. Worm activity also helps to mix the soil.

J.R. Escritt (U.K.)

I am surprised that Mr. van der Horst does not put on sand in winter, as we find it is useful then to improve traction, to dry the ground, and to maintain surface permeability. We have no trouble with layering on football grounds, presumably because of the effect of the studs in players' boots.

J.P. van der Horst (Netherlands)

In winter time we do no oversanding because with the summer measures I have described the top soil stays permeable. In winter, we only need to put sand on the goal areas.

W.H. Daniel (Indiana, U.S.A.)

We can now, by repeated use of aerators, work top-dressings of pure materials sufficiently well into the top soil to achieve the physical conditions we desire.

R.E. Engel (New Jersey, U.S.A.)

I should like to comment on the subject of working in top-dressings of sand. I agree this might be done on turf receiving heavy wear, such as football fields, but I disagree with the practice for turf such as putting greens. Cultural practices cannot dissipate this layer quickly enough to avoid serious deficiencies in performance.

R.A. Keen (Kansas, U.S.A.)

It is possible with currently available equipment, such as an aerator, to deal with a surface application of organic matter, or up to 1 in. of wind-blown dust, by diluting them with sand and working them in.

J.R. Escritt (U.K.)

I agree with Dr. Engel about the disadvantages of sand top-dressings on golf greens. Dressings of sand can cause layering, and we advocate dressing greens with a compost similar to the U.S.G.A. recommended mixture.

SESSION 6D: ESTABLISHMENT PRACTICES

(Chairman: Prof. P. Boeker)

SPORTS GROUND CONSTRUCTION

J.R. Escritt,

Director, Sports Turf Research Institute, Bingley, Yorkshire, U.K.

SUMMARY

An outline is presented of the methods used in producing sports grounds in the British Isles.

INTRODUCTION

Bad sports ground construction is widespread and is not confined to any one country. The chief faults arise not from unwise choice of fertilizer or seed (although these may contribute) but from difficulties in retaining or restoring natural soil properties (especially drainage) after the use of heavy equipment for grading, etc., in the prevailing weather conditions and with time limits imposed by user demand and by economics. The ultimate answer may be in non-grass surfaces. An intermediate answer may be found in "artificial" soils as in the USGA specification for golf greens and the ideas which have followed, but in Britain, at any rate, a great many sports turf areas will continue to be made by grading out and grassing down "natural" sites as economically as possible. It is, perhaps, not unprofitable therefore to examine the procedures which are proving reasonably successful.

CONSTRUCTION

Choice of site

Availability and cost are often the deciding factors in choosing a site but accessibility to the population concerned is very important as well as availability of services such as electricity, gas, water and drainage. Drainage outfalls are required for land drainage as well as for foul drainage from pavilions, etc. It would be ideal if a level, regularly-shaped site with good natural drainage could be picked but quite frequently it makes good sense to reclaim waste land despite any extra cost involved.

Organisation of construction

British practice is for the engineer or architect in charge to be provided with a brief of the facilities desired on the area. He can then submit for approval a layout based on his brief and on the final levels he proposes. Once all this has been agreed he can prepare detailed specifications of work, drawings (with drainage plans) and bills of quantities for which tenders can be invited from firms believed to be qualified to carry out the work. Conditions of contract should prohibit work when site conditions are unsatisfactory, e.g. too wet.

Grading

Sports grounds seldom need to be horizontal and there are usually advantages in cost and ease of drainage if sites are not made horizontal. Acceptable falls differ with the purpose for which the turf is intended but for general purposes a gradient of about 1:60 may prove satisfactory provided that it is transverse to the direction of play. Grading usually involves removal of top soil and regulating the subsoil before returning top soil. It is of course important to ensure a sufficient depth of fertile top soil.

Drainage

Most sports turf needs drainage: this has been found true for Mediterranean golf courses as well as Scottish football grounds. Sports turf drainage has special requirements: the accepted standards for agricultural drainage need to be improved upon and, in particular, special attention must be paid to speedy removal of excess surface water. Important aspects of this are getting the water through the earth and having somewhere for it to go. The latter usually means land drains and, partly because of the poor falls, herringbone pattern pipe drainage systems are frequently used, the main drains running with the maximum fall of the land and the laterals, generally at a depth of 2 ft. (60 cm), joining them at an angle through purpose-made junctions. Plastic drain pipes are now competing with the old-established baked clay pipes and with the more modern concrete pipes. To facilitate rapid surface drainage the drains are usually covered with graded aggregate to within 6 in. (15 cm) of the surface. In practice it is important to install drains after return of top soil, not before, since spreading the top soil involves considerable risk to the drains. On sites with very bad sub-surface drainage a 6 in. (15 cm) layer of graded aggregate is sometimes laid below the top soil but this must also be provided with drains. Trials at Bingley have shown that such a layer has a water-holding capacity equivalent to only about 1-1½ in. (2.5 - 3.75 cm) of rainfall. The layer should also be covered with gritty ash or small gravel before return of the top soil.

It has recently been suggested that about 3-6 in. (7.5 - 15.0 cm) of sand mixed with fertilizer and placed below only about 3 in. (7.5 cm) of top soil will be a good construction to facilitate aeration and drainage. This resembles an old method formerly used in British bowling green construction which seems to have been abandoned. Possibly this procedure may have to come back in modified form. Throughout the world there is at the present time a considerable interest in the drainage of sports turf areas.

Subsoil cultivations

On a graded site use of heavy equipment results in a highly compacted subsoil which severely restricts moisture penetration. Subsoil cultivation to alleviate this condition is carried out by means of a subsoil cultivator after top soil has been spread. A normal procedure is to cultivate the subsoil at 2 ft. (60 cm) centres to a depth of 1½ ft. (45 cm), usually with the fall of the land: but this amount of cultivation can usefully be increased by doing the operation in two directions at right angles or at closer centres. Thorough subsoiling is carried out before drainage to avoid damage to drains but nowadays a further subsoiling at the rather shallower depth of 12 - 15 in. (30 - 47 cm) is often done during the latter stages of soil cultivations, i.e. after drains have been installed.

Subsoil cultivation can be carried out satisfactorily on established playing fields, quite often without undue disturbance of the surface, although occasionally disruption can be such as to necessitate cultivation and re-seeding. Subsoil cultivation of existing pitches is often helped by feeding sand into the slits made by the subsoiler and good results were obtained for example at the Rugby Union Football Ground at Twickenham. A variation on this has been suggested by some people, namely to install 3 in. (7.5 cm) bands of gravel by cutting narrow slits with special equipment and filling with gravel to help get the water away from the surface quickly. This procedure has been used for many years by amateur technicians in Britain but it has not always given very good results. However, with proper organisation it may have possibilities.

Top soil

Normal agricultural operations of ploughing, tine cultivation, disc harrowing, rolling and chain harrowing seem to produce the best results. Rotary cultivators are attractive to some people but difficulties with drainage are frequently encountered after their use, this being related apparently to the severe soil pulverisation and also to the compacted layer which the machines frequently produce below the loosened earth.

Surface grading

Blade grading is necessary to produce a smooth finish free of appreciable mounds or depressions and it is important to ensure that sufficient top soil is retained and that cultivations remove the marked surface compaction which usually results from this operation.

Soil improvement

(a) Physical

The use of large amounts of coarse sand to improve the permeability of heavy soils adds considerably to the cost of construction but this cost has to be related to the extra value likely to be obtained in terms of use, relative to the total capital outlay i.e. including the cost of land and buildings. The S.T.R.I. has tended to restrict its recommendations to 100-200 tons/acre of sand (250 - 500 tonnes/ha) worked into the immediate surface soil because of the cost but this may be a mistake. (In the U.S.A. there are those who are making putting greens on "earth" which may be in fact over 90% imported sand, and even this does not guarantee free drainage for ever, since compression under wet conditions ultimately results in a state when even a low proportion of fines will fill the voids between the coarse particles). Incorporation of 5-10 tons/acre of granulated peat (12.5 - 25.0 tonnes/ha) confers resiliency and helps to offset compaction (1). On thin sandy soils, peat and dried sewage or other suitable organic wastes can be incorporated with advantage to help conserve moisture.

Other materials are now being suggested for soil improvement, including sintered fly ash from power stations, globules of burnt brick clay and granules of foamed synthetic materials, e.g. cellular polystyrene.

(b) Chemical

Lime and fertilizer applications are based on soil tests but a useful "normal" treatment is granular fertilizer containing 10% N, 15% P_2O_5 and 10% K_2O at 6 cwt./acre (750 kg/ha). There is international interest in new types of fertilizers, particularly gradual release nitrogen fertilizers, but these are not widely accepted in Britain.

Suitable cultivations are necessary to incorporate the soil improvement materials and a further light blade grading may be desirable. This should not be permitted to move about, and cause uneven distribution of, the soil ameliorants. Stone picking is a laborious task which has also to be undertaken:

stone picking machines are useful but do not seem to provide a complete answer to the problem.

Grass establishment

Turfing is unacceptably expensive for large areas and usually these are established by sowing grass seeds. In selecting grass seed, speed of establishment has to be taken into account as well as resistance to and recovery from wear, tolerance of mowing, ability to stand the local climate, resistance to disease and weed invasion, etc., and with all these in mind the following general purpose mixture is useful:

> 40% perennial ryegrass (<u>Lolium</u> <u>perenne</u> L.)
> 20% Chewings fescue (<u>Festuca</u> <u>rubra</u> L. ssp. <u>commutata</u> Gaud.)
> 20% creeping red fescue (<u>Festuca</u> <u>rubra</u> L. ssp. <u>rubra</u>)
> 10% smooth-stalked meadow-grass (<u>Poa</u> <u>pratensis</u> L.)
> 10% browntop bent (<u>Agrostis</u> <u>tenuis</u> Sibth.)

This is sown at 1½ cwt./acre (188 kg/ha). It is worth naming persistent leafy varieties suitable for local conditions. A feature of the present time in the international turf research field is the tremendous interest in new varieties of the common turf-forming grass species. Many new varieties are available with advantages claimed for them and in each country it is wise to make enquiries before specifying the actual varieties to be used.

Fine turf areas

Special standards of construction (2) are usually required for fine turf areas. These may be sown at 1 oz./sq. yd. (34 g/sq m) with good varieties of fine grass seeds, e.g.

> 80% Chewings fescue
> 20% browntop bent

but quite frequently they are turfed with the best available turf. There are few turf producers in the British Isles and it is usually a question of obtaining the best available natural turf, from old pastures or park land or, in the case of bowling greens, from sheep-grazed sea marsh land. Construction has to be tailored to suit user requirements. Since these always include quick drainage, drainage layers of graded aggregate are frequently used. For bowling greens a very sandy soil is required with the accent on rapid drainage but for cricket tables the requirements of the game call for a heavy surface soil which with heavy rolling will give the right degree of bounce. Tennis court requirements are somewhat intermediate but are much closer to the requirements for a cricket table than to those for a bowling green.

Timing of operations

In Britain the aim is to start construction work in spring to ensure the late summer sowing which is most satisfactory under British conditions. Turfing of special areas is usually carried out in the autumn. For a general sports ground this means going out to tender in January and February with preliminary administrative work tuned to this as far as possible.

Quality of work

To obtain satisfactory results good quality work is required and this is not easily obtained in the British Isles or elsewhere. Weather very much influences the position and in Britain there are years with very little suitable weather. Contractors are therefore almost compelled to work when conditions are unsuitable because of wetness, with irretrievable damage to the soil, particularly in respect of drainage properties. In this mechanical age there are decreasing numbers of people with understanding of soil handling and skill in ordinary agricultural or horticultural operations and this has a considerable bearing on the results obtained in sports ground construction.

DEVELOPMENT

Experience has made it essential to recognise a definite development period. When the contractor has completed his work as described and possibly cut the grass once or twice the newly established area needs a good deal of attention, particularly fertilizing and mowing, in the first few years of its life. Since the area is usually not ready for use in less than one year from sowing early development is sometimes neglected.

REFERENCES

1.   ANON. (1966) Playing fields and hard surface areas. Department of Education and Science Building Bull. No. 28.

2.   ANON. (1965) Sports Ground Construction - Specifications for Playing Facilities. The National Playing Fields Association and The Sports Turf Research Institute.

TURFGRASS SEED IN THE FORM OF PELLETS AND GRANULES

H. Grimm and J.C. Knolle,

Saat- und Erntetechnik G.m.b.H., D 344 Eschwege, Box 748, West Germany.

SUMMARY

The paper describes the advantages of granulating seed and gives details of several experiments which helped determine how the granulating process could give these advantages. Certain proportions of organic and inorganic granulating compounds were particularly tested. The effects of several fungicides on the germination and growth rate of young plants were also tested. In addition detailed experimental tests were conducted with nutrients added in the form of slow-acting fertilizers to the granulating materials at various concentrations.

There are many advantages in putting turfgrass seed into granules or pellets; the following are noteworthy:-

1. It is made easier to sow low seed rates, particularly on plots for seed growing and multiplication.

2. Improvement is possible in sowing techniques using aeroplanes in arid regions, in order to reclaim natural pastures.

3. Techniques for amateur gardeners to sow turfgrass mixtures are made simpler.

4. The various components of a mixture are prevented from separating out during sowing with turfgrass seeders.

5. Fine seeds are not blown away.

6. Germination and early growth can be improved by the addition of nutrients, insecticides, fungicides, etc.

7. Germination under extreme soil and climatic conditions can be improved.

The process of granulating Agrostis tenuis Sibth. consists of thoroughly mixing one part seed and ten to twenty parts of granulating compound. Water is added in order to obtain a moist mixture which can then be formed into granules in a conventional granulator. The granules then have to be dried to the original humidity of the seed (6 - 9%) in order to obtain the most favourable conditions for keeping. Usually, organic material such as peat, wood-powder or similar products are used for granulating. Unfortunately, these materials alone are unsuitable because they are not plastic enough during the granulating process. Inorganic mineral powder, such as bentonite and kaolin, must then be added. The proportions used in this mixture determine the germination power of Agrostis tenuis. The optimal proportions are determined by tests to give the seed in granules the same germination power as the natural seed.

Table 1 shows the results of tests with various granulating compounds. Germination tests were conducted in a conventional Jacobson germinator to determine the effect of mineral powders on seed germination, measured by the number of germinated seeds per gram of granules. The greater the amount of mineral

Table 1: germination of seed of _Agrostis tenuis_ in granules made with different compounds (Germination test in Jacobson apparatus: alternating temperature (10 - 20°C) with light: final count after 21 days: 4 replicates each of 1 g granules).

Components of granules (kg)	Number of germinated seeds per g granules	Percentage relative to standard (100)
1 peat + 0.4 kaolin	425	86
1 " + 0.3 "	432	88
1 " + 0.2 "	465	95
1 peat + 0.4 bentonite	372	76
1 " + 0.3 "	421	85
1 " + 0.2 "	436	89
1 " + 0.1 "	492	100

germination of granulated seed of <u>Agrostis tenuis</u> with different fungicides mixed into the granular material (Germination test on soil with high organic content: 3 days at 6°C , then 25 days alternating temperature ($10 - 20^{o}$C) with light: Final count after 28 days: 4 replicates each of 1 g granules).

Fungicide	Weight of fungicide (g) per kg granules	Number of germinated seeds per g granules	Percentage relative to standard (100)
untreated (standard)	0	317	100
TMTD (pure tetramethyl-thiuram-disulphide)	1.0	375	118
	4.0	389	122
Mancozeb (trade name: Dithane ultra)	0.06	375	118
	6.0	368	116
	18.0	316	99
Chloroneb (trade name: Demosan)	0.6	329	104
	6.0	317	100
	18.0	304	96
Mercury (trade name: Ceresan)	0.03	320	101
	0.06	359	113
	0.3	317	100

Table 3: germination of seed of _Agrostis tenuis_ in granules containing a slow-acting nitrogenous fertilizer (conditions as in Table 1)

Nitrogen content as g per kg granules	Number of germinated seeds per g granules	Percentage relative to standard (100)
0 (standard)	482	100
30	579	121
80	351	73
160	79	16

Table 4: germination of seed of _Agrostis tenuis_ in granules containing slow-acting nitrogenous (N), potassic (K), and phosphatic (P_2O_5) fertilizer

Content of nutrients as g per kg granules			Number of germinated seeds per g granules	Percentage relative to standard (100)
N	K_2O	P_2O_5		
0	0	0 (standard)	371	100
0	10	10	345	93
0	20	20	306	82
0	40	40	304	82
25	10	10	357	96
25	20	20	344	93
25	40	40	323	87
50	10	10	345	93
50	20	20	321	86
50	40	40	311	84

material, the greater the reduction of germination capacity. The reason is that granules with a high bentonite or kaolin content have such a high saturation content that the seeds in the granules are suffocated. The effect on germination can be compared to the effect of a soil crust. In granules where the diameter is about 2.5 mm, the kaolin and bentonite content can be greater than in granules having a 3.5 - 5.0 mm diameter. The content of kaolin or bentonite in the granulating material should be adjusted to the expected rainfall. If heavy rainfall is expected after sowing, followed by a longer dry period, then binding components have to be added to the mixture. These binders prevent the disintegration of the granules (and hence the freeing of the seed) during the rain period. When granules are sown on light, sandy soil, they should be of a relatively dense consistency. If the soil consists of heavy clay, however, more porous granules are to be preferred.

Normally, field germination of turfgrass seed is much lower than laboratory germination. Several tests were conducted to find fungicides which could be mixed into the granulating material to improve germination. Laboratory tests preceded tests under field conditions. These germination tests were carried out, not in the Jacobson germinator but on top of soil having a high organic content.

As can be seen from Table 2, most of the chemicals used in the tests were well tolerated by the seed. With TMTD and mancozeb better results were obtained than with the standard. In addition to their effects during germination, the possible effects of the fungicides on the seed during storage is of great importance. Test storage for six months did not reveal any adverse effect on germination. Further tests are at present being carried out and will be extended for a storage time of at least 18 months.

When the major nutrients are incorporated in the granulating material, there is again the possibility of the seed being hindered in its germination. High concentrations of nutrients usually have a negative effect on germination, and therefore from the beginning only slow-acting nutrients have been used. If they are to be used in the granulating process, these substances should, if possible, be in a non-hygroscopic form; otherwise a completely moisture-proof packing is needed.

The effects of slow-acting nitrogen is shown in Table 3. Nitrogen at 30 g per kg of granules showed a definite positive effect during the germination period, but a reduction in germination was caused by 80 g/kg granules. Nitrogen at 30 - 50 g/kg granules should be sufficient to improve the development of the young plants in soil deficient of nitrogen.

The addition of potash and phosphate to the granules, even in slow-acting form, distinctly reduces the germination capacity (Table 4).

Although the germination figures in the tests in the Jacobson apparatus were relatively low, field experiments with granules with the same nutrient content have shown much better results. Higher amounts may be added to the granules when there is sufficient rainfall. The exact amount of nutrients added depends on the sufficiency of rainfall during the germination period. In the absence of sufficient rainfall, the addition of nutrients should be carefully controlled. The best results would be obtained, of course, if the nutrients in the granules were to be coated with a substance which prevents disintegration until after germination occurs. It is unfortunate that a substance of this type has not been developed to date.

The experiments of which the results are presented in the four Tables are only a small part of the comprehensive experimental programme conducted by the Saat- und Erntetechnik with granulated seeds. Numerous additional problems are being intensively investigated.

One important aspect of the seed granulating process is the "mixture ratio" (Streckungsfaktor) which is the proportion of powder to seed (eg. 1:10, 1:11, 1:20, etc.). This ratio has to be adjusted according to the conditions under which the granulated seeds are to be used. By adjusting "mixture ratio" it is possible to regulate the number of viable seeds per granule on the average to 3-7 or 2-4. It is important that the user of granulated seeds conducts preliminary tests to determine the number he wants in the final processing. The germination power of seed before granulating varies greatly, but adjustment can easily be made during the granulating process. It is possible to produce granules which contain a fixed number of viable seeds per unit weight. Thus, a uniform quality of granulated seed can be produced even though the quality of the seed itself varies from year to year. To obtain uniform seed material, it is necessary to conduct intensive laboratory tests on the seed to be granulated, under normal and adverse germination conditions.

Various types of grass seed present problems of flow because of the awns and glumes, and the normal sowing process is made difficult. The ease of sowing this type of seed can, however, be improved through pelleting and granulating.

SOD DEVELOPMENT OF KENTUCKY BLUEGRASS*

Lowell E. Moser,

Assistant Professor, The Ohio State University, Columbus, Ohio, and the
Ohio Agricultural Research and Development Center, Wooster, Ohio, U.S.A.

SUMMARY

The development of Poa pratensis sod is dependent upon rhizome formation and to a lesser extent on tiller formation. These are affected pro-
foundly by environmental factors and the genetic potential of the plant.
P. pratensis does not need a cold treatment or a short photoperiod to
bring about rhizome initiation. Long photoperiods, soil temperatures near
16-21°C, moderate nitrogen levels, moderate to high potassium levels, high
mowing, and adequate moisture all favour rhizome production. There is considerable genetic variation among P. pratensis cultivars in both the rate
and method of sod formation. The method of sod formation is dependent on
the relationship of rhizome to tiller production. Rhizome and tiller production often vary inversely since they both develop from similarly situated crown buds. The stimulus causing ligule formation on cataphylls and
subsequent rhizome emergence is not identified.

INTRODUCTION

Poa pratensis L. (Kentucky bluegrass) develops an excellent turf in
the cooler temperate regions of the United States. It is the basic lawn and
golf course fairway grass in the central and northern United States. Establishment is rather slow compared to species like Lolium perenne L. but P. pratensis
forms a more dense and well-knit turf. The density can be attributed to the
plant's rhizome and tiller production which results in thickening. The rapid
development of P. pratensis sod from seedlings to thick well-knit turf is of
special importance to the sod producer who wants a well-knit sod for marketing.
The length of time required for sod formation varies since rhizome and tiller
production are affected by environmental factors as well as the genetic potential
of the plant.

METHOD OF SOD FORMATION

Lobenstein (10) reported that dense turf formation by P. pratensis resulted
from extensive rhizome development. The number and linear extent of rhizomes
was considered as important as, if not more important than, tiller production
in evaluating turf potential of P. pratensis cultivars. He described three different patterns of sod formation by P. pratensis clones, all showing the importance of rhizome production.

One type of sod formation is characterized by the production of a large
number of tillers from the original crown and considerable secondary branching
by these tillers. Rhizomes produced by this type were generally shorter than
those of other clones and emerged close to the original crown. The result was
a bunch-type growth. The sod expanded slowly but these clones formed dense sods
as they spread. Merion was an example.

---

*Published with the permission of the Associate Director of the Ohio Agricultural
Research and Development Center as Journal Article No. 76-69.

The second type of sod formation involved plants that produced a large number of tillers and also developed a number of long rhizomes. The long rhizomes enhanced the spreading potential of the plant. The plants formed a dense sod as they spread.

The third type of sod formation came from those clones that produced fewer tillers but successive orders of long rhizomes. These clones invaded a new area and rapidly formed a low density sod. The sod thickened as new cycles of rhizomes formed, emerged, and developed new crowns which tillered.

The percentage of unemerged rhizomes did not relate to aggressiveness so much as to the production of continuing cycles of new crowns. The production of large numbers of rhizomes may have been due to the juvenility factor present in the new young crowns. Lobenstein (10) and Melkerson (11) emphasized that initial rhizome and tiller formation by P. pratensis seedlings was not necessarily a true reflection of the sod-forming characteristic of the clone. Actual field observations are necessary to establish sod development patterns.

RHIZOME AND TILLER FORMATION

Since rhizome and tiller formation and growth are major factors controlling the rate of P. pratensis sod formation they will be discussed in detail, especially rhizome formation and growth.

The above-ground part of a P. pratensis seedling consists of leaves. The apical meristem is at the base of the shoot. The stems remain as an area of compressed nodes and internodes that is called the crown. The buds from which tillers and rhizomes develop are located in this crown area (10). Stem buds are usually located higher on the crown than rhizome buds, but there is considerable overlap. All buds can be classified as either one type or the other. Intermediate type structures were initially rhizomes but some environmental stimulation caused them to grow upward and emerge early in their growth (6).

Intra-vaginal tillers are formed if the new tiller develops inside the leaf sheaths of the primary plant. If these new tillers break through the enclosing sheaths before emergence they are referred to as extra-vaginal tillers (10).

Rhizome buds are located in the axils of aerial leaves or the axils of cataphylls on other rhizomes (6). Fisher (6) reported that P. pratensis seedlings do not produce rhizomes until a number of aerial tillers have formed. In experiments at the Ohio State University this did not always hold true, especially with vigorous varieties grown under long photoperiods. Often three to four week old plants had no evident additional tillers but had one to three short rhizomes.

Fisher (6) reported three stages of rhizome growth. The primary stage began when the rhizome buds started to elongate and ended when an invagination along one side of the cataphyll appeared. The second stage started at this point and ended with the appearance of the rudimentary ligule on the newest cataphyll. The third stage was the transitional stage at which time the rhizome grew upward and gained more shoot characteristics. Once a ligule was formed on the newest cataphyll the rhizome began to grow upward. The importance of recognizing these stages when discussing rhizome growth and physiology has been emphasized. Some discrepancies might be avoided by determining the stage of rhizome growth (6).

The mode of rhizome growth and penetration has also been studied (7). Soil penetration by rhizomes especially in compacted areas was attributed to circumnutational (rotational) growth movements and not to torsional twisting or straight penetration by growing force (7).

The mystery still remaining in rhizome growth and development concerns the stimulus that causes rhizomes to enter stage three of Fisher's growth description. Exactly what causes new cataphylls to develop a rudimentary ligule and the subsequent change to negative geotropism remains unsolved. Short daylengths and ample nitrogen (8) or possibly hormone production (3) have been suggested as stimulating rhizome emergence. Light and air caused rhizomes to emerge prematurely. Rhizomes of P. pratensis elongated only in total darkness and with high carbon dioxide concentrations (5). Once a rhizome was exposed to light, internode elongation ceased and a crown was formed (10).

ENVIRONMENTAL FACTORS AFFECTING RHIZOME AND TILLER PRODUCTION

Spring-seeded P. pratensis produces a weak sod during the seeding year in the United States. Sod grown on mineral soil and harvested in the seeding year will generally not hold together. A large number of rhizomes elongate during the late spring season of the following year. This general field observation has lead to the inference that P. pratensis must pass through a winter season before an appreciable number of rhizomes form, i.e. that a short photoperiod or cold temperature, or both, are needed to stimulate rhizome initiation under field conditions. Several authors have reported that most rhizome production occurred under long days (2, 4), but most of these data were from field studies where other environmental factors were confounded with photoperiod.

In research conducted in controlled environment chambers, the development of P. pratensis rhizomes was considerably greater under long days than under short days (12). Generally the number and length of primary and secondary rhizomes increased as photoperiods increased within the range of 8 to 18 hours (Table 1). This supports previous reports that rhizome production is greater under long photoperiods.

In a subsequent experiment where P. pratensis plants initiating rhizomes received either short (8 hr.), intermediate (12 hr.), or long (16 hr.) photoperiods followed by a long photoperiod (16 hr.), rhizome numbers were greatest in plants that received long photoperiods in the rhizome initiation phase. Evidently short photoperiods did not stimulate rhizome initiation. In the same experiment plants were treated with a cold treatment (1^0C) ranging from 10 to 40 days in conjunction with 8, 12 and 16-hour photoperiods. The cold treatment did not induce rhizome initiation at any photoperiod (12).

The effects of photoperiod could possibly be attributed to a true photoperiodic response involving the phytochrome system or to a difference in total light energy received by the plants. Later experiments were designed to elucidate the mechanism involved in the photoperiodic response on rhizome production. P. pratensis produced fewer primary and secondary rhizomes under an interrupted light scheme (8 hours daylight, 7 hours dark, 2 hours light, 7 hours dark) than under 17 or 10-hour photoperiods.

Table 1: the total number and length of rhizomes per *Poa pratensis* plant 85 days after planting (12) (Superscripts refer to Duncan's Multiple Range Test at the 5% level)

	Cultivar							
	Merion		Windsor		Delta		Average	
Photoperiod	No.	Length (cm)	No.	Length (cm)	No.	Length (cm)	No.	Length (cm)
8 hr.	3.2	8.5	8.1	33.4	3.5	12.7	4.9^a	18.2^x
12 hr.	3.2	12.5	11.8	84.7	3.1	13.3	6.0^a	36.8^y
18 hr.	6.8	23.7	18.1	118.4	7.0	44.6	10.6^b	62.2^z
Average	4.4^a	14.9^x	12.7^b	78.8^y	4.6^a	23.5^x		

Table 2: total number and length of rhizomes per *Poa pratensis* plant 85 days after planting (Superscripts refer to Duncan's Multiple Range Test at the 5% level)

	Cultivar							
	Merion		Windsor		Fylking		Average	
Photoperiod	No.	Length (cm)	No.	Length (cm)	No.	Length (cm)	No.	Length (cm)
10 hr.	8.1	47.3	6.6	34.9	7.7	39.7	7.4^b	40.6^y
8 + 2 hr (interrupted)	4.2	16.6	4.4	17.5	6.8	24.7	5.1^a	19.6^x
17 hr.	10.9	69.7	12.1	70.7	13.4	69.2	12.1^c	69.8^z
Average	7.7^a	44.5^x	7.7^a	41.0^x	9.3^b	44.5^x		

Table 3: number of developed crown buds (primary rhizomes plus primary tillers) and percentage of developed crown buds forming primary rhizomes per *Poa pratensis* plant 85 days after planting (12) (Superscripts refer to Duncan's Multiple Range Test at the 5% level)

	Cultivar							
	Merion		Windsor		Delta		Average	
Photoperiod	No.	% rhizomes	No.	% rhizomes	No.	% rhizomes	No.	% rhizomes
8 hr.	23.7	13.1	26.2	29.5	26.8	12.2	25.6^a	18.2^x
12 hr.	43.1	6.5	32.7	29.5	23.5	8.7	33.1^b	14.9^x
18 hr.	28.7	19.1	28.9	39.3	19.9	31.0	25.8^a	29.8^y
Average	31.8^b	12.9^x	29.3^b	32.8^z	23.4^a	17.3^y		

Plants receiving a 17-hour photoperiod produced the most rhizomes. This suggests that the phytochrome system is not involved since the interrupted treatment did not evoke as much rhizome production as the long photoperiod treatment (Table 2). At the present time the difference between the interrupted treatment and the short day treatment is unexplained since plants received the same amount of light energy within a 24-hour period.

Tillering of P. pratensis often is inversely proportional to rhizome production. Twelve-hour photoperiods enhanced tiller production somewhat compared to 8 or 18 hour photoperiods (Table 3). (The number of primary rhizomes, i.e. rhizomes originating at the crown of the original plant, and the number of tillers at the original crown were combined and referred to as the number of developed crown buds.) Often the number of developed crown buds differed very little between photoperiods. The main difference in number of developed crown buds in Table 3 was due to the profuse tillering of Merion at the 12-hour photoperiod. The plants having the most rhizomes often had the fewest tillers. Therefore, it appeared that photoperiod does not influence crown bud initiation as much as it affects differentiation into rhizomes or tillers.

P. pratensis did not have to be subjected to short photoperiods and/or a cold treatment for rhizome initiation and elongation. Short photoperiods and cold treatment generally reduced rhizome numbers and length. Cold treatment increased tiller numbers corresponding to the decrease in rhizome production. Cold treatment affected bud differentiation more than bud initiation.

Temperature has a very profound influence on the P. pratensis plant. P. pratensis roots and rhizomes grew very little if the air and soil temperature exceeded $27-32^{0}C$ (1). Brown (2) stated that rhizome numbers increased most at soil temperatures of $16-21^{0}C$. In greenhouse work where the soil temperature was held at a constant $21^{0}C$, total rhizome weight declined slightly as the air temperature went to $29^{0}C$ but declined rapidly to nearly zero with a further rise to $38^{0}C$. From field observations and studies, Evans (4) concluded that cool temperatures of $2-10^{0}C$ favour shoot formation and temperatures of $16-21^{0}C$ favour rhizome formation. However, photoperiodic differences were also present.

Nitrogen levels markedly affect rhizome production. Numerous studies have shown that high soluble nitrogen levels result in less rhizome production than moderate or moderately low levels (5, 9, 13). The strength of sod has been reduced by adding excessive amounts of nitrogen. Over a period of one year the underground parts of P. pratensis were reduced as much as 50% by high nitrogen (143 ppm in nutrient solution) (13). High levels of nitrogen also accented the deleterious effects of temperature on rhizome growth (8). A narrow ratio of nitrogen to soluble carbohydrate reserves favoured shoot rather than root development in P. pratensis (14). Tiller formation is generally enhanced with high levels of nitrogen at the expense of root and rhizome production.

Phillippe (13) reported that with a mixture of elements rhizome weight seemed to follow the potassium level more than it did the nitrogen or phosphorus levels. For optimum rhizome production in Poa pratensis a moderate level of nitrogen (57 ppm nutrient solution) and a moderate to moderately high level of potassium (41-142 ppm) seemed most desirable. Rhizome production was not affected as greatly by phosphorus levels (13).

Low mowing generally reduces root and rhizome growth of P. pratensis by reducing the carbohydrate production. Mowing P. pratensis at 2 cm compared to

5 cm reduced rhizome production. With a combination of low mowing and high nitrogen (25+ ppm soluble nitrogen in the tissue) rhizome production almost ceased (9). Clipping reduced the total rhizome length but the highly rhizomatous clones maintained their superiority under mowing (10).

Adequate moisture must be available for rhizome growth. The mid-summer growth of P. pratensis rhizomes is largely dependent on moisture and temperature. If ample moisture is present the long photoperiods of early and midsummer enhance rhizome initiation and elongation providing high temperature does not evoke dormancy.

GENETIC POTENTIAL

There is a considerable amount of genetic difference in P. pratensis in the rapidity of tiller and rhizome formation as discussed earlier (10). In controlled environment studies at the Ohio State University, the cultivar Windsor generally produced rhizomes more quickly than did the cultivar Merion (12), although in a later experiment Fylking had slightly more than Merion or Windsor (Table 2). Merion generally tillered more quickly than Windsor.

REFERENCES

1. BROWN, E.M. (1939) Some effects of temperature on the growth and chemical composition of certain pasture grasses. Missouri agric. Exp. Stn. Res. Bull. 299.

2. BROWN, E.M. (1943) Seasonal variations in the growth and chemical composition of Kentucky bluegrass. Missouri agric. Exp. Stn. Res. Bull. 360.

3. ETTER, A.G. (1951) How Kentucky bluegrass grows. Ann. Mo. bot. Gdn. 38, 3, 293.

4. EVANS, M.W. (1949) Vegetative growth development and reproduction in Kentucky bluegrass. Ohio agric. Exp. Stn. Res. Bull. 681.

5. FISHER, J.E. (1965) The growth of rhizomes in Kentucky bluegrass. II. Form and structure during the main stages of growth. Greenhouse, Garden, Grass 5, 4, 1.

6. FISHER, J.E. (1965) Morphologically distinct stages in the growth and development of rhizomes of Poa pratensis L. and their correlation with specific growth responses. Can. J. Bot. 43, 10, 1163.

7. FISHER, J.E. (1964) Evidence of circumnutational growth movements of rhizomes of Poa pratensis L. that aid in soil penetration. Can. J. Bot. 42, 3, 293.

8. HARRISON, C.M. (1934) Responses of Kentucky bluegrass to variations in temperature, light, cutting, and fertilizing. Pl. Physiol. 9, 1, 83.

9. JUSKA, F.V., et al. (1955) The competitive relationship of Merion bluegrass as influenced by various mixtures, cutting heights, and levels of nitrogen. Agron. J. 47, 11, 513.

10. LOBENSTEIN, C.W. (1964) Sod-forming characteristics of Kentucky bluegrass as affected by morphological and physiological factors. Ph.D. Diss. Purdue Univ. (Libr. Congr. Card No. Mic. 64-12, 764) Univ. Microfilms, Ann. Arbor, Mich. (Diss. Abstr. 25, 3195).

11. MELKERSON, E.J. (1963) Comparative performance of vegetative and seedling bluegrasses for turf. M.S. Thesis. Purdue University.

12. MOSER, L.E., et al. (1968) Rhizome and tiller development of Kentucky bluegrass (Poa pratensis L.) as influenced by photoperiod, cold treatment, and variety. Agron. J. 60, 6, 632.

13. PHILLIPPE, P.M. (1942) Effects of some essential elements on the growth and development of Kentucky bluegrass (Poa pratensis). Ph.D. Diss. The Ohio State University.

14. SPRAGUE, H.B. (1934) Utilization of nutrients by Colonial bent (Agrostis tenuis) and Kentucky bluegrass (Poa pratensis). New Jersey agric. Exp. Stn. Bull. 570.

DISCUSSION

DEVELOPMENT OF POA PRATENSIS TILLERS FROM RHIZOMES

W.R. Adams (U.K.)

Does Dr. Moser know how long young tillers of Poa pratensis L. developing from rhizomes depend upon energy from the parent plant?

L.E. Moser (Ohio, U.S.A.)

I have noticed that rhizomes seem to degenerate rather quickly upon emergence. So I would expect that a new plant ceases to receive carbohydrates, etc., from the parent plant quite soon after the rhizome has emerged.

W.H. Daniel (Indiana, U.S.A.)

When we studied rhizome terminal fragments, pieces with one leaf left on them grew twice as rapidly as pieces without leaves. This suggests that there is a low energy reserve in new rhizomes.

J.H. Madison (California, U.S.A.)

It has been found that once a rhizome shoot emerged it appeared to be independent of the parent plant. If the shoot emerged in soil deficient of a nutrient the shoot was deficient of that nutrient even when the parent plant was in fertile soil.

PELLETED SEED

W.H. Daniel (Indiana, U.S.A.)

What is the effect of the concentration of salts on pelleted seed?

J.C. Knolle (West Germany)

If we store pelleted seed in polythene bags and at not more than 8% humidity, there is no effect on germination from the fertilizers in the coating.

R.W. Miller (Ohio, U.S.A.)

With grasses that do not form rhizomes and stolons, at what spacing do pelleted seeds need to be placed to give a good turf?

J.C. Knolle (West Germany)

This depends on location and variety. It is for the user to decide.

R.L. Morris (U.K.)

Does the practice of coating seed in New Zealand have any advantage in practice? I understand that lawn grass seeds coated with phosphate and fungicide are available in New Zealand.

G.S. Robinson (New Zealand)

Pelleting of turf seeds is not a normal practice in New Zealand where pelleting is mainly restricted to agricultural sowing of legumes. Pelleting can improve nodule development if bacteria are included in the pelleting material.

J.C. Knolle (West Germany)

In Australia grass seed has been pelleted with lime to make it heavier, for sowing in windy conditions. But this has proved costly and not always satisfactory. Our aim is to ensure uniform seed rates and the best use of seed. We also incorporate fungicides to improve establishment.

D.B. White (Minnesota, U.S.A.)

Does pelleting affect the storage life of seed?

J.C. Knolle (West Germany)

Pelleted seed remains viable as long as ordinary seed, if kept dry (7-9% humidity) in polythene bags.

SESSION 7: ROADSIDES

(Chairman: Dr. J. R. Watson)

TURFGRASSES FOR ROADSIDES

P. Boeker,

Professor of Crop Husbandry, Friedrich-Wilhelms Universität, Bonn,
West Germany.

SUMMARY

Seed mixtures for roadsides are in most cases still rather poorly
adapted for their special purpose. Investigations on this problem started
about 35 years ago. Taking into consideration the composition of the adjacent grassland, the first mixtures contained nearly 20 species, including
not only grasses but also legumes and herbs. In later years these mixtures
became more simple. At present, mixtures of 3-4 species seem to be sufficient. These species are Agrostis tenuis, Festuca ovina s.l., Festuca
rubra s.l. and Poa pratensis.

Turf at the roadside should fulfil the following conditions: it should
fasten the loose soil quickly to prevent erosion; it should be adapted to the
vegetation of the environment, meaning that it must not be in strong contrast
to the adjacent grassland; and it should remain low-growing in order not to
obscure the view at crossings and road bends. Low growth of the grasses also
means low costs for maintenance, especially for mowing. Best of all would be
if this maintenance work could be saved completely, by the use of growth control
substances and herbicides.

Unfortunately many or perhaps most of the new and old turf grasses do not
fulfil these requirements. Because of their tall growth they are very costly
in maintenance and therefore there is now a tendency to replace them by planting shrubs and bushes or even trees. Such planting is sometimes justified when
it is necessary to fasten a soil by deep rooted plants, as grasses have the
main part of their roots only in the upper layer of the soil down to a depth of
20-30 cm. But in many situations grasses and turf should be preferred.

The antipathy against turf which is held by road authorities is very often
due to seeds mixtures which were not adapted to the above-mentioned purposes.
This can easily be checked by sampling mixtures proposed for sowing, or by a
survey of the roadsides. In spring 1968 a survey of the seeds mixtures in
Northern Wurttemberg showed that at that time 25 grasses and 9 legumes were in
use. The most frequently used were Agrostis tenuis Sibth., Festuca rubra L. ssp.
rubra, Poa pratensis L., Festuca ovina L., Lolium perenne L., Poa annua L.,
Festuca rubra L. ssp. commutata Gaud., Trifolium dubium Sibth., and Trifolium
repens L. Other species were: Agrostis alba L., Lolium multiflorum Lam.,
Deschampsia flexuosa (L.) Trin., Dactylis glomerata L., Poa trivialis L.,
Arrhenatherum elatius (L.) J. & C. Presl, Bromus secalinus L., Cynosurus crist-
atus L., Festuca tenuifolia Sibth., Poa nemoralis L., Lotus corniculatus L.,
Medicago lupulina L., Onobrychis viciifolia Scop. and Trifolium hybridum L.
Only once were the following recorded: Bromus erectus Huds., Cynodon dactylon
(L.) Pers., Festuca arundinacea Schreb., Festuca pratensis Huds., Poa compressa
L., Poa palustris L., Trisetum flavescens (L.) Beauv., Medicago varia Martyn,
Melilotus officinalis (L.) Lam. and Trifolium pratense L.

It is rather astonishing how many species were sown which are completely useless and wrong at the roadsides, e.g. Bromus secalinus, a former weed of the rye-fields, or Lolium multiflorum, a short-lived grass for leys. Besides this, on many roadsides one has the definite impression that only seed cleanings were sown. One curiosity was a roadside several kilometres long with a pure stand of Alopecurus myosuroides Huds.

These examples may show that real knowledge on adequate seed mixtures is very restricted. Only in the recent years has there developed more uniformity.

The first to deal with these seeds mixtures were plant sociologists. In 1935 at the request of the authorities building the autobahnen, R. Tüxen (8) developed the first four mixtures to take into consideration the composition of the adjacent grassland. His mixtures contained 5 - 15 grasses, 3 - 4 legumes and 2 herbs. But Tüxen's aim was not to sow complete plant communities, as is at present the aim of some landscape architects. He intended only to sow the most important species. Later, E. Preising (6) developed for the same purpose eleven mixtures which were adapted to the forestcommunities which the roads passed. He developed mixtures for raw soil, to establish pioneer communities on them, and mixtures for good humus-rich soils to establish permanent communities. His mixtures were already simpler, containing 2 - 12 species.

Unfortunately at no time has anybody followed up the development of the mixtures in the years after sowing. Thus in the survey of the vegetation at the sides of autobahnen published in 1961 by R. Tüxen and W. Lohmeyer (9), this information was unknown. But from their survey they concluded that it was possible to use for the whole of Western Germany only 4 mixtures, with only 6 grasses in them. These mixtures were a very big improvement but they remained nearly unknown in the files of the road authorities. On the other hand these same authorities ordered the formulation of a new regulation for making roadsides green again; for this R. Hansen and L. Roemer (3) developed 110 various mixtures, containing altogether 47 species of which 27 were grasses, 8 legumes and 12 herbs. As these mixtures proved very soon to be much too complicated in their composition and much too difficult to choose appropriately, the authors reduced the number of mixtures in 1967 (4) to 20 and the number of species to 25, of which 14 were grasses, 6 legumes and 5 herbs. But even these mixtures still contain some species of which little or no seed is available.

The author's own observations at the sides of main roads and autobahnen in 1962 to 1964 led to the same conclusions as Tüxen and Lohmeyer. They proved that the main grasses for roadsides should be only the following 4 species: Agrostis tenuis, Festuca ovina s.l., Festuca rubra s.l. and Poa pratensis. These grasses are the corner stones of all grassland communities used as pastures in West Germany. With the exception of Festuca ovina they can be found in more than 80% of all pasture stands, and by their nature form a low-growing turf. They are adapted to a great variation of soil, pH, nutrient supply and water supply. They can be found from the lowlands to high in the mountains. Moreover it is useful that Festuca rubra ssp. rubra and Poa pratensis have stolons by which they can easily and quickly recolonize gaps in the turf and fill them. Therefore it is justified to put the emphasis on using these species in the mixtures for roadsides, which is in agreement with the publications of modern plant sociologists in Germany (5, 7). Only for special cases in difficult environments may it be necessary to use some additional species. To use legumes, as is sometimes recommended in order to make use of their capacity for fixing nitrogen, will involve the possibility of attracting game to the roadsides which may cause danger to traffic. Herbs, which are also sometimes suggested for sowing, are as a rule not much deeper rooting at first than the grasses. Normally their seed is very expensive, and very often sufficient seed is not available.

The two seeds mixtures in Table 1 are proposed for roadsides. Mixture A should be used where there is a reasonably adequate water supply and where the soil is not too light or extremely acid. Mixture B is proposed for especially dry soils, very sandy or stony, and situations with unfavourable soil reaction; therefore it contains higher amounts of Festuca ovina and Festuca rubra ssp. commutata.

Table 1: recommended roadside mixtures (g/sq m)

	Mixture A	Mixture B
Agrostis tenuis	2	2
Festuca ovina	-	3 - 5
Festuca rubra ssp. rubra	3 - 6	3 - 4
Festuca rubra ssp. commutata	3 - 6	4 - 6
Poa pratensis	4 - 6	3
Total	12 - 20	15 - 20

The amount of seed varies because time of sowing may not always be best for germination; the same may apply to the preparation of the soil as a seed-bed or when suitable equipment is not used for sowing. Under very favourable conditions the amounts of seed in the Table may even be reduced.

As it will take about 2 to 3 weeks after sowing for the new grass to make the ground green, it may be advisable in some cases, where the soil is very inclined to erosion, to use in addition to the recommended grasses a small amount of a quick germinating grass like Lolium perenne. As this grass has the tendency to suppress slower growing components the amount should not be higher than 1 - 2 g/sq m. In this case it is also advisable to use a cultivar which is known to be short-lived so that it may vanish in 1 - 2 years to leave a stand of the more useful grasses.

The mixtures described have been tested in comparison with several others offered by the seed trade or proposed by the road authorities. A trial sown in spring 1966 in Hohenheim in Southern Germany proved that, of all the various grasses used, Festuca rubra and Festuca ovina were the most reliable right from the beginning. They formed a good dense short turf in which Agrostis tenuis and Poa pratensis increased their percentage share of the sward with the years. In this respect it may even be worthwhile to consider starting to reseed with a pure sowing of _Festuca rubra_, as it was found that after only 2 years 9 additional species had invaded these plots, though they were the densest of all. These demonstrations even convinced the civil servants of the road and watercourse authorities to introduce the mixtures officially in some bigger districts of Southern Germany.

But seed mixtures are only a part, though a very important one, of the solution of the problem of reseeding roadsides. Another question is whether to use the top soil or not. In most cases it seems better, because of the high amount of dormant seed in it, not to replace it but to sow on the bare subsoil. Otherwise one gets unwanted plants some of which may be rather tall-growing and therefore must be regarded as weeds. This form of sowing requires only a sufficient amount of nutrients to give the new grass a good start, but in every case fertilizing is not only useful but necessary for the establishment of a good dense turf.

REFERENCES

1. BOEKER, P. (1965) Einfache oder sehr vielseitige Mischungen im Strassenbau? Neue Landschaft 11, 260.

2. BOEKER, P. (1968) Einige Grundsätze für die Ansaaten von Strassen, auf Böschungen und ähnlichen Standorten. Saatgutwirtschaft 20, 189.

3. HANSEN, R., and ROEMER, L. (1964) Rasenmischungen. In: Richtlinien für Strassenbepflanzung. Teil 2, Köln.

4. HANSEN, R., and ROEMER, L. (1967) Rasensaatenmischungen für Grunflächen von Strassen in der freien Landschaft. Garten und Landschaft 77, No. 2.

5. LOHMEYER, W. (1968) Über die Ansaat niedrigbleibender Rasen an Strassen und Autobahnen. Natur und Landschaft 3.

6. PREISING, E. (1940) Über die Aufstellung von Rasenmischungen für offene Böden nach pflanzensoziologischen Gesichtspunkten unter besonderer Berücksichtigung der Reichsautobahnen. Dissertation Berlin.

7. TRAUTMANN, W., and LOHMEYER, W. (1969) Pflanzensoziologische Grundsätze für die Aufstellung von Rasenmischungen (unpublished manuscript)

8. TÜXEN, R. (1935) Pflanzensoziologie im Hinblick auf den Strassenbau in Deutschland. Die Strasse 2.

9. TÜXEN, R., and LOHMEYER, W. (1961) Kritische Untersuchungen von Rasen an den Autobahnen des Bundesrepublik. Manusckript Stolzenau.

SEEDING TECHNIQUES FOR ESTABLISHING GRASS ON SWEDISH ROADSIDES

Bjarne Langvad, M.Sc.,

W. Weibull AB, Landskrona, Sweden.

SUMMARY

Experiments and practical work on a big scale in Sweden have shown that the establishment of grass on road embankments and similar areas can be carried out by a method totally different from the traditional one. The costs entailed in the new method are considerably lower than those encountered with the traditional procedure, and at the same time the resulting areas are better established and require less maintenance, or even none at all. Two versions of this method are briefly described and details given of the grass and other seed which it is desirable to use.

GREEN BORDERS FOR SCANDINAVIAN ROADS

The extension of the Scandinavian road network means that every year large areas are claimed for road embankments, central reserves and other refuge areas, stopping places, etc. In Sweden alone the amount of land taken annually for such areas probably amounts to between 1,000 and 1,400 ha. These green areas are a part of the road and are as a rule laid out simultaneously with road construction or road improvement. In Sweden there are about 8,000 miles of national highway and 55,000 miles of so-called provincial roads. If one takes the green areas to be a minimum of 6 sq m per metre of roadway for provincial roads, 12 sq m for national highways and 22 sq m for motorways, the total green area connected to the road network is 650 sq km.

In addition to their aesthetic function, the green areas are of technical importance in relation both to road construction and to the traffic itself. In the first case, they help to stabilise the surface of embankments. Secondly, embankments and central reserves can, when suitably designed, be a safety zone for a vehicle which for one reason or another runs off the road. Grass also provides an aesthetically attractive transition between the road and the adjacent countryside. The method of preparing the ground and establishing the grass vegetation is of decisive importance if these areas are to fulfil the two technical functions as well as the purely aesthetic function.

TRADITIONAL METHODS OF ROADSIDE SEEDING
AND THE SEARCH FOR NEW TECHNIQUES

The establishment of grass vegetation on roadsides has been traditionally an operation involving much work and heavy expenditure. In Sweden the problem was, until 1963, solved in the following way. A layer of top soil, 5 cm thick, was added on top of the underlying material, after which the grass seed was sown and covered over. Most of the work was generally done by hand. The cost per sq. m with this traditional method was about 1.50 - 2 Swedish crowns. As early as 1958 the Turfgrass section at Weibullsholms Plant Breeding Institute had already begun experimental work on a special method of establishing grass, in co-operation with the Swedish Highway Department. The chief questions these Swedish experiments and investigations aimed to answer were as follows:

1. Is it possible to eliminate completely the use of top soil for the sowing and establishment of grass on roadsides?

2. What method or methods might be devised to replace the traditional method of using top soil?

3. What method and what machinery should be used for the sowing of embankments?

4. Are the species, varieties and mixtures of grass seed which have been used for many years suitable for the sowing of modern road embankments?

The experimental programme has had four different stages of development:

1. Preliminary experiments on sowing in different kinds of soil, and experiments with different species and varieties, in the period 1958-60.

2. Experiments in sowing grass both as mixtures and as pure stand of species, and experiments with fertilizing programmes, etc., in various parts of Sweden during the years 1961-62.

3. Experiments with the mechanical mixing and sowing of grass seed, fertilizing agents, etc., in 1962.

4. Sowing on a large scale to apply the experience gained in experiments. The aim has been to try out the method on bigger areas, with machines designed for large scale use. The development of the work is shown by the following figures:

1962	2.5 million sq m
1963	6.5 " " "
1964	10.5 " " "
1965	14.0 " " "
1966	14.0 " " "
1967	14.5 " " "
1968	15.0 " " "

In 1969 it is planned to sow 15 million sq m. In Norway and Denmark together, 6 million sq m have been sown and in France and Germany the S/48 Company from Denmark has sown large areas by using the Swedish method.

The experiments have shown that the establishment of grass on road embankments and similar areas can be done by a method totally different from the traditional one. The costs entailed in the new method are considerably lower than those encountered with the traditional procedure, and at the same time the resulting areas are more thickly established, and require much less maintenance or even none at all.

THE NEW SWEDISH METHODS

These methods may be briefly described as follows:

Method A, for stable surfaces:

Grass seed (Weibulls Vägslänt) and fertilizer (PK 15/30 and ureaformaldehyde) are carried on a lorry which is driven along the edge of the road; as
it goes, a machine scatters grass seed and fertilizer over the embankment
surfaces, using a stream of air.

Method B, for areas subject to erosion:

Materials intended to prevent surface erosion, such as peat, binding agent
and water, as well as seed and fertilizer, are measured and mixed in a mixing
plant. The finished product which is a half-dry, viscous mass, is stored at
the place of manufacture.

The material is loaded on a lorry and driven to the site. The lorry is
coupled to a spreader machine and the material is tipped into the latter. The
lorry and the spreader are driven along the edge of the road, and the machine
spreads the half-dry viscous mass on the embankment surface to a thickness of
4-6 mm. If it is needed to spread more than 16-18 mm, a hydroseeder is used.

An additional advantage of the new simplified method is that it avoids
the germination of weed and coarse grass seeds which were always found in the
top soil added by the old method, and which frequently formed an undesirable
element in the resulting vegetation.

Until 1963, the grass species generally sown on road cuttings over the
greater part of the country were still timothy (Phleum pratense L.), meadow
fescue (Festuca pratensis Huds.) and perennial ryegrass (Lolium perenne L.).
These tall, coarse or otherwise undesirable grasses are not used nowadays, but
are replaced by a creeping variety of red fescue (Festuca rubra L.), common
bent (Agrostis tenuis Sibth.), a low growing variety of meadow grass (Poa
pratensis L.) and Evergreen turf timothy (Phleum bertolonii DC.). The advantage of using these species is obvious: when mixed and well established they
form a low, close-growing mat, which needs no mowing or cutting. A matter of
pressing importance is also to ascertain which of the more decorative Swedish
wild plants are most suitable for sowing in grass seed mixtures in order to make
newly sown embankments attractive in the shortest possible time. From many
points of view, it is desirable to attempt to hasten the process of restoration
by the sowing of these additional species. Under extreme conditions it may
be several years, or even decades, before the natural growth on embankments has
become either an aesthetically attractive covering or a protection against
erosion. Measures aimed at quick restoration using suitable, low growing
grasses and ornamental plants are therefore urgently necessary.

The new methods afford good opportunities of establishing a sward, the
composition of which is not incompatible with the flora of the surrounding
countryside. The sowing is done in a medium or material free of weeds. The
vegetation which is established by sowing and encouraged by balanced fertilizing will quickly form a close growing ground cover preventing or resisting the
invasion of the area by undesirable plants. In this way it is possible from
the outset to establish the desired balanced grass community.

These new methods can also be readily adapted for more general purposes
of improving appearance, e.g. for covering abandoned gravel pits, spoil dumps,
slag heaps and so on.

TURFGRASS ESTABLISHMENT ON ROADSIDES

W.B. Gilbert,

North Carolina State University, Raleigh, North Carolina, U.S.A.

SUMMARY

In erosion prevention on roadsides, the protection of the roadway core, its slopes and drainage ways is of first importance. The establishment of grasses and legumes is the most economical means of preventing and controlling erosion. Successful establishment and maintenance of a suitable turf depends upon the adaptation of plant species to all the factors that affect plant growth. The performance of any one turf species is associated with soil, climatic, and biotic factors and their inter-relationships. The modification of these factors is discussed, including liming and seedbed fertilization, the various mulching materials to aid germination and seedling growth, the use of ditch liners for erosion control, and the selection of a species or mixture for a particular site.

In erosion prevention work for highway departments, the item of first importance has to be the protection of the roadway core, its slopes and its drainage ways. The shoulder slopes are the most important; for erosion quickly exposes road core material, endangers the stability of the surfaced shoulder, of the roadway itself, and of a vehicle leaving the surfaced areas (Foote, 1968).

The shoulder slopes are most exposed to the view of the travelling public, and are most frequently mowed. These areas are the most difficult to protect and on which to establish and maintain a satisfactory turf. The unfavourable factors present are poor growing media; heavy surface flows of water from the roadway; concentrations of salt; concentration of wet snow resulting in ice sheets and smothering; rapid and extreme changes in temperature resulting from the nearness of the surfaced areas, and high variable winds from the passing vehicles.

After the shoulder slopes, the other areas in order of importance are: fill slopes, ditches, cut slopes, and other areas outside the rounded tops of the cuts, toes of the fills, and slopes of the ditches and drainage ways.

Fill slope surfaces protect and are another part of the road core. They are often subject to gravitational erosion, slides, slips and slumps, besides gullies and sheet erosion caused by raindrop impact and flowing water.

The ditches and drainage ways remove moisture, the greatest hazard to a stable road core. Drainage structures are costly and necessary to the planned, orderly removal of water. The soil around these structures must be completely protected from erosion.

Cut slopes are important as eroding material from these areas may affect the drainage flow. Cut slopes are also quite important aesthetically as they are in full view of the motorist.

The establishment of grasses and legumes on highway rights-of-way is the most economical means of preventing and controlling erosion and providing pleasant scenery for motorists. For rapid establishment of vegetative cover, the proper plant species, nutrients, soil, climate and engineering features must be brought together.

Successful establishment and maintenance of a suitable turf along road-sides on various slopes, through cuts and fills, depends upon the adaptation of plant species to all the factors that affect plant growth. The performance of any one turf species or variety is associated with soil, climatic and biotic factors and their interrelationships.

The soil factors include: native fertility; acidity; compaction and aeration; texture as related to moisture and nutrient-holding capacity; erodibility; and the availability of top soil or suitable subsoil for slope dressing, if and when needed.

The climatic factors are: temperature as influenced by slope exposure, latitude and elevation; potential rainfall and evapotranspiration as influenced by longitude, latitude, elevation and nearby large bodies of water; wind intensity; and light intensity.

The biotic factors are: plant species as influenced by soil and climatic factors; morphology of species, including size, rooting depth, method of propagation, longevity and growth habits; adaptation of species as related to diseases and insect tolerance; rate of seedling emergence and its growth rates; and date of seeding as interrelated to temperature and moisture.

Seedbed fertilization

The soil factors may be modified to some extent through liming and proper fertilization. Subsoils that are exposed when roadsides are cut and filled are almost always low in nitrogen and vary widely in their phosphate and potash content. Fertilizers may be the only source of nutrients for the small seedlings as they struggle to get established under unfavourable conditions (Beers, 1962). The value of adding inorganic chemical fertilizers to soils for plant growth promotion has been known for over 100 years. Fertilizers have been shown to increase primary vegetative cover established on roadsides of new construction projects (Jackobs et al., 1967). In 1959, Daniel reported for the sub-committee on fertilization for the American Road Builders Association by summarizing six principles for roadside fertilization in the Midwest. These were:

1. Use maximum fertilization to produce dense turf quickly.

2. Provide an adequate supply of nutrients for the least fertile soil in the area.

3. Expect all soils to be deficient in nitrogen.

4. Phosphorus is most needed mixed into the rootzone before planting.

5. Suggested standard is 112 kg/ha each of N, P_2O_5, K_2O as seedbed application.

6. Get a soil test before liming.

The above principles have been confirmed by subsequent investigation in the humid Southeast, where the soil materials are invariably low in nitrogen and phosphorus. In North Carolina when phosphorus was not included in the fertilizer applied in the seedbed (Table 1, treatment 3), grass stands were very poor or non-existent in large areas.

Table 1: sod establishment on cut slopes with different rates of N, P, K, and lime (Station 310, U.S. 1, Raleigh, N. C.: seeded 25 Oct. 1963 with _Festuca arundinacea_ Schreb. at 170 kg/ha)

Treatment number	kg/ha			Lime (tons/ha)	Grass cover after 7 months (%)
	N	P_2O_5	K_2O		
1	112	112	112	2.24	58.0
2	112	112	0	2.24	65.0
3	112	0	112	2.24	20.0
4	112	224	112	2.24	83.6
5	112	448	112	2.24	76.6
6	112	112	112	0	51.6
7	112	112	112	8.96	60.0

A dose of 224 kg/ha of phosphorus (treatment 4) produced a significant increase over the standard 112 kg/ha. The omission of potassium (treatment 2) had little effect on the percent coverage at 7 months, as did the absence of lime (treatment 6). However, these two treatments were rated lower during the second year (Gilbert and Davis, 1967).

In the adjacent State of Virginia, Blaser (1962a) suggests 4.5 tons/ha lime and 1120 kg/ha of a 10-20-10 fertilizer to supply ample nitrogen and phosphorus for rapid seedling growth and the establishment of a grass dominant sod. However, he states that legumes of northern origin (_Trifolium_ spp., _Lotus_ _corniculatus_ L., _Coronilla_ _varia_ L., and _Melilotus_ spp.) require more lime and more phosphorus and potassium fertilization for establishment than grasses. Legumes of southern origin, such as _Lespedeza_ _cuneata_ (Dumont) G. Don, are very tolerant of acid soils and liming may retard growth.

Mulches

Failures in establishing new turf areas are more often attributed to low moisture than any other factor. Surface mulches improve moisture availability and, consequently, germination and subsequent seedling growth. In addition to conserving moisture, mulches increased water infiltration from 6 mn per hour on bare soil to 18 mm on mulched soil (Duley and Kelley, 1939). Mulches, because of better water infiltration, reduce water run-off and concurrent soil erosion.

High temperatures often prevent satisfactory establishment of grass cover, especially on south-facing slopes, because they damage seedlings and reduce moisture supply to the point where growth ceases (McCalla and Duley, 1946). Soil temperatures are moderated by good mulching materials by reducing the build-up of temperatures during the day and retarding heat loss during the night. The lower temperatures of mulched soils reduce rates of evaporation.

Mulches tend to assure successful turf establishment by improving the rate of germination and seedling growth and shorten the period for developing a suitable turf. The more difficult the environment or moisture stress, the greater the benefits from surface mulching. Straw applied at a rate of 2 - 4 tons/ha has been one of the best mulches for establishing stands and increasing yields (Jacks et al, 1955). Results with straw mulches have been unsatisfactory with heavy applications or uneven distribution. Unthreshed small grains or weedy species in hay mulches are objectionable, since the rapid germination and seedling growth of small grains may exterminate the stands of the desirable seeded species. Instead of working on a basis of x tons/ha, a better criterion is to leave 25 to 50% of the soil exposed (Blaser, 1962b). The best way to stabilize straw or hay mulches against air draughts from fast-moving vehicles and on slopes is to use asphalt.

Considerable concern has been expressed by personnel involved with turf establishment on roadsides as to the future availability of straw, both in quantity and quality. Mulches of various kinds are used and new mulch materials are being developed and evaluated in conjunction with seeding. Brant (1961) compared the mulches used in the United States and gave an evaluation of the newer mulching materials.

In a recent experience in Nebraska, Dudeck et al (1967) compared the effect of various mulch treatments as to soil temperatures, soil moisture, seedling emergence, and percent cover (Table 2). The plots treated with the Excelsior mat had the highest minimum soil temperature and the lowest maximum soil temperature with a range of 13.2°C. This was because the mat provided more insulation. The thinner mulches had a higher range, with asphalt having a 25.2° range, going from 13.5° to 38.3°C. The soil moisture percentages, taken 6 days after seeding, indicate the mulches' influence on moisture infiltration rather than an effect on retarding evaporation, since plots did not have an opportunity to dry during this 6 day period. The plots with Excelsior mat had the highest soil moisture percentage, apparently because the mat intercepted more rainfall and allowed less run-off from the plots. Because of the favourable amount and distribution of rainfall following seeding, many of the mulch treatments were not significantly different in seedling stand from the plots with no mulch. Due to differences in seedling maturity and degree of tillering, the grass cover percentage is considered to be more valid for evaluating this experiment. Five treatments were better in cover than the no-mulch plots.

A similar experiment was conducted in Virginia by Barkley et al (1965). Under these more humid conditions, the wood fibre cellulose produced results comparable to those of straw. Their summary states: "Straw, sawdust, and Turfiber (wood fibre cellulose) mulches moderated the soil temperature of the seed zone, thereby improving germination, emergence, and growth of grass seedlings. Soilset mulches (elastic emulsion) were not beneficial to grass development. Straw mulch tended to moderate soil temperature and conserve more soil moisture than the other mulches."

Table 2: effect of mulch treatments on soil temperature, soil moisture, seedling stand and grass cover (Firth, Nebraska, 1965: sown with 1,300 live seed/sq m of Bromus inermis Leyss.) (Any two means with different letters are significantly different at the 5% level)

Mulch treatment	Soil temperature range (°C)	Soil moisture (%)	Seedlings/sq m after 26 days	Grass cover after 14 months (%)
Excelsior mat	13.2a	28.0a	1041a	89.2a
Fibreglass and asphalt	19.8def	20.5bcd	680ab	45.8c
Prairie hay and asphalt	17.0bc	25.0ab	711ab	74.2ab
Corncobs and asphalt	17.8cd	22.0bcd	919ab	71.7b
Jute netting	18.1cde	22.6bcd	822ab	70.0b
Asphalt	25.2g	24.9abc	188c	30.0d
Woodchips and asphalt	18.6cdef	22.6bcd	834ab	69.2b
Latex	18.9cdef	21.4bcd	596b	47.5c
Wood cellulose and asphalt	20.7f	20.8bcd	725ab	53.3c
Medium paper netting	18.6cdef	21.6bcd	678ab	47.5c
Fibreglass	20.0ef	20.8bcd	766ab	46.7c
Wood cellulose	19.7def	19.6d	756ab	43.3cd
No mulch	19.8def	20.4cd	575b	38.3cd

587

Ditch linings for sod establishment and erosion control

The most critical need for erosion control in ditches, as on cut slopes and other areas along highways, is between seeding and sod establishment. Ditches along interstate and certain other highways with more than a 3 to 5% grade are generally paved, thus eliminating the erosion problem. Grass sods are much less expensive and are used whenever practical.

In an experiment at Raleigh, North Carolina, Gilbert and Davis (1967) constructed simulated median ditches 9 m long with a 3% linear slope; each ditch was 2.5 m wide with 10:1 shallow cross-section slopes. At the lower end of each ditch, a 10 cm pipe carried the run-off water into 150 l sediment-collecting drums. The ditches were prepared for seeding with 1,400 kg/ha of an 8-8-8 fertilizer, and 168 kg/ha tall fescue (Festuca arundinacea Schreb.) was sown.

A total of 32 different materials or combinations were evaluated in pilot trials, with the following 4 treatments being selected for the final runs:

1. Excelsior mat: stapled every 1.5 m at sides and 0.75 m in centre.

2. Jute net: stapled as treatment 1.

3. Fibreglass at ± 10 kg/100 sq m; covered with Mulchnet; stapled as treatment 1; then tacked with RC2 asphalt at 17 l/100 sq m.

4. RC2 asphalt sprinkled on ditch bottom at 34 l/100 sq m; Fibreglass at ±10 kg/100 sq m; then tacked with RC2 asphalt at 17 l/100 sq m.

The ditch bottom contours were measured at 3 points in each ditch after the liners were applied and again after the following water applications were made:

1. Entire area sprinkled for 1 hour, equalling 2.5 cm of rain.

2. Each ditch washed for 1 hour with 6,000 l water.

3. The rate increased to 18,000 l/hr. for 1 hour.

4. The rate decreased to 6,000 l/hr. for 1 hour.

The results are given in Table 3.

Table 3: results of trial on ditch linings

Treatment	Velocity (m/second)	Manning's n	Sediment in cm Range	Average	Grass stand %
1. Excelsior mat	0.30	0.0603	0.48 - 0.15	0.28	64*
2. Jute net	0.52	0.0279	17.47 - 1.90	6.12	70
3. Fibreglass 10 kg: net: RC2	0.55	0.0256	0.84 - 0.30	0.51	85
4. RC2: Fibreglass 10kg: RC2	0.61	0.0227	0.64 - 0.30	0.48	84

*Fine net suppressed grass stand: net size has since been increased

The Excelsior mat gave the best erosion control and the standard jute net failed to control the erosion. The asphalt-fibreglass-asphalt treatment, No. 4, was the most satisfactory when both economics and effectiveness in preventing erosion are considered.

Grasses and legumes for roadside turf

Many types of herbaceous material have some adaptation for roadside use. Many factors need to be considered before the final selection of a species or mixture for a particular location. There are material differences in the rate of establishment between the grasses and legumes. This is important because of the necessity of producing a protective cover as quickly as possible. The margin in time for establishment is quite wide. The best grasses will produce a good cover in 2 to 3 months, while the legumes require from one to two full seasons to become well established, and are usually not seeded alone for this reason. It is standard procedure in North Carolina to hydroseed Lespedeza sericea into a thinned-out turf several years after establishment rather than including the legume in the original seeding.

Foote (1963) gives methods and examples of classifying grasses and legumes. The origin is important because it largely governs the climatic pattern adaptation of the species. All legumes used in the United States, and most of the grasses, have a European or Asian origin and are adapted to the climatic pattern of their home of origin and not to the U.S.A. These species have also had their adaptation affected by man's cultivation and use. The native species, especially the grasses, are excellently adapted to U.S. climatic patterns but are not adapted to manipulation by man because they have not been cultivated to any great extent. The seed of many of the natives is hard to collect, clean, or sow. Establishment of these species is often quite difficult. However, a much greater and better use could be made of them than has been done so far.

The method of plant spread affects the use of a species. Species which reproduce only by seed often produce numerous seeds that establish readily. Plants that spread only by vegetative parts are generally easy to establish, but laborious to obtain and plant. Plant species which spread by both seed and vegetative parts have an advantage in usage since they tend to fill in bare areas and compete strongly with weed invasion.

The life cycle of a plant species is very important in management. Annual species can increase or decrease very rapidly in numbers in a short time. Perennials differ greatly in their life span. They may produce seed the first year of growth but generally produce more after the first year. Short-lived perennial grasses can be used as long-term nurse or companion species to long-lived perennial legumes, obtaining quick stabilization and a permanent cover.

The ease of establishment of a species indicates the amount of care, effort and expense needed in seeding and establishment work. Ease of maintenance has a direct effect on maintenance costs, equipment, and on roadside appearance. The difficulty of maintaining the turf depends on the individual species which make up the turf.

The strength and depth of the plant's root system is an important item which has often been overlooked. Plants with strong deep root systems should be used where slips and slides are possible or where ground water problems are anticipated. Most native grasses have a deeper root system then the introduced species.

The seasonal growth patterns of the plant species can be used effectively in forming mixtures for roadside appearance and erosion control. The cool-season grasses start growth in early spring, produce a seed stalk in June, and are largely dormant in midsummer. They produce a low green growth in the fall. However, if the turf is not strong and vigorous, it will be invaded by summer annual grasses which give a bad appearance and require more frequent mowings.

The warm-season grasses start growth in late spring, make their greatest growth in midsummer, and end growth in early fall. These grasses are not as subject as the cool-season grasses to invasion by warm-season annuals, but are apt to be invaded by the winter annuals, giving the turf a ragged appearance in the early spring.

The legumes have an intermediate growth pattern, starting growth early in the spring and continuing through the summer and fall, though varying greatly between species. Most legumes produce attractive flowers that add to the attractiveness of the roadside.

When all the soil, climatic, and biotic factors have been considered or altered, the differences in adaptation can be used to fit the proper plant or plants to the specific site conditions.

REFERENCES

1. BARKLEY, D.G., BLASER, R.E., and SCHMIDT, R.E. (1965) Effect of mulches on microclimate and turf establishment. Agron. J. 57, 189.

2. BEERS, Z.H. (1962) Fertilizers an important factor in establishing and maintaining roadside turf. Twenty-first Short Course on Roadside Development, Ohio Department of Highways and Ohio State University. p.94.

3. BLASER, R.E. (1962a) Methods of maintaining and reseeding deteriorated highway slopes. Twenty-first Short Course on Roadside Development. Ohio Department of Highways and Ohio State University. p.87.

4. BLASER, R.E. (1962b) Soil mulches for grassing. Roadside Development, Highway Research Board, National Academy of Sciences - National Research Council, publication 1030:15.

5. BRANT, F.H. (1961) Mulching practices and materials. Roadside Development, Highway Research Board, National Academy of Sciences-National Research Council, publication 928:24.

6. DANIEL, W.H. (1959) Principles of roadside fertilization. Better Crops with Plant Food. 43, 1, 14.

7. DUDECK, A.E., SWANSON, N.P., and DEDRICK, A.R. (1967) Mulches for grass establishment on steep construction slopes. HRB Roadside Development, Highway Research Record No. 206, 53.

8. DULEY, F.L., and KELLEY, L.L. (1939) Effect of soil types, slope, and surface conditions on intake of water. Nebraska agric. Exp. Stn. Res. Bull. 112.

9. FOOTE, L.E. (1968) Turf establishment on highway right-of-way slopes. Twenty-seventh Short Course on Roadside Development, Ohio Department of Highways and Ohio State University. p. 83.

10. GILBERT, W.B., and DAVIS, D.L. (1967) An investigation of critical problems of establishing and maintaining a satisfactory sod cover along North Carolina highways. Project ERD-110-S Final Report. N.C. State University.

11. JACKOBS, J.A., ANDREWS, O.N. Jnr., MURDOCH, C.L., and FOOTE, L.E. (1967) Turf establishment on highway right-of-way slopes: a review. HRB Roadside Development, Highway Research Record No. 161. 71.

12. JACKS, G.V., BRIND, W.D., and SMITH, R. (1955) Mulching Technology, Communication No. 49, Commonwealth Bureau of Soil Science, Farnham Royal.

13. MCCALLA, T.M., and DULEY, F.L. (1946) Effect of crop residues on soil temperature. Agron. J. 38, 75.

SPECIES EVALUATION AND ECOLOGY IN ROADSIDE STABILIZATION

Wayne W. Huffine,

Dept. of Agronomy, Oklahoma State University, Stillwater, Oklahoma, U.S.A.

SUMMARY

The ecological considerations are very important in using plants for revegetation, and it may be necessary to make initial establishment with plants of a lower order of succession than those intended for the permanent cover. Examples are given. Mulches can be very important, and results of an experiment in Virginia are summarized. Various grasses are compared in their suitability for use on slopes in Oklahoma.

The successful use of any plant for revegetation purposes is dependent upon an understanding of its site requirements and tolerances. The relationship between the plant and its environment serves as the basis of ecology. The creation of cut and fill slopes in highway construction alters the ecological environment in each climatic zone of a country. Erosion resistant plants successfully grown on arable lands within an area may be undesirable for use on 3:1, or steeper, north-facing, or south-facing slopes. Similarly, but perhaps with less drastic effect on species adaptation on roadsides within an area, a west exposure slope may be much hotter and drier in mid-summer than adjacent level lands.

Plant growth is controlled by two groups of factors, one hereditary and the other environmental, or a combination of the two. Important environmental factors are moisture, temperature, light, gases, and nutrients. The soil may affect all these factors except light. All variations in quantity and quality of plant growth are caused by variations in internal physiological processes or conditions.

Before planting any species for revegetation purposes the ecological factors such as temperature, soils, and rainfall must be considered, reported Johnson et al (3). The soil, which consists of physical, chemical, and biological components, is probably as great a determining factor in plant growth as climate. The types of plants found in a particular area are determined to a great extent by the major environmental factor, temperature. The minimum winter temperatures, the average date for the last killing frost in the spring and the length of the growing season all help to determine the distribution of plant species. Proximity of great river systems and large bodies of water exert profound effects upon local temperature norms. Plant species are rated for hardiness in particular areas primarily on the basis of experience. In Minnesota, Johnson et al report a generally decreasing precipitation gradient from northeast to southwest across the state. The prairie species of grasses and forbs found in the southwest area are important because of their ability to withstand heat and drought and should be considered as potential material for roadside planting.

In this report Johnson et al point out that within the major vegetation divisions of Minnesota conditions exist which alter to some degree the direct environmental effects of local climate. One important condition that affects the growth of highway plantings is slope direction and angle. They point out that since maximum solar effect occurs only when the sun's rays strike at right angles to the surface of the earth, the greater the angle the less radiant

592

energy will reach a unit area. They report that, in the northern hemisphere, a slope of as little as 5 degrees towards the north reduces soil temperature as much as a shift of 300 miles northward on level land. On the other hand a 5 degree slope to the south will receive as much solar heating as a comparable level site 300 miles further south. The steepness, direction of slope, and composition of the soil will affect the waterholding capacity of the soil. Cool north slopes generally retain moisture well which explains why species adapted to more northern regions are occasionally found on northfacing slopes considerably south of their usual range.

Treatment of roadsides with vegetation is essentially the same thing that nature does as she revegetates a disturbed site, Young reports (4). These natural disturbances of sites have been occurring throughout time.

The very nature of building a highway with the grading, drainage establishment, surfacing, and other construction activities ranges from mild to catastrophic disturbance of the site. Young points out that a 30 ft. cut on the highway can expose material as difficult to treat with vegetation as a lava flow.

Nature replaces plants on new or disturbed sites in a definite successive order. Young says that experience has shown that it is usually easier to succeed in the establishment of plants for the protection of a disturbed area if plants of a lower order of succession are used to begin with than if higher order plants are used initially. This is fortunate in roadside treatment because grasses are usually wasted for the base cover.

To secure a permanent grass cover, it is sometimes desirable to start with annuals or temporary grass even though the ultimate aim is a perennial or another grass. In the Southeast U.S. crown vetch (Coronilla varia L.) is commonly established with an annual such as the cereal rye (Secale cereale L.). The crown vetch soon will become dominant. The same is true with Sericea lespedeza (Lespedeza cuneata (Dumont) G. Don). It is often started with weeping lovegrass (Eragrostis curvula (Schrad.) Nees).

Most grasses that are likely to be used on disturbed areas produce short seedling leaves. Generally they do not emerge through a heavy mulch. The seedlings must have light soon after they germinate in order to survive. Mulch, then, to be effective must be in sufficient quantity to provide a protective cover for the seed and seedling, but thin enough for the seedling to be exposed to light upon germination. Young reports that about 2 tons/acre (4,500 kg/ha) of grain straw will provide the proper kind of cover.

Many materials both natural and manufactured are being used for mulches to promote plant growth. Desirable mulches function to conserve soil moisture, moderate soil temperature, reduce soil erosion, improve soil properties, and usually improve stands and plant production, report Barkley et al (1).

Plant growth is influenced by soil temperature and moisture, both of which are influenced by mulches. Barkley et al present data on microclimate and growth of grass seedlings with various mulches.

Twenty treatment combinations (4 mulching materials and no mulch with 4 grass treatments in all combinations) were used with and without irrigation. The grasses and seeding rates were Kentucky 31 fescue (Festuca arundinacea Schreb.) 60 lb./ac. (67 kg/ha), Kentucky common bluegrass (Poa pratensis L.) 40 lb./ac. (45 kg/ha), and redtop (Agrostis alba L.) 10 lb./ac. (11 kg/ha). The seed was applied by hand on 5 July and rolled with a light roller; the mulches were then applied. Barley (_Hordeum vulgare_ L.) straw mulch was applied by hand at 2,500 lb./ac. (2,800 kg/ha) leaving approximately 25% bare ground. Two-year-old hardwood sawdust was applied to a depth of 1/8 in. (3 mm). Turfiber was sprayed on in a water slurry with a hydro-seeder at a rate of 1,200 lb./ac. (1,340 kg/ha). Soilset was diluted 9:1 by volume with water and applied with a sprinkling can at 800 lb./ac. concentrate (900 kg/ha).

Soil temperatures were obtained by 3 thermocouples connected in parallel, placed before mulching ¼ in. (6 mm) below the soil surface in each replicate. The average temperature of the 3 thermocouples was recorded by a Leeds–Northrup 16 point temperature recording potentiometer.

The results of these investigations showed that a moderation of soil temperature and conservation of soil moisture was produced by straw, wood cellulose fibres, and sawdust which resulted in quicker turf establishment than no mulch or elastomeric emulsion treatment in the summer seedings of Kentucky 31 fescue, Kentucky bluegrass, and redtop. Irrigation improved all treatments, but was most beneficial to those grasses mulched with straw, wood cellulose fibres, and sawdust.

Research on roadside development and erosion control in Oklahoma showed weeping lovegrass to be better adapted for use in eastern Oklahoma on north facing slopes than any other grass tested for erosion control. Bermudagrass (_Cynodon dactylon_ (L.) Pers.) is better adapted for use on all slopes except those that face north. In the western half of the State sideoats grama (_Bouteloua curtipendula_ (Michx.) Torr.) is the most widely adapted grass for erosion control on all slopes of any species tested, reported Huffine et al (2). Weeping lovegrass is as well adapted as sideoats grama on south-facing slopes in this area. Switchgrass (_Panicum virgatum_ L.) is as well adapted for erosion control purposes in western Oklahoma as sideoats grama on north-facing slopes. Buffalograss (_Buchloe dactyloides_ (Nutt.) Engelm.) works as well as sideoats grama for erosion control on west-facing slopes.

REFERENCES

1. BARKLEY, D.G., BLASER, R.E., and SCHMIDT, R.E. (1965) Effect of mulches on microclimate and turf establishment. Agron. J. 57, 2, 189.

2. HUFFINE, W.W., REED, L.W., and ROACH, G.W. (1968) Maintenance of vegetative ground covers on Oklahoma highways. (Part II Final Report). Roadside Development and Erosion Control. Oklahoma agric. Exp. Stn. Rep.

3. JOHNSON, A.G., WHITE, D.B., and SMITHBERG, M.H. (1965) Development of ground covers for highway slopes (Interim Report). Minnesota agric. Exp. Stn. Misc. J. 1259.

4. YOUNG, W.C. (1967) Ecology of roadside treatment. Twenty-Sixth Short Course on Roadside Development, Columbus, Ohio, October, 1967.

GRASS SPECIES SUITABLE FOR ROADSIDES

M. Petersen (Denmark)

Can Poa pratensis L. establish itself, or make any contribution to erosion control on slopes, if sown on subsoil? In my experience Poa pratensis will establish itself on slopes on good top soil, but not on sand or poor top soil. Moreover, botanical analyses in Denmark have shown that Poa pratensis does not contribute to erosion control on slopes in Danish conditions.

P. Boeker (West Germany)

Poa pratensis will establish itself rather slowly, and it will always contribute only a small proportion of the population. But it is of value because its rhizomes may close gaps.

B. Langvad (Sweden)

The Poa pratensis used in mixtures on highway embankments will mostly establish itself close to the concrete or asphalt highway itself.

H. Vos (Netherlands)

I question whether it is advisable to use Poa pratensis on poor sandy soil.

P. Boeker (West Germany)

On very acid sandy soils one should use Festuca ovina L. instead of Poa pratensis, which needs a substantial amount of nutrients, including bases.

C. Eisele (West Germany)

I am of the opinion that on roadside slopes one has to use the soil which is at hand, including the top soil. The top soil may have to be removed from below the highway, because it contains organic matter which it is undesirable to have beneath the concrete. It is too expensive to take it away, so it must be distributed on the slopes.

G.G. Fisher (U.K.)

There are a variety of demands made upon the vegetation found on roadsides, as follows:-

1. The highway engineer requires protection from erosion, and appearance is of little importance except to relieve monotony for the driver.

2. The motorist asks for pleasant appearance, aided perhaps by landscaping.

3. The conservationist sees in the roadside one of the few remaining environments for many of our wild flowers.

A vegetation type to satisfy all these demands is difficult, but in my opinion is most likely to be given by a grassland sward which requires the minimum in maintenance either by mowing or by chemical treatment.

J.R. Watson (Minnesota, U.S.A.)

In some states of the U.S.A., for example Minnesota, Nebraska and the Dakotas, roadsides are also used for game animals such as pheasants.

LEGUME SPECIES FOR ROADSIDES

D.B. White (Minnesota, U.S.A.)

Lotus corniculatus L. (birdsfoot trefoil) and Coronilla varia L. (crown vetch) perform very well on barren sandy soils when appropriate inoculum is used. The U.S. Soil Conservation Service has selected types for flower colour and other characters important in roadside use.

C.E. Wright (U.K.)

White clover (Trifolium repens L.) is a plant indigenous to many temperate regions. It is low-growing, capable of spreading and can supply its own nitrogenous fertilizer. Has anyone experience of using this species as a monoculture. for roadside verges and slopes?

D.B. White (Minnesota, U.S.A.)

Trifolium repens maintains a very unstable population from year to year and for that reason is not recommended for pure seeding.

P. Boeker (West Germany)

Legumes are inadvisable on roadsides as they attract game.

G.S. Robinson (New Zealand)

In New Zealand white clover is often included in roadside sowings, especially on very infertile volcanic soils where it gives a quick cover in the first year so long as phosphate is applied. If grasses are sown too, they take over at a later stage.

G.M. Wood (Vermont, U.S.A.)

I would like to add a word of caution on the use of Lotus corniculatus for highway seedings. This species has a very low seedling vigour, particularly the variety Empire which is best suited for roadsides because of low growth and greater winter hardiness. Therefore, serious erosion may result if Lotus corniculatus is sown alone. One or more grasses that are not too aggressive should be included, such as Agrostis alba L. and Festuca rubra L.

W.W. Huffine (Oklahoma, U.S.A.)

We do not advocate the use of legumes on the highway because they attract bees. These insects enter open windows of vehicles, creating a real driving hazard.

STEEPNESS OF SLOPES

G.S. Robinson (New Zealand)

None of the speakers has mentioned the need for roadside slopes to be eased back near the top. Do highway engineers take care that this is done in high rainfall areas to avoid the top of the slope being undercut, with consequent difficulties in establishing cover?

W.W. Huffine (California, U.S.A.)

If slopes exceed 3:1, there will be difficulties, and we discourage engineers from creating steeper slopes. On slopes steeper than 3:1 I believe supplemental irrigation is needed for establishing cover. Also, with long slopes it is necessary to provide berms with interception ditches to collect and discharge in an orderly fashion the water which falls on the face of the slope.

D.B. White (Minnesota, U.S.A)

In Minnesota, slopes are designed to deal only with the water that falls on them. The drainage systems are laid out to avoid water washing down slopes.

MINUTES OF BUSINESS MEETING, 18 JULY 1969.

Present - <u>Organizing Committee</u> - Dr. J. B. Beard (Chairman)
                                       Mr. J. R. Escritt
                                       Mr. B. Langvad
                                       Dr. J. R. Watson

          <u>Conference Treasurer</u> - Mr. B. M. Wood

          <u>Conference Secretary</u> - Mr. J. P. Shildrick

          and 47 other Conference participants.

1.   <u>Vote of thanks to committee members</u>

     Dr. Beard expressed his thanks individually to the Members of the
Organizing Committee, and Mr. Escritt did the same for Members of his Local
Arrangements Committee, and also expressed appreciation of the work done by
Dr. Beard. These thanks were warmly endorsed by the Meeting.

2.   <u>Conference expenses</u>

     The Treasurer outlined the provisional income and expenditure account for
the Conference (excluding the banquet and tours). Income from the Registration
fees of the 80 participants and from trade donations totalled £1,100. Expenditure on pre-conference meetings and correspondence, preparation of the Papers
given to delegates, and Conference expenses totalled about £625, with some items
still unknown. There was provisionally a balance in hand of about £475. A
final account would be prepared and put on record as soon as it could be drawn
up. A major item still to be decided was the cost of publishing the Proceedings.

3.   <u>Conference Proceedings</u>

     Dr. Beard outlined plans to publish the Proceedings which would include
a record of the discussions. He had received a letter from Gordon and Breach,
publishers, of Washington D.C., outlining an arrangement whereby the editor
(Mr. Escritt) would deliver material to the firm ready for printing, and would
undertake proof reading. The firm would ensure publication about 6 - 9 months
after receipt of material, and would recover the cost of publication by selling
the Proceedings, at a figure between 2½ and 4 cents per page, to libraries and
other interested organizations. Copyright would rest with the publishers.
Dr. Beard then said that the Organizing Committee had already discussed this
letter. They suggested that he should make enquiries on their behalf about the
status of Gordon and Breach, and, if satisfied, proceed to negotiate a contract,
sending copies to the Organizing Committee. If negotiations failed, other
arrangements would have to be considered by the Organizing Committee. One important point would be to ensure that each participant at the Conference
received a copy of the Proceedings.

     Dr. Beard outlined the following course of action for editorial work:-

1.   The record of discussions would be prepared by Mr. Escritt and his
colleagues, and the draft circulated to Members of the Organizing Committee to
act as a review board.

2.   Authors' final corrections of their papers should be sent to Mr. Escritt
by August 31st. Such corrections should only be of minor details. If there
were anything to be withdrawn from publication this should also be notified to
Mr. Escritt by August 31st. The texts of Papers delivered in the introductory
session and session 5 should also be sent in by the same date.

3. All papers delivered at the Conference, and the discussion record, would be published as soon as possible, either by Gordon and Breach or in other appropriate form. It was hoped that the complete Volume of Proceedings could then be supplied to each participant in the conference without further charge. The group photograph of participants would be included.

Dr. Davis proposed, and it was agreed, that the Organizing Committee should have full authority to negotiate and decide on the publication of the Proceedings. Dr. Engel asked that the matter of copyright of papers from public stations should be particularly checked. Dr. Beard said that Experiment Station numbers would be shown on papers where appropriate. Dr. White said that he would be willing to pay, if necessary, a small extra charge for the bound Volume of Proceedings. Dr. Beard said he was glad to know this, although he hoped such a charge would not be necessary. Mr. Eschauzier said he would like reprints to be available, and as he was supported by about half of those present, Dr. Beard agreed that the Organizing Committee would do what it could to meet their wishes.

4. Formation of the International Turfgrass Society

Dr. Beard said the Organizing Committee suggested setting up an international structure to improve communications between turfgrass research workers, to organize future international meetings, and to create more common ground in terminology and trial procedures. He asked if the Meeting wished to establish such a body, and if so, what form it should take and what should be its object-ives.

The Meeting unanimously voted in favour of setting up such a body. Various names were suggested: the Meeting finally approved "The International Turfgrass Society". It was agreed that all registered participants of the Conference should be the founder members of the International Turfgrass Society, which thus came into being.

Dr. Rieke asked what funds would be available to the Society. Dr. Beard replied that the Society would have any surplus remaining from the Conference funds and any royalties from the Proceedings. Dr. Keen suggested that other bodies might contribute dues.

Dr. Beard then explained that the Organizing Committee had recommended that there should be two bodies within the Society -

a)   a small Executive Committee, of 5 - 7 members, and

b)   a larger International Turfgrass Advisory Board, with a member from each
      of the fifteen countries represented at the Conference.

It was suggested that members of the Executive Committee should, if possible, be different from members of the Advisory Board, but that all members should be chosen from the Conference participants.

After some discussion, in which Dr. Beard said that a country could have the same man representing it on both bodies, if it wished, the Meeting approved the proposals for an Executive Committee and an Advisory Board.

Dr. Beard then called on Dr. Keen to report the views of a small ad hoc group co-opted by the Organizing Committee to propose names for the Executive Committee. This ad hoc group had already met and made recommendations under Dr. Keen's chairmanship. (The other members were Mr. Eisele, Mr. van der Horst, Mr. Morris and Mr. Schweizer.)

Dr. Keen said his group recommended that the Executive Committee should consist of seven members, and proposed three members of the existing Organizing Committee and four others, namely:-

Dr. Davis (Chairman)
Dr. Beard
Dr. Daniel
Mr. Escritt
Mr. van der Horst
Mr. Langvad
Dr. Switzer

Dr. Keen asked the meeting to accept these recommendations and discharge his group. Dr. Engel suggested that no country should have more than two representatives on the Executive Committee, but it was pointed out that the U.S.A. were given three representatives in view of the likelihood that the next Conference would be held there. Dr. Beard said he envisaged that the Committee would be re-elected at each Conference. Dr. White considered the Committee's main task was to prepare a constitution for the Society, and proposed adoption of the nominations made by Dr. Keen. These were approved on a vote, and the seven Members, with Dr. Davis as Chairman, were elected to serve as the Executive Committee for at least the next four years, and to undertake the preparation of a constitution for the Society and the running of the Society as they might see fit until the next Conference. Dr. Keen's group was discharged, with the thanks of the Meeting.

Dr. Beard then asked for suggestions for the Executive Committee's terms of reference and future activities. The following suggestions were made:-

<u>General terms of reference</u>: To promote communication among turfgrass research workers through publications and meetings: to standardize terminology and unite procedures: and to encourage and sometimes assist any research and education which would lead to effective production and maintenance of turfgrasses. (Dr. Madison)

<u>Suggestions for specific tasks</u>:

1. International rules for seed testing of turfgrasses. (Mr. Eisele)
2. Standardization of units of weight and area. (Dr. Adams)
3. Suggestions on adoption of metric units. (Dr. Keen)
4. Standard procedures for trials, e.g. standard cutting heights, levels of fertility and control varieties. (Dr. Schweizer)
5. Publication of a reference list of turfgrass research establishments. (Mr. Fisher)

The proposed terms of reference were accepted, and the suggestions referred to the Executive Committee.

5. Other business

Dr. Beard sought the views of the Meeting on the next Conference. It was agreed that it should be held in 1973, in the U.S.A. Mr. Morris suggested greater concentration on selected items, but Dr. Schery suggested, and the Meeting agreed, that the programme be left to the Executive Committee, with the sole proviso that there should be no split sessions.

Mr. Morgan asked about subscriptions to the Society, but Dr. Daniel suggested, and it was agreed, that this matter should be deferred until the final account of this Conference was drawn up.

Dr. Beard pointed out that although the Executive Committee had been elected, nominations were required from each country for the Advisory Board. These should be submitted before the end of the Conference to the Conference Secretary, or subsequently to the Chairman of the Executive Committee.

The Meeting was then adjourned.

Nominations made to the Advisory Board before the end of the Conference were:-

West Germany	- Prof. P. Boeker
Great Britain	- Mr. J. R. Escritt
New Zealand	- Mr. G. S. Robinson
Sweden	- Mr. E. Helmbring
U.S.A.	- Dr. G. C. Horn

LIST OF PARTICIPANTS

Dr. W. A. Adams	Soil Science Unit, University College of Wales, Penglais, Aberystwyth, U.K.
Mr. G. Akesson	AB Hammenhögs Frö, S 270-50, Hammenhog, Sweden.
Mr. D. T. A. Aldrich	National Institute of Agricultural Botany, Huntingdon Road, Cambridge, CB3 0LE, U.K.
Mr. J. Andringa	Zwaan & de Wiljes Ltd., Stationstraat 124, Scheemda, Holland.
Dr. James B. Beard	Department of Crop Science, Michigan State University, East Lansing, Michigan 48823, U.S.A.
Mr. William H. Bengeyfield	United States Golf Association, Green Section, P.O. Box 567, Garden Grove, California 92642, U.S.A.
Dr. S. W. Bingham	Department of Plant Pathology and Physiology, Virginia Polytechnic Institute, Blacksburg, Virginia 24061, U.S.A.
Prof. Peter Boeker	Institut für Pflanzenbau der Rheinischen Friedrich-Wilhelms Universität, 53 Bonn, Katzenburgweg 5, West Germany.
Mr. A. V. Bogdan	Commonwealth Bureau of Pasture and Field Crops, Hurley, Maidenhead, Berks., U.K.
* Mr. Gunnar Borg	The Swedish Seed Association, Svalöf, Sweden.
Mr. P. Bowen	Fisons Ltd., Levington Research Station, Levington, Ipswich, Suffolk, U.K.
* Mr. F. E. Bunn	The Murphy Chemical Co. Ltd., Wheathampstead, St. Albans, Herts., U.K.
Dr. John F. Cornman	Professor of Ornamental Horticulture, Cornell University, Ithaca, New York, U.S.A.
Dr. William H. Daniel	Department of Agronomy, Purdue University, Lafayette, Indiana 47907, U.S.A.
Dr. Richard R. Davis	Department of Agronomy, Ohio Agricultural Research and Development Center, Wooster, Ohio 44691, U.S.A.
Mr. J. L. Dawson	Scottish Agricultural Industries Ltd., Seeds Development Unit, Ingliston, Newbridge, Midlothian, U.K.
Miss. M. L. Denecke	Institut für Grünlandlehre, Technischen Hochschule München, 805 Freising-Weihenstephan, West Germany.
Dr. Edith Ebert-Jehle	J.R. Geigy S.A., Agricultural Chemicals Research Dept., CH 4000, Basle 21, Switzerland.

* Registered but not attending

Dr. T. Eggers	Pflanzenschütz Urania G.m.b.H., D-2000, Hamburg 36, Alsterterrasse 2, West Germany.
Dr. Kaoru Ehara	Faculty of Agriculture, Kyushu University, Fukuoka, Japan.
Mr. C. Eisele	Hesa G.m.b.H., 61 Darmstadt, Bismarckstrasse 59, West Germany.
Dr. R. E. Engel	Rutgers University, New Brunswick, New Jersey, U.S.A.
Dr. Ernst. L. Entrup	Deutsche Saatveredelung Lippstadt-Bremen G.m.b.H., 478 Lippstadt, Landsbergerstrasse 2, West Germany.
Ir. W. A. Eschauzier	n.v. H. Mommersteeg's Zaadteelt en Zaadhandel, Wolput 72a, Vlijmen, The Netherlands.
Mr. J. R. Escritt	The Sports Turf Research Institute, Bingley, Yorkshire, BD16 1AU, U.K.
Mr. G. G. Fisher	Land and Water Management Ltd., 88a Girton Road, Cambridge, U.K.
Dr. T. E. Freeman	Plant Pathology Dept., University of Florida, Gainesville, Florida 32601, U.S.A.
Dr. William B. Gilbert	Crop Science Dept., North Carolina State University, Raleigh, North Carolina 27607, U.S.A.
Mr. D. J. Glas	Plant Breeding Station, D.J. van der Have N.V., Rilland-Bath, The Netherlands.
Dr. Roy L. Goss	Western Washington Research and Extension Center, Puyallup, Washington 98371, U.S.A.
Mr. E. Helmbring	J. E. Ohlsens Enke AB., Skogholmsvägen, 21479, Malmoe, Sweden.
Dr. Paul R. Henderlong	Ohio State University, Agronomy Dept., 1827 Neil Avenue, Columbus, Ohio 43210, U.S.A.
Dr. G. C. Horn	401 Newall Hall, University of Florida, Gainesville, Florida 32601, U.S.A.
Ir. J. P. van der Horst	Nederlandse Sport Federatie, Burg. van Karnebeeklaan 6, 's Gravenhage, The Netherlands.
Dr. J. E. Howland	700 Forest St., Reno, Nevada 89502, U.S.A.
Dr. Wayne W. Huffine	Agronomy Dept., Oklahoma State University, Stillwater, Oklahoma 74074, U.S.A.

Dr. Lars-Eric Janson	Vattenbyggnadsbyran (VBB), P.O. Box 5038, S-10241 Stockholm, Sweden.
Ir. M. Kamps	Gebr. van Engelen Zaadteelt en Zaadhandel N.V., P.O. Box 35, Vlijmen, The Netherlands.
Dr. Ray A. Keen	Dept. of Horticulture, Waters Hall, Kansas State University, Manhattan, Kansas 66502, U.S.A.
Mr. Jack L. Kidwell	J. L. Kidwell Landscape Corporation, Route 3, Box 16A, Culpeper, Virginia 22701, U.S.A.
Mr. Jürgen C. Knolle	Saat - und Erntetechnik G.m.b.H., D - 3440 Eschwege, Industriehof, Postfach 478, West Germany.
Dipl. Ing. Bretislav Konicek	Praha 6 - Dejvice, Komornická 18, Czechoslovakia.
Dr. L. H. J. Korsten	Cebeco, Seed Dept., P.O. Box 182, Rotterdam 1, The Netherlands.
Dr. Z. Brzywczy - Kuninska	Institute of Public Utility Services, Warszawa, Bracka 4, Poland.
Mr. Bjarne Langvad	W. Weibull, Plant Breeding Institution, Landskrona, Sweden.
Dr. John H. Madison	Department of Environmental Horticulture, University of California, Davis, California 95616, U.S.A.
Dr. R. W. Miller	Agronomy Dept., Ohio State University, Columbus, Ohio 43210, U.S.A.
Mr. Wayne C. Morgan	Kellogg Supply Inc., 23924 South Figueroa St., Wilmington, California 90744, U.S.A.
Mr. R. L. Morris	Fisons Ltd., Levington Research Station, Levington, Ipswich, Suffolk, U.K.
Dr. L. E. Moser	Assistant Professor, Agronomy Dept., Ohio State University, Columbus, Ohio 43210, U.S.A.
Mr. Robert C. O'Knefski	Co-operative Extension Agent, Nassau County, 30 Willis Avenue, Mineola, New York, U.S.A.
Mr. R. W. Palin	Sutton and Sons Ltd., London Road, Reading, Berks., U.K.
Dr. A. Pap	Hurst Gunson Cooper Taber Ltd., Witham, Essex, U.K.
Mr. Martin Petersen	L. Daehnfeldt Ltd., Faaborgvej 248, Dyrup, Odense, Denmark.
* Dr. R. Pietsch	Wolf-Geräte G.m.b.H., 524 Betzdorf/Sieg, Postfach 860, West Germany.
Mr. K. Potter	Hurst Gunson Cooper Taber Ltd., Witham, Essex, U.K.

---

* Registered but not attending   608

Dr. Paul E. Rieke	Soil Science Dept., Michigan State University, East Lansing, Michigan, 48823, U.S.A.
Mr. G. S. Robinson	Agronomy Dept., Massey University, Palmerston North, New Zealand.
Ir. G. J. Ruychaver	Nederlandse Sport Federatie, Burg. van Karnebeeklaan 6, 's Gravenhage, The Netherlands.
Dr. C. W. H. M. Schaepman	Barenbrug's Zaadhandel N.V., Bakenbergse Weg 268, Arnhem, The Netherlands.
Dr. R. W. Schery	The Lawn Institute,Route 4, Kimberdale, Marysville, Ohio 43040, U.S.A.
Dr. Richard E. Schmidt	Agronomy Dept., Virginia Polytechnic Institute, Blacksburg, Virginia 24061, U.S.A.
Dipl. Ing. Edgar W. Schweizer	Eric Schweizer Seeds Ltd., P.O. Box 360, 3601 Thun, Switzerland.
Mr. J. P. Shildrick	The Sports Turf Research Institute, Bingley, Yorkshire, BD16 1AU, U.K.
Mr. John F. Shoulders	Extension Specialist (Turf), Agronomy Department, Virginia Polytechnic Institute, Blacksburg, Virginia 24061, U.S.A.
Mr. James A. Simmons	Research Division, O. M. Scott & Sons Co., Marysville, Ohio 43040, U.S.A.
* Dr. W. Skirde	Rasenforschungsstelle am Institut für Grünlandwirtschaft und Futterbau der Universität Giessen, 63 Giessen, Ludwigstrasse 23, West Germany.
Mr. Derek Soper	May & Baker Ltd., Research Station, Ongar, Essex, U.K.
Dr. V. I. Stewart	Soil Science Unit, University College of Wales, Penglais, Aberystwyth, U.K.
Dr. J. Stubbs	Plant Protection Ltd., Fernhurst, Nr. Haslemere, Surrey, U.K.
Dr. Clayton M. Switzer	Department of Botany, University of Guelph, Guelph, Ontario, Canada.
Dr. J. Troll	University of Massachusetts (Temporarily c/o Fisons Ltd., Levington Research Station, Levington, Ipswich, Suffolk, U.K.)
Mr. R. Vijn	Gebr. van Engelen Zaadteelt en Zaadhandel N.V., P.O. Box 35, Vlijmen, The Netherlands.

---

* Registered but not attending

Ir. H. Vos
Institute for Research on Varieties of Field Crops (I.V.R.O.), Postbox 32, Wageningen, The Netherlands.

Dr. James R. Watson
Director of Agronomy, Toro Manufacturing Corporation, 8111 Lyndale Avenue South, Minneapolis, Minnesota, 55420, U.S.A.

Dr. Bernhard Werminghausen
Badische Anilin- und Soda-Fabrik AG., 6703 Limburgerhof (Pfalz), Weinbietstrasse 36, West Germany.

Dr. Donald B. White
Department of Horticultural Science, University of Minnesota, St. Paul, Minnesota 55101, U.S.A.

Dr. H. Hamilton Williams
County of Los Angeles Department of Arboreta and Botanic Gardens, 301 North Baldwin Avenue, Arcadia, California 91006, U.S.A.

Dr. Glen M. Wood
Plant and Soil Science Dept., Hills Science Building, University of Vermont, Burlington, Vermont, U.S.A.

Mr. M. A. Wood
Richardsons (Ulster) Ltd., 1 Short Strand, Belfast BT 5 4BS, Northern Ireland, U.K.

Dr. Charles E. Wright
Plant Breeding Station, Ministry of Agriculture for Northern Ireland, Loughall, Armagh, N. Ireland, U.K.

Dr. Isao Yoshikawa
Kansai Golf Union Research Center, 1303-2 Kurando, Takarazuka, Hyogo Pref., Japan.